ADDISON WESLEY
Chemistry 11

**Addison Wesley
Science Authors**

Ray Bowers
Eric Brown
Sadru Damji
Dean Eichorn
Ute Goering-Boone
Art Last
Dale Parker
Robert Perkins
Geoff Rayner-Canham
Mark van Roode
Len Silverman
Gail de Souza
Elgin Wolfe
Rob Young

Advisory Panel

Ray Bowers
Shawna Hopkins
Heather Mace
Philip Marsh
Graham Satterthwaite
Gail de Souza
Elgin Wolfe

Geoff Rayner-Canham

Grenfell College, Memorial University of Newfoundland
Corner Brook, Newfoundland

Sadru Damji

Upper Canada College
Toronto, Ontario

Ute Goering-Boone

Peel District School Board
Mississauga, Ontario

Contributing Authors

Marietta (Mars) Bloch

Toronto District School Board
Toronto, Ontario

Peter Bloch

Toronto District School Board
Toronto, Ontario

Toronto

Publisher   Susan Green
Managing Editor   Cecilia Chan
Product Manager   Donna Picheca
Developmental Editors   Nancy Andraos, Jackie Dulson, Ph.D.
Coordinating Editor   Lynne Gulliver
Editorial Team   Howard Harper, Karen Kligman, Cynthia Young
Editorial Assistant   Judy Wilson
Indexers   Kate Baltais, Harold Otto
Marketing Manager   Dawna Day-Harris
Production Manager   Theresa Thomas
Production Coordinator   Sandra Magill
Art Direction   Alex Li
Cover Design   Anthony Leung
Interior Design   Anthony Leung, Alex Li
Page Layout   Heather Brunton & Ruth Nicholson/ArtPlus Limited
Photo Researcher   Nancy Cook, Karen Taylor

Illustration   ArtPlus Limited/Imagineering Scientific and Technical Artworks Inc.

ISBN 0-201-70812-4

Printed and bound in Canada

1 2 3 4 5 –TCP– 05 04 03 02 01

Cover Image: NASA/Science Photo Library

Cover picture shows colour satellite map of atmospheric ozone in the southern hemisphere between mid August and early October 1998.

Acknowledgements

Curriculum and Assessment Consultant

Marietta (Mars) Bloch
Toronto District School Board

Senior Science Consultant

Philip Marsh
Peel District School Board

Technology Consultant

Mike Newnham
Thames Valley District School Board

Accuracy Reviewers

Michael C. Baird, Ph.D.
Department of Chemistry, Queen's University

Norman Colin Baird, B.Sc., Ph.D.
Department of Chemistry, University of Western Ontario

Stanislaw Skonieczny, Ph.D., D.Sc.
Department of Chemistry, University of Toronto

Ates Tanin, B.Sc., Ph.D.
Department of Chemistry, University of Toronto

Safety Reviewer

John Henry
Hamilton-Wentworth District School Board

Catholicity Reviewers

Bernie Zweerman
Regina Pacis C.H.S., Downsview

Review Panel

Kyn Barker
York Region District School Board

Leslie Barton
Toronto French School, Toronto

Robin Howard
Mother Teresa C.S.S., Nepean

John Purificati
St. Patrick's H.S., Ottawa

Reviewers

Roman Charabaruk
Albert Campbell C.I., Scarborough

Chuck Cohen
Wm. Lyon Mackenzie, C.I., North York

Marcel Dufresne
Monsignor John Pereyma C.S.S., Oshawa

Denise Edney
Etobicoke, C.I., Etobicoke

Barry Fawcett
John McCrae S.S., Nepean

Anthony Hack
Runnymede C.I., Toronto

Paul Inwood
Marathon H.S., Marathon

Andrew Liptak, L.L.B.
St. Martin's S.S., Mississauga

Robert McIntosh
St. Mary C.S.S., Pickering

Don Mullins
Kirkland Lake C.V.I., Kirkland Lake

Lily Nguyen-Moreira
Branksome Hall, Toronto

Sherry Semeniuk
Sir Robert Borden H.S., Nepean

Niels Walkau
Cobourg D.C.I. West, Cobourg

Teresa Zaw-Tun
Hawthorn School For Girls, North York

Reginald Zeller, B.S.P.
West Hill S.S., Owen Sound

Contributing Writers

Gabriel Roman Ayyavoo, M. Ed.
Francis Libermann C.H.S., Scarborough

Julie Czerneda
Professional Writer

Heather Mace
Ottawa-Carleton District School Board

Contents

UNIT 5
Hydrocarbons and Energy

436

1

Matter and Chemical Bonding

OVERALL
EXPECTATIONS

*By the end of this unit,
you will be able to:*

■ demonstrate an understanding of
the relationship between periodic
tendencies, types of chemical
bonding, and the properties of
ionic and molecular compounds

■ carry out laboratory studies of
chemical reactions, analyze
chemical reactions in terms of
the type of reaction and the
reactivity of starting materials,
and use appropriate symbols and
formulas to represent the
structure and bonding of
chemical substances

■ describe how an understanding
of matter and its properties can
lead to the production of useful
substances and new technologies

Chemistry began at the birth of the universe. It is widely accepted that the universe formed during what is called the "big bang." Astrophysicists have provided strong evidence that, when matter first formed between 10 and 20 billion years ago, the only two elements that existed were hydrogen with a small proportion of helium. So where did all the other chemical elements come from? They came from the death of stars. The larger the star, the shorter its life. In that first generation of stars, each massive star shone brightly for only a billion years or so before its gravitational field caused a catastrophic collapse followed by an explosion that could be seen across the galaxy.

In that explosion, protons and neutrons collided together to form enormous quantities of all the remaining nuclei in the periodic table, as well as larger nuclei that have long since decayed away. Star after star exploded, and the atoms drifted through space until they became trapped by the gravitational field of younger, smaller stars such as our own sun. The atoms accumulated to form the bodies in our solar system, including Earth. But this is just the beginning of the chemical story. It is the combination of the atoms of those elements into millions of different compounds that has formed the rocks under our feet, the water of our seas, the air we breathe, the plants and animals around us, and, of course, ourselves.

Now chemists go beyond nature. For our technological society, we need materials that are stronger, more flexible, more heat resistant, more electrically conductive, more water absorbent, or better in hundreds of other ways than nature can supply. To make these compounds, it is necessary to understand the properties of the chemical elements, discover the ways in which elements can combine, and predict the types of chemical reactions these compounds can undergo. This is where your journey into chemistry begins.

CHEMISTRY HEADLINES

New Material Covers Space Probe

A tough, black composite material called "carbon-carbon" covers the Solar Probe craft, NASA's latest project to study the sun. Carbon-carbon is made by laying a cloth of carbon fibres into a mould, wetting it with an epoxy resin, and burning away the epoxy in an oven. This material is extremely stiff and lightweight, and can endure extremely high temperatures.

Green Plastics Cause Concern for Environmentalists

Certain types of plastics can be grown in the leaves and stems of corn plants. Although some biochemical engineers believed they were the environmental answer to having completely biodegradable plastics, the energy required to produce them and the carbon dioxide and methane released when they break down pose serious environmental concerns. In fact, harvesting and processing the plastic uses more non-renewable resources than current plastic manufacturing practices.

Are Molecular Semi-Conductors Possible?

Scientists are working on building molecules that function exactly like or similar to semi-conductor devices, such as diodes, transistors, and conductors, in computers. Because computer chips keep shrinking in size, problems such as heat dissipation, stray signals, and limits of chip fabrication using current technologies might be solved by molecular semi-conductors. Although this technology is still in its infancy, scientists are striving to make computers capable of performing complex tasks at incredible speeds.

ACHIEVEMENT TASK — PREVIEW

At the end of the unit, you will demonstrate your learning by completing the task "Calcium Carbonate—A Viable Product?" As a consultant to a company, you will research how the compound is manufactured and what its uses are in agriculture, synthesize it and analyze some of its chemical properties, prepare a cost-benefit analysis, and prepare a presentation for the company executives on your findings. See page 118.

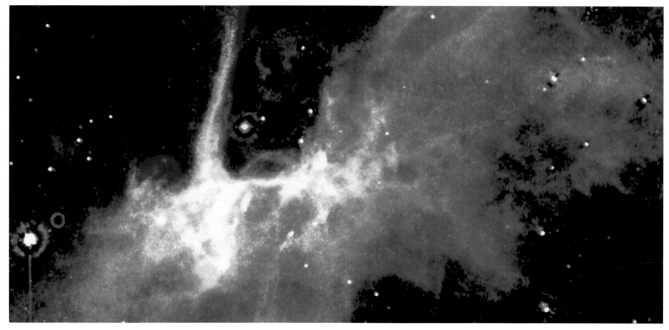

The Cygnus Loop supernova exploded 15 000 years ago, leaving behind remnants of oxygen atoms (blue), hydrogen atoms (green), and sulfur atoms (red). This supernova remnant is 2600 light-years away and lies within our Milky Way galaxy.

CHAPTER 1

SPECIFIC EXPECTATIONS

By the end of this chapter, you will be able to:

- define and describe the relationship among atomic number, mass number, atomic mass, isotope, and radioisotope (1.1)

- demonstrate an understanding of the periodic law, and describe how electron arrangement and forces in atoms can explain periodic trends such as atomic radius, ionization energy, electron affinity, and electronegativity (1.1, 1.2, 1.3)

- relate the reactivity of a series of elements to their position in the periodic table (1.2, Investigation 1, Investigation 2)

- use appropriate vocabulary to communicate ideas related to chemical reactions (1.2, 1.3)

- analyze data involving periodic properties such as ionization energy and atomic radius in order to recognize general trends in the periodic table (1.3)

- identify chemical substances and reactions in everyday use or of environmental significance (1.2)

The Periodic Table

Science is concerned with discovering knowledge, organizing it, and explaining the "why." The discovery and explanation aspects are always discussed, but the organizing of knowledge is often taken for granted. Yet without organization, the knowledge would not make sense. The division of science into different areas of study—biology, chemistry, physics, geology, and so on—is itself an overall way of categorizing scientific information. Knowledge does not always fit into neat boxes, and so we invent "in between" categories such as biochemistry, the study of the chemistry of living organisms. Each science discipline, in turn, has its own key organization. Geologists classify rocks as sedimentary, igneous, and metamorphic; physicists classify forces as gravitational, magnetic, electrostatic, and so on. Classification is so important to biologists that it is a whole subdiscipline called taxonomy.

There are many ways of organizing knowledge, but scientists want ways that are predictable. This means that the method of organization can be used to predict things that are not already known. In fact, you use predictable organization in many aspects of your life. For example, when you go shopping in a supermarket, you assume that the goods are arranged by food type: meats, vegetables, fruit, etc. But the store could organize the contents in alphabetical order, by brand name, or by country of origin. The advantage of organizing the goods by food type is that similar foods are clustered together and you can always predict where to find a particular item.

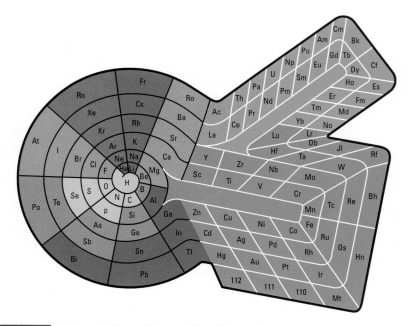

FIGURE 1.1 This spiral form of the periodic table was devised by Dr. Theodor Benfey, an American chemist. What do you think are the advantages and disadvantages of this particular design as compared to the more traditional representation of the periodic table found on the inside back cover of this text?

Chemistry is the study of the chemical elements and the compounds they form. During the 19th century, as the number of known elements increased, chemists realized that it was essential to find some means of organizing the elements. Even more importantly, chemists were eager to find a method of predicting whether more elements existed and what the properties of those elements were likely to be. In that way, the search for new elements could be focussed rather than just hit or miss. The discovery of chemical periodicity and the development of the periodic table was the key. The periodic table is one of the great monuments of science, a triumph of human intellect, which is still the core of our organization of chemical knowledge.

Discovering Chemistry

Metals, Metals, Everywhere!

Most of the chemical elements are metals. What are their similarities and differences?

Materials
   safety goggles
   samples of calcium, copper, and iron metals
   dilute hydrochloric acid
   distilled water
   3 test tubes
   tweezers

1. Take samples of the metals and describe their physical appearance. Look up their densities in data tables.
2. Place a piece of calcium in one dry tube with tweezers, copper in the next, and iron in the third. Add a few millilitres of water to each. Note your observations.
3. In the tubes where nothing happened, pour off the water and add about 2 mL of dilute hydrochloric acid to each. Again note your observations.

■ Compare your observations with the location of the elements in the periodic table. What are the trends in density?

■ What are the trends in chemical reactivity?

■ Which do you think would be the least dense metal in the fourth row?

■ Which do you think would be the most chemically reactive metal in the fourth row?

■ Copper has one physical property that only one other metal has. What is that property, and which other metal has that same property?

■ Where are these two metals located relative to each other in the periodic table?

CHECK**POINT**

Draw a sketch of the periodic table and shade in the areas of the table that represent the location of the following:

noble gases
alkali metals
halogens
hydrogen
metalloids
metals
non-metals

Describe how the periodic table can be used to predict the properties of elements and the types of compounds that they form.

1.1 The Development of the Periodic Table

Key Understandings

When you have completed this section, you will be able to:

- define atomic number, mass number, atomic mass, isotope, and radioisotope
- describe the relationship among atomic number, mass number, atomic mass, isotope, and radioisotope
- define periodic law and describe its significance in relation to the organization of elements in the periodic table
- understand how scientific theories develop over time as more information becomes known

FIGURE 1.2 Timeline of our technological development

    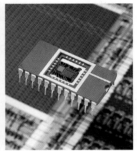

Stone Age: begins 2 600 000 B.C.

Bronze Age: begins 3200 B.C.

Iron Age: begins 1200 B.C.

Synthetic Polymer Age: begins in 1903 with the invention of Bakelite

Silicon Age: begins in 1954 with the invention of the silicon transistor

INFO BIT

French researchers recently analyzed eye-makeup residues preserved inside tiny vases taken from ancient Egyptian tombs. They discovered that the makeup, which the Egyptians called mesdemet, contained compounds nearly nonexistent in nature. Ancient chemists must have painstakingly synthesized these substances. The researchers believe their discovery provides strong evidence that the ancient Egyptians may have been the world's first chemists.

One way to organize human history is by the materials that we use, as you see in Figure 1.2. Over time, knowledge about the types and properties of materials on our planet was passed on to different generations and added to by different people. Our social history also developed, in part from the application of this knowledge in new inventions and ways of thinking about our world. Today, we can choose exactly the right element or compound that has the specific properties that make it suitable for a particular use. Think about motor vehicles and aircraft; why do we make one out of iron and the other out of aluminum? Why do we use the compound iron oxide (Fe_2O_3) in videotape, floppy disks, and hard drives, and not some other metal oxide? The properties of elements and the compounds they form depend on their location in the periodic table. But the excitement of chemistry is not what we know but what we have yet to discover. One of the great challenges in the 21st century is to find a material that will conduct an electric current without resistance (a superconductor) at room temperature. Such a material would enable scientists and technologists to develop faster computers, better magnetic resonance imaging (MRI) instruments, and levitating mass transit vehicles, all with substantially lower energy usage, and would have applications that are currently unimaginable in other fields. Chemists believe the key to making such a material is to find which elements need to be combined and in what proportion. The answer must lie in the periodic table.

The Organization of Elements

How could the growing number of elements be organized? The story is one of the best examples in science of scientists building on the advances of their predecessors. The history is actually quite complex, so this is a somewhat simplified version. By the late 18th century, chemists realized that each element had a characteristic mass. At that time, they arbitrarily assigned the atomic mass of hydrogen to be exactly 1 because hydrogen was the element with the least mass. The atomic mass of every other element was then measured by comparison with the value for hydrogen, giving a **relative atomic mass**, A_r. As each new element was discovered, one of the first properties to be reported was its atomic mass.

One of the first scientists to organize the elements was Johann Döbereiner, a German chemist. In 1817, he noticed that some sets of three elements displayed a certain regularity in their properties, so he grouped these together and called them **triads**. He found three such triads in which the middle element had an atomic mass that was approximately equal to the average mass of the other two. Some of the chemical and physical properties of the middle elements were also midway between those of the first and third elements. One of these triads consisted of chlorine, bromine, and iodine.

TABLE 1.1 One of Döbereiner's Triads

Element	Relative Atomic Mass (A_r)	Boiling Point (°C at standard pressure)	Properties
chlorine	35.5	−34	green, toxic, reactive gas
bromine	79.9	59	red-brown, toxic, reactive liquid
iodine	126.9	185	violet, toxic, reactive solid

Eighty percent of the elements known in 1829 did not fit into a triad, which suggested to most chemists that Döbereiner's observations were pure coincidence. However, organizing elements by atomic mass and looking for patterns in properties were crucial steps in themselves.

John Newlands, a British chemist, took the next step. In 1864, he arranged the known elements in order of increasing atomic mass and showed that every eighth element formed part of a set of elements with similar chemical and physical properties. This **law of octaves**, as Newlands called it, contained each of Döbereiner's three triads. Unfortunately, Newlands assumed that all elements were known, and, as new elements were discovered that did not fit into Newlands's table of elements, most chemists again dismissed the patterns as coincidence.

The Periodic Table Organizes the Elements by Their Properties

In 1869, Lothar Meyer, a German chemist, and Dmitri Mendeléev, a Russian chemist, independently developed a method for organizing the elements, laying the basis for the modern periodic table. Both found that they could arrange the elements based on the periodicity in their properties. **Periodicity** means "patterns that repeat at definite intervals." In chemistry, periodicity

WEBLINK

The periodic table is still the crucial centrepiece of chemistry today. Contrast the lives of its two discoverers, Lothar Meyer and Dmitri Mendeléev. Investigate why Mendeléev's name is the one usually associated with the discovery of the periodic table. Begin your research at **www.pearsoned.ca/chemistry11**.

refers to the occurrence of similar physical and chemical properties of elements at regular intervals in the periodic table. Organizing the elements in this way made it easier to predict the properties of the elements, the kinds of reactions they could participate in, and the kinds of compounds they were likely to produce. Mendeléev is generally credited for the development of the periodic table, partly because he maintained a higher public profile and partly because Meyer did not pursue or use this research to the same extent.

Mendeléev constructed his periodic table based on the atomic mass of the elements because it was the only quantity that could be measured reliably. At that time, atoms were thought to be indivisible, and protons, neutrons, and electrons had yet to be discovered. He stated that the properties of the elements were a periodic function of their atomic masses. This led to the **periodic law**, which states that elements arranged in order of increasing atomic mass show a periodic repetition of properties.

FIGURE 1.3 One of the versions of the periodic table devised by Mendeléev. Why does it look very different from the one we use today?

1 I	2 II	3 III	4 IV	5 V	6 VI	7 VII	8 VIII
H							
Li	Be	B	C	N	O	F	
Na	Mg	Al	Si	P	S	Cl	
K	Ca		Ti	V	Cr	Mn	Fe Ni Co Cu
Cu?	Zn			As	Se	Br	
Rb	Sr	Yt	Zr	Nb	Mo		Ru Pd Rh Ag
Ag?	Cd	In	Sn	Sb	Te	I	
Cs	Ba		Ce				
		Er	La	Ta	W		Os Pt Ir Au
Au?	Hg	Tl	Pb	Bi	U		
			Th				

There were two key points that Mendeléev observed that none of his predecessors had:

- When he placed elements in order of increasing atomic mass, sometimes an element did not resemble the element above or below it, but did match the ones in the next column. He would leave a space and conclude that there was a missing element needed for that space. In so doing, Mendeléev used the periodic table as a powerful tool to predict the existence of missing elements. At the time, only 70 elements were known.
- Mendeléev also predicted the properties of these unknown elements by using the averaging concept of Döbereiner's triads. For example, in his table, there was a blank space below aluminum and above indium. By comparing the properties of aluminum and indium, Mendeléev deduced the properties of the missing element. In 1875, the element gallium was discovered, and its chemical properties closely matched those predicted by Mendeléev (see Table 1.2).

TABLE 1.2 Predicted and Observed Properties of Gallium

Property	Predicted by Mendeléev	Observed by Paul-Émile Lecoq de Boisbaudran (discoverer of gallium)
atomic mass	69	69.7
density (g·cm^{-3})	6.0	5.90
melting point (°C)	low	29.78
boiling point (°C)	high	2400
formula of oxide	M_2O_3	Ga_2O_3

EXAMPLE 1

In the periodic table, strontium is directly below calcium and above barium. From the following physical properties of calcium and barium, predict some of the properties of strontium.

TABLE 1.3

Element	Appearance	Density	Melting Point	Boiling Point
calcium	silvery metal	1.54 g·cm^{-3}	845°C	1484°C
strontium	?	?	?	?
barium	silvery metal	3.60 g·cm^{-3}	725°C	1640°C

Given
properties of calcium and barium

Required
properties of strontium

Analysis
You would predict that the properties of strontium would be the average between those of calcium and barium.

Solution
predicted appearance = silvery metal
predicted density of strontium = (1.54 g·cm^{-3} + 3.60 g·cm^{-3})/2 = 2.57 g·cm^{-3}
predicted melting point of strontium = (845°C + 725°C)/2 = 785°C
predicted boiling point of strontium = (1484°C + 1640°C)/2 = 1562°C

Statement
Strontium is predicted to be a silvery metal with a density of approximately 2.57 g·cm^{-3}, a melting point of about 785°C, and a boiling point of about 1562°C.

In fact, strontium is a silvery metal with a density of 2.58 g·cm^{-3}, a melting point of 775°C, and a boiling point of 1367°C. Therefore, three of your four predictions are very close to the measured values. That the boiling point of strontium is less than that of either calcium or barium shows that periodicity has its limitations.

PRACTICE PROBLEM

Use the averaging approach introduced by Döbereiner to predict the properties of germanium (Ge) given the properties of silicon (Si) and tin (Sn). Compare your predictions with the accepted values in data tables.

TABLE 1.4

Element	Density (g·cm^{-3})	Melting Point (°C)	Boiling Point (°C)
silicon (Si)	2.33	1410	2355
germanium (Ge)	?	?	?
tin (Sn)	7.31	231.9	2507

Though you may have the impression that everything in chemistry is predictable, not all trends are as consistent as those already shown. Each element is unique, and it is the uniqueness that makes the study of the elements so interesting. For example, one of the most reactive elements is phosphorus, yet this would not be predicted from the properties of its unreactive neighbours, nitrogen and arsenic.

Mendeléev realized that placing the elements strictly in order of increasing atomic mass resulted in some elements appearing in the wrong column of his periodic table. Based on the measured atomic mass, potassium with a relative atomic mass of 39.1 should appear before argon (relative atomic mass of 39.9), but to do this would place potassium in the same column as the gases helium, neon, and so on. This would obviously be incorrect since potassium has properties similar to those of lithium and sodium but argon does not. Can you find two other pairs of elements that are in reverse order? Discrepancies in science are sometimes a clue that there is something fundamentally wrong with the concept or theory. These anomalies in the ordering of elements worried the chemists of the time. They checked and rechecked the values of the atomic masses in case errors had been made. But the values were correct. However, there was a more fundamental question: why was there periodicity? The explanation needed advances in physics and a realization that the atom was not indivisible but contained subatomic particles.

FIGURE 1.4 The modern periodic table

Atomic Structure and the Modern Periodic Table

To explain the "why" of the modern periodic table, it is essential to understand the structure of the atom, since it is the subatomic particles within the atom that determine its properties. Chemists were happy with the idea of the indivisible atom, and it came as a great shock when physicists showed that there were particles—electrons—smaller than an atom. In 1911, Ernest Rutherford, a New Zealand physicist, outlined the essential features of our modern model of atomic structure. He proposed that each atom contained a positively charged nucleus, around which travelled negatively charged electrons.

The next crucial step happened in 1913 with the work of Henry Moseley, an English physicist. When the atoms of different elements were bombarded with electrons and the wavelengths of the X-rays emitted by the atoms were studied, Moseley found that these wavelengths were related by an integer that he called the **atomic number** (symbol Z). Rutherford realized that this number represented the number of positive charges in the nucleus and the number of orbiting electrons in an atom.

The discovery of a fundamental number to represent each element was almost as important as the work by Mendeléev. Now chemists could place the elements in a numerical order that did correctly match the properties. There was no need for switching the order as Mendeléev had had to do. When the elements were placed in order of increasing atomic number, they all matched with the correct group. Furthermore, after the discovery of the noble gases, chemists had wondered if there were other whole groups of unknown elements still to be discovered. Because there were few missing atomic numbers, it was later concluded that more groups did not exist. Nearly all the elements up to uranium had already been found. The **modern periodic law** can be stated as follows:

> **Elements arranged in order of increasing atomic number show a periodic repetition of properties.**

Organizing the elements based on atomic number and atomic structure creates columns in the periodic table called **groups**. These families of elements have similarities in the way their electrons are arranged. They also exhibit many periodic trends in the formulas and properties of the compounds that they form. Although there are only 90 naturally occurring elements, nuclear physicists have created new elements by colliding atoms (such as lead and krypton) at high speeds. The existence of the atoms of these new elements is often short-lived, but chemists have devised special rapid techniques to determine key properties of each new element and the formulas and properties of one or more of its compounds. These findings are then compared with those predicted from the location of the element in the periodic table. Explanations are then proposed for any differences between theory and experiment. As an example, using data tables, you should be able to predict the approximate density, melting point, and boiling point of element 118.

Isotopes

The next problem facing chemists was radioactivity. In 1898, French scientists Pierre Curie and Marie Curie discovered the elements radium and polonium. These elements were found to give off radiation and were called radioactive elements. The major difficulty arose when it was realized that, as the radiation was released, the atoms of the element were transformed into atoms of a different element, which in turn released radiation to form

FIGURE 1.5 Ernest Rutherford played a major role in determining the structure of the atom. Part of his early work was accomplished at McGill University in Montreal.

WEBLINK

Choose one of the more obscure elements and find out who discovered it, where and when it was discovered, why it was given its particular name, and what its physical properties are. Begin your research at **www.pearsoned.ca/chemistry11**.

atoms of another element, and so on, until a non-radioactive element was formed. Because these new "elements" had different atomic masses than those of known elements, they had to have their own place in the periodic table. Dozens of new elements, such as ionium, were claimed to exist. The answer was found in 1906 by Frederick Soddy, a British chemist. He predicted that lead could have atomic masses other than the "normal" value of 207.2. When lead was extracted from different radioactive ores, the lead from uranium ores had a mass of 208 and that from thorium had a mass of 206, making his predictions correct. Soddy named these different types of atoms isotopes. The need for all the new spaces in the periodic table disappeared because these new "elements" were just different varieties of existing elements. The isotopes that are radioactive are called **radioisotopes**. With the discovery of isotopes, it was now possible to provide a good definition of radioactivity. **Radioactivity** is the release of radiation when the atoms of an isotope of an element are transformed into atoms of an isotope of another element or of a different isotope of the same element.

With the discovery of the neutron in 1932, all became clear: isotopes have different numbers of neutrons in their atomic nuclei but the same number of protons. The total number of neutrons and protons in a nucleus is called the **mass number** (symbol A). So the modern definition of an **isotope** is two or more forms of the same element that differ in their mass number because they have different numbers of neutrons in their nuclei.

Although neutrons have no charge, they add to the mass and size of the atomic nucleus. Isotopes can be written in word form with the mass number attached as a suffix separated by a hyphen or in symbolic form with the number of protons (atomic number) to the lower left of the chemical symbol and the mass number to the upper left. For example, hydrogen occurs as 3 different isotopes (Table 1.5). Each hydrogen isotope has been given its own name, making hydrogen unique among the elements.

TABLE 1.5 Isotopes of Hydrogen and their Relative Abundance in Nature

Isotope	Common Name	Protons	Neutrons	Abundance	Symbol
hydrogen-1	protium	1	0	99.984%	$^1_1$H
hydrogen-2	deuterium	1	1	0.016%	$^2_1$H
hydrogen-3	tritium	1	2	trace	$^3_1$H

Chemists were then able to explain why the atomic mass of iodine was less than that of tellurium, even though the atomic numbers were in the reverse order. It just happens that the only isotope of iodine in nature has 74 neutrons, while the two most common isotopes of tellurium have 76 and 78 neutrons, making the average atomic mass of tellurium greater than that of iodine.

On the scale of relative atomic mass, a proton and a neutron each have a mass close to 1. For example, the atomic mass of helium is close to 4, what one would expect for the sum of the masses of 2 protons and 2 neutrons (the electrons having negligible mass). But there are many elements whose atomic mass is not an integer. The discovery of isotopes solved this problem as well. For example, chlorine has an atomic mass of 35.5. This was found to result from a mixture of chlorine-35 (76%) and chlorine-37 (24%) giving a measured atomic mass of 35.5.

Then & NOW

Harriet Brooks: Canadian Pioneer in the Study of Radioactivity

When you read about a scientific discovery, it is usually linked to one person (e.g., Newton, Einstein). Yet in modern times, research has largely been undertaken by groups of researchers working with a "famous name" scientist. It is often one of the unknown researchers who made the discovery, but the discovery becomes associated with the famous name scientist. Harriet Brooks, a Canadian scientist, was one such unknown researcher.

Harriet Brooks was born in 1876, in Exeter, Ontario, and completed her grade school education in Seaforth, Ontario, before enrolling at McGill University in Quebec in 1894. In those days, it was quite difficult being a female student. In many universities, women had to sit in the front row of the class and had to enter through a separate doorway. Some professors refused to have women in their class. Despite the challenges that she faced, Brooks was an outstanding student, and she graduated with an honours degree in mathematics and science. She became Ernest Rutherford's first research assistant when he arrived in Canada to undertake research at McGill.

At the time, the radioactive element thorium was known to give off something that was given the name "emanation." Brooks showed that this substance was a gas and made the first measurement of its atomic mass. We now know that she had discovered radon. This discovery was crucial to the progress of research into radioactivity. At the time, it was believed that radioactive substances did not change their elemental structure when they gave off radioactive rays. Brooks's research showed this was not true—a different element or isotope was formed as the rays were released.

She made several other discoveries at McGill, but as research employment opportunities for women were limited, Brooks accepted a teaching position at Barnard College, a women's college affiliated with the all-male Columbia University in New York. She died prematurely in 1933.

It is almost certain that Brooks died prematurely as a result of her exposure to the radiation emitted from the radioactive isotopes that she studied. In the first half of the 20th century, the hazards of radiation were not appreciated. For example, when it was discovered that the radiation from radium caused a glow, the numbers on watch dials were painted with radium compounds so the time could be read in the dark. Many of the hundreds of young women employed as watch painters, called the "radium girls," died agonizing deaths from the effects of the radiation they received.

X-rays were treated in an equally casual fashion. Even into the 1950s and early 1960s, shoe stores had X-ray machines so that children's feet could be X-rayed to see if the shoes fit correctly. The child, parent, and shop assistant could see the live image of the child wiggling his or her toes to make sure they were not crunched together. There was minimal protection from the X-ray radiation, and it is probable that many shoe store employees of the time developed radiation-related illnesses.

Now we are well aware of the hazards of all forms of radiation. Because chemists have improved the sensitivity of X-ray film so much, dental X-ray machines now use very small levels of radiation. In addition, the patient is usually draped with an X-ray absorbing lead apron to protect the remainder of the body, particularly the reproductive organs, from X-ray radiation. Federal government regulations now control the availability of radioactive material. Any institution wishing to possess radioactive elements must explain exactly what they are to be used for and must designate a safety officer to be responsible for the materials. Government inspectors are sent from time to time to check whether the elements are stored safely and used appropriately. Find out where radioactive materials are being used nearby, such as your local hospital or university. What are they used for? What safety precautions are employed?

FIGURE 1.6 Harriet Brooks (1876–1933) in her graduation photograph from McGill University

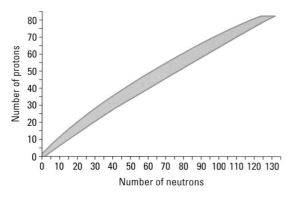

FIGURE 1.7 The coloured area on this graph represents the region of stability for atomic nuclei. As the number of protons in the nucleus increases, the number of neutrons must increase at a greater rate if the nucleus is to be stable.

If you look at the composition of the oxygen-16 nucleus, you will see that it has 8 protons and 8 neutrons—an equal number. On the other hand, the uranium-238 nucleus contains 92 protons and 146 neutrons. Why so many more? Neutrons play an important role in the nucleus, acting as a sort of nuclear "glue." On their own, the positively charged protons in the nucleus would repel one another and the nucleus would disintegrate. It is the role of the neutrons to pack between the protons, holding the nucleus together. For the elements listed at the beginning of the periodic table, about the same number of neutrons as protons suffice. However, as the number of protons increases, the number of neutrons increases at an even greater rate to provide a stable nucleus. As a result, the ratio of neutrons to protons becomes greater and greater (Figure 1.7).

Section 1.1 Review

Understanding Concepts

1. Make a chart defining each of the following and its significance in understanding the properties of the elements: atomic mass, atomic number, mass number, isotope, and radioisotope.

2. Describe how the periodic law can help to determine the properties of a set of given elements.

3. Explain how the principle of pattern recognition played an important role in the evolution of the periodic table.

4. Describe how new scientific discoveries led to the revisions of Mendeléev's periodic table.

5. Lead is one of the best X-ray absorbers, while beryllium is almost completely transparent to X-rays. Suggest what might be the major factor for lead's ability to absorb X-rays. Describe any practical advantages lead has for its use in X-ray absorption.

Applying Inquiry/ Communication Skills

6. Given the data in Table 1.6, predict the specific gravity, melting point, and boiling point of niobium (atomic number 41), and explain the rationale for your predictions.

Making Connections

7. One of the most dangerous products from a nuclear explosion is strontium-90. This radioactive isotope is absorbed by plants and enters the food chain. Given that strontium is closely related to calcium, suggest where you think the strontium would be deposited. Explain why this location would be particularly life-threatening. Write your ideas in a paragraph that informs others of the possible dangers and suggests a possible treatment.

TABLE 1.6

Element	zirconium	molybdenum
Atomic Number	40	42
Specific Gravity	6.4	10.2
Melting Point	1700°C	2600°C
Boiling Point	2900°C	3700°C

1.2 Chemical Properties and Electron Arrangement

Key Understandings

When you have completed this section, you will be able to:

- describe the electron arrangement in atoms and how this arrangement is related to the physical and chemical properties of the atom
- use appropriate vocabulary to communicate ideas related to elements and their properties
- relate the reactivity of a series of elements to their positions in the periodic table
- recognize the occurrence and abundance of elements found in nature
- understand the importance of assessing risks and benefits when using elements and compounds for everyday use

In the periodic table, groups 1, 2, and 13 through 18 are referred to as the **main** (or representative) **groups**. The elements in the middle of the periodic table are called the **transition metals**. The two rows of 14 elements placed below the main part of the table are called the **lanthanoids** and the **actinoids**. Most of our studies will be about the main group elements. Four of the main groups of elements have specific names: group 1 elements, except for hydrogen, are the **alkali metals**; group 2 elements are the **alkaline-earth metals**; group 17 elements are the **halogens**; and group 18 elements are the **noble gases**.

INFO**BIT**

The lanthanoids and actinoids are traditionally called the lanthanides and actinides. However, as you will see in the next chapter, the ending *-ide* is used only for a negative ion. That is why the ending for the elements themselves were changed to *-oid*. Some chemists have proposed that they be called lanthanons and actinons, and you may see these terms being used.

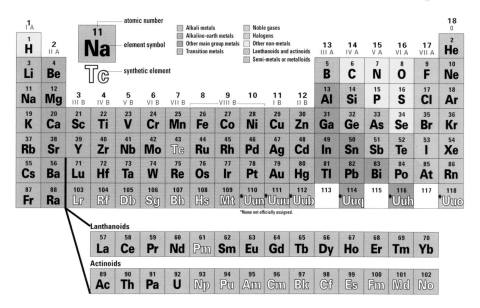

FIGURE 1.8 Names are given to each part of the periodic table.

Most of the elements are metals; that is, they are reflective and conduct heat and electricity. Many metals can also be beaten into sheets (malleable) and drawn into wires (ductile). With the exception of one form of carbon, non-metals do not show any of the above properties. In general, the solid non-metals are brittle and brightly coloured. Several non-metals exist as gases at room temperature. Research which is the most malleable metal. How thin can sheets of this metal be made?

Investigation

Refer to page 27,
Investigation 1

Classifying elements as metals or non-metals is often convenient, and a thick line is drawn on many periodic tables to show the division between the two classes. In reality, however, there is no sharp dividing line between metals and non-metals. There is, instead, a border area in which we see a gradual change in the properties of elements from metallic to non-metallic. The elements in this border area are poor conductors of electricity and are shiny and brittle. They are called **semi-metals** or metalloids. The semi-metals form a steplike pattern diagonally through the right side of the periodic table. This means that in a group such as 15, the properties of the elements in the group change from non-metallic at the top (N, P), through semi-metallic (As, Sb), to metallic at the bottom (Bi).

FIGURE 1.9 Though you may think all metals are hard, the alkali metals are so soft they can be cut with a knife. The alkali metals are usually stored under oil to protect them from air and moisture because they are very reactive.

FIGURE 1.10 The non-metal phosphorus exists in two forms (called allotropes). The red form is a red-brown, air-stable, powdery solid, while the white (sometimes called yellow) form spontaneously burns in air. For this reason, the white form is stored under water.

Elements can be classified according to their phases (solid, liquid, or gas) at normal ambient (room) temperature. The majority of the elements exist as solids. The periodic table inside the back cover of this text shows the phase of each element at room temperature. You can see that the elements that exist as gases at this temperature are clustered in the upper right-hand corner of the periodic table. They are all non-metals. Only two elements, bromine and mercury, are liquids at room temperature (Figure 1.11). Three other elements, cesium and francium of group 1 and gallium of group 13, melt between 25°C and 30°C.

The Arrangement of Electrons

It was Niels Bohr, a Danish physicist, who discovered that the properties of atoms could be explained if the electrons were considered to occupy fixed energy levels (shells) around the nucleus. In the Bohr model of the atom, each shell or energy level can hold only a certain maximum number of electrons. The first shell can have a maximum of 2 electrons, as in the element helium. The next shell can have a maximum of 8 electrons, the third 18, and the fourth 32. In fact, the number of electrons per shell can be determined using the formula $2n^2$, where n is the number for the shell. The atomic number gives us both the number of protons and electrons in the neutral atom. The **electron configuration** can be determined simply by filling the shells according to the maximum number (Table 1.7). For example, the electron arrangement of selenium (element 34) will be 2, 8, 18, 6—a total of 34 electrons.

However, the outermost shell can never contain more than 8 electrons. For example, argon (element 18) has the electron arrangement 2, 8, 8. The next element, potassium, has one more electron. As the outermost shell cannot contain more than 8 electrons, this additional electron must therefore go into the next shell. So the electron arrangement of potassium is 2, 8, 8, 1. Calcium (element 20) has the arrangement of 2, 8, 8, 2, and then the third level is "backfilled" as the transition metal series is crossed. For example, scandium (element 21) has the configuration 2, 8, 9, 2.

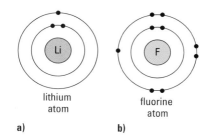

a)   b)

FIGURE 1.11 The electron arrangement of an atom can be represented by shell diagrams. The electron arrangement of lithium is shown in a) and that of fluorine is shown in b).

TABLE 1.7 The Electron Arrangement of the First 22 Elements in the Periodic Table

Element	Atomic Number	1st Energy Level	2nd Energy Level	3rd Energy Level	4th Energy Level
hydrogen	1	1			
helium	2	2			
lithium	3	2	1		
beryllium	4	2	2		
boron	5	2	3		
carbon	6	2	4		
nitrogen	7	2	5		
oxygen	8	2	6		
fluorine	9	2	7		
neon	10	2	8		
sodium	11	2	8	1	
magnesium	12	2	8	2	
aluminum	13	2	8	3	
silicon	14	2	8	4	
phosphorus	15	2	8	5	
sulfur	16	2	8	6	
chlorine	17	2	8	7	
argon	18	2	8	8	
potassium	19	2	8	8	1
calcium	20	2	8	8	2
scandium	21	2	8	9	2
titanium	22	2	8	10	2

Electron Arrangement of Alkaline-Earth Metals

What is the pattern in the electron arrangement of the first four alkaline-earth metals?

Find the group 2 elements on a periodic table. Write the electron arrangements of each element in group 2 up to strontium.

- What similarity can you observe among the arrangements?
- Predict what the similarity would be for the halogens. Check your predictions by writing the electron arrangements for the first three of those elements.

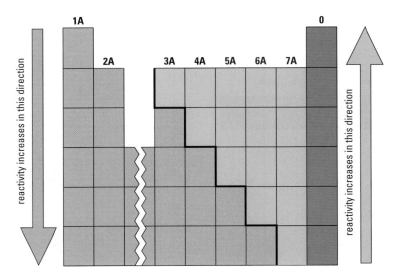

FIGURE 1.12 This diagram visually represents the relative reactivities of the main group elements down a group.

From the above activity, were you able to recognize a pattern based on how the number of electrons in the outer shell relate to the group number? If you were to write the electron arrangements for all the main group elements, you would see a consistent pattern in the way the outermost electrons are arranged. These patterns in occupancy of the outermost electron shell determine the chemistry of the element. Therefore, when the elements in a group react, they will most probably react in the same way. The intensity of the reaction, however, does change as you go down a group.

At the beginning of this unit, you saw what happened when calcium, copper, and iron were combined with water and with acid. In which direction of the periodic table did metal reactivity increase? If you had the time to study all of the chemical elements, you would find the following trends: for the main group metals, reactivity increases down the group; for non-metals, reactivity decreases down the group (Figure 1.12). Reactivity is greater to the far left and right of the periodic table (except for the noble gases). That is, the most reactive elements are those with either 1 or 7 electrons in their outer shell. On the basis of these trends and excluding the noble gases and the radioactive elements, which metallic element is the most reactive? Which non-metallic element is the most reactive?

The Number of Chemical Elements

It is unlikely that any more naturally occurring elements will be found in the universe. The stability of an atom is determined by the composition of its nucleus, and there appears to be a maximum number of protons that a nucleus can contain and still remain stable. This upper limit seems to be 83 protons (the element bismuth). Only 81 elements have stable isotopes. Two elements with lower atomic numbers than bismuth have no stable isotopes. These are technetium (atomic number 43) and promethium (atomic number 61).

All elements with atomic numbers greater than 83 are unstable. Atoms of these elements disintegrate at a rate that is not influenced by temperature, pressure, or any other physical or chemical effect. Such unstable atoms are radioisotopes because they disintegrate by the process of radioactivity. The

Investigation

Refer to page 28, Investigation 2

stability of the elements above atomic number 88 generally decreases as the atomic number increases. This stability is expressed in terms of the half-life of the element. The **half-life** is the time required for half the nuclei in a sample of an element to disintegrate and form different elements. The greater the half-life, the more stable the element. The half-life of uranium-238 is 10^9 years, that of californium-249 is 360 years, and that of lawrencium-257 is 8 seconds.

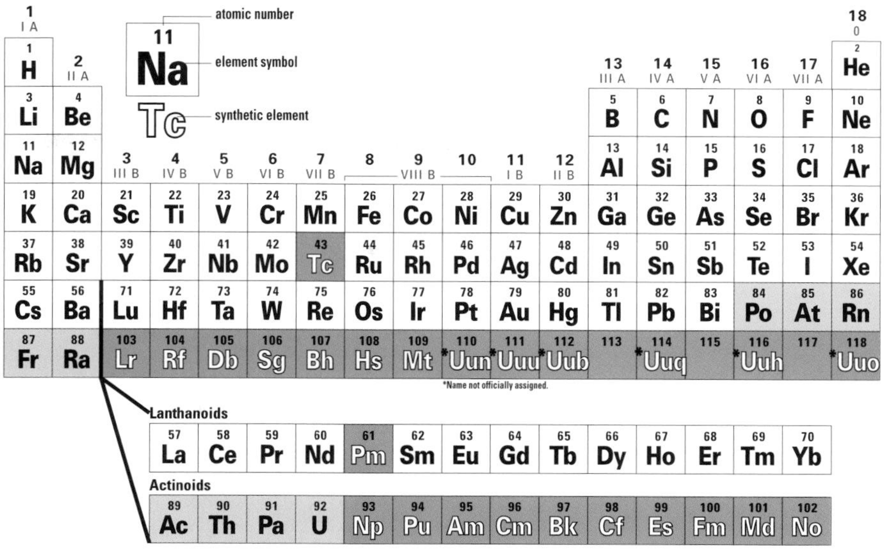

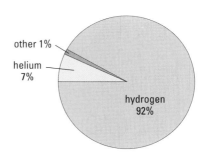

FIGURE 1.13 There are only 81 elements that have stable isotopes. All those in colour exist only as radioactive isotopes. The pink-coloured elements exist on Earth, while those in red have been synthesized by nuclear physicists.

The Abundance of the Elements

Hydrogen is the most abundant element in the universe. Of all atoms in the universe, approximately 92% are hydrogen atoms! In the past, this percentage was even higher. It is believed that all the other elements were produced from hydrogen as a result of nuclear reactions within stars. Helium is the second most abundant element, comprising 7% of the atoms in the universe. In general, elements become less abundant as their atomic number increases. The abundance of the group 16 elements is as follows: oxygen, 6×10^{-2}%; sulfur, 1×10^{-3}%; selenium, 3×10^{-7}%; and tellurium, 2×10^{-8}%.

There is a difference between the abundance of an element on Earth and in the universe. Most of the low-density gases, hydrogen and helium, escaped from Earth's atmosphere millions of years ago, leaving nitrogen (78%) and oxygen (21%) as the two major components of the present atmosphere. (You will learn more about Earth's atmosphere in Chapter 9.) Most of the hydrogen that remains on Earth is combined with oxygen in the form of water.

From Table 1.8, 8 elements alone account for more than 98% of Earth's crust. They are not present as the elements themselves. For example, some of the oxygen is found combined with hydrogen as water, and some is combined with silicon to form silicon dioxide (sand or quartz). If every element were distributed uniformly throughout Earth's crust, then the resulting low concentrations of many of the elements would make it completely uneconomical to extract and refine them. For example, gold is only present at a concentration of about 10^{-6}%.

Fortunately, the crust is very heterogeneous, and elements and compounds are concentrated in ore bodies. It is the task of prospectors and geochemists to find localized concentrations of elements that can be used for the needs of the economy.

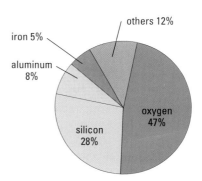

FIGURE 1.14 The percent composition of the universe

FIGURE 1.15 The percent composition of Earth's crust

TABLE 1.8 The Most Abundant Elements in Earth's Crust

Element	O	Si	Al	Fe	Ca	Na	K	Mg
Percentage	46.6	27.6	8.3	~5.0	3.6	2.8	2.6	2.1

Section 1.2 Review

Understanding Concepts

1. Write a paragraph describing how electron arrangements in atoms can explain periodic trends.
2. Describe what the numbers 2, 8, 8 tell you about the chemical properties of an element.

Applying Inquiry/ Communication Skills

3. New elements with atomic numbers 114, 116, and 118 have been synthesized, but, as yet, there is still little information about them. Predict the group of elements each would belong to, and predict some of its properties. Write your predictions in the form of a short journal article for chemists.

Making Connections

4. The element aluminum may have a role in the biochemical disorder Alzheimer's disease. Research the uses of aluminum in our society, and outline its importance to the economy, our health, and the environment. Prepare a risk assessment concerning the use of this element.

1.3 Periodic Trends

Key Understandings

When you have completed this section, you will be able to:

- analyze data involving periodic properties, such as ionization energy and atomic radius, in order to recognize general trends in the periodic table
- identify chemical properties of substances that have led to useful purposes for these substances in everyday life

So far, you have seen some qualitative ways in which the properties of the elements differ within any one **period** in the periodic table. There are also quantitative characteristics across a period, called **periodic trends**, regarding the arrangement of the elements. The properties that you will be examining are atomic radius, ionization energy, electron affinity, and electronegativity.

Atomic Radius

An atom does not have a sharply defined boundary that sets the limit of its size, but we can indirectly *estimate* a value for the atomic radius using the distance between atoms in compounds. Because atomic radii are so small, they are measured in picometres (pm), where one picometre equals 10^{-12} m. The **atomic radius** of an element is an estimate of the size of an atom from its nucleus to its outer perimeter.

Figure 1.16 shows the atomic radii of the main group elements. Notice that the atomic radii decrease from left to right across the period. From sodium in the first group through argon in the eighth group, the number of protons in the nucleus increases

Discovering Chemistry ***Periodic Trends in Atomic Radii***

What is the periodic trend in atomic radii in the periodic table?

Materials

Figure 1.16
spreadsheet program or graphing calculator

Using the atomic radii listed in Figure 1.16, graph the atomic radii versus the atomic number.

- Describe the trend you see down a group. Explain how you would account for this using the atomic model.
- Describe the trend you see across a group. Suggest an explanation using the atomic model.

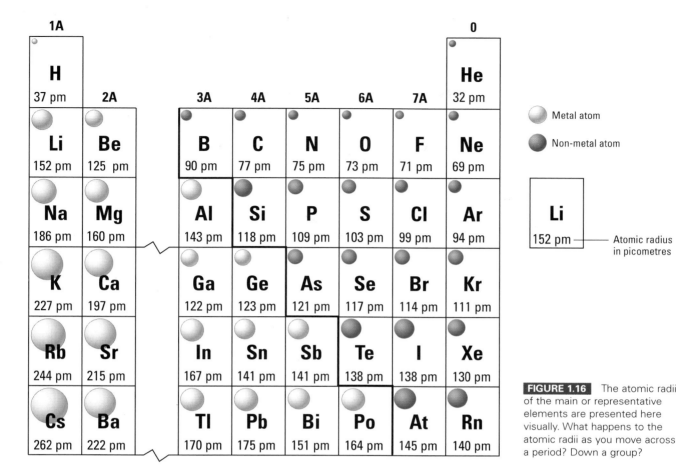

FIGURE 1.16 The atomic radii of the main or representative elements are presented here visually. What happens to the atomic radii as you move across a period? Down a group?

by 1. As the nuclear charge increases, the outermost electrons are more strongly attracted to the nucleus. This decreases the average distance between these electrons and the nucleus. Consequently, there is a decrease in the size of the atoms.

Furthermore, atomic radii increase as you go down a group. This increase in size within a group can be explained in terms of the Bohr model of the atom. As you go down a group, the nucleus of each element contains more and more protons, and this, of course, means that there are correspondingly more electrons, which will occupy more shells. These outer electrons are farther away from the nucleus, and although they feel the attractive pull of the positive protons in the nucleus, they also feel the repulsion of the inner electrons. The net attractive pull is therefore weaker, and the radii of the lower members of a group are greater than if there were no inner electrons. This reduction in attractive force due to inner electrons is called a **screening effect**.

Ionization Energy

When an atom gains or loses an electron, it is called an **ion**. If the atom loses an electron, the ion has a positive charge; if it gains an electron, it has a negative charge. Positively charged ions are called **cations**, and negatively charged ions are called **anions**. Gaseous ions are very short-lived, while ions that are in solution or the solid phase are more stable.

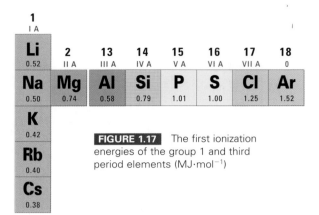

1 I A	2 II A	13 III A	14 IV A	15 V A	16 VI A	17 VII A	18 0
Li 0.52							
Na 0.50	**Mg** 0.74	**Al** 0.58	**Si** 0.79	**P** 1.01	**S** 1.00	**Cl** 1.25	**Ar** 1.52
K 0.42							
Rb 0.40							
Cs 0.38							

FIGURE 1.17 The first ionization energies of the group 1 and third period elements (MJ·mol⁻¹)

One of the properties of an element that can be measured very precisely is ionization energy. **Ionization energy** is the energy needed to remove an electron from a gaseous atom. The actual value depends on which electron is being removed. For example, the first ionization energy of an element is the amount of energy required to remove the least attracted electron from a gaseous atom of that element. The first electron that is least attracted is in the outer shell of the atom. It is the removal of the first electron that is most commonly studied. For the first ionization energy, the process can be written as follows:

$$Na(g) + energy \rightarrow Na^+(g) + e^-$$

Figure 1.17 shows the first ionization energies of the elements in group 1 and in the third period. Recall that the number of protons increases from left to right across a period and that the electrons are attracted more strongly to the increasingly larger nuclei. The number of electrons also increases across a period, and these additional electrons are usually at the same energy level. So the outer electrons in atoms on the right side of a period will be attracted more strongly to the nucleus than those in atoms on the left side. Therefore, across a period, the ionization energy tends to increase as the atomic radius decreases.

Notice how the ionization energy decreases down the group. This decrease is related to the increase in size of the atoms as you go down that group; this pattern occurs in all the groups in the periodic table. We know that as the atomic radius increases, the outermost electron becomes progressively farther from the nucleus. Since the attraction between this outer negative electron and the positive nucleus (shielded by the inner electrons) becomes weaker, the removal of this electron requires less energy. Therefore, as the atomic radius increases down a group, the ionization energy decreases.

FIGURE 1.18 The first ionization energies of the first five periods in the periodic table show a periodic trend. Use this graph to explain what is meant by "shows a periodic trend." What is the general trend across a period? Down a group?

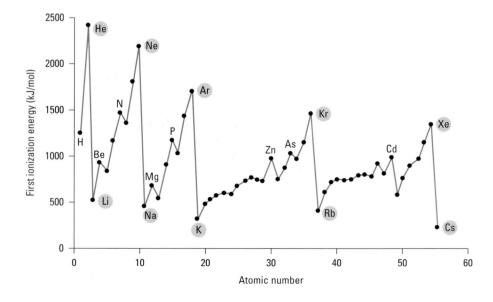

You will notice from Figure 1.18 that there are deviations from the expected general increase across a period. These zigzags within the general trend cannot be explained by the simple Bohr model of the atom. In fact, the variations suggest that there are energy sublevels within each energy level. Chemists use the simplest model that will explain their observations. For this level of chemistry, the Bohr model explains what you need to understand. It is only toward the end of your grade 12 chemistry course that you will need to know about a more sophisticated model of the atom.

WEBLINK

You have studied the first ionization energies of a few periods, but what do the patterns look like for the rest of the periodic table? Using graphs, report on the trends in the later periods. Begin your research at **www.pearsoned.ca/ chemistry11**.

Multiple Ionization Energies

It is possible to remove every electron from an atom. For example, the second ionization energy is defined as the energy required to remove the second electron; the third ionization energy, the energy to remove the third; and so on. For any atom, the number of possible ionization energies is equal to the number of electrons present in that atom. As an example of the trends, Table 1.9 shows all the ionization energies for lithium, beryllium, and boron—the elements at the beginning of the second period of the periodic table.

TABLE 1.9 Ionization Energies for Lithium, Beryllium, and Boron (MJ·mol^{-1})

Element	Ionization Energies				
	1st	2nd	3rd	4th	5th
lithium	0.5	7.3	11.8		
beryllium	0.9	1.8	14.8	21.0	
boron	0.8	2.4	3.7	25.0	32.8

The trends in multiple ionization energies are consistent with our current model of the atom. As each successive electron is removed, the ionization energy increases. Notice that it is much easier to remove the outermost electrons—that is, the highest energy electrons—than those from inner energy levels.

Electron Affinity

Just as it is possible to remove an electron from a gaseous atom, it is also possible to add an electron. Energy is usually released in this process because there is a force of attraction between the nucleus and the added electron. This energy is called the electron affinity of the atom, and, like ionization energy, it can be measured very precisely. **Electron affinity** is the energy released when an electron is added to a gaseous atom. The process can be represented as follows:

$$F(g) + e^- \rightarrow F^-(g) + \text{energy}$$

Looking at the periodic table, there is an increase in the amount of energy released when an electron is added to an atom across a period going from left to right. In other words, the electron affinity increases. Therefore, the electron affinities of the metals are less than those of the non-metals.

There is a relationship between ionization energy and electron affinity. A large value of ionization energy indicates that the removal of an electron

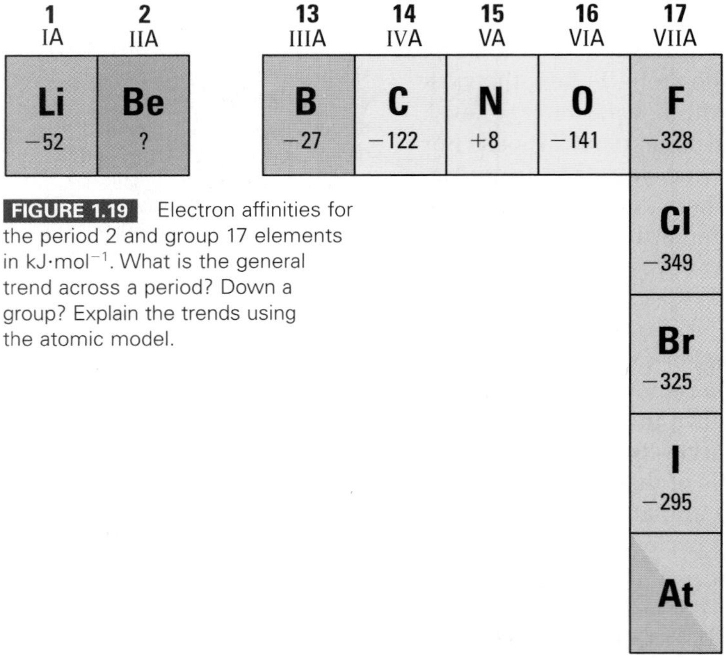

1 IA	2 IIA		13 IIIA	14 IVA	15 VA	16 VIA	17 VIIA
Li −52	**Be** ?		**B** −27	**C** −122	**N** +8	**O** −141	**F** −328
							Cl −349
							Br −325
							I −295
							At

FIGURE 1.19 Electron affinities for the period 2 and group 17 elements in kJ·mol⁻¹. What is the general trend across a period? Down a group? Explain the trends using the atomic model.

from a gaseous atom is difficult and that it is unlikely to occur for that element. On the other hand, a large value of electron affinity indicates that a lot of energy is released when an electron is added to a gaseous atom, and that such a process is very likely to occur.

Although each element has a unique ionization energy and electron affinity, chemists can make combinations of elements so that, when subjected to an electric current, electrons leap from an atom of one element to an atom of the other element, releasing light in the process. These combinations are called light-emitting diodes (LEDs). An LED containing the elements gallium and phosphorus in a 1:1 ratio, GaP, gives a green light when electricity is passed through it. The element below phosphorus in the periodic table is arsenic. By substituting a proportion of the atoms of phosphorus with arsenic (As), the difference in energies is changed. This means that the wavelengths of light emitted will be altered. Consequently, if the composition of Ga:P:As is 1.0:0.4:0.6, the LED will emit red light, while an in-between ratio will give yellow light. Red, yellow, green: do these colours look familar? They are the colours of traffic lights. New traffic lights consist of arrays of LEDs rather than light bulbs. The LEDs are brighter and longer lasting and use a tiny fraction of the electrical energy of traditional bulbs. Through the understanding of ionization energies and electron affinities, chemists have made a product that is safer and more energy-efficient.

Electronegativity

Knowing the properties of the elements in the periodic table is interesting, but creating new materials and understanding how and why chemical reactions occur is really at the heart of chemistry. Being able to predict the properties of a chemical compound provides us with incredible knowledge about how it may react. It was through the study of a wide range of compounds that Linus Pauling, an American chemist, deduced that the electrons in chemical bonds were not always shared equally by the adjacent atoms. He suggested that this unequal sharing of electrons was due to a property, called electronegativity, that was different for each element. Electronegativity is not a fundamental property of an atom; however, it is a useful concept when you try to understand the behaviour of compounds. **Electronegativity** is the property that determines the relative strength of attraction by an atom of a bonding electron pair in a chemical compound.

For example, when hydrogen and fluorine share electrons to form a compound, the fluorine has a greater attraction for the shared electrons than hydrogen. By comparing the experimental values of the energies holding atoms together in compounds with those predicted theoretically, Pauling devised a relative numerical scale. He chose to assign fluorine a value of 4.0.

According to this scale, hydrogen has a value of 2.1. Later chemists showed that the electronegativities of various elements matched well with their corresponding ionization energies and electron affinities. This provided a theoretical basis for the electronegativity concept.

The most electronegative elements are in the upper right corner of the periodic table; the least electronegative elements are in the lower left. Electronegativity tends to increase from left to right across a period and decrease down a group. Again, the periodic property can be explained in terms of atomic structure. Going from left to right across a period, the number of protons increases, therefore, any shared electrons on the periphery of the atom will be attracted more strongly, giving a higher electronegativity. Notice that the extremes of electronegativity values correlate with chemical reactivity; that is, the most reactive chemical elements are those with the highest (fluorine) and lowest (cesium) electronegativities.

As you go down a group, the number of protons increases, but there are also more electron shells. The outermost electron shell will be farther away, and the inner electrons will create a shielding effect, which will decrease the overall attraction between the shared electrons and the nucleus. This, in turn, means that the electronegativity will decrease as you go down a group.

Why are these periodic properties useful? They help us understand why an element forms certain types of compounds and not others, and why elements react the way they do. You will discover in the next chapter that combinations of atoms with very different electronegativities form different types of compounds compared to those formed by atoms with similar electronegativities.

WEBLINK

For a simulation to show how periodic trends work in the periodic table, go to **www.pearsoned.ca/chemistry11**.

TABLE 1.10 Electronegativity Values for Main Group Elements

1 IA	2 IIA	13 IIIA	14 IVA	15 VA	16 VIA	17 VIIA
H 2.1						
Li 1.0	Be 1.5	B 2.0	C 2.5	N 3.0	O 3.5	F 4.0
Na 0.9	Mg 1.2	Al 1.5	Si 1.8	P 2.1	S 2.5	Cl 3.0
K 0.8	Ca 1.0	Ga 1.6	Ge 1.8	As 2.0	Se 2.4	Br 2.8
Rb 0.8	Sr 1.0	In 1.7	Sn 1.8	Sb 1.9	Te 2.1	I 2.5
Cs 0.7	Ba 0.9	Tl 1.8	Pb 1.9	Bi 1.9		

Section 1.3 Review

Understanding Concepts

1. Write a paragraph outlining the significance of understanding periodic trends.

2. Copy and complete the table at the bottom of this section.

3. Give the reason for the decrease in the first ionization energy for the alkaline-earth metals when moving down group 2 from beryllium to radium.

4. Although silicon is used in computer chips, there are other chemical elements that can be used in semiconductor devices. Identify these elements and give reasons for your choices. Suggest why silicon is used even though the other elements are superior in certain properties.

Applying Inquiry/ Communication Skills

5. Of all the elements discovered so far, state which one probably has the largest atomic radius. Explain your reasoning.

6. The graphs in Figures 1.20 and 1.21 show the relationship between the electronegativities and the first ionization energies for some period 2 and period 3 elements. Ignore the steps created by boron, oxygen, aluminum, and sulfur.

   a) State the general trend in the relationship between these two properties in each period.

   b) Propose an explanation for this trend.

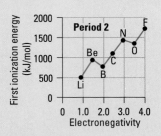

FIGURE 1.20

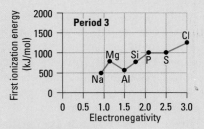

FIGURE 1.21

Making Connections

7. The alkali metals react very vigorously with water. They tarnish quickly on contact with air. Suppose you are a marketing manager for a shipping company that is willing to transport alkali metals. Prepare an information pamphlet for your customers that describes:

   a) how these materials are stored and prepared

   b) special instructions to ensure there are no harmful effects to your employees, customers, and the environment

Property	Periodic Trend	Group Trend	Explanation
atomic radius			
ionization energy			
electron affinity			
electronegativity			

Inquiry Skills

▶   Initiating and Planning
▶   Applying Technical Skills
      Using Tools, Materials, and Equipment
▶   Conducting and Recording
▶   Analyzing and Interpreting
▶   Concluding and Communicating

Investigation 1 (Section 1.2)

Trends in Periodicity

You are a research chemist with one of the nuclear physics groups who is synthesizing new elements. The group members hope to prepare enough atoms of elements 116, 118, and 119 to be able to measure their physical properties. But how will you know if you really have made these elements? You recall the predictable concept of periodic properties and decide to extrapolate plots of melting and boiling points and densities to determine the likely values. The physicists can then check your estimated values with the measured ones and see whether the new elements have really been synthesized.

Problem

How do trends differ across the periodic table?

Materials

- spreadsheet program or graphing calculator
- density data for the alkali metals and noble gases and group 16 elements (to be supplied by the teacher)
- melting and boiling point data for the alkali metals, noble gases, and group 16 elements (to be supplied by the teacher)

Procedure

1. Develop a procedure to determine the periodic trends down a group.

2. Select the independent variable you will use to determine these trends.

3. Have the teacher review your procedure before you carry it out.

Analyzing and Interpreting

1. Present your data in the form of a set of graphs.

2. Describe the trends in densities, melting points, and boiling points that you observe.

Concluding and Communicating

3. In the form of a table, indicate your predicted values for the density, melting point, and boiling point for elements 116, 118, and 119.

Extending

4. In view of its very low density, lithium should be useful for building unsinkable ships. Give two reasons why it is not used.

5. Helium is used for filling party balloons. Predict what would happen if you filled a balloon with xenon instead of helium.

6. In well-sealed houses, a potential danger is radon gas. This radioactive gas leaks in through cracks and crevices in the basement floor. Explain why this gas accumulates in the basement. Suggest the best solution for the removal of radon gas. Investigate why the gas is so harmful.

Investigation 2 (Section 1.2)

Inquiry Skills

Initiating and Planning

Applying Technical Skills

▶   Using Tools, Materials, and Equipment

▶   Conducting and Recording

▶   Analyzing and Interpreting

▶   Concluding and Communicating

Patterns of Chemical Reactivity

Problem

How do the elements lithium, sodium, magnesium, and calcium differ from common metals, such as iron and copper? What patterns are there in their reactivity with water?

Materials

- safety goggles
- samples of lithium, sodium, magnesium, calcium, and aluminum metals
- distilled water
- five 250-mL beakers
- knife
- litmus paper (red and blue)
- tweezers
- wire screen

> **CHEMICAL DISPOSAL: Make sure all the metal has reacted and rinse out all solutions with water. Place any leftover solids in a designated waste container.**

Procedure

1. Fill each of the five beakers about three-quarters full of distilled water.

2. Using a knife, scrape the outside surface of a small piece of calcium. Using tweezers, place the piece of calcium in one beaker and a 2-cm strip of magnesium in another. Record your observations.

3. Using tweezers, place a strip of aluminum in another beaker. Record your observations.

4. Your teacher will supply you with a sliver of lithium. Blot the sliver with paper towel to remove the oil on the outside.

5. Using the tweezers, carefully drop the sliver of lithium in one beaker. Record your observations.

6. Your teacher will demonstrate the addition of sodium to water, covering the beaker with a wire screen to prevent any fragments from escaping. Record your observations.

7. Test each of the beakers with a piece of red litmus paper and a piece of blue litmus paper. Note any colour changes.

8. Tabulate your results in the following table:

Metal	Degree of Reactivity	Litmus Colour Changes (initial colour → final colour)	Order of Reactivity 1 (most) → 5 (least)
lithium			
sodium			
magnesium			
calcium			
aluminum			

State the order of reactivity for the metals.

Analyzing and Interpreting

1. Discuss how the density of lithium and sodium compares with the density of water.

2. Determine if common metals (e.g., iron, copper) have high or low densities.

3. Describe the hardness of sodium compared to that of common metals.

4. Compare the reactivity of the following pairs of metals: magnesium and calcium, lithium and sodium, and sodium and magnesium.

5. Determine which element would be harder, calcium or magnesium.

Concluding and Communicating

6. Locate the metals on a periodic table. Assuming these reactions represent trends in the properties of elements, determine the relative reactivity of potassium with water compared with sodium. Determine the relative reactivity of strontium with water compared with calcium. Explain your answers.

7. Predict which metal you would expect to be the most reactive in the periodic table.

8. Describe how you can tell if the reactions created a chemical change and not just a physical change.

Extending

9. Mark on a periodic table the locations of the elements with a density greater than 15 $g \cdot cm^{-3}$. Record their densities and melting points.

CHAPTER SUMMARY

Key Terms

actinoid	electron configuration	ionization energy	period
alkali metal	electronegativity	isotope	radioactivity
alkaline-earth metal	group	lanthanoid	radioisotope
atomic number	half-life	noble gas	relative atomic mass
atomic radius	halogen	periodic law	semi-metal
electron affinity	ion	periodic trend	transition metal

Essential Understandings

■ Recognizing patterns is an important skill for scientists and helps them to make discoveries and search for answers.

■ The periodic table is an organizational tool that chemists use to predict the properties of elements, how the elements react to form compounds, and the types of compounds the elements are likely to form.

■ Atomic number is more accurate than atomic mass for predicting the periodicity of elements.

■ Elements can have the same number of protons but different numbers of neutrons, which results in variations in the physical and chemical properties of those elements.

■ Knowing the properties of elements helps us understand why certain elements form certain compounds and why they react as they do.

■ Risk assessments help us to analyze the potential environmental risks and benefits of using a particular substance.

Consolidate Your Understanding

1. Describe how the periodic table can explain the periodic repetition of physical and chemical properties of the elements.

2. Construct a concept map starting with the term "periodic table."

3. Think of circumstances when recognizing patterns has helped you understand a particular situation. Explain how.

4. Name the factors that should be considered when analyzing potential environmental risks and benefits of substances. Explain why it is important to consider points of view from different perspectives.

CHAPTER 1 REVIEW

Understanding Concepts

1. Choose which statement about the alkali metals lithium to cesium is correct.
   a) As the atomic number increases, the electronegativity of the elements increases.
   b) As the atomic number increases, the melting point of the element increases.
   c) As the atomic number increases, the first ionization energy of the element decreases.
   d) As the atomic number increases, the atomic radius decreases.
   e) As the atomic number increases, the electron affinity increases.

2. The following elements and ions have the same number of electrons. Determine which of the following shows the correct order of their increasing radii.
   a) $K^+ > Ar > Ca^{2+}$
   b) $Ar > K^+ > Ca^{2+}$
   c) $Ca^{2+} > K^+ > Ar$
   d) $Ca^{2+} > Ar > K^+$
   e) They all have the same radii.

3. Determine which element you would expect to have the lowest first ionization energy.
   a) Li
   b) Cs
   c) H
   d) He
   e) Ba

4. Identify which atom should have the largest value for electron affinity.
   a) He
   b) F
   c) Na
   d) Si
   e) Mn

5. The following is a list of the usual charge found on the ions of a series of elements:

   $$Y^- \quad W^{2+} \quad Z^{2-} \quad V^{3+} \quad X^+$$

   State which elements are most likely to be metals.

   a) V, W, and X
   b) V and W
   c) X and Y
   d) Y and Z
   e) only X

6. Describe the relationship between the group number and the electron configuration of the elements in a group.

7. Explain the difference between the following:
   a) isotope and radioisotope
   b) atomic number and atomic mass

8. Arrange the following elements in order of decreasing atomic size: sulfur, chlorine, aluminum, and sodium. Explain if your arrangement demonstrates a periodic trend or a group trend.

9. Explain how the outer electron configuration of an element is related to its position in the periodic table.

10. The following properties show periodic variation as a result of changing electron configuration: metallic/non-metallic character, atomic radii, ionization energy, electron affinity, and electronegativity. On a block diagram of the periodic table, use arrows and words to show the trends. Use the atomic model to account for the trends.

11. List the properties common to metals, and compare them to the properties of non-metals.

12. Explain why magnesium has an atomic mass of about 24.3 instead of 24 or 25.

13. Indicate whether the following properties increase or decrease from left to right across the periodic table. Account for the trend using the atomic model.
    a) atomic radius (excluding noble gases)
    b) metallic character
    c) first ionization energy
    d) electron affinity
    e) electronegativity

14. Indicate whether the following properties increase or decrease as you descend a group in the periodic table:
    a) ionic radius
    b) first ionization energy
    c) electron affinity
    d) electronegativity

15. Explain why Mendeléev used atomic mass rather than atomic number to arrange the elements in his periodic table.

16. Describe the relationship between Newlands's law of octaves and the modern periodic table. (Remember that the noble gases had not been discovered in Newlands's time.)

17. The first, second, and third ionization energies for a certain element are 0.736 MJ·mol^{-1}, 1.45 MJ·mol^{-1}, and 7.72 MJ·mol^{-1} respectively.
    a) State in which group of the periodic table you would expect to find this element. Explain your answer.
    b) Predict if the fourth ionization energy would be greater or smaller than 25 MJ·mol^{-1}. Explain your reasoning.

Applying Inquiry/ Communication Skills

18. Predict which element you think is the most reactive in the periodic table, and outline your reasons.

19. In an activity, you will be using qualitative observations to compare the reactions of elements in two groups: the alkali metals and the halogens. Design a data table for recording your observations.

20. Write an introduction for the qualitative lab exploring the properties of the halogens, alkali metals, and third period elements. Your introduction should include a definition of the problem(s) or research question(s). You should formulate hypothesis(es) about the relative reactivity of the elements based on their positions in the periodic table. Identify the relevant data you will gather to answer your research question(s). You should include any background information that is pertinent to your hypothesis(es). Outline how you will gather the necessary data, indicating any assumptions you are making.

21. Melting points and boiling points show periodic trends. Gather suitable data to help you predict the values for the melting and boiling points of the radioactive halogen astatine.

22. Use a graphing calculator or spreadsheet to plot a periodic property. Use the software or calculator to analyze the trends in the data. Evaluate the possibility of representing the trend mathematically.

23. The graph below represents the number of elements discovered during different periods throughout history. Using this information, complete the following:
   a) Identify the characteristic common to the elements discovered before 1750.
   b) Determine during which period the most elements were discovered.
   c) Explain how Mendeléev's work contributed to the discovery of many elements.

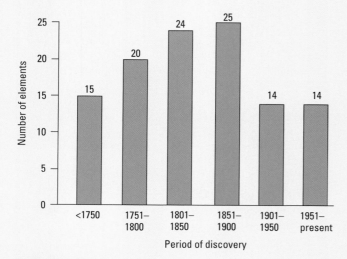

FIGURE 1.22

24. The element with atomic number 119 has not yet been isolated. You are a member on the team who has just achieved that goal. Suggest to which group it would belong. Identify its physical state (gas, liquid, or solid) at room temperature. Determine whether it would be metallic or non-metallic, and reactive or non-reactive. Comment on the number of outer electrons you would expect it to have and its stability. Briefly explain your reasoning. Assign a name and symbol for the element. Design a stamp to celebrate the discovery of this new element.

25. Use the Internet to find the following properties of the alkaline-earth metals and the group 16 elements: density, relative atomic mass, atomic radius, and first ionization energies. Justify the placement of the elements in either group 2 or 16 based on this data.

Making Connections

26. Explain if there is a limit to the number of elements. Write a persuasive essay that presents a position on the value to science and to society of funding research to create new and heavier elements.

27. Forensic scientists are often required to analyze substances that are found at the scene of a crime. Write a PMI (plus, minus, interesting) on whether or not analysis of these elements and compounds should be submissible evidence at a trial.

28. Write a 400 to 800 word report on the semi-metals (metalloids). Your report should include a discussion of why these elements are called "semi-metals" or "metalloids." You should also discuss the impact these elements have had on technology and society. Other sets of elements to which you might apply this assignment are the coinage metals, chromium, manganese, iron, cobalt, nickel, the noble gases, or the halogens.

29. Platinum is a rare and expensive metal used in automobile catalytic converters to decrease pollution, in several chemical industries, in jewellery, and in collectors' coins. There are only a few places in the world where the concentration of platinum is high enough for economic extraction. A group of geochemists have speculated that it would be profitable to mine platinum in a small town in northern Ontario. Prepare a chart showing the positive and negative impacts the mine could have on the community and the environment.

CHAPTER 2

Chemical Compounds and Bonding

If all that existed were the elements, the universe would be a lifeless place. It is the formation of compounds that has provided us with the array of substances around us. But why do compounds form? This is a question that baffled early chemists. The answer lay with the charged subatomic particles and, specifically, with the attractions between charges of opposite sign—the subject of electrostatics. Although electrostatics is considered a physics topic, its principles are at the core of chemistry.

One of the marvels of chemistry is that by combining elements, the compounds they form have completely different properties from their constituent

FIGURE 2.1   What is causing this person's hair to stand on end?

elements. For example, oxygen gas combines with flammable hydrogen gas to give water, the most important liquid on the planet. The properties of water are totally unlike those of either oxygen or hydrogen. And what determines whether a compound is a solid, liquid, or gas? It is the way in which atoms combine. In fact, there are two very different ways in which atoms can form compounds. The way atoms combine determines the properties that the compound will possess.

The way atoms combine also determines the way in which chemists name a compound. Each chemical compound has a systematic name and sometimes one or more common names. It is a lot easier to say "Pass the Aspirin™" than "Pass the acetylsalicylic acid." The systematic name is unique to that compound. Many chemical compounds have the same chemical formula (but different atomic arrangements), but each one has a unique name. The American Chemical Society has a register of the names and formulas of every known chemical compound—a list that increases by thousands of compounds each day. This online registry of millions of compounds is vital to today's chemists. For example, before attempting to make a new compound, a chemist would check the registry to see whether that compound is already known. Environmental chemists consult the registry to determine whether there are any established hazards associated with a particular compound. In fact, information science is now a crucial component of modern chemistry.

Discovering Chemistry

To Glow or Not to Glow? That Is the Question

What types of compounds, when dissolved in water, conduct electricity?

Materials

    solutions (distilled water, tap water, table salt in water, baking soda in water, sugar in water, antifreeze in water)
    conductivity tester
    spot plate

1. Place a few drops of the solution in labelled depressions of the spot plate.
2. Keeping the probes 1 cm apart, determine the brightness of the bulb using a scale from 0 (bulb did not glow) to 3 (bulb was very bright). Group the solutions based on the degree of brightness.

- What do you observe about the variation of bulb brightness? Look for patterns and hypothesize about what the results might indicate.

- Try a selection of other compounds dissolved in water. What types of compounds, when dissolved in water, do you think would cause the bulb to glow?

- Can you generalize your results for all compounds? What factors would you have to consider?

CHECK**POINT**

You are given the chemical formula H_2SO_4. List as many facts about this compound as you can determine just by looking at its formula. Explain how you deduced each fact.

2.1 Chemical Bonds and Ionic Compounds

Key Understandings

When you have completed this section, you will be able to:

- use the octet rule to explain the stability of ions
- understand how ionic bonds form
- identify the elements on the periodic table likely to form ionic bonds
- describe the physical and chemical properties of ionic compounds
- draw Lewis structures for ionic compounds
- identify some chemical reactions in the body

In the previous chapter, you saw the relationship between the properties of the elements and the development of our modern periodic table. In your study of periodic trends, you learned that some gaseous elements are likely to lose electrons while others are likely to gain them. Furthermore, the elements on the left side of the periodic table have lower electronegativities than those on the right side. It is these properties that form the basis of our understanding of bonding. **Bonding** is the term chemists give to the electrostatic attraction between pairs of atoms or ions.

In the world around us, very few substances are in the form of pure elements. Elements combine to form new substances that we refer to as **compounds**. These compounds are formed because a **chemical bond** has formed between the elements.

Why do compounds form? A chemical bond forms if a combination of atoms has a lower energy state than if the the atoms remained isolated. The lower energy state may be attained by the transfer of electrons from one atom to another, producing a pair of ions. This type of bond is called an **ionic bond**, the topic of this section. However, pairs of electrons may be shared between atoms. This, too, can result in a lower energy state. This type of bond is called a **covalent bond**, the focus of the next section.

The Electron Arrangement of Ions

In the formation of compounds, metal atoms lose electrons. For example, the lithium atom loses 1 electron to become the lithium ion.

Notice that the outer shell of the lithium ion, Li^+, has 2 electrons just like its nearest noble gas, helium. Helium is very stable because it won't react with any other atom, and chemists attribute this to the fact that it has a filled outer shell, in this case, with 2 electrons. Therefore, the lithium ion will have the same stable electron arrangement as helium (Figure 2.2).

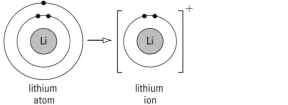

FIGURE 2.2 When the lithium atom loses its outermost electron to form the lithium ion, it has the same electron arrangement as helium.

lithium
atom

lithium
ion

helium
atom

Main group metals of other periods also lose all of their outer electrons when they form ions. In this way, they will attain the electron arrangement of the preceding noble gas. Each of the noble gases after helium has 8 electrons in its outermost shell.

The non-metals form stable ions by gaining enough electrons to achieve the same 8 electrons as the following noble gas.

In Figure 2.3, a fluorine atom gains 1 electron to have the same electron configuration as the noble gas neon.

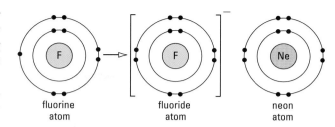

FIGURE 2.3 When the fluorine atom gains an electron, its electron arrangement is the same as that of neon.

How to Draw Lewis Structures

When atoms combine to form compounds, the only electrons that are involved in the interaction are those in each atom's outermost shell. It is much easier to look at electron arrangements if a simple method is used for depicting electron structures. Such a method was devised by Gilbert Lewis and is known as drawing **Lewis structures** or **electron-dot diagrams**. To construct the Lewis structure for an atom, the following rules are used:

- The symbol of the element is used to represent the core (protons and neutrons) and the inner electrons.
- The symbol is assumed to have four sides, and the electrons in the outermost energy level are placed as dots on each of the sides.
- Dots are placed singly on each side and are then paired on each side until the number of outer electrons has been attained.

The Lewis structures for the third period main group elements are shown below. What is the Lewis structure of each of the second period elements?

Na·   ·Mg·   ·Al·   ·S̈i·   ·P̈:   ·S̈:   :C̈l: :Är:

FIGURE 2.4 Lewis structures of the period 3 elements

The Octet Rule

If you draw the Lewis structures for the elements in group 18, you will find that, with the exception of helium, they all have 8 outer electrons. Because they are known as the noble gases, we often refer to their electron arrangements as **noble gas configurations**. For a long time, chemists thought that the noble gases did not react and form compounds. They attributed this characteristic to the fact that all noble gases, except for helium, have 8 outer electrons, an octet, and claimed that this configuration made them too stable to react. This theory dominated scientists' thinking for a long time.

Many atoms react with each other in a way that leaves them with 8 electrons in their outer shells. One such reaction involves transferring electrons from a metallic atom to a non-metallic atom to form ions and ionic compounds. A second reaction involves the sharing of electrons between non-metallic atoms to form neutral molecules. This is discussed in section 2.2. The **octet rule** states that when atoms combine, electrons are transferred or shared so that each atom ends up with 8 electrons in its outermost occupied shell. This is a good rule to follow when drawing Lewis structures of compounds. However, you will learn that other compounds can exist in which an atom can have less than 8 or more than 8 outer electrons.

Case Study

Can an Element Save Lives?

Decision-Making Skills

Defining the Issue

Developing Assessment Criteria

➤ Researching the Issue

➤ Analyzing Data and Information

➤ Proposing a Course of Action

➤ Justifying the Course of Action

➤ Communicating Your Proposal

BACKGROUND INFORMATION

Every chemical element is unique, and almost every element touches your life in one way or another. Some elements, such as oxygen, have very positive roles; others, such as mercury, have very negative roles; while a few, such as chlorine, have both benefits and risks. Risk assessment is an important part of environmental science, and chlorine provides an excellent example.

Chlorine is a dense, pale green gas. It is a severe irritant even at levels as low as 0.5 parts per million. At higher concentrations, it causes a painful death, destroying the surface of your lungs. In fact, in World War I (1914–1918), it was used as the first poison gas in warfare, killing tens of thousands of soldiers and injuring hundreds of thousands of others.

Even so, well over a million tonnes of chlorine gas are produced every year in Canada. The usefulness of chlorine is deemed to outweigh the hazards —and there are hazards. The chlorine is produced in one location, then liquefied, placed in railcars, and shipped to manufacturing plants, where it is mainly used in the manufacture of certain plastics, such as polyvinylchloride (PVC).

In 1979, a freight train derailed in Mississauga. When one of the chlorine-containing tank cars rup-tured, over 200 000 people had to be evacuated from their homes. The area residents were fortunate. Another tank car containing a flammable chemical caught fire, and the updraft from the flames carried much of the chlorine gas upward rather than horizontally. Also, heat energy is needed to enable the chlorine liquid to evaporate, and the cool November weather slowed the rate of evaporation.

Over the last 100 years, chlorine has been a lifesaver. The addition of low levels of chlorine to water supplies has eradicated such water-borne diseases as cholera, typhoid, and dysentery. Whenever illnesses related to water supplies break out, such as in Walkerton, Ontario, in 2000, the first question to ask is whether there has been adequate chlorination. Even in this realm, chlorine is not totally innocuous. Some water supplies contain high levels of natural organic matter (mainly humic acids) from the rotting of vegetation. Chlorine reacts with humic acids to form chloro-compounds, some of which are known to be hazardous to health in high concentrations. The most well-known of these compounds are the trihalo-methanes (THMs), and there are now strict limits on the levels of THMs in drinking water.

Analyzing the Issue

1. Make a chart identifying the positive and negative effects of chlorine gas.

2. Many industrial processes, such as the manufacture of white paper products, use chlorine. There is controversy over claims of increased incidences of breast cancer in both men and women living near factories that use chlorine in their manufacturing processes. Research the main uses of chlorine in Canada, and prepare a chart outlining the risks and benefits of its use.

3. Although chlorine is commonly used for water treatment, other elements and compounds can also be used.

For example, the compounds ozone and chlorine dioxide can be used as a water disinfectant. Research one of these alternatives, and compare the risks and benefits of its use with the risks and benefits of chlorine use.

4. Based on your research, choose a water treatment option that will maximize health, economic, and environmental benefits but minimize risks.

5. Write a persuasive letter to the Public Utilities Commission presenting your choice in question 4. In your letter, identify the health, economic, and environmental consequences of implementing your choice.

Ionic Compounds

The existence of stable ions provides the model for one of the two types of bonds—the ionic bond. Walter Kossel, a German chemist, hypothesized that the driving force behind the formation of ions was the tendency of an atom to reach a more stable electron arrangement. As an example, look at the ions formed from sodium and chlorine atoms. Sodium has 1 outer electron. By losing this electron, the resulting sodium ion will have the same electron configuration as neon (Figure 2.5). This process can be represented as follows:

$$Na\cdot \longrightarrow \left[Na\right]^{+} + e^{-}$$

FIGURE 2.5

Chlorine, on the other hand, has 7 outer electrons. By gaining 1 electron, the resulting chlorine ion, Cl^{-}, will also have the same electron configuration as argon. This process can be represented as follows:

$$:\overset{..}{\underset{..}{Cl}}\cdot + e^{-} \longrightarrow \left[:\overset{..}{\underset{..}{Cl}}:\right]^{-}$$

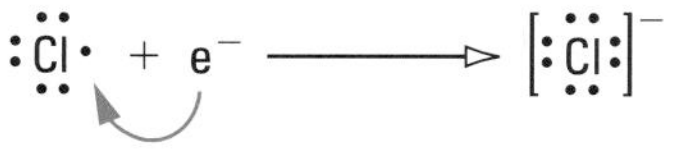

FIGURE 2.6

Electrons cannot just appear or disappear. So some atoms must gain electrons while other atoms lose electrons. But which ones? The elements with the lower ionization energies—the metals—will lose electrons while the elements with the high electron affinities—the non-metals—will gain electrons. The formation of a compound is driven by the need to attain the lowest energy state, and the transfer of electrons from metal to non-metal does exactly that.

When atoms combine and form ions, ionic compounds are formed. An **ionic compound** is a substance that consists of positive ions and negative ions held together by electrostatic attractive forces. The transfer of 1 or more electrons from a metallic atom to a non-metallic atom creates the ions and forms an ionic bond.

The formation of the ionic compound sodium chloride from atoms of sodium and chlorine can be depicted as follows:

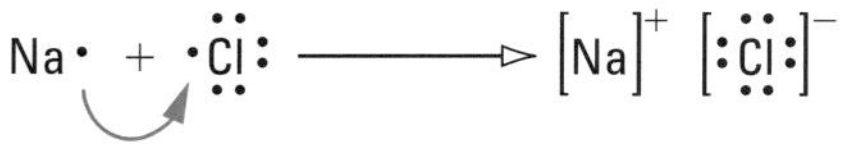

$$Na\cdot + \cdot\overset{..}{\underset{..}{Cl}}: \longrightarrow \left[Na\right]^{+} \left[:\overset{..}{\underset{..}{Cl}}:\right]^{-}$$

FIGURE 2.8

This simple diagram does not show the most amazing part of chemistry: by forming the ions, the very nature of the substances has changed. Sodium is a soft, shiny metal that reacts with water, while chlorine is a poisonous, green gas. However, the transfer of electrons between sodium and chlorine produces a white solid that is essential to life.

Another example of an ionic compound is magnesium chloride. In this case, to create an electrically neutral compound, 2 chlorine atoms must be present for every magnesium atom. The 2 outer electrons from the magnesium atom are more strongly attracted to the more electronegative chlorine atoms. So you would draw the Lewis structure for the compound as follows:

FIGURE 2.7 If a positively charged sphere and a negatively charged sphere are brought near each other, the electrostatic attraction brings the opposite charges together. It is the same electrostatic attraction that holds cations and anions together.

WORD**ORIGIN**

Salt comes from the Latin word *sal*. Salt was so important in the ancient world (and in parts of the world even today) that Roman soldiers had part of their pay in the form of blocks of salt. Payment in salt was called *salarium* from which we get the word "salary."

$$\ddot{\text{Cl}}\cdot \; + \; \cdot\text{Mg}\cdot \; + \; \cdot\ddot{\text{Cl}}\ddot{} \longrightarrow \left[:\ddot{\text{Cl}}:\right]^{-} \left[\text{Mg}\right]^{2+} \left[:\ddot{\text{Cl}}:\right]^{-}$$

FIGURE 2.9

The formula of magnesium chloride would be written as $MgCl_2$, and the subscript shows that there are 2 chloride ions for each magnesium ion.

The Crystal Lattice and Ionic Radii

Ionic compounds are crystalline solids at room temperature, and the arrangement of the ions in the crystals is studied by specialized chemists called X-ray crystallographers. When X-rays are passed through a single crystal of an ionic compound, they are scattered or diffracted by the ions. Crystallographers analyze the X-ray pattern using powerful computers to determine the location of the ions (Figure 2.10). For each ionic compound, it has been found that the cations and anions are packed together in a three-dimensional array called a **crystal lattice**, which has a specific shape.

Figure 2.11 shows the crystal lattice for sodium chloride. The larger, green spheres are the chloride ions, Cl^-, while the smaller, grey spheres are the sodium ions, Na^+. Why is a cation almost always smaller in radius than an anion? The reason is that the location of the outermost electrons determines the radius of an atom or, in this case, an ion. A cation has its outer electrons removed, and so its ionic radius will be less than the atomic radius of that element. Table 2.1 shows the comparative radius of the common third period cations with those of the corresponding atoms.

WEBLINK

X-ray crystallography has enabled scientists, such as Dorothy Hodgkin (winner of a Nobel prize in chemistry), to discover the structure of molecules such as penicillin and vitamin B12. Write a report on her life and work. Begin your research at **www.pearsoned.ca/chemistry11**.

FIGURE 2.10 X-ray crystallography is a chemist's most powerful tool for the study of solid compounds. By shining a beam of X-rays through a crystal of a compound and "photographing" the resulting X-ray diffraction pattern, it is possible to determine exactly how the ions are arranged.

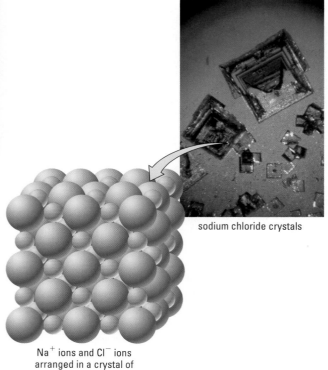

sodium chloride crystals

Na^+ ions and Cl^- ions arranged in a crystal of sodium chloride

FIGURE 2.11 A salt crystal is formed from sodium cations (in green) and chloride anions (in brown) being arranged in a three-dimensional array called a crystal lattice. Not all ionic compounds have the same crystal lattice as the one shown.

TABLE 2.1 Some Comparative Radii of Atoms and their Cations in Picometres

Atom	Na	Mg	Al
	157 pm	140 pm	117 pm
Cation	Na^+	Mg^{2+}	Al^{3+}
	98 pm	65 pm	45 pm

Potassium, calcium, scandium (Sc), and titanium (Ti) all form cations. Consult a periodic table to determine the likely charge on each ion. Which is likely to be the smallest ion of the four? The largest ion? Is any ion likely to be larger than the sodium ion, Na^+? If so, why?

In the case of an anion, the ionic radius is greater than the corresponding atomic radius because there is a greater electrostatic repulsion between the outermost electrons. Table 2.2 shows the comparative radii of some common third period anions with those of the corresponding atoms.

TABLE 2.2 Some Comparative Radii of Atoms and their Anions in Picometres

Atom	S	Cl
	104 pm	99 pm
Anion	S^{2-}	Cl^-
	190 pm	181 pm

In the sodium chloride crystal lattice, each sodium ion has 6 chloride ions equidistant from it, and, similarly, each chloride ion has 6 sodium ions equidistant from it. Therefore, it is impossible to say that a given chloride ion "belongs with" any specific sodium ion. All you can say is that sodium chloride contains equal numbers of sodium ions and chloride ions. Alternatively, you could say that both the sodium and chloride ions are present in a 1:1 ratio. Chemists use the term **formula unit** to represent the smallest unit of an ionic compound that still has the properties of that compound. For example, the smallest unit of sodium chloride would be 1 sodium ion and 1 chloride ion, corresponding to the formula NaCl.

Properties of Ionic Compounds

Heating an ionic compound until it melts allows it to conduct electricity. If an ionic compound can dissolve in water, the resulting solution will also conduct electricity (Figure 2.12). These observations give the best evidence that ionic compounds really do consist of ions. But this idea of ions was not readily accepted at first. In 1884, Svante Arrhenius, a young Swedish chemist, first tried to explain these facts using the concept of ions. He referred to any substance that could conduct electricity in the molten state or in solution as an electrolyte. An **electrolyte** is a substance that conducts electricity in the molten state and in solution.

Arrhenius suggested, as part of his Ph.D. thesis, that the particles of a salt such as sodium chloride were not made of atoms but of charged particles called ions, which were responsible for the conduction of electricity. This was a revolutionary concept because at that time, the atom was viewed as being structureless and indivisible. So where would the electric charge on these

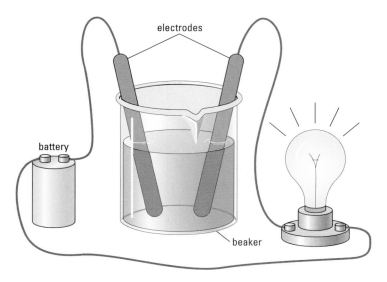

electrodes

battery

beaker

ions come from? His conservative examiners grudgingly gave him the lowest possible mark for his doctorate degree. However, his ionic theory was soon to explain so much in chemistry that, in 1903, he received the Nobel prize in chemistry for it.

In the solid phase, the ions of an ionic compound are held in fixed places in a crystal lattice. However, heating an ionic compound until it melts causes it to conduct electricity. In the liquid phase, the ions are free to move and conduct an electric current. Very high temperatures are needed to melt an ionic compound because the ionic bonds holding the ions in place in the crystal lattice are so strong. In fact, salt (sodium chloride) does not melt until the temperature is increased to 804°C.

FIGURE 2.12 Simple apparatus for testing the conductivity of a solution

WORD**ORIGIN**

Ion comes from a Greek word meaning "wanderer," since these particles carry electricity through the aqueous solution of an ionic compound, as well as through its molten state.

WEB**LINK**

Zinc is probably the most ignored element in our diets. Research the role of zinc in the human body and the adverse health effects associated with zinc deficiency. Begin your research at **www.pearsoned.ca/chemistry11**.

Metal Ions and Our Health

Our lives depend on ions. In fact, one of the arguments for life originating in the sea is that our blood serum and seawater have similar ionic compositions. The two most common ions in our bodies are those of two of the alkali metals, sodium and potassium. Sodium ions are present mostly in the blood serum, while potassium ions are found mainly within cells. Nerve impulses are transmitted by the sudden influx of sodium ions into nerve cells. As the cell walls allow the ions to pass through, up to half of your basic metabolic energy is utilized operating the cell pumps to pump sodium ions out of cells and potassium ions into cells. When you go into shock, the ion pumps shut down and ions flood through the cell walls, disrupting your biochemical processes and producing the characteristic symptoms of shallow breathing, profuse sweating, faintness, and a rapid pulse that becomes weak.

Two of the alkaline-earth metal ions, magnesium and calcium, parallel the locations in the body of sodium and potassium. In this case, the magnesium ions are within cells and the calcium ions are in the blood serum. Calcium ions are particularly important for bone formation, and a major health problem is calcium deficiency. With insufficient calcium ion intake, a porous bone structure is formed, leading to easily fractured bones together with the development of the disease osteoporosis.

Although most people have heard of the importance of the Na^+, K^+, Mg^{2+}, and Ca^{2+} ions, not as many are aware that the zinc ion, Zn^{2+}, is another essential ion. Our bodies rely on enzymes to speed up the chemical reactions that take place within our bodies. Over 100 of these different enzymes require zinc ions in order to function. Zinc deficiency is now more common than it used to be as a result of our modern diets. Research which foods are rich in zinc. Suggest reasons why many people are zinc-deficient. Zinc deficiency is associated with fatigue and lower resistance to infection. What is another metal ion that our body needs? What is one of its roles in the body? What foods contain it?

Understanding Concepts

1. Describe the characteristics of ionic bonds.

2. Show the relationship between the Lewis structure of an element and the location of the element on the periodic table.

3. The alkali metals Na and Cs are chemically similar, but the compounds NaCl and CsCl have different crystal structures. Conversely, Na and Mn are chemically different, but the compounds NaCl and MnS have the same crystal structures. Suggest a possible reason why this is the case.

Applying Inquiry/ Communication Skills

4. Draw the Lewis structures for the following atoms. Deduce the ions that they will form, and draw the Lewis structures of those ions.

   a) calcium
   b) oxygen
   c) aluminum
   d) bromine

5. Draw the Lewis structures and write the chemical formulas for the following ionic compounds:

   a) lithium and oxygen
   b) magnesium and sulfur
   c) lithium and iodine
   d) barium and chlorine
   e) sodium and sulfur
   f) lithium and nitrogen

6. Describe how you would go about identifying whether an unknown compound is ionic. Include in your description any instruments you would use in your identification and why you would use them.

Making Connections

7. Salt, NaCl, is commonly used to melt snow and ice in many Ontario cities. Research the environmental impact of using salt, and find safer alternatives that are being used in other countries.

8. Many different ions are important to the proper functioning of your body. Choose one ion and find out why it is important in your body. Research which foods are the best sources of that ion and the health risks associated with a diet deficient in those foods. Write a health brochure informing others of the importance of your research and the consequences of not eating a healthy diet.

2.2 Covalent Compounds

Key Understandings

When you have completed this section, you will be able to:

- understand how covalent bonds form using the octet rule
- describe why some covalent compounds are exceptions to the octet rule
- identify the elements on the periodic table likely to form covalent bonds
- describe the physical and chemical properties of covalent compounds
- draw Lewis structures and structural formulas for covalent compounds with single, double, and triple bonds
- predict whether a bond is ionic or covalent using electronegativity values
- determine the polarity of a covalent bond using electronegativity values
- use appropriate vocabulary to communicate ideas related to chemical reactions

If ionic compounds are formed from combinations of metals and non-metals, how do non-metals combine together? It is not by giving and taking electrons but by sharing electrons. The purpose is the same: atoms attain a noble gas configuration. These compounds are called **covalent compounds**, and the atoms are held together by covalent bonds. Covalent molecules are very prolific in nature (Figure 2.13). The gases in air are covalent compounds; so is gasoline. Sugar and edible oils are covalent compounds. Many tissues of your body are also composed of covalent compounds, for example, proteins in muscle tissue.

In a covalent bond, the nuclei of the individual atoms are electrostatically attracted to the shared electrons. The smallest part of a covalent compound is a **molecule**. If a molecule contains 2 atoms, it is said to be a **diatomic molecule**, while a molecule containing 3 atoms is said to be a **triatomic molecule**.

The smallest component of a covalent compound is a molecule. Each molecule contains atoms whose nuclei are electrostatically attracted to the shared electrons. These shared electrons form a covalent bond.

A very common example of a covalent molecule is water, H_2O. Because oxygen is in group 16, it requires 2 more electrons to form an octet, 1 from each hydrogen atom. The 2 electrons shared between each oxygen atom and hydrogen atom are called **bonding pairs**. Since there is only 1 pair of electrons involved in each bond, it is said to be a **single bond**. The 2 pairs of electrons on the central oxygen atom that are not involved in bonding are called **lone pairs**.

$$H\cdot \;+\; \cdot\ddot{\underset{..}{O}}\cdot \;+\; \cdot H \longrightarrow H\!:\!\ddot{\underset{..}{O}}\!:\!H \qquad \boxed{\textbf{FIGURE 2.14}}$$

If only 1 atom of an element is present in a chemical formula, whether it is covalent or ionic, no subscript is used after the symbol of that element. So the water molecule is represented by H_2O, not H_2O_1. The formula tells us exactly how many atoms of each element are contained in 1 molecule of that compound (Figure 2.15).

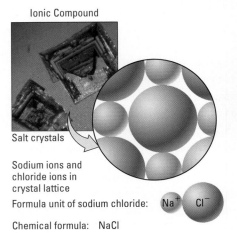

Ionic Compound

Salt crystals

Sodium ions and chloride ions in crystal lattice

Formula unit of sodium chloride: Na^+ Cl^-

Chemical formula: NaCl

Molecular Compound

Drop of water

Arrangement of water molecules in liquid water

Molecule of water: H O H

Chemical formula: H_2O

EXAMPLE 1

Draw the Lewis structure for NH_3.

Given
NH_3, formula for ammonia

Required
Lewis structure for NH_3

Analysis
The ammonia molecule is formed in a fashion similar to that for water. The nitrogen atom has 5 outer electrons and will share 3 of them with the electrons from the 3 hydrogen atoms to attain a noble gas configuration.

Solution
Therefore, the nitrogen and each of the 3 hydrogen atoms will share a pair of electrons. The nitrogen will also have 1 pair of unshared electrons.

Statement

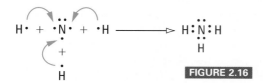

FIGURE 2.16

In the process, 3 covalent bonds are formed between hydrogen and nitrogen.

PRACTICE PROBLEM

Draw the Lewis structure for SCl_2.

EXAMPLE 2

Predict the formula of the compound formed by oxygen and fluorine.

Given
elements in the compound, oxygen and fluorine

Required
formula of compound

Analysis
The Lewis structure of oxygen in group 16 is:

$$\cdot \overset{\cdot\cdot}{\underset{\cdot\cdot}{O}} \cdot$$

FIGURE 2.17

and that of fluorine in group 17 is:

$$\overset{\cdot\cdot}{\underset{\cdot\cdot}{:F}} \cdot$$

FIGURE 2.18

The oxygen atom needs 2 electrons to acquire a noble gas configuration, and the fluorine atom needs 1.

Solution
Both requirements can be met if the oxygen atom shares 2 of its outer electrons, 1 with each of 2 fluorine atoms. In return, each fluorine atom shares 1 of its outer electrons with the oxygen atom. Its Lewis structure is:

PRACTICE PROBLEM

Predict the formula of the compound formed between silicon and hydrogen.

$$:\overset{..}{\underset{..}{F}}:\overset{..}{\underset{..}{O}}:\overset{..}{\underset{..}{F}}:$$

FIGURE 2.19

Statement
The formula of the covalent compound oxygen fluoride is OF_2. Note that the oxygen is written first because it is the accepted convention to write the least electronegative element first.

Investigation

Refer to page 67, Investigation 1

Multiple Covalent Bonds

To provide complete octets, the sharing of more than 1 pair of electrons is sometimes necessary. This is called forming multiple bonds. If 2 pairs of electrons are shared, a **double bond** is formed, while a **triple bond** involves the sharing of 3 pairs of electrons.

An example of a molecule containing double bonds is carbon dioxide. The carbon dioxide molecule consists of a central carbon atom and 2 oxygen atoms. Carbon has 4 outer electrons and hence requires 4 more to attain a noble gas configuration. Oxygen has 6 outer electrons and therefore requires 2 more to have an octet. For all the atoms to reach a noble gas configuration, each oxygen atom must share 2 of its electrons with the carbon atom. At the same time, carbon must share 2 of its electrons with each oxygen. Consequently, you have:

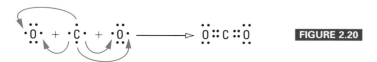

FIGURE 2.20

INFO**BIT**

Most covalent bonds are single bonds; double bonds are common, but triple bonds are rare. Chemists have managed to synthesize a few compounds with quadruple bonds, that is, 4 pairs of shared electrons. These are extremely rare and do not occur in nature.

When 6 electrons are shared by 2 atoms, a triple bond is formed. The nitrogen molecule, the major component of air, is an example of a molecule with a triple bond. A nitrogen atom has 5 outer electrons and is 3 electrons short of a noble gas configuration. You can picture the bonding as a three-step process: (1) the pairing of 2 electrons, (2) then of 4 electrons, (3) then of 6 electrons to form the 3 bonding electron pairs that represent the triple covalent bond:

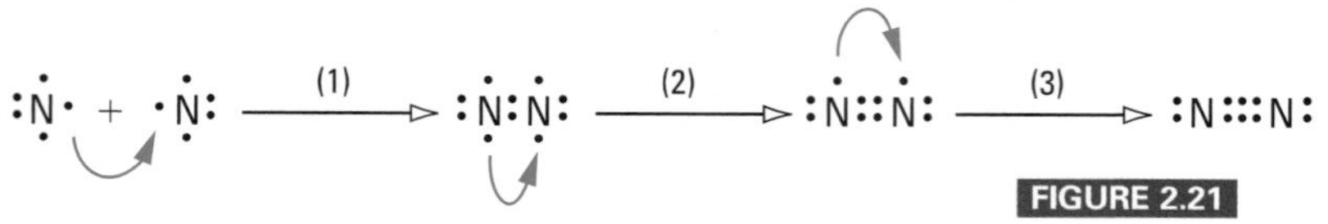

$$:\overset{.}{N}\cdot \; + \; \cdot\overset{.}{N}: \xrightarrow{(1)} :\overset{.}{N}:\overset{.}{N}: \xrightarrow{(2)} :\overset{.}{N}::\overset{.}{N}: \xrightarrow{(3)} :N:::N:$$

FIGURE 2.21

Exceeding the Octet Rule

The octet rule is never exceeded for the covalent compounds of the second period elements, but for the later periods where up to 18 electrons can be accommodated in the third electron shell, the central atom in a compound can possess more than 8 electrons. In fact, many such compounds have been synthesized. Chemists have found that these atoms will often add the same number of electrons that they already possess in their outer shell. An example is PCl_5 (Figure 2.22). Each chlorine atom has 7 electrons, and it shares 1 electron with the central phosphorus atom. The phosphorus atom has 5 electrons, and it, in turn, contributes 1 electron to each chlorine atom. Each chlorine atom will then have 8 electrons while the phosphorus atom has a total of 10 electrons in its outer shell.

FIGURE 2.23

The octet rule is useful because it applies to most covalent compounds you will encounter in this course. Nevertheless, as you saw above, there are exceptions. In fact, an obsession with the octet rule delayed research into the chemistry of the noble gases for at least 30 years.

Other Ways of Representing Molecules

Drawing Lewis structures for compounds is time-consuming, especially if there are several atoms in a molecule. Chemists overcome this by drawing **structural formulas**, in which a solid line is used to represent each pair of bonding electrons. Below, you can see how ammonia, NH_3, is represented by this method:

FIGURE 2.24

If a double or triple bond is present in a molecule, we still use one solid line for each bonding pair of electrons. Carbon dioxide and nitrogen gas are represented as follows:

$$O = C = O \quad N \equiv N$$

FIGURE 2.25

One disadvantage of such formulas is that they do not show the outer electrons that are not involved in covalent bonding. A modified version of the structural formula can be used to show these lone pairs of electrons. The modified formula for the ammonia molecule, which has one lone pair of electrons, is shown below:

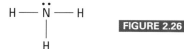

FIGURE 2.26

Diagrams on paper do not convey the overall three-dimensional shape of the molecule. For this reason, molecular models are used. There are two types: **space-filling models** that give a good impression of what the molecule looks like, and **ball-and-stick models** that show the type of covalent bond (single, double, or triple) between each pair of bonded atoms (Figure 2.29, page 47). Ball-and-stick models show the shape of the molecule more clearly.

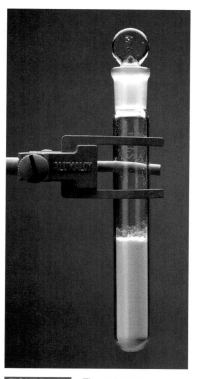

FIGURE 2.22 The existence of compounds like phosphorus pentachloride, PCl_5, requires us to modify our simple model of covalent bonding.

Challenging the Octet Rule

Chemists had traditionally argued that the noble gases could not form compounds because that would violate the octet rule. In 1962, Neil Bartlett, a British chemist, decided to challenge this long-held belief. Working as a professor at the University of British Columbia (UBC) in Vancouver, he assigned his first research student the task of identifying an unknown compound that he, himself, had prepared as a graduate student. The unknown compound proved to be O_2PtF_6, which is composed of O_2^+ and PtF_6^- ions. The interesting thing about this compound was that PtF_6 had an electron affinity greater than the ionization energy of the oxygen molecule. So the PtF_6 must have reacted with the oxygen in the atmosphere to form this new compound.

While preparing to teach a class of second-year university students, Bartlett happened to glance down a list of first ionization energies. He noticed that almost the same amount of energy was required to remove an electron from radon or xenon atoms as was required to remove an electron from oxygen molecules. As the radioactive gas radon was unavailable at UBC, Bartlett asked his colleagues if any of them had some xenon gas. He was greeted with laughter when he told them that he proposed to form a chemical compound with xenon because everyone *knew* that the element was completely inert.

Bartlett, however, managed to obtain some xenon gas, and on 23 March 1962 was ready to try preparing a xenon compound. When the xenon and fluorine gas mixed, a yellow-orange crystalline solid rapidly formed. Bartlett had indeed synthesized the first ever compound of a noble gas. Despite the "known fact" that noble gases did not react, he had the courage to try and reaped the rewards of opening up a whole new area in chemistry—the chemistry of noble gas compounds. Once Bartlett's work was published, hundreds of other chemists began frantically working in the field, desperately trying to discover other new compounds of xenon and even of krypton.

FIGURE 2.27   Neil Bartlett (1932–)

Many chemists concluded that the existence of these compounds contradicted the concept of periodicity. However, if you look at two of the known compounds of xenon, XeO_3 and XeF_2, you see that their formulas are quite compatible with periodic concepts. Table 2.3 gives the formulas of some of the fifth period oxides. As you can see, XeO_3 completes the trend across the period.

TABLE 2.3   Formulas of Some Fifth Period Oxides

Element	Sb	Te	I	Xe
Oxide Formula	Sb_2O_3	TeO_2	I_2O_5	XeO_3
Ratio of Element: Oxygen	1:1.5	1:2	1:2.5	1:3

Another way to look at periodicity is to study series of molecules in which the central atom is surrounded by the same number of electrons. The later fifth period fluorides form such a series; each central atom has 10 outer electrons (Table 2.4). Notice that XeF_2 fits the expected trend of the fifth period series.

TABLE 2.4   Formulas of Some Fifth Period Fluorides

Element	Sb	Te	I	Xe
Fluoride Formula	SbF_5	TeF_4	IF_3	XeF_2
Ratio of Element to Fluorine	1:5	1:4	1:3	1:2

You can see that the existence of xenon compounds reinforces, rather than contradicts, the usefulness of the periodicity concept. However, you should not fall into the trap of assuming a compound has to exist just to fit a periodic trend. Many factors are involved in the existence of compounds, and part of the excitement of chemistry is to understand what these factors are. We must keep open minds and be receptive to new ideas and evidence that disproves current theories and perceptions.

At the time of the discovery of noble gas compounds, chemists anticipated a great future for them: they would revolutionize chemistry, and every school laboratory would have a bottle of one or more noble gas compounds. So what happened? It was a victory of hype over substance. Chemists could get large research grants by making extravagant promises. The media loves to hear of great breakthroughs promising to revolutionize our lives. Though such things do happen, most new discoveries serve useful but unexciting purposes. For example, XeF_2 is a very useful compound for adding fluorine to other molecules, the other product being non-toxic recyclable xenon gas. And, of course, the discovery of noble gas compounds teaches chemists never to say "never."

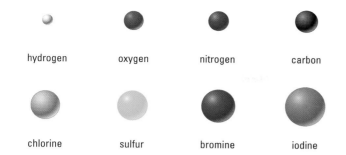

hydrogen oxygen nitrogen carbon

chlorine sulfur bromine iodine

FIGURE 2.28 These are the comparative atomic sizes with the colour codes used for molecular models.

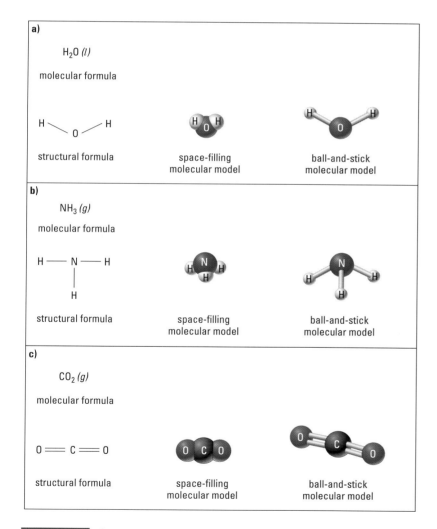

a)

H₂O (l)

molecular formula

H — O — H

structural formula

space-filling molecular model

ball-and-stick molecular model

b)

NH₃ (g)

molecular formula

H — N — H
|
H

structural formula

space-filling molecular model

ball-and-stick molecular model

c)

CO₂ (g)

molecular formula

O = C = O

structural formula

space-filling molecular model

ball-and-stick molecular model

FIGURE 2.29 Some molecules represented by space-filling and ball-and-stick molecular models: a) water, H_2O; b) ammonia, NH_3; c) carbon dioxide, CO_2.

WEBLINK

SIMULATION

For a simulation to show atoms combine, go to **www.pearsoned.ca/chemistry11**.

Is solid air freshener an ionic or covalent compound? It won't dissolve in water, so another method will have to be used.

Materials

small pieces of a solid air freshener
hot water
ice
two 100-mL beakers
dish or large beaker
thermometer

CAUTION: Handle the air freshener with tweezers or tongs. Do not inhale the vapour.

1. Place one 100-mL beaker in the dish or large beaker.
2. Insert a few pieces of solid air freshener into the 100-mL beaker.
3. Half-fill the second 100-mL beaker with ice, and carefully balance it on top of the first beaker.
4. Pour hot water to a depth of about 2 cm into the dish or large beaker. Ensure the water temperature is above 45°C.
5. Observe the base of the upper beaker. It may take some time before anything can be observed.

■ On the basis of your observation, decide if air freshener is an ionic or covalent compound. Give evidence in your answer.

■ Describe the phenomenon you have just observed. Explain it in terms of the kinetic-molecular theory of matter.

■ If you used a coloured air freshener, examine both the bottom of the upper beaker and the contents of the lower beaker. Record your observations.

Properties of Covalent Compounds

Covalent compounds can be gases, such as CO_2, liquids, such as H_2O, or solids, such as SiO_2, at room temperature. They are unlike ionic compounds, which are always high-melting solids. For example, water has a melting point of 0°C and has a boiling point of 100°C, which is well below the melting point and boiling point of salt (804°C and 1413°C respectively). But a few covalent compounds have very high melting points. The most common example is SiO_2 (sand), which has a melting point of 1610°C.

If you set up a conductivity experiment, you would find nearly all covalent compounds produce non-conducting solutions if they can be dissolved in water; for example, a sugar solution is non-conducting. These solutions are classified as non-electrolytes. There are a few rare exceptions of covalent compounds that do form electrolytes when they are dissolved in water, for example, HCl. In the process of dissolving, HCl changes from a covalent gaseous compound to an ionic compound in water.

So is there really any one chemical property that distinguishes ionic compounds from covalent ones? The answer is no. A decision on the type of bonding relies on a combination of evidence: solubility, melting and boiling points, and conductivity data. Table 2.5 shows a comparison of the properties of a typical ionic compound with those of a typical covalent compound.

TABLE 2.5 Comparison of an Ionic Compound with a Covalent Compound

Compound	magnesium chloride (MgCl₂)	sulfur dichloride (SCl₂)
Bonding Type	ionic	covalent
Melting Point	714°C	−122°C
Boiling Point	1417°C	60°C
Electrical Conductivity When Liquid	high	negligible

Polar Covalent Bonds and the Electronegativity Scale

Covalent bonding implies the sharing of electrons. But the electron pairs are not always shared equally, and it is the unequal sharing of electron pairs that accounts for many aspects of chemical behaviour. How do chemists know whether electron pairs are shared equally or unequally? The key is the electronegativity scale that was introduced in Chapter 1. In any covalent bond, the atom with the higher electronegativity will attract the bonding electrons more strongly.

A simple example is HCl (Figure 2.30). Because hydrogen has a lower electronegativity than chlorine, the shared electron pair will be pulled closer to the chlorine atom. This will slightly unbalance the way the electron charge is distributed throughout the molecule. As a result, the chlorine atom will have a fraction of an excess negative charge, and the hydrogen atom will have a fraction of an excess positive charge. This slight difference in charge within a covalent molecule is called a **dipole**. The Greek symbol lower-case delta (δ) is used to indicate a partial (fractional) charge.

Such molecules have **polar covalent bonds**, and we say that the molecule is **polar**. The electronegativity difference determines how polar the bond is. For example, in a hydrogen–fluorine bond, the electronegativity difference is $4.0 - 2.1 = 1.9$. This bond is very polar. On the other hand, a carbon–hydrogen bond has an electronegativity difference of only $2.5 - 2.1 = 0.4$. This bond has such a low polarity as to be almost non-polar. Any bond with an electronegativity difference of less than 0.5 would be considered slightly polar. This low polarity of the C–H bond becomes very important in Unit 5. The only time a covalent bond is completely non-polar is when the 2 atoms are identical, as in the case of hydrogen gas, H_2.

Water is the most important polar molecule to all living creatures. With an electronegativity difference of $3.5 - 2.1 = 1.4$, the bonds are significantly polar. The oxygen atom is partially negative and the hydrogen atoms are partially positive (Figure 2.31). This electronegativity difference is sometimes called the **ionic character** of the bond, and the O–H bond has an ionic character of 1.4.

At what point does the unequal sharing of electrons become so extreme that the compound is ionic? For a compound such as sodium chloride with an electronegativity difference between sodium and chlorine of $3.2 - 0.9 = 2.3$, the elements definitely exist as independent ions. In fact, an electronegativity difference (ionic character) of more than 1.7 is commonly used to indicate the bond is ionic (Figure 2.32). Electronegativity differences are not a perfect way of distinguishing between an extremely polar covalent bond and an ionic bond. It is far simpler to rely on the general observation that compounds formed between non-metals are covalent, while those between metals and non-metals are ionic.

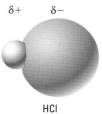

$\delta+$ $\delta-$

HCl
hydrogen chloride

FIGURE 2.30 HCl is a polar molecule.

$\delta+$ $\delta+$

$\delta-$
H₂O
water molecule

FIGURE 2.31 Many of the properties of the water molecule arise from the high polarity of its bonds.

Investigation

Refer to page 68, Investigation 2

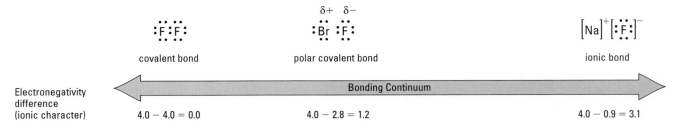

covalent bond   polar covalent bond   ionic bond

Electronegativity
difference
(ionic character) $4.0 - 4.0 = 0.0$ $4.0 - 2.8 = 1.2$ $4.0 - 0.9 = 3.1$

FIGURE 2.32 The progression from a pure covalent bond through a polar covalent bond to an ionic bond

EXAMPLE 3

Predict the polarity of a covalent bond between oxygen and chlorine. Will the bond be slightly polar or very polar?

Given
elements bonded together, oxygen and chlorine
electronegativity table

Required
polarity of bond

Analysis
The electronegativities are O = 3.5 and Cl = 3.0.

Solution
The oxygen is more electronegative than chlorine. Therefore, oxygen will have a stronger attraction for the bonding electron pair. Oxygen will have a partial negative charge and chlorine a partial positive charge. The electronegativity difference is $3.5 - 3.0 = 0.5$, so the bond is only slightly polar.

Statement
The oxygen–chlorine bond is only slightly polar with the following polarity:

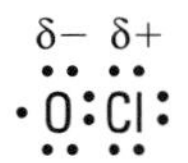

δ– δ+
·Ö:Cl:

FIGURE 2.33

PRACTICE PROBLEMS

1. Use electronegativity values to decide whether the bonds between the following pairs of elements will be non-polar, polar covalent, or ionic:
   a) calcium and chlorine
   b) nitrogen and bromine
   c) carbon and fluorine

2. Deduce the bond polarity in the compound IF. Will the bond be slightly polar or very polar?

The Polarity of Water and Microwave Ovens

Have you ever wondered how a microwave oven worked? It is one of the most important technological applications of water polarity in our daily lives. Microwaves are absorbed by polar materials; the greater the polarity, the more the microwaves are absorbed. Since water is a very polar molecule, it is a particularly good absorber of microwaves. Microwaves are part of the electromagnetic spectrum—between infrared (which is the energy source in a conventional oven) and radiowaves. A typical microwave oven converts about half of the electrical energy into microwaves, the remainder being released as heat (hence the need for a blower fan). The microwaves are selectively absorbed by water molecules in the food. The energy is largely converted to molecular vibrations or what we would call heat. What evidence do you have that the microwaves are selectively absorbed by water molecules? Devise some experiments to test this.

FIGURE 2.34 Chemists now use specially adapted and explosion-proof microwave ovens for certain types of chemical reactions.

Section 2.2 Review

Understanding Concepts

1. Make a chart describing the similarities and differences between ionic and covalent bonds.

2. Outline the kind of information a structural formula reveals about the compound it represents.

3. Explain in a paragraph how you can use electronegativity values to classify a bond as non-polar, covalent, polar covalent, or ionic.

4. Explain why compounds containing C-N and C-O single bonds can form covalent bonds with H^+ but compounds containing only C-H and C-C single bonds cannot.

5. Compound X melts at $-57°C$ and boils at $126°C$. Compound Y melts at $640°C$ and boils at $1304°C$.

   a) Determine which of the two compounds is most likely to be ionic.

   b) Of the two compounds, state which is most likely to consist of two or more non-metals. Explain your reasoning.

6. Ionic compounds have high melting points, while covalent compounds usually have lower ones. Propose an explanation for the difference in melting points.

Applying Inquiry/ Communication Skills

7. Identify the types of bonds present in these molecules. Draw the corresponding Lewis structures and structural formulas. Indicate the presence of any dipoles that exist in your drawings.

   a) Cl_2

   b) LiF

   c) CO

   d) HCl

   e) NO_2

   f) AgCl

   g) KI

8. Predict what happens to the strength of a covalent bond if 2 electron pairs are shared instead of 1. Predict what happens to the strength of a covalent bond if 3 electron pairs are shared. Rank the bond strengths from weakest to strongest. Describe how you would go about testing your predictions.

2.3 Chemical Formulas and Names

Key Understandings

When you have completed this section, you will be able to:

- name compounds using the classical and Stock systems
- relate common names of substances to their IUPAC names
- recognize the formulas of compounds in various contexts
- demonstrate an understanding of the need for the safe use of chemicals in everyday life
- use appropriate vocabulary to communicate ideas related to chemical formulas and names

Language is a key part of chemistry, as it is in all sciences. In fact, chemistry has its own unique words, such as "base," "lanthanoid," "covalent bond," and "electronegativity." These words carry specific meanings. As chemistry is largely the study of chemicals, the names of chemicals are part of the chemical language and they have their own rules. Exact spelling is particularly important since a difference of one letter in a name can represent the difference between a harmless chemical and a dangerous one.

The Origins of Chemical Names

Until the late 18th century, there was no systematic method of assigning names to chemical compounds (called nomenclature). Some substances were named after places, such as Epsom salts, some after people, such as Glauber's salt, and some were given names related to the appearance of the substance, such as oil of vitriol and butter of arsenic. Many compounds were known by more than one name, which caused some confusion. Some of the old names, such as muriatic acid, quicklime, and methyl hydrate, are still in use today and still cause confusion.

In 1787, Guyton de Morveau, a French chemist, devised a systematic approach to naming compounds. His **classical system** of nomenclature named compounds using words from Greek and Latin, two languages that could be understood by scholars and scientists throughout Europe. He decided to name metallic elements first. The name of a compound gave specific information about the chemical composition of that compound, with a key part of the name being the word ending (the suffix), such as *-ous*, *-ic*, *-ate*, and *-ite* (Table 2.6). For the names of a few compounds, he used prefixes, such as *per-* and *hypo-*. A convention was established where the least electronegative element was always given first in a chemical name. Some of our current chemical naming system is based on the rules devised by de Morveau.

TABLE 2.6 Classical Names Used to Distinguish Different Ions of the Same Metal

Metal	Ion of Lower Charge	Ion of Higher Charge
iron	ferrous, Fe^{2+}	ferric, Fe^{3+}
copper	cuprous, Cu^+	cupric, Cu^{2+}
tin	stannous, Sn^{2+}	stannic, Sn^{4+}
lead	plumbous, Pb^{2+}	plumbic, Pb^{4+}
mercury	mercurous, Hg_2^{2+}	mercuric, Hg^{2+}

The Stock System of Naming Compounds

As more and more compounds were discovered, it became apparent that the classical system had reached the limits of its capabilities. In 1919, Alfred Stock, a Prussian chemist, devised a new system of naming chemical compounds, which became known as the **Stock system**. This involved using Roman numerals in parentheses rather than prefixes and suffixes to represent charges, for example, (II) to represent 2+ and (IV) to represent 4+. The Stock system removed the ambiguity of the prefix and suffix method (Table 2.7).

When the International Union of Pure and Applied Chemistry (IUPAC) was organized in 1920, one of its objectives was to obtain international agreement on a system for naming chemical compounds. The IUPAC still meets occasionally to make recommendations about the names of chemical compounds, and it published its latest complete set of *Nomenclature of Inorganic Chemistry, Recommendations* in 1990 (Figure 2.35). The rules allow some flexibility in the use of the classical and Stock systems. In North America, a hybrid Stock-classical system is used, with the Stock system used for cations only. But in some countries, such as the United Kingdom, the pure Stock system with only Roman numerals is employed.

Common Ions and Their Names

When metals (elements with 1, 2, or 3 outer electrons) form compounds, they lose their outer electrons and form positive ions or cations. For example, a potassium atom will lose its 1 outer electron to give the K^+ ion. The name of a cation is usually the name of the element followed by the word "ion." Accordingly, the K^+ ion is referred to as the "potassium ion."

When non-metals (elements with 5, 6, or 7 outer electrons) form compounds, they gain electrons to form negative ions. The name of a simple anion *always* has the suffix *-ide*, but the element name is sometimes shortened. Consequently, the O^{2-} ion is called the "oxide ion" and the N^{3-} ion is called the "nitride ion."

The charges on most of the main group elements were discussed earlier in this chapter, and they are quite predictable. For example, calcium is in group 2 and forms a Ca^{2+} ion, while sulfur in group 16 forms a S^{2-} ion. However, the two bottom members of group 14 (tin and lead) can both form ions of charges 2+ and 4+. An ionic charge of 4+ is to be expected since this corresponds to a loss of all the element's outer electrons. Why a lead or tin ion can have a charge of 2+ is more difficult to explain and is beyond the scope of this course. To differentiate between ions of the same element that have different charges, the Stock system makes it very easy: the name of the element is written followed by the charge in Roman numerals enclosed in parentheses. Therefore, Pb^{4+} is called lead(IV) while Pb^{2+} is called lead(II). From the charges of the lead ions, use a periodic table to deduce the charges of the 2 ions that the element thallium, Tl, forms.

The transition elements iron, copper, silver, zinc, and mercury will be used in several examples throughout this text. The charges on the ions of these metals cannot be predicted from simple atomic theory. Iron, copper, and mercury each form 2 ions with different charges. For example, iron forms an Fe^{2+} ion, iron(II), and an Fe^{3+} ion, iron(III). Mercury forms a simple Hg^{2+} ion and

TABLE 2.7 Roman Numerals Used in the Stock System of Naming and Their Equivalent Arabic (Modern) Numbers

I	1
II	2
III	3
IV	4
V	5
VI	6

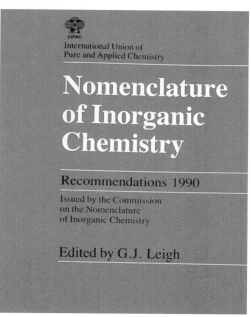

FIGURE 2.35 The rules for naming compounds are made by the International Union of Pure and Applied Chemistry.

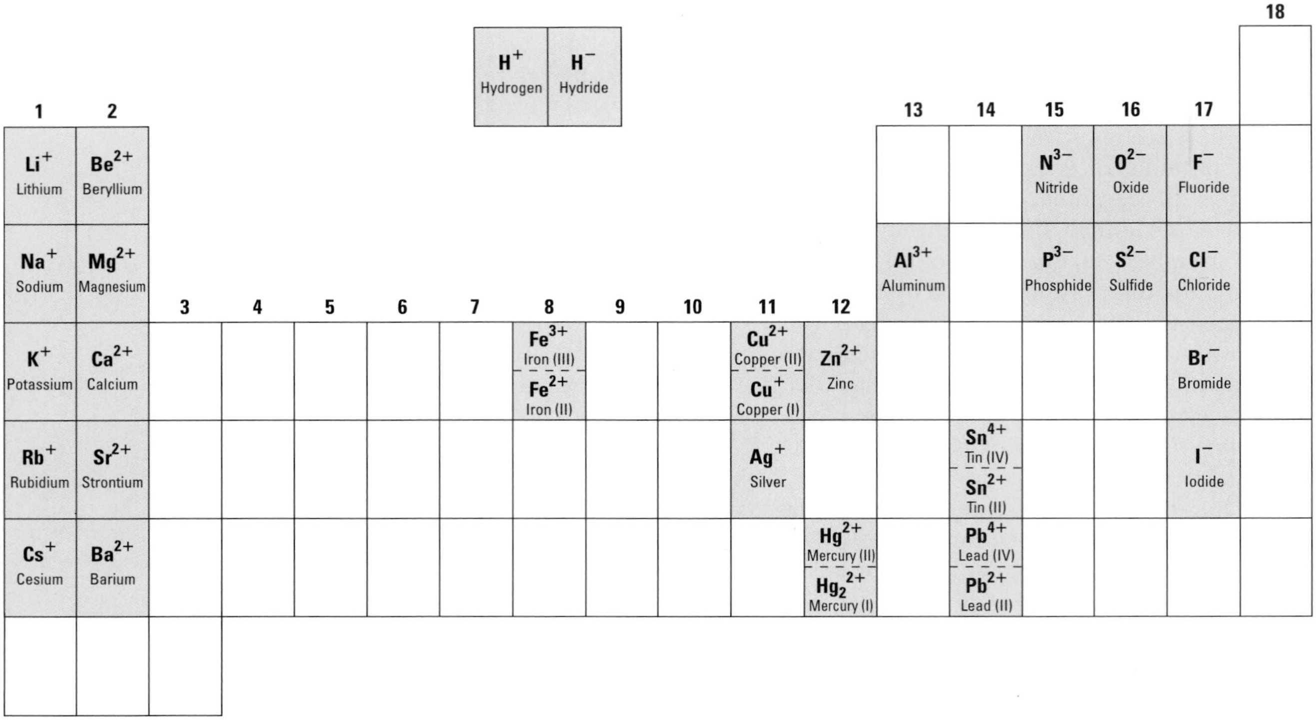

1	2	3	4	5	6	7	8	9	10	11	12	13	14	15	16	17	18
															H^+ Hydrogen / H^- Hydride		
Li^+ Lithium	Be^{2+} Beryllium													N^{3-} Nitride	O^{2-} Oxide	F^- Fluoride	
Na^+ Sodium	Mg^{2+} Magnesium											Al^{3+} Aluminum		P^{3-} Phosphide	S^{2-} Sulfide	Cl^- Chloride	
K^+ Potassium	Ca^{2+} Calcium						Fe^{3+} Iron (III) / Fe^{2+} Iron (II)			Cu^{2+} Copper (II) / Cu^+ Copper (I)	Zn^{2+} Zinc					Br^- Bromide	
Rb^+ Rubidium	Sr^{2+} Strontium									Ag^+ Silver			Sn^{4+} Tin (IV) / Sn^{2+} Tin (II)			I^- Iodide	
Cs^+ Cesium	Ba^{2+} Barium										Hg^{2+} Mercury (II) / Hg_2^{2+} Mercury (I)		Pb^{4+} Lead (IV) / Pb^{2+} Lead (II)				

FIGURE 2.36 Names and charges of some common anions and cations

another ion that is written as Hg_2^{2+}. The latter is a diatomic ion that contains 2 mercury(I) ions bonded together. Although this diatomic ion is often written as Hg^+, this text will use the more appropriate symbol Hg_2^{2+}. Some common ions and their corresponding names are shown in Figure 2.36.

In many industries, the classical system for naming ions is still used extensively. The metals that can have more than one ion are referred to by their Latin names, and suffixes are used to identify the charge on the ion. The suffix *-ic* is used for ions with the higher charge and *-ous* for ions with the lower charge.

Formulas and Names of Binary Ionic Compounds

You learned that when an ionic compound was formed from two elements (a **binary compound**), the cation lost its outer electrons and the anion filled its outer electron shell. Figure 2.36 provides the formulas of the common ions, making it very easy to determine the formula of such a compound. All you have to do is balance the number of cations and anions to give an electrically neutral compound. For example, to find the formula of the compound between lithium and oxygen, you look at Figure 2.36. The lithium cation is Li^+ while the oxygen anion is O^{2-}. To balance the charges, you will need 2 lithium ions for each oxide ion. The formula is therefore Li_2O.

If an element, such as copper, can form 2 different cations, Cu^{2+} and Cu^+, it can form 2 different compounds with any given anion. For example, there will be 2 compounds of copper with chlorine: $CuCl_2$ and $CuCl$.

To determine the name of a binary ionic compound from the formula is relatively easy using Figure 2.36. For example, the name of $BaBr_2$ would simply be barium bromide. The only complication arises with the cations that can have more than one possible charge (Figures 2.38 and 2.39). The compound CuO can be used to illustrate the problem. The name could be

FIGURE 2.37 Since there are two compounds of iron and chlorine, the Stock system uses Roman numerals to distinguish them. The blue-green compound (upper left) is iron(II) chloride, and the yellow-brown compound (lower right) is iron(III) chloride. Using the classical system, these compounds would be named ferrous chloride and ferric chloride respectively.

copper(I) oxide or copper(II) oxide. But the charge on the oxide ion is always $2-$. Since there is only 1 copper ion combined with each oxide ion, each copper ion has to have a charge of $2+$. Accordingly, the correct name has to be copper(II) oxide.

EXAMPLE 4

What is the formula and name of the compound containing aluminum and sulfur?

Given
Figure 2.36 and elements in compound, aluminum and sulfur

Required
formula of compound

Analysis
You can see in Figure 2.36 that aluminum forms the aluminum ion (Al^{3+}) and sulfur forms the sulfide ion (S^{2-}).

Solution
To balance the charges, you will need 3 sulfide ions (each with a $2-$ charge) to give a total charge of $6-$ to balance 2 aluminum ions (each with a $3+$ charge), which have a total charge of $6+$.

Statement
The formula will therefore be Al_2S_3, and the compound name will be aluminum sulfide. In this compound, no Roman numerals are necessary because there is only one possible cation for aluminum, namely Al^{3+}.

PRACTICE PROBLEM

Determine the formula of the compound formed between:
a) barium and oxygen
b) zinc and nitrogen

Several artists' paints are mixtures of binary inorganic compounds (the pigments) with an oil base. For example, the pigment for the white paint shown is titanium(IV) oxide and for the yellow paint is cadmium(II) sulfide.

FIGURE 2.39 Tin forms two cations: tin(II) and tin(IV). Some toothpastes use tin(II) fluoride to toughen teeth enamel while tin(IV) sulfide is used to mimic the appearance of gold in the frame of a painting. What are the formulas of the two compounds?

EXAMPLE 5

What is the formula and name of each of the two compounds containing lead and oxygen?

Given
Figure 2.36 and elements in compound, lead and oxygen

Required
formula of compounds

Analysis
You see in Figure 2.36 that lead forms the lead(II) ion (Pb^{2+}) and the lead(IV) ion (Pb^{4+}), and oxygen forms the oxide ion (O^{2-}).

Solution
To balance the charges, you will need 1 oxide ion (O^{2-}) for the Pb^{2+} ion and 2 oxide ions (each with a 2− charge) to balance the charge of 4+ on the lead(IV) ion. The lead(II) ion (Pb^{2+}) can combine with the oxide ion (O^{2-}) in a 1:1 ratio because the ions have equal but opposite charges. However, the lead(IV) ion will combine with the 2 oxide ions to balance the charges in a ratio of 1:2.

Statement
The formula of the Pb^{2+} compound formed will be PbO, and its name will be lead(II) oxide. The formula of the Pb^{4+} compound formed will be PbO_2, and its name will be lead(IV) oxide.

PRACTICE PROBLEM

Determine the formulas and names of the two compounds containing iron and oxygen.

Polyatomic Ions and Their Compounds

It is possible for a cluster of atoms to be joined together by covalent bonds and yet have a charge. These species are known as **polyatomic ions**. A large number of common ions fit in this category, and it is important that you know their names and formulas and how to predict the chemical formulas of compounds containing polyatomic ions.

The Bonds in Polyatomic Ions   Although equal sharing of electrons can be used to explain the bonding in most simple covalent compounds, the concept cannot be successfully applied to polyatomic ions. In 1923, Nevil Sidgwick, a British chemist, showed that covalent bond formation could involve the sharing of an electron pair donated by only 1 of the 2 atoms. This situation occurs in the formation of the ammonium ion (NH_4^+) from the ammonia molecule (NH_3) and the H^+ ion:

NH_3	H^+	NH_4^+
ammonia	hydrogen ion	ammonium ion

FIGURE 2.40

In the ammonia molecule, the nitrogen has 3 bonding electrons plus 1 lone pair of electrons that is not involved in bonding. The H^+ ion, which is the nucleus of a hydrogen atom, has no electrons. It has a positive charge and is attracted to the lone pair of electrons on the nitrogen atom. The resulting single covalent bond is, in all respects, equivalent to the other 3 covalent bonds between the nitrogen and hydrogen atoms. In this case, however, both of the electrons involved in bond formation come from the nitrogen atom. Sidgwick called this type of bond a **co-ordinate covalent bond**. The positive charge is spread out over the entire ion. This is represented by writing the Lewis structure inside square brackets with the net ionic charge shown as a superscript outside the brackets.

Other polyatomic ions can be represented in the same way. For example, the hydroxide ion (OH^-) is represented by the following Lewis structure:

$$\left[: \overset{\cdot\cdot}{\underset{\cdot\cdot}{O}} : H \right]^-$$ **FIGURE 2.41**

while the sulfate ion (SO_4^{2-}) is represented as follows:

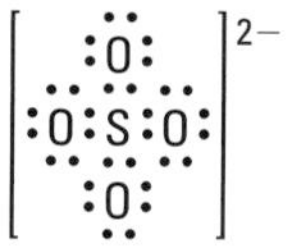

FIGURE 2.42

Formulas and Names of Some Oxyanions

Almost all of the common polyatomic ions contain oxygen and only one other element, and they have a net negative charge. These oxygen-containing ions are called **oxyanions**. There are patterns in the formulas of the most common oxyanions (Figure 2.43). For example, the formulas in the second row of the table (CO_3^{2-} and NO_3^-) have 3 oxygen atoms combined with 1 atom of another element, whereas those in the third row (PO_4^{3-}, SO_4^{2-}, and ClO_4^-) have 4 oxygen atoms combined with 1 atom of another element. Also, the charge on the ions decreases in increments of 1 unit from left to right across a period.

The names of the common oxyanions consist of the name of the element other than oxygen with the *-ate* suffix, for example, SO_4^{2-} is called sulf*ate*. Notice that chrom*ate*, CrO_4^{2-}, and sulf*ate*, SO_4^{2-}, in groups 6 and 16 have corresponding formulas.

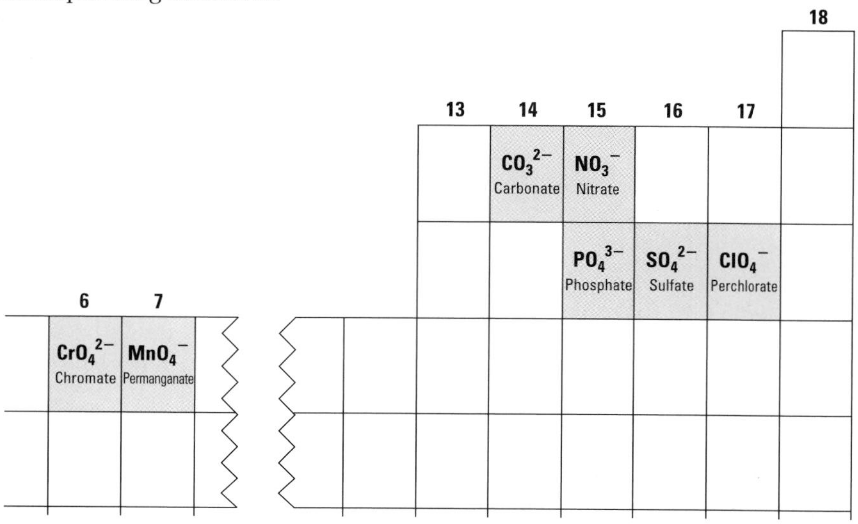

FIGURE 2.43   Some common oxyanions

TABLE 2.8 Oxyanions of Nitrogen

nitrate	NO_3^-
nitrite	NO_2^-

TABLE 2.9 Oxyanions of Chlorine

perchlorate	ClO_4^-
chlorate	ClO_3^-
chlorite	ClO_2^-
hypochlorite	ClO^-

TABLE 2.10 Oxyanions of Sulfur

sulfate	SO_4^{2-}
sulfite	SO_3^{2-}
thiosulfate	$S_2O_3^{2-}$

TABLE 2.11 Other Important Anions

hydroxide	OH^-
cyanide	CN^-
acetate	$CH_3CO_2^-$

Some elements form more than one oxyanion. To distinguish between two oxyanions of the same element, the suffix is changed (Table 2.8). If there are more than two oxyanions, then prefixes are added. The rules are shown below:

	Prefix	Suffix
One more oxygen atom:	*per-*	*-ate*
"Normal" atom:		*-ate*
One less oxygen atom:		*-ite*
Two less oxygen atoms:	*hypo-*	*-ite*

Chlorine forms one of the most extensive series of oxyanions as is shown in Table 2.9. Just as group 6 parallels group 16, so group 7 parallels group 17. Thus the name of MnO_4^- is *per*manganate, and the name of ClO_4^- is *per*chlorate.

Sulfur forms two regular oxyanions (Table 2.10): sulfate and sulfite. In addition, it is possible to replace an oxygen atom in sulfate (SO_4^{2-}) by a second sulfur atom to give $S_2O_3^{2-}$. To indicate this change, the prefix *thio-* is used. Thiosulfate is a key ion in the traditional photographic development process. In addition to oxyanions, there are three other anions that you need to know. These are listed in Table 2.11.

Compounds Containing Oxyanions

Calcium carbonate is a particularly common compound containing a polyatomic ion (Figure 2.44). It exists naturally as chalk, marble, or limestone and is an example of an ionic compound containing the polyatomic ion (CO_3^{2-}). The Ca^{2+} and CO_3^{2-} ions are held together by an ionic bond, but in the CO_3^{2-} ion, covalent bonds exist between the carbon and oxygen atoms. Therefore, when you see $CaCO_3$ written, you must picture it as $[Ca]^{2+}[CO_3]^{2-}$.

The formula for a compound containing a polyatomic ion is determined in the same way as the formula for a binary ionic compound. You combine the cations and anions in a ratio that will balance the charges and give you a neutral compound (Figure 2.45).

For example, a compound consisting of the sodium ion (Na^+) and the sulfate ion (SO_4^{2-}) must contain twice as many sodium ions as sulfate ions for the charges to balance. The formula of the compound will therefore be Na_2SO_4 (Figure 2.46). For some combinations of ions, more than one polyatomic ion is required to balance the charges. To show this, the formula of the polyatomic ion is placed in parentheses with the number of ions written as a subscript. For example, a compound containing the calcium ion (Ca^{2+}) and the nitrate ion (NO_3^-) requires 2 nitrate ions to balance the charge on the calcium ion. Therefore, its formula is $Ca(NO_3)_2$.

FIGURE 2.44 Limestone, chalk, and marble rocks all consist of calcium carbonate, $CaCO_3$.

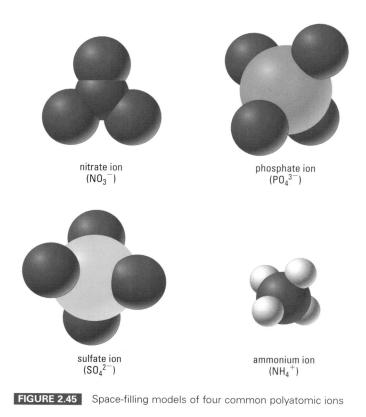

nitrate ion
(NO_3^-)

phosphate ion
(PO_4^{3-})

sulfate ion
(SO_4^{2-})

ammonium ion
(NH_4^+)

FIGURE 2.45 Space-filling models of four common polyatomic ions

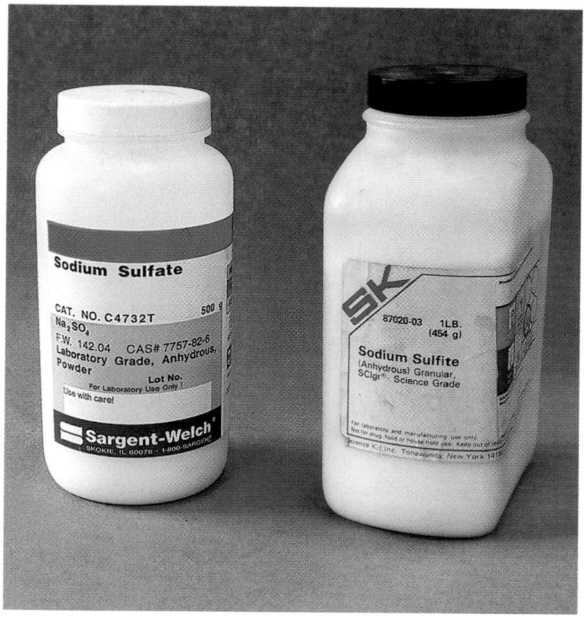

FIGURE 2.46 Although the names of these two compounds are very similar, their chemical properties are quite different. You must be particularly careful in identifying the names and formulas of common oxyanions. Sodium sulfate is used in many detergent formulations, while sodium sulfite is used as a fruit preservative.

To name compounds containing polyatomic ions, you simply combine the name of the cation with the name of the anion. For example, the compound formed from the sodium ion and the sulfate ion is called sodium sulfate. Similarly, the compound $Ca(NO_3)_2$ is calcium nitrate.

EXAMPLE 6

Write the name of K_2CO_3.

Given
formula of compound, K_2CO_3

Required
name of compound

Analysis
Identify the ions present in K_2CO_3. This compound contains K^+ ions and CO_3^{2-} ions.

Solution
The potassium ion and carbonate ion are present.

Statement
The name of the compound is potassium carbonate.

PRACTICE PROBLEM

Write the name of $HgCrO_4$.

PRACTICE PROBLEM

Write the name of the $Mg(ClO_2)_2$.

FIGURE 2.47 a) Sodium hypochlorite, NaClO, is the active ingredient in bleach. b) Many fertilizers contain phosphate, nitrate, or sulfate ions.

You should be able to identify compounds that contain polyatomic ions from their formulas (Figure 2.47). For example, when you see the formula Na_2SO_4, you should be able to identify it as a compound that is composed of sodium ions and sulfate ions, *not* just as a compound of sodium, sulfur, and oxygen. To determine the formula of a compound from its name, you always need to know the charges on the ions before you can decide how many of each ion is required.

PRACTICE PROBLEM

Write the formula of lithium phosphate.

EXAMPLE 9

Write the formula of iron(III) sulfate.

Given
name of compound, iron(III) sulfate

Required
formula of compound

Analysis
Iron(III) is the name of the Fe^{3+} ion, and sulfate is the $SO_4{}^{2-}$ ion.

Solution
To balance the charges in this compound, you will need 3 sulfate ions for every 2 iron(III) ions.

Statement
The formula is $Fe_2(SO_4)_3$.

PRACTICE PROBLEM

Write the formula of tin(IV) perchlorate.

Hydrated Salts

Many salts form crystals that contain molecules of water within the crystal structure. Such salts are called **hydrated salts** (Figure 2.48). For example, if you gently heat some blue copper(II) sulfate crystals, a white powder forms while a vapour is produced that condenses to form liquid droplets on the walls of a test tube (Figure 2.49, page 62). Analysis of the liquid shows it to be pure water. Once the test tube has cooled, adding a drop of water to the white solid turns it blue again. The chemical structure of blue copper(II) sulfate must have contained water molecules. In fact, for each copper(II) sulfate unit in the crystal, there are 5 water molecules.

The presence of the water molecules in crystalline compounds is indicated by including the word "hydrate" in the name of the compound. Therefore the blue copper(II) sulfate is sometimes called hydrated copper(II) sulfate. Greek prefixes are attached to the word "hydrate" to show the exact number of water molecules per formula unit (see Table 2.12). For example, the correct name for hydrated copper(II) sulfate is copper(II) sulfate pentahydrate. When writing the formula of a hydrated salt, a raised dot is used to separate the formula of the salt from the formula for water. The number of water molecules per formula unit is written in front of the formula for water. Therefore, the formula of copper(II) sulfate pentahydrate is written as $CuSO_4 \cdot 5H_2O$.

FIGURE 2.48 Many salts exist in hydrated form, with water molecules being part of their structure. One example is washing soda (sodium carbonate decahydrate, $Na_2CO_3 \cdot 10H_2O$).

TABLE 2.12 Greek Prefixes

Greek Prefix	Number	Greek Prefix	Number
mono-	1	*hexa-*	6
di-	2	*hepta-*	7
tri-	3	*octa-*	8
tetra-	4	*ennea-* (or *nona-*)	9
penta-	5	*deca-*	10

a)

b)

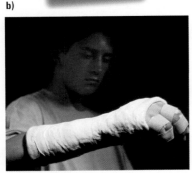

FIGURE 2.49 When copper(II) sulfate pentahydrate is heated, the blue crystals crumble to form anhydrous copper(II) sulfate. The water that is driven off can be tested with blue cobalt(II) chloride paper. The blue cobalt(II) chloride is the anhydrous form. It picks up water to form pink $CoCl_2 \cdot 6H_2O$. What is the name of the pink form of cobalt(II) chloride?

FIGURE 2.50 a) The chemical name for plaster of Paris is calcium sulfate hemihydrate (*hemi-* means "one-half"). b) Plaster of Paris reacts with water to give calcium sulfate dihydrate. It is the formation of long, intertwined crystals of the dihydrate that gives a plaster cast its strength. What are the formulas of the two hydrates?

EXAMPLE 10

Write the name of the hydrated salt $MgSO_4 \cdot 7H_2O$.

Given
formula of compound, $MgSO_4 \cdot 7H_2O$

Required
name of compound

Analysis
The formula is made up of three parts: a magnesium ion, a sulfate ion, and 7 water molecules.

Solution
Without any water molecules in the compound, the salt would be called magnesium sulfate. Because the hydrate has 7 molecules of water associated with each formula unit, the word "heptahydrate" must be added to the salt's name.

Statement
The hydrated salt's full name is magnesium sulfate heptahydrate.

PRACTICE PROBLEM

Write the name for $FeCl_2 \cdot 6H_2O$.

WEBLINK

Plaster of Paris is used for many other purposes, such as to make casts of footprints at crime scenes. Investigate the uses of plaster of Paris and the modern materials that are being used to replace it. Begin your research at **www.pearsoned.ca/chemistry11**.

Acid Salts

There is a family of salts whose anions contain one or more covalently bonded hydrogen atoms (Table 2.13). These salts are called **acid salts**, and the anions are called acid anions. Acid anions combine with cations in the same way as other anions do. For example, the sodium cation, Na^+, will combine with the hydrogen carbonate anion, HCO_3^-, to give sodium hydrogen carbonate, $NaHCO_3$.

This compound is also known as sodium bicarbonate, sodium hydrogen carbonate, or baking soda (Figure 2.51). Why is there no acid anion of the nitrate ion?

TABLE 2.13 The Names and Formulas of Common Acid Anions

Formula	Name
HCO_3^-	hydrogen carbonate
HSO_4^-	hydrogen sulfate
HSO_3^-	hydrogen sulfite
HPO_4^{2-}	hydrogen phosphate
$H_2PO_4^-$	dihydrogen phosphate

FIGURE 2.51 The hydrogen carbonate oxyanion (HCO_3^-) is sometimes used as an antacid as well as in cooking. Sodium hydrogen carbonate's common name is baking soda.

Formulas and Names of Binary Covalent Compounds

For most ionic compounds, there is only one possible combination of elements. For example, $MgCl_2$ can be called magnesium chloride because magnesium always forms the 2+ ion and chloride always the 1− ion. Therefore, there is no need to stipulate how many of each ion are present in the name. However, the formulas of covalent compounds are often very hard to predict (Figure 2.52). For example, sulfur and chlorine form the compounds S_2Cl_2 and SCl_2, while the compounds of sulfur and fluorine are SF_4 and SF_6. To distinguish between these compounds, prefixes must be used. Fortunately, the prefixes are the same as those used for the hydrates, that is, *mono-*, *di-*, *tri-*, and so on. As for binary ionic compounds, the name of the second element in the formula is given the ending *-ide*. If there is no prefix before the first name, as in the two examples just given, you assume there is only one atom of that element in the compound. The prefix *mono-* is attached to the name of the second element in a compound when only one atom of the second element is present in the molecule. For example, CO is called carbon monoxide (the second "o" is omitted from mono-oxide). Note that in binary covalent compounds, the less electronegative element is usually written first in both the formula and the chemical name. Carbon–hydrogen and nitrogen–hydrogen compounds are exceptions. For example, chemists have retained the pre-systematic ordering of the formulas CH_4 (common name: methane) and NH_3 (common name: ammonia).

To illustrate the method of naming covalent compounds, the examples in the previous paragraph have been used:

a)

S_2Cl_2	*di*sulfur *di*chlor*ide*
SCl_2	sulfur *di*chlor*ide*
SF_4	sulfur *tetra*fluor*ide*
SF_6	sulfur *hexa*fluor*ide*

FIGURE 2.52 Carbon forms two oxides, both of which are colourless, odourless gases: a) carbon dioxide, the non-poisonous product from respiration, and b) carbon monoxide, the toxic product from the incomplete burning of fuels, such as gasoline. **b)**

Case *Study*

What You Don't Know *Can* Hurt You

Decision-Making Skills

▷ Defining the Issue
▷ Developing Assessment Criteria
▷ Researching the Issue
▷ Analyzing Data and Information
▷ Proposing a Course of Action
▷ Justifying the Course of Action
▷ Communicating Your Proposal

BACKGROUND INFORMATION

Everyday we eat, drink, spray, and apply many products without questioning their ingredients. When was the last time you read the label on a tube of lipstick or a can of pop? What are those ingredients, some of which you can't even pronounce? According to Health Canada, you have the right to know what's in most of the products you use, and the manufacturer must tell you. Yet, there are things in your house right now that can kill you without your knowing. Which ones? Maybe the information is on the label.

Unfortunately, this is not always the case. If you clean the sink or oven with a cleaning product, there are powerful chemicals at work. These chemicals cut down on the amount of scrubbing involved, which saves time. But some products contain ingredients that are carcinogens (cancer-causing agents), such as crystalline silica and trisodium nitrilotriacetate, or neurotoxins, such as formaldehyde. These products are not just harmful, but also deadly.

What about products you put on or in your body? Cosmetics' labels list some product ingredients but don't reveal which are carcinogenic. The same is true for hair colour and fragrance labels, which contain some ingredients that are also potentially neurotoxic, teratogenic, or carcinogenic. As for the things we put in our bodies, have you ever seen a fish labelled "may contain carcinogens"? Even hot dogs contain nitrite preservatives, precursors of carcinogenic nitrosamines. Studies show that if a child eats a dozen hot dogs a month, the risk of leukemia is nine times higher than usual. If the meat industry were forced to label hot dogs stating that nitrite preservatives are carcinogenic, what would happen? If the government can force tobacco manufacturers to put labels stating that "tobacco kills" on cigarette packs, isn't it time it does the same for hot dogs and all other consumer products?

Analyzing the Issue

1. Identify the different stakeholders affected by the content appearing on product labels of manufactured goods. Write a statement describing the issue from the perspective of each stakeholder.

2. Identify the criteria you think should be applied to the labelling of manufactured goods, such as cosmetics and cleaning solvents, and justify your choice of criteria.

3. Discuss your criteria with other members of your class. Have other class members considered criteria different from your own? Describe how these influenced your criteria. After the discussion, re-examine your criteria,

describe any changes you made to your list, and explain why.

4. Research the policy of product labelling in Canada. Discuss why you agree or disagree with this policy. Describe how your research required you to evaluate or even rethink your criteria.

5. Write a magazine article that describes your criteria and why they should be part of product labelling policy in Canada. Include in your article your point of view about consumers' rights to know the contents of the products they purchase.

Formulas and Names of Binary Acids

Acids have their own rules of naming. There are two types of acid: those containing hydrogen and one other element (binary acids), and those that contain hydrogen joined to an oxyanion (ternary acids).

The most common example of a binary acid is HCl(aq). Because HCl itself is a gas at room temperature, HCl(g) would be called hydrogen chloride. It is only when hydrogen chloride is dissolved in water that it becomes an acid. To name a binary acid, the prefix *hydro-* is placed in front of the other element's name, and the suffix *–ic acid* is added to the end. For example, HCl(aq) is called hydrochloric acid.

The other common binary acid is HF(aq), hydrofluoric acid. There are two other acids named using the rules for binary acids: $H_2S(aq)$, hydrosulfuric acid; and HCN(aq), hydrocyanic acid. Look at the names of the other binary acids to determine the names of HBr(g) and HBr(aq), and HI(g) and HI(aq).

Formulas and Names of Ternary Acids

Most common acids are ternary acids containing oxyanions. To form their names, the anions ending in -*ate* are changed to -*ic*, and anions ending in -*ite* are changed to -*ous*. The word "acid" is then added. The names and formulas of common ternary acids are given in Table 2.14. Note that when writing the chemical formula for acids, the symbol *(aq)* must be added after the formula. This indicates that the acid has been mixed with water (aqueous), hence the symbol *(aq)*. You will learn more about acids in Unit 3. Look at the names of the other ternary acids to determine the names of $HNO_2(aq)$, $HBrO_2(aq)$, $H_3PO_4(aq)$, and $H_2CO_3(aq)$.

TABLE 2.14 Some Common Ternary Acids

Formula	Name
$HNO_3(aq)$	nitric acid
$H_2SO_4(aq)$	sulfuric acid
$H_2SO_3(aq)$	sulfurous acid
$HClO_4(aq)$	perchloric acid
$HClO_3(aq)$	chloric acid
$HClO_2(aq)$	chlorous acid
$HClO(aq)$	hypochlorous acid

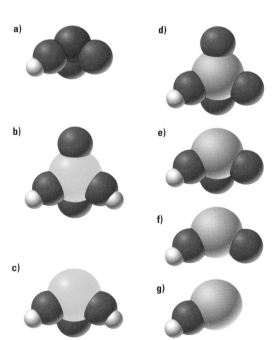

FIGURE 2.53 Space-filling models for the molecules listed in Table 2.14. a) HNO_3, b) H_2SO_4, c) H_2SO_3, d) $HClO_4$, e) $HClO_3$, f) $HClO_2$, and g) $HClO$.

Section 2.3 Review

Understanding Concepts

1. Explain why de Morveau's system of naming compounds is not preferred by the IUPAC.

2. You are given the chemical formula $Fe_2(SO_4)_3$. List six facts about this compound that you can determine just by looking at its formula, and explain how you deduced each fact.

3. Describe how the formulas for compounds formed by elements of the same group compare. Repeat the question for compounds formed by elements of the same period.

Applying Inquiry/ Communication Skills

4. Write the formula for the following compounds and ions:
   a) tin(IV) sulfate
   b) potassium ion and carbonate ion
   c) copper(II) nitrate
   d) aluminum nitrate
   e) calcium ion and perchlorate ion
   f) potassium chlorite
   g) aluminum ion and sulfite ion
   h) ammonium carbonate
   i) zinc ion and chromate ion
   j) iron(III) ion and nitrate ion
   k) calcium permanganate
   l) ammonium ion and phosphate ion

5. Name the following compounds using both the classical and Stock systems where applicable:
   a) SO_3
   b) $CaSO_3$
   c) Li_3PO_4
   d) XeF_6
   e) P_2O_3
   f) $Hg(CN)_2$
   g) $PbCrO_4$
   h) $H_2CO_3(aq)$
   i) $CaCl_2 \cdot 2H_2O$
   j) P_4O_{10}
   k) $KHSO_4$
   l) $Ca(HCO_3)_2$
   m) $HBrO_3(aq)$
   n) $Na_2CO_3 \cdot 10H_2O$
   o) NO_2
   p) $NaClO_3$
   q) NH_4HS
   r) N_2O
   s) $SnSO_4$
   t) Cl_2O
   u) N_2O_5

6. Determine the formulas and names (both Stock and classical where applicable) of the compounds formed between:
   a) lithium and sulfur
   b) iron and chlorine
   c) copper and sulfur
   d) aluminum and fluorine
   e) zinc and oxygen
   f) calcium and phosphorus
   g) mercury and oxygen

7. Chromatography is a very valuable technique that helps chemists identify the chemical compounds present in an unknown sample. Illustrate the way chromatography works using a diagram, and show how you would identify an unknown sample.

Making Connections

8. Prepare a list of five common food chemicals (preservatives, additives, colours, etc.). Using the *Merck Index*, determine how these chemicals affect our health. Visit the Health Canada Web site and search the excerpts from the *Food and Drug Act* to determine the laws that regulate the disclosure of these chemicals on consumer product labels. In the form of a chart, evaluate the advantages and shortcomings of such laws from the consumer point of view. Note that Parts B and E and the Appendix of the *Food and Drug Act* are the sections relevant to this question.

Investigation 1 (Section 2.2)

Inquiry Skills

▶ Initiating and Planning
Applying Technical Skills
▶ Using Tools, Materials, and Equipment
▶ Conducting and Recording
▶ Analyzing and Interpreting
▶ Concluding and Communicating

Ionic and Covalent Compounds

You are part of a research team that is trying to classify a compound produced by mixing a piece of magnesium metal with a solution of iodine.

Problem

To determine if the magnesium-iodine compound is ionic or covalent.

Materials

- safety goggles
- a piece of magnesium ribbon
- iodine solution
- conductivity tester
- deflagrating spoons
- small beaker
- stirring rod
- test tube
- gas burner

CHEMICAL DISPOSAL: Make sure all the magnesium has reacted. All mixtures can be dissolved in water and poured down the drain.

Experimental Design

1. Combine the magnesium and iodine in a test tube. Record your observations.

2. Develop a procedure to obtain and dry your product.

3. Develop a procedure to test if your compound is ionic or covalent. What points must you consider?

4. Show your procedure to the teacher before testing the compound.

5. Carry out your procedure and record your results.

Analyzing and Interpreting

1. Present your observations in a data table.

2. Discuss sources of error in your activity that can be attributed to weaknesses in experimental design. Explain what improvements you would make to the design.

Concluding and Communicating

3. Classify the compound as ionic or covalent. Explain your reasoning.

4. Give the chemical formula of the compound and draw its Lewis structure.

5. Prepare a lab report of your experimental design, results, and conclusions.

Extending

6. Obtain an unknown sample from the teacher and determine experimentally if it is ionic or covalent.

Investigation 2 (Section 2.2)

Inquiry Skills

Initiating and Planning
▶ Applying Technical Skills
▶ Using Tools, Materials, and Equipment
▶ Conducting and Recording
▶ Analyzing and Interpreting
▶ Concluding and Communicating

Using Bond Polarity to Identify Compounds in a Mixture

Most substances in our surroundings are mixtures, and a major task of chemists is to separate these mixtures into their individual components. Chromatography is a technique that makes it possible to separate the components in an unknown sample. It relies on the fact that each compound has a different degree of polarity in the bonds of its molecules. This difference enables the components to be separated.

Problem

To identify the components in plant leaves using paper chromatography.

Materials

- safety goggles
- a selection of leaves (variegated leaves; plain leaves, such as spinach or red cabbage; maple leaves)
- sand
- acetone
- 250-mL Erlenmeyer flask and watch glass
- glass tube
- paper clip
- pipette
- chromatographic paper or filter paper
- mortar and pestle

> **CHEMICAL DISPOSAL: Leaf paste can be dissolved with water and poured down the drain.**

Procedure

1. Chop some leaves very finely, and place them to about a 2-cm depth in a mortar.
2. Add a pinch of sand and about 6 drops of acetone from a pipette.
3. Grind the mixture with a pestle for at least 3 min.
4. Obtain a piece of filter paper, and cut it into 3-cm by 25-cm strips. Trim one end to a point.
5. On a strip of chromatographic paper (or filter paper), draw a pencil line 5 cm from the point at the bottom of the strip.
6. Use a fine glass tube to put liquid from the leaf extract onto the centre of the line. Keep the spot as small as possible.

7. Allow the spot to dry; then add another spot on top. Allow to dry, and repeat until you have done this five times.
8. Put a small amount of acetone in the flask, and hang the paper from a pencil or glass rod so that the end of the paper is dipped in the acetone but the spot is still well above the liquid surface. Secure the paper upright in the flask with a paper clip.
9. Cover the flask with a watch glass and leave until the acetone has moved to the top.
10. Mark how high the acetone reaches on the paper with a pencil.
11. Remove the strip and allow to dry in a well-ventilated space.

Analyzing and Interpreting

1. Describe the colours that you see. Identify the colour that has moved the farthest.
2. For each colour, calculate the ratio of the distance the compound travelled to the distance the acetone travelled. Compare your answers with the others in the class. Explain why this ratio is useful.

Concluding and Communicating

3. Repeat the experiment with different leaves, including maple leaves. Discuss what you notice about the colours from the maple leaves. Suggest what happens when the leaves turn colour in the fall.
4. Research the class of chemical compounds to which these coloured pigments belong.

Extending

5. You used paper for this chromatography activity. Liquid chromatography using columns is another technique used in many commercial and industrial labs. Research how liquid chromatography is accomplished in research laboratories.
6. Research the different types of chromatography that chemists use to identify the components in mixtures.

CHAPTER SUMMARY

Key Terms

acid salt
ball-and-stick model
binary compound
bonding pair
chemical bond
classical system
compound
co-ordinate covalent bond
covalent bond

covalent compound
crystal lattice
dipole
double bond
electrolyte
formula unit
hydrated salt
ionic bond
ionic compound

Lewis structure (electron-
   dot diagram)
lone pair
molecule
noble gas configuration
octet rule
oxyanion
polar
polar covalent bond

polyatomic ion
single bond
space-filling model
Stock system
structural formula
triple bond

Essential Understandings

- The octet rule explains why the ions that form from elements in certain groups in the periodic table are stable.

- Compounds that are exceptions to the octet rule indicate that we need to revise our theory about how and why they form.

- The position of the elements in the periodic table allows chemists to predict the type of compounds likely to form from certain element combinations.

- Knowing the ionic character of a bond helps us predict the likely physical and chemical properties of a compound.

- There is no single way to determine if a compound is ionic or covalent, and there are always compounds that have properties that do not fit our predictions.

- IUPAC chemical names and formulas provide valuable information to chemists about the type of compound, the atoms present, and the way those atoms are arranged.

- Understanding common and IUPAC chemical names helps us be more informed consumers when we look at product labels.

Consolidate Your Understanding

1. Explain how you can predict the type of compound likely to be formed from elements based on their position in the periodic table.

2. Construct a concept map starting with the term "chemical bonding."

3. List possible sources of errors when conducting a scientific experiment. Describe how such errors may affect your results and conclusions.

4. Scientific theories are absolute truths. State whether you agree or disagree with this statement. Give supporting evidence for your opinion.

Understanding Concepts

1. State which substance would form electrolytes when dissolved in water.
   I   calcium chloride, used to keep dust down on rural roads
   II sulfur dioxide, a by-product of burning coal that is involved in forming acid rain
   III sodium hydrogen carbonate, commonly known as baking soda
   IV nitric acid, used for making explosives and cauterizing warts
   a) I only
   b) I and II only
   c) III and IV only
   d) I, III, and IV only

2. Choose the pair of elements that will form a compound having bonds with the most ionic character.
   a) Li and I
   b) C and O
   c) Fr and F
   d) Cl and Br
   e) K and Cl

3. State which compound involves one or more co-ordinate covalent bonds.
   a) O_2, produced by green plants
   b) $POCl_3$, used as a chlorinating agent
   c) $AlBr_3$, used to speed up some chemical reactions
   d) H_2S, an insidious poison that has a "rotten egg" odour
   e) NI_3, a contact explosive

4. The elements calcium and oxygen both combine with 2 atoms of fluorine. Identify which combination of name and formula is correct.
   a) fluorine calcide (F_2Ca) and fluorine oxide (F_2O)
   b) calcium fluoride (CaF_2) and fluorine oxide (F_2O)
   c) calcium fluoride (CaF_2) and oxygen fluoride (OF_2)
   d) fluorine calcide (F_2Ca) and oxygen fluoride (OF_2)
   e) It depends on the system of nomenclature used.

5. Ionic bonds are usually formed between two elements with the following combination of properties:
   a) low ionization energy and low electron affinity
   b) low ionization energy and high electron affinity
   c) high ionization energy and low electron affinity
   d) high ionization energy and high electron affinity
   e) none of the above

6. Describe the differences in physical properties between ionic and covalent compounds.

7. Explain how electronegativity values help us to predict whether a bond is purely covalent, polar covalent, or ionic.

8. Element L is near the left side of the periodic table. Elements M and N are near the right side. Identify compounds LM_2 and NM_2 as ionic or covalent. Justify your classification.

9. Baking soda and washing soda are related compounds. Examine their formulas, and point out the similarities and differences. List specific examples of how these substances are used in the home. Link the properties of the substances to how they are used. Prepare an advertisement for the products based on your findings.

10. Write the electron configuration for each of the following ions, and in each case identify the inert gas that has the same electron configuration:
    a) Li^+ b) Mg^{2+} c) Cl^- d) S^{2-}

11. An unknown compound, A, is a solid at room temperature and does not melt when heated in a gas flame. When it is dissolved in water, it is a good conductor of electricity. Identify the compound as ionic or covalent, and give your reason. Predict whether it would conduct electricity if it were melted.

12. Since oceans contain enormous quantities of dissolved ionic compounds, you could expect that they would conduct electricity. Explain whether this statement is true. Justify your explanation.

13. All chemical activity is related directly to electrons. Explain this statement.

14. Predict whether each of the following compounds would be predominantly ionic or covalent:
    a) KCl   b) $C_6H_{12}O_6$ c) BaS
    d) $CrCl_3$ e) NO_2 f) CCl_4

15. You usually start by gathering individual bits of information. When the collection gets large enough, you impose some organization on the bits. You saw this process in the development of the periodic table earlier in this unit. You have likely used this process for a music or card collection. However, once the information is organized and patterns are developed, then your interest turns to the exceptions. You observed that for the representative elements, electronegativity increased across a period, but the electronegativity of zinc is 1.66 and for copper, which precedes it, it is 1.75. Also, the electronegativity of the main group elements decreases moving down a group, but gallium has an electronegativity of 1.82, and aluminum above it has a value of 1.47. Give reasons that would account for these exceptions.

Applying Inquiry/ Communication Skills

16. Draw Lewis structures for each of the following atoms and ions:
    a) B   b) Mg   c) Ar   d) I   e) Ca^{2+}
    f) N^{3-} g) Br^- h) Si   i) P   j) Cs
    k) S   l) Mg^{2+} m) Sc^{3+} n) O^{2-}

17. Draw the structural formula for each of the following:
    a) Br_2 b) PH_3 c) CBr_4 d) H_2S e) CS_2

18. Each of the following compounds contains a polyatomic ion. Draw the Lewis structure for each polyatomic ion:
    a) Na_2CO_3 b) NH_4OH c) KNO_3

19. Give the formula of the following oxyanions:
    a) carbonate   b) perchlorate
    c) chlorite   d) dichromate

20. Give the name of each of the following:
    a) NO_2^- b) MnO_4^- c) CrO_4^{2-} d) HSO_4^-
    e) ClO^- f) HS^- g) SO_3^{2-} h) ClO_3^-

21. Predict the formula and name of the binary compound that is likely to be formed by each of the following pairs of metals and non-metals:
    a) potassium and iodine   b) lithium and oxygen
    c) barium and fluorine   d) zinc and sulfur
    e) tin and chlorine (two possibilities)

22. Name the following compounds:
    a) LiCl   b) NH_4Br c) Na_2S d) $Fe_3(PO_3)_2$
    e) $Na_2CO_3 \cdot 10H_2O$ f) CO
    g) $BaCl_2$ h) Cl_2O_7 i) $SnCl_2$ j) Al_2O_3

23. The following compounds each have more than 8 electrons around their central atoms. Draw Lewis structures for each. Name each compound.
    a) XeO_2 b) SF_6

24. Write the formula for each of the following salts, and identify each as being either an acid salt or a hydrated salt:
    a) barium chloride dihydrate
    b) potassium hydrogen sulfate
    c) zinc chloride tetrahydrate
    d) calcium hydrogen carbonate

25. Provide the IUPAC name for each of the following compounds:
    a) HgS, cinnabar   b) $Al_2O_3 \cdot 2H_2O$, bauxite
    c) Fe_2O_3, hematite   d) $MgSO_4 \cdot 7H_2O$, Epsom salts
    e) $AsCl_3$, butter of arsenic
    f) $Na_2SO_4 \cdot 10H_2O$, Glauber's salt

26. Using the table at the bottom of this page and a graphing calculator or spreadsheet, plot percent ionic character versus difference in electronegativity. Use the software or calculator to analyze the trends in the data. Evaluate the possibility of representing the trend mathematically. Determine the electronegativity difference that represents the border between ionic and covalent bonds.

27. An unknown crystalline substance crumbles to a white powder when heated. Cobalt chloride paper turns from blue to pink when held at the mouth of the test tube while the solid is heated. Students heated 4 samples of the unknown crystals. The results of their trials are plotted in Figure 2.54.

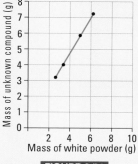

FIGURE 2.54

Analyze the graph using the following questions:
a) Determine if the unknown crystals are a compound. Give evidence to support your claim.
b) State whether the unknown crystals are a hydrate. Explain your answer.
c) A fifth trial was also done, but the students forgot to record the mass of the unknown compound. If the mass of the white powder was 8.6 g, deduce what the mass of the compound must have been. Explain how you got your answer.

Making Connections

28. Make a list of the cleansers and pesticides found in your home and in the homes of others in your class. Group the products and rank them based on the problems they present to humans and to the environment. Write an action plan to inform the community of the problems and to provide possible solutions.

29. Identify the manufacturers of the pesticides and cleansers used in your home. Research what is meant by the phrase "cradle to grave." Examine the Web site of the manufacturers for their policies regarding "cradle to grave." Prepare a report on your research. State your opinions on how effectively manufacturers consider the "cradle to grave" impact for their products. Be prepared to support your opinions with data you have researched.

30. Many people have to be very careful about their intake of sodium ions. Since many foods contain the sodium ion, these people often use salt substitutes as flavour enhancers. Use the library and the Internet to research why sodium ions are necessary but create problems in the body when consumed in excess. Find out the ingredients of salt substitutes and if there are any health risks associated with their use. Write a report of your findings for the school newsletter. Offer to give a brief presentation on the topic at a senior citizens' residence.

31. Sodium fluoride can be used to help prevent cavities in teeth. Where there is not enough natural fluoride in drinking water, sodium fluoride may be added to the water by local authorities. Compounds containing fluoride are also added to some toothpastes and mouthwashes. Yet fluoridation is still a controversial topic. Use the Internet and library to find out more about this subject. Write a position paper on whether or not sodium fluoride should be added to the drinking water in your community. Support your position with the findings from your research.

TABLE 2.15

Difference in Electronegativity	0.1	0.3	0.5	0.7	0.9	1.1	1.3	1.5	1.7	1.9	2.1	2.3	2.5	2.7	2.9	3.1
Percent Ionic Character	0.5	2	6	12	19	26	34	43	51	59	67	74	79	84	88	91

Chemical Reactions

There are many common observations that you may not think of in the context of chemistry: the changing colours of leaves in the fall, rust spots on your bicycle, bubbles from the bottom of a stagnant pool of water, the fading of jeans. Yet each one is a chemical process. Chemical reactions are occurring all around us. Some are very slow, such as the dissolving away of rocks on mountains; others are fast, such as the explosion of gasoline in an internal combustion engine.

FIGURE 3.1 Signs of a chemical reaction. In this case, the green chlorophyll in the leaf has changed to a colourless compound, revealing the red and yellow pigments that are always present in the leaf.

Our own bodies are chemical factories, taking in the components of food —proteins, carbohydrates, fats, vitamins, and minerals—and using them to synthesize all the different components of our body, such as the calcium compounds of our bones, hemoglobin molecules in the blood, and DNA molecules. The food that we eat has usually undergone chemical reactions that we refer to as cooking. Even something as simple as toasting bread is a chemical reaction: the surface carbohydrate molecules are converted to more tasty sugars. In fact, a chef is part artist and part food chemist.

But chemistry is also a major driving force of our economy. The extraction of metals, such as aluminum and iron, and the synthesis of materials, such as cement, Teflon™, and semi-conductors, are vital to our society. Many of the chemical reactions needed to produce the commodities in our society are performed on a gigantic scale, providing employment to hundreds of thousands of people, while export of the products plays a key role in the Canadian economy. Historically, the priority of industry was to produce marketable chemicals, no matter what the cost to the environment. In this century, the chemical industry faces the challenge of developing new and improved chemical processes to synthesize the products our society needs with the least possible environmental impact. This is the study of "green chemistry," the merger of industrial chemistry and environmental chemistry, one of the most important branches of science today.

Discovering Chemistry

Signs of Chemical Change

How can you tell if a chemical reaction has taken place?

Materials
     safety goggles
     copper(II) sulfate pentahydrate
     sodium carbonate decahydrate
     dilute sulfuric acid
     distilled water
     wooden splint

1. Place some crystals of copper(II) sulfate pentahydrate in a test tube, add some water, and shake the tube until all the crystals have dissolved.
2. Dissolve some sodium carbonate decahydrate in water in another tube.
3. Add the sodium carbonate solution to the copper(II) sulfate solution. Then carefully and slowly add some dilute sulfuric acid while stirring. Test the gas produced with a burning wooden splint.

- List four criteria of a chemical reaction that you have observed.

- Suggest the identity of one of the final products of the reaction. Suggest the identity of the gas produced.

> **CHECKPOINT**
>
> Describe three chemical reactions in your daily life. Classify each reaction by type. Give evidence that the reactions are occurring, and predict what you think the products are.

3.1 Chemical Reactions and How to Represent Them

Key Understandings

When you have completed this section, you will be able to:

- understand the different types of reactions that take place in everyday life
- recognize the difference between a physical and a chemical change
- describe the observations that indicate that a chemical reaction took place
- understand how the atomic arrangement of the products differs from that of the reactants
- write chemical equations to represent chemical reactions
- use appropriate vocabulary to communicate ideas related to chemical reactions

INFOBIT

Why does peeling an onion make your eyes sting? Molecules from the sliced onion rise up through the air and react with the salty solution in your eyes. The result is that sulfuric acid is produced. No wonder you cry!

It is a common misconception that chemical reactions occur only in chemistry labs. **Chemical reactions** are events that describe specific changes in substances. You exist because of chemical reactions. The surface of Earth has its present composition because many chemical processes took place over hundreds of millions of years. From the time that Earth solidified, the rains on the surface of the planet and the high pressure and temperature deep in Earth's crust transformed the simple combinations of elements into the thousands of different minerals that you can find today. These minerals were the result of **geochemical reactions**.

FIGURE 3.2 The colours of the rocks in Painted Desert National Park, Arizona, are the result of geochemical reactions.

Every part of your being is the result of **biochemical reactions**. For example, there would be no oxygen in the air without photosynthesis, the process by which plants convert carbon dioxide and water to carbohydrates and oxygen gas (see Figure 3.3). Your body is a mobile chemical factory, taking in proteins, carbohydrates, fats, minerals, and vitamins and producing cells, which are themselves miniature chemical factories that synthesize enzymes, DNA, RNA, keratin, bone, and so on.

What are your clothes made from? Are they made from cotton, wool, or silk fibres? These materials are produced by the biochemical reactions in cotton plants, sheep, and silkworms respectively. Or perhaps your clothing is synthetic, and the fibres were produced in a chemical factory. Look around your classroom. Everything from the flooring to the paint on the ceiling has been synthesized by industrial chemical reactions.

Some of the food that you ingest is used to keep your body temperature close to 37°C. This process is a **thermochemical reaction**, a reaction in which there is a significant heat change. In our bodies, it is the breaking down of food into simple molecules, such as carbon dioxide and water, that releases heat. Thermochemical reactions are also needed to heat our homes. There, energy in fuels, such as oil or natural gas, is released on burning. You probably rely on thermochemical reactions for transportation since buses, trains, and automobiles use these reactions to provide the energy of motion.

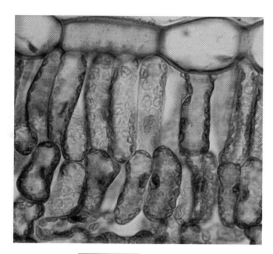

FIGURE 3.3 Photosynthesis is a crucial biochemical reaction that occurs in plants. The chemical reactions involved take place within chloroplasts (structures found within the cells of green leaves and stems).

Recognizing a Chemical Reaction

When two or more substances have been mixed together, how do you know if a chemical reaction has taken place? Most often, you will be able to see physical changes, and sometimes these changes indicate that a chemical change has taken place. Generally, you will see evidence of one or more of the following observations:

- colour change
- formation of a solid
- formation of a gas
- heat change

Colour change, formation of a solid, and production of a gas are usually good indications of a chemical change. For example, the brown colour that appears on a cut apple after awhile is evidence that a chemical reaction is occurring. When two solutions are mixed in a lab and a fine white solid is formed in the mixture, that is a chemical reaction. And when carbon dioxide gas is produced in the familiar reaction between baking soda and vinegar, that too is an indication of a chemical reaction. The observation of gas bubbles can occasionally be misleading. For example, if you warm a glass of ice-cold water to room temperature, you often see bubbles on the side of the glass. This is not a chemical reaction. Gases dissolve better in cold water than hot water; the bubbles are simply dissolved air escaping from the water.

FIGURE 3.4 Blue jeans placed in bleach turn white. The colour change indicates that a chemical reaction has taken place.

FIGURE 3.5 Dropping a piece of zinc metal in hydrochloric acid causes bubble formation. This, too, is an indication of a chemical reaction.

Similarly, the formation of a solid can be an indication of a physical process—crystallization—not a chemical reaction. The term **precipitate** is used specifically for solids that form when two solutions are mixed.

Heat changes in solutions containing water are the least reliable indicator of a chemical reaction. Most compounds, when they dissolve in water, either absorb or release heat during the dissolving process. For example, dissolving sodium hydroxide pellets in water releases a lot of heat, but the heat is simply the result of the sodium and hydroxide ions breaking free from the crystal lattice and dissolving in the water. Only when heat is absorbed or released following the mixing of two solutions, can you say that the heat change is caused by a chemical reaction.

Writing Chemical Equations

How do we represent chemical reactions? All chemical reactions can be described by **chemical equations** using established conventions in chemistry. Chemical equations are a shorthand method of describing reactions. Before you study the different types of equations, here is a review of how to write a chemical equation.

- **Reactants** are the substances that you start with. They react with each other and are written on the left. **Products** are the substances you end up with. They are produced during the reaction and are written on the right. An arrow is used to separate the reactants from the products.

- The products of a chemical reaction must be composed of the same number of atoms of each element as the reactants. This is required by the **law of conservation of matter**, which states that atoms can be neither created nor destroyed in a chemical reaction. The chemical equation must be balanced so that each element has the same number of atoms on each side of the equation.

- Finally, symbols representing the state of each substance (solid, liquid, gas, or aqueous) are added. "Aqueous" means that the substance is dissolved in water. The symbols are listed in Table 3.1.

TABLE 3.1 Symbols Used to Represent the Physical State of Elements and Compounds

State	Symbol
gas	(g)
liquid	(l)
solid	(s)
aqueous	(aq)

The steps in the process can be illustrated using the photosynthesis reaction mentioned earlier. Green plants use the carbon dioxide gas in the air and liquid water from the ground to make oxygen gas and a type of sugar called glucose, $C_6H_{12}O_6$. The **word equation** for this reaction is:

$$\textbf{Reactants} \qquad\qquad \textbf{Products}$$

carbon dioxide + water → oxygen gas + glucose

To write the chemical equation, the appropriate chemical formulas are substituted for the words. Remember that the following gases usually exist as diatomic molecules: H_2, O_2, N_2, F_2, and Cl_2. The first draft of the chemical equation is:

$$CO_2 + H_2O \rightarrow O_2 + C_6H_{12}O_6$$

The above unbalanced equation is also known as a skeleton equation. The atoms are then balanced according to the law of conservation of matter:

$$6\ CO_2 + 6\ H_2O \rightarrow 6\ O_2 + C_6H_{12}O_6$$

Next, the states of the substances are added:

$$6\ CO_2(g) + 6\ H_2O(l) \rightarrow 6\ O_2(g) + C_6H_{12}O_6(aq)$$

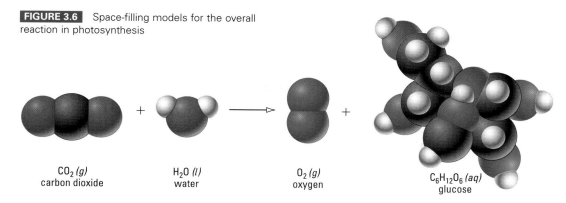

CO_2 *(g)*
carbon dioxide

H_2O *(l)*
water

O_2 *(g)*
oxygen

$C_6H_{12}O_6$ *(aq)*
glucose

Finally, symbols are placed over the arrow to provide information about the chemical reaction. Since light and chlorophyll must be present for photosynthesis to occur, we write the words "visible light" above the arrow and "chlorophyll" below the arrow. So the chemical equation will look like this:

$$6\ CO_2(g) + 6\ H_2O(l) \xrightarrow[\text{chlorophyll}]{\text{visible light}} 6\ O_2(g) + C_6H_{12}O_6(aq)$$

Table 3.2 shows the meanings of the different symbols used.

TABLE 3.2 Showing Experimental Conditions in Chemical Reactions

Symbol	Meaning
$\xrightarrow{\Delta}$	The reactants are heated.
$\xrightarrow{850°C}$	The reactants are heated to a particular temperature (in this case, 850°C).
$\xrightarrow{Fe}$	The reaction is performed in the presence of a substance (in this case, iron) used to make the reaction go faster.
$\xrightarrow{uv\ light}$	Light energy is necessary for the reaction (in this case, ultraviolet light).

How do we know what products are formed in a chemical reaction? The identity of the products can be determined by studying their properties. In the example above, if you collected the gaseous product, you would find that a glowing wooden splint would re-ignite in its vicinity. This would show that the gas is oxygen. You can determine the presence of sucrose by mashing up the green part of a plant and then performing a chemical test for sucrose on the liquid released.

But does the carbon of the sugar come from the carbon dioxide? To test this hypothesis, chemists use radioactive tracers, that is, compounds containing a radioactive element. There is an isotope of carbon, carbon-14, that is radioactive. The radioactive carbon is reacted with oxygen to form radioactive carbon dioxide. The plant is then placed in a container into which the radioactive carbon dioxide is pumped. After leaving the plant in light for some time, chemists find that the sugar extracted from the leaves is also radioactive. Therefore, the carbon in the sugar produced by photosynthesis has to come from the carbon in the carbon dioxide.

EXAMPLE 1

Hydrogen gas burns in the oxygen of air to form a liquid that boils at 100°C. Write a balanced chemical equation for this reaction.

Given
The information can be written as a word equation:

hydrogen + oxygen → liquid

Required
balanced chemical equation

Analysis
hydrogen gas = H_2

oxygen gas = O_2

The only liquid that contains hydrogen and oxygen and boils at 100°C is water, H_2O. So that must be the product.

Solution
Write the skeleton equation:

$H_2 + O_2 → H_2O$

Apply the law of conservation of matter:

$2 H_2 + O_2 → 2 H_2O$

Write the physical states of all the substances:

$2 H_2(g) + O_2(g) → 2 H_2O(l)$

Statement
The balanced chemical equation for the reaction is:

$2 H_2(g) + O_2(g) → 2 H_2O(l)$

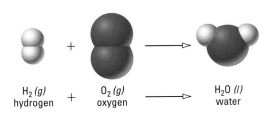

$H_2 (g)$ + $O_2 (g)$ ⟶ $H_2O (l)$
hydrogen   oxygen   water

FIGURE 3.7 Space-filling models for the reaction producing water

PRACTICE PROBLEMS

1. When water is added to liquid silicon tetrachloride, a solid and a gas are produced. The solid is the only oxide of silicon, while the gas dissolves in water to form hydrochloric acid. Deduce the identity of the products, and write a balanced chemical equation for the reaction.

2. When an aqueous solution of sodium chloride is added to an aqueous solution of silver nitrate, a precipitate is formed. The precipitate is analyzed and found to contain silver ions and chloride ions. Determine the identity of the two products, and write a balanced chemical equation for this reaction.

Understanding Concepts

1. List three types of observations that you can use of which you can be reasonably confident of indicating a chemical change has occurred.

2. Explain why the observation of a heat change is an unreliable indicator of a chemical change.

3. Classify the following as chemical reactions or physical changes.

   a) A tablet is dropped in water, bubbles form, and a fizzing noise is heard.

   b) A white solid was obvious on the grass at dawn but by 9:00 a.m. had disappeared.

   c) You found some old colour family photos, but the red had faded, leaving everything looking blue.

4. Describe how the law of conservation of mass is related to the balancing of a chemical equation.

Applying Inquiry/Communication Skills

5. Write a balanced chemical equation for each of the reactions below.

   a) Solid carbon burns in fluorine gas to give gaseous carbon tetrafluoride.

   b) Heating aluminum metal in oxygen gas gives aluminum oxide.

   c) Sulfur dioxide gas reacts with oxygen gas at 200°C in the presence of platinum to give a gaseous sulfur trioxide.

6. Write sentences that completely describe each of the chemical reactions shown in these skeleton equations.

   a) $NH_3(g) + O_2(g) \xrightarrow{\text{Pt}} NO(g) + HCl(aq)$

   b) $H_2SO_4(aq) + BaCl_2(aq) \rightarrow BaSO_4(s) + HCl(aq)$

   c) $N_2O_3(g) + H_2O(l) \rightarrow HNO_2(aq)$

3.2 Synthesis and Decomposition Reactions

Key Understandings

When you have completed this section, you will be able to:

- recognize when a synthesis or decomposition reaction is likely to occur by looking at the reactants
- predict the products of synthesis and decomposition reactions
- perform an experiment to experimentally determine the products in synthesis and decomposition reactions
- write chemical equations to represent synthesis and decomposition reactions
- give examples of synthesis and decomposition reactions in everyday life
- use appropriate vocabulary to communicate ideas related to chemical reactions

For every chemical reaction, it would be possible to take the products, determine their identity by chemical analysis, and then write the corresponding chemical equation. This process would be incredibly time-consuming. Fortunately, most chemical reactions fall into categories. By understanding which category a reaction would fit into, it is possible to predict the products of the reactions with a strong (but not absolute) degree of certainty. For inorganic reactions (those excluding compounds containing carbon and hydrogen), there are four main categories: synthesis (sometimes called combination), decomposition, single displacement (sometimes called substitution), and double displacement.

Synthesis (Combination) Reactions

A **synthesis reaction** occurs when two or more simple substances combine to produce a more complex substance. The most common type of synthesis reaction involves two elements reacting together to form a compound. Synthesis reactions generally look like this:

$$A + B \rightarrow AB$$

Rusting is one synthesis reaction that has had a great impact on our society. Rust costs the economy literally billions of dollars a year. The formula for rust is iron(III) oxide, a binary ionic compound of iron and oxygen. The way it forms is by combining with the oxygen in the air:

$$4\ Fe(s) + 3\ O_2(g) \rightarrow 2\ Fe_2O_3(s)$$

FIGURE 3.8 The Lions Gate Bridge, Vancouver. Bridges exposed to the corrosive effect of salt spray must be repainted on an annual basis to stop them from rusting away. For some long bridges, as soon as the painters finish at one end, they must restart at the other. Chemists have recently devised a new type of paint that protects such structures for much longer periods of time.

INFO**BIT**

When iron or steel reacts with oxygen, iron oxide (or rust) forms. The rust then flakes away and exposes fresh metal underneath to react with the oxygen. The problem of rusting can be eliminated if the metal is coated with a thin layer of a metal, such as zinc, that reacts more readily with oxygen. Zinc reacts with oxygen to form an oxide layer but unlike rust it stays in place and protects the metal from any corrosion. This process is called galvanization.

Many non-metal oxides will combine with water to form acids. "Acids" are substances that will turn blue litmus paper red. Non-metal oxides, such as carbon dioxide, sulfur trioxide, and dinitrogen pentoxide, react with water to form acids that are called **acidic oxides**. An example is the reaction of carbon dioxide with water to form carbonic acid:

$$CO_2(g) + H_2O(l) \rightarrow H_2CO_3(aq)$$

It is the carbonic acid in carbonated water that provides the sharp taste.

Just as non-metal oxides react with water to form acids, so do some metal oxides react with water to form bases. Bases are substances that will turn red litmus paper blue. Such oxides are called **basic oxides**. For example, solid lithium oxide reacts with water to give a solution of lithium hydroxide:

$$Li_2O(s) + H_2O(l) \rightarrow 2\ LiOH(aq)$$

Acidic oxides and basic oxides can react with each other in a synthesis reaction to form a salt containing an oxyanion. For example, solid calcium oxide (a basic oxide) reacts with carbon dioxide gas (an acidic oxide) to give the salt known as calcium carbonate that is found in marble and limestone:

$$CaO(s) + CO_2(g) \rightarrow CaCO_3(s)$$

EXAMPLE 2

Aluminum metal reacts violently with chlorine gas to produce a white solid.
Write a balanced chemical equation for the reaction.

Given
aluminum + chlorine → ?

Required
balanced chemical equation

Analysis
$Al + Cl_2 →$?

This is a synthesis reaction of two elements. The product has to be aluminum chloride. Since aluminum forms Al^{3+} and chloride is Cl^-, the formula of the product must be solid $AlCl_3$.

Solution
Write the skeleton equation:

$Al + Cl_2 → AlCl_3$

Apply the law of conservation of matter:

$2 Al + 3 Cl_2 → 2 AlCl_3$

Add the states:

$2 Al(s) + 3 Cl_2(g) → 2 AlCl_3(s)$

Statement
The balanced chemical equation is:

$2 Al(s) + 3 Cl_2(g) → 2 AlCl_3(s)$

PRACTICE PROBLEM

Predict the products and write the balanced equation for the synthesis of lithium metal and chlorine gas.

EXAMPLE 3

In sealed systems such as submarines and spacecraft, the buildup of carbon dioxide gas from the exhaled air of the inhabitants is a real problem. To prevent the concentration of this gas from reaching unhealthy levels, one route is to cycle the air through canisters of lithium oxide. Write a balanced chemical equation for the synthesis reaction that occurs between solid lithium oxide and gaseous carbon dioxide.

Given
lithium oxide + carbon dioxide → ?

Required
balanced chemical equation

Analysis
$Li_2O + CO_2 →$?

This is a synthesis reaction of a basic (metallic) oxide with an acidic (non-metallic) oxide to give a salt containing an oxyanion. The only carbon-containing oxyanion is carbonate. Therefore, the product might be lithium carbonate, Li_2CO_3.

Solution
Write the skeleton equation:

$Li_2O + CO_2 \rightarrow Li_2CO_3$

The atoms are balanced already as required by the law of conservation of matter.

Add the states. As salts are solids, lithium carbonate must be solid.

$Li_2O(s) + CO_2(g) \rightarrow Li_2CO_3(s)$

Statement
The balanced chemical equation for the synthesis reaction is:

$Li_2O(s) + CO_2(g) \rightarrow Li_2CO_3(s)$

PRACTICE PROBLEM

Predict the products and write balanced equations for the following synthesis reactions:
a) solid barium oxide and sulfur dioxide gas
b) solid potassium oxide and water

Decomposition Reactions

A **decomposition reaction** can be considered as the reverse of a synthesis reaction. In a decomposition reaction, a complicated substance is broken down into two or more simpler substances. Decomposition reactions in which elements are produced are quite rare. The general form of this type of reaction is:

$AB \rightarrow A + B$

For example, 18th century chemists prepared oxygen gas by heating solid mercury(II) oxide, leaving behind globules of shiny mercury metal. The chemical equation for the reaction (shown in Figure 3.9) is:

$$2\ HgO(s) \xrightarrow{\Delta} 2\ Hg(l) + O_2(g)$$

Decomposition reactions that occur as a result of heating are called **thermal decompositions**. For example, some acids such as carbonic acid decompose when heated. Carbonic acid is an aqueous mixture that also contains carbon dioxide and water. By changing the reaction conditions, the relative amounts of carbon dioxide, water, and carbonic acid can change. Heating causes more of the carbonic acid to decompose:

$$H_2CO_3(aq) \xrightarrow{\Delta} CO_2(g) + H_2O(l)$$

Although it is quite rare for acids to decompose to form acidic oxides and water, most bases decompose on heating to form basic oxides and water. For example, strong heating of calcium hydroxide produces calcium oxide (commonly called quicklime) and water vapour:

$$Ca(OH)_2(s) \xrightarrow{\Delta} CaO(s) + H_2O(g)$$

INFOBIT

Strongly heating a lump of quicklime (CaO) causes it to glow brightly. About 100 years ago, the intense light from glowing quicklime was used as stage lighting in theatres, hence the origin of the saying "being in the limelight."

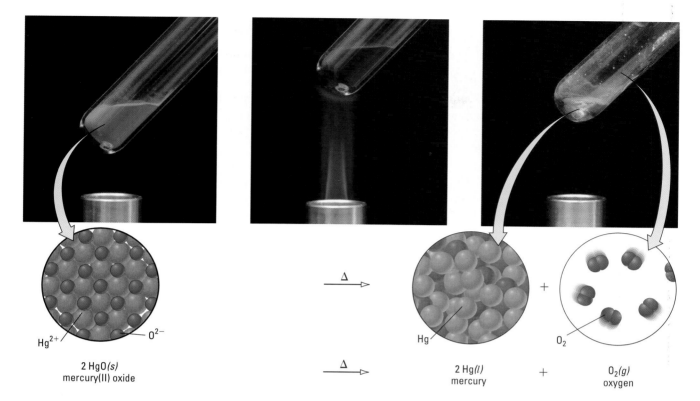

$$2\ HgO(s) \qquad\qquad\qquad\qquad 2\ Hg(l) \qquad + \qquad O_2(g)$$
mercury(II) oxide   mercury   oxygen

FIGURE 3.9 The thermal decomposition of mercury(II) oxide causes its colour to change from red to black. Oxygen gas is released and liquid mercury begins to collect on the sides of the test tube.

Several salts, particularly carbonates, can be thermally decomposed to form an acidic oxide and a basic oxide. For example, strong heating of solid calcium carbonate decomposes the salt into solid calcium oxide and carbon dioxide gas:

$$CaCO_3(s) \xrightarrow{\ \Delta\ } CaO(s) + CO_2(g)$$

It is not always easy to make predictions about the products that will be formed in a decomposition reaction. For example, if solid ammonium nitrate is heated, water vapour and dinitrogen oxide gas are produced:

$$NH_4NO_3(s) \xrightarrow{\ \Delta\ } 2\ H_2O(g) + N_2O(g)$$

Ammonium nitrate is used as both a fertilizer and an explosive and must be handled carefully. Some disastrous explosions have occurred when bulk quantities of ammonium nitrate have been accidentally heated. One example occurred in 1947 in Texas City, Texas. A ship carrying ammonium nitrate caught fire, and the heating of the cargo caused a massive explosion, which destroyed the city and killed over 600 people.

The bleach and disinfectant hydrogen peroxide solution also decomposes into simpler substances. A hydrogen peroxide solution is quite stable for a long while, but in the presence of manganese(IV) oxide, it froths and foams, decomposing into water and oxygen gas (Figure 3.10):

$$2\ H_2O_2(aq) \xrightarrow{\ MnO_2\ } 2\ H_2O(l) + O_2(g)$$

WEBLINK

What exactly happened during the Texas City explosion? Taking the role of the safety officer for Texas City, write a report listing your recommendations to prevent such an accident from happening again and explain your reasoning. Begin your research at **www.pearsoned.ca/chemistry11**.

What Whitewash and Chemistry Have in Common

The term "whitewash" is often used today to indicate some story or event that has been covered up. Whitewash is actually a suspension of calcium hydroxide in water, and it provided early Canadian settlers with a material to paint their houses and fences. The process involved decomposition and synthesis reactions. Calcium carbonate (limestone, chalk) is found in many parts of the country. Heating it gives calcium oxide and carbon dioxide:

$$CaCO_3(s) \xrightarrow{\Delta} CaO(s) + CO_2(g)$$

The calcium oxide was then mixed with an excess of water to give a slurry of calcium hydroxide:

$$CaO(s) + H_2O(l) \rightarrow Ca(OH)_2(aq)$$

The calcium hydroxide was then painted on the fences and wood siding where it would dry. The white colour became more intense with time as the calcium hydroxide reacted with the carbon dioxide in air to give the intense white colour of chalk, calcium carbonate.

$$Ca(OH)_2(s) + CO_2(g) \rightarrow CaCO_3(s)$$

Did the use of whitewash contribute at all to increasing atmospheric levels of carbon dioxide. If not, why not? If so, would the contributions have been significant?

FIGURE 3.10 The decomposition of hydrogen peroxide. a) Hydrogen peroxide decomposes very slowly on its own. b) Some manganese(IV) oxide is added to speed up the reaction. Very rapid decomposition of the hydrogen peroxide occurs. Sufficient heat is produced to cause the water of the hydrogen peroxide solution to boil. The white "smoke" that is escaping from the mouth of the test tube is actually condensed water vapour.

FIGURE 3.11 The White House got its name after it was whitewashed in 1814. It had been burned that year after a British force invaded Washington, D.C., during the War of 1812.

EXAMPLE 4

When solid lithium hydroxide is heated, two products are formed: one is a solid, and the other is a gas that condenses into a liquid on the cool walls of a test tube. Write a balanced chemical equation for this reaction.

Given
lithium hydroxide $\xrightarrow{\Delta}$?

Required
balanced chemical equation

Analysis

LiOH $\xrightarrow{\Delta}$?

This is a decomposition reaction of a base. The lithium hydroxide will decompose to a basic (metallic) oxide and water. Since lithium forms the Li^+ ion, the metallic oxide must be Li_2O.

Solution
Write the skeleton equation:

LiOH $\xrightarrow{\Delta}$ Li_2O + H_2O

Apply the law of conservation of matter:

2 LiOH $\xrightarrow{\Delta}$ Li_2O + H_2O

Add the states:

2 LiOH(s) $\xrightarrow{\Delta}$ Li_2O(s) + H_2O(l)

Statement
The balanced chemical equation is:

2 LiOH(s) $\xrightarrow{\Delta}$ Li_2O(s) + H_2O(l)

PRACTICE PROBLEM

Predict the products and write the balanced chemical equation for the thermal decomposition of solid silver oxide.

EXAMPLE 5

When solid zinc carbonate is heated, two products are formed: one a solid and one a gas. Write a balanced chemical equation for this reaction.

Given
zinc carbonate $\xrightarrow{\Delta}$?

Required
balanced chemical equation

Analysis
This is a decomposition reaction of a salt. The zinc carbonate will decompose into a basic (metallic) oxide and an acidic (non-metallic) oxide. Since

zinc forms the Zn^{2+} ion, the metallic oxide must be ZnO. The acidic oxide corresponding to the carbonate ion is carbon dioxide, CO_2.

Solution
Write the skeleton equation:

$$ZnCO_3 \xrightarrow{\Delta} ZnO + CO_2$$

The atoms are already balanced as required by the law of conservation of matter.

Add the states. Since carbon dioxide is a gas, then zinc oxide must be a solid (as expected for an ionic compound).

$$ZnCO_3(s) \xrightarrow{\Delta} ZnO(s) + CO_2(g)$$

Statement
The balanced chemical equation is:

$$ZnCO_3(s) \xrightarrow{\Delta} ZnO(s) + CO_2(g)$$

PRACTICE PROBLEM

Predict the products and write balanced chemical equations for the following decomposition reactions:
a) heating zinc hydroxide
b) heating iron(II) carbonate

Section 3.2 Review

Understanding Concepts

1. Explain what is meant by the following terms, and give an example of each.
   a) synthesis reaction
   b) decomposition reaction

2. Describe the product that is formed and identify the type of chemical reaction when copper(II) oxide and carbon are combined.

Applying Inquiry/ Communication Skills

3. Predict the products and write a balanced equation for each reaction. Classify each reaction, and identify whether the product is an acid, a base, a salt, an acidic oxide, or a basic oxide.

   a) $Zn(s) + Cl_2(g) \rightarrow$
   b) $AgCl(s) \xrightarrow{\Delta}$
   c) $Mg(OH)_2(s) \xrightarrow{\Delta}$
   d) $CaO(s) + H_2O(l) \rightarrow$
   e) $Li_2O(s) + CO_2(g) \rightarrow$
   f) $Mg(s) + O_2(g) \rightarrow$
   g) $MgCO_3(s) \xrightarrow{\Delta}$

4. Identify the chemical reaction that takes place when silver tarnishes. Write a balanced chemical equation for the reaction.

5. Describe the information that is conveyed in the following equations:
   a) $2\ CO(g) + O_2(g) \rightarrow 2\ CO(g)$
   b) $PCl_3(l) + Cl_2(g) \rightarrow PCl_5(g)$

3.3 Single and Double Displacement Reactions

Key Understandings

When you have completed this section, you will be able to:

- demonstrate an understanding of the relationship between the type of chemical reaction and the nature of the reactants
- write chemical equations to represent single and double displacement reactions
- predict the products of single and double displacement reactions, and test the predictions through experimentation
- investigate through experimentation the reactions of elements to produce an activity series
- evaluate and compare the reactivity of metals and alloys
- explain why most metals are found in nature as compounds
- understand the need to use chemicals safely in everyday life
- use appropriate vocabulary to communicate ideas related to chemical reactions

The reactions in the previous section were among the simplest, with only one product (synthesis) or one reactant (decomposition). However, much more important in chemistry are the other two categories of reactions, single displacement and double displacement.

Single Displacement Reactions

In **single displacement reactions**, also called single replacement reactions, one element replaces another element in a compound. Single displacement reactions have the following general form:

$$A + BC \rightarrow AC + B$$

One example of industrial importance involves the reaction of iron metal with a solution of copper(II) sulfate to give copper metal and iron(II) sulfate. Copper is an expensive metal, so it is economically important to collect copper-containing waste solutions from copper mines and pass the solution through towers of scrap iron. The metals switch places and the copper can be collected and melted down.

$$Fe_{(s)} + CuSO_{4(aq)} \rightarrow FeSO_{4(aq)} + Cu_{(s)}$$

Using the Activity Series to Predict Metal Reactivity

If you add a lump of copper to a solution of iron(II) sulfate, will any reaction happen? The answer is no. So how can you predict whether a reaction will occur? The answer is found in the relative reactivities of metals. Metals can be placed in an order known as the **activity series**. Knowing this order enables you to predict whether or not a particular single displacement reaction will occur.

The activity series (or electrochemical or electromotive series, as it is also called) consists of an ordering of metallic elements plus hydrogen. Any metal to the left will displace a metal ion to the right from a compound. You can usually predict when a single displacement reaction is likely to occur by referring to the activity series.

FIGURE 3.12 The iron in the bolt is switching places with the copper in solution. The green colour of the solution is characteristic of the Fe^{2+} ion.

Li K Ba Ca Na Mg Al Zn Fe Ni Sn Pb H Cu Hg Ag Au

metal   metal ion

Discovering Chemistry — Metals Displacing Metals

In this activity, you will be given small pieces of metal and corresponding solutions of compounds of the metal. Your job will be to predict which reactions will occur and then design a way to provide evidence to support your predictions.

Materials
  spot plate
  tweezers
  wash bottle to rinse the spot plate

1. Use the tweezers to place a small piece of metal into 3 or 4 drops of a metal solution in a depression of the spot plate. Record any evidence of a reaction.

2. Repeat for all possible pairs of metal and metal compound solution provided.

3. Use the wash bottle to rinse the spot plate into a container provided by your teacher. Place all unreacted metal into a separate container.

- Order the metals in a chart so that the metal at the top will displace all metals from a compound below it.

TABLE 3.3

Metal*	Mg	Zn	Cu	Sn	Fe
Solution of Metal Compound in Dropper Bottles	$MgSO_4$	$ZnSO_4$	$CuSO_4$	$SnCl_2$	$FeSO_4$

* must be clean

EXAMPLE 6

Will zinc metal react with tin(II) nitrate, and if so, what will the products be?

Given
zinc + tin(II) nitrate → ?

Required
prediction of reaction taking place and products

Analysis
Zinc metal, Zn(s), is to the left of tin(II), Sn^{2+}(aq), metal ion; therefore, a reaction will occur.

The metals will switch to give zinc ion, Zn^{2+}(aq), and tin metal, Sn(s).

Solution
Write the skeleton equation:

$Zn + Sn(NO_3)_2 \rightarrow Sn + Zn(NO_3)_2$

The atoms are already balanced as required by the law of conservation of matter.

Add the states:

$Zn(s) + Sn(NO_3)_2(aq) \rightarrow Sn(s) + Zn(NO_3)_2(aq)$

Statement
The products will be tin metal and zinc nitrate.

PRACTICE PROBLEM

Predict which of the following displacement reactions will occur. Write a balanced chemical equation for the reaction you predict will occur.
a) copper metal with silver nitrate solution
b) copper metal with iron(II) chloride solution

Using the Activity Series to Predict Reactions with Acids

The element hydrogen is located among the metals of the activity series. Having this element in the series enables the series to be used for a second purpose—to identify which metals react with dilute acids to produce hydrogen gas. Those metals to the left of hydrogen in the series react with acids, while those to the right do not.

Li K Ba Ca Na Mg Al Zn Fe Ni Sn Pb H Cu Hg Ag Au

$\longleftarrow$ react with acids $\longrightarrow$ $\longleftarrow$ do not $\longrightarrow$
react
with
acids

For example, you can predict that zinc metal will displace hydrogen gas from hydrochloric acid because zinc is to the left of hydrogen in the series. This prediction proves to be correct experimentally. The reaction is actually an excellent method for the small-scale preparation of hydrogen gas.

$$Zn(s) + 2\ HCl(aq) \rightarrow ZnCl_2(aq) + H_2(g)$$

EXAMPLE 7

Predict the products from the reaction of magnesium metal with sulfuric acid.

Given
magnesium + sulfuric acid → ?

Required
prediction of products

Analysis
Magnesium metal, Mg(s), is to the left of hydrogen in the activity series; therefore, a reaction will occur.

The metal and the hydrogen ion will switch to give the magnesium ion, $Mg^{2+}(aq)$, and hydrogen gas, $H_2(g)$.

Solution
Write the skeleton equation:

$Mg + H_2SO_4 \rightarrow H_2 + MgSO_4$

The atoms are already balanced as required by the law of conservation of matter.

Add the states:

$Mg(s) + H_2SO_4(aq) \rightarrow H_2(g) + MgSO_4(aq)$

Statement
The products will be hydrogen gas and magnesium sulfate.

PRACTICE PROBLEM

Predict which one of copper and aluminum will react with nitric acid. Write a balanced equation for the case where the metal reacts.

FIGURE 3.13 A violent reaction occurs when a piece of potassium is added to water.

Using the Activity Series to Predict Reactions with Water

A third use of the activity series is to indicate those metals that react with water. These are the very reactive alkali metals and the lower members of the alkaline-earth group (calcium through barium).

Li K Ba Ca Na Mg Al Zn Fe Ni Sn Pb H Cu Hg Ag Au

⟵ react with ⟶
water

For example, potassium metal reacts violently with water to give hydrogen gas and a solution of potassium hydroxide. You can picture this reaction better as a single displacement if you think of water as H-OH ("hydrogen hydroxide"). The potassium atom replaces the "H" of H-OH to form KOH, and the displaced hydrogen atoms combine to form H_2 molecules (hydrogen gas).

$$2 \text{ K}(s) + 2 \text{ HOH}(l) \rightarrow 2 \text{ KOH}(aq) + H_2(g)$$

EXAMPLE 8

Predict the products from the reaction of calcium metal with water.

Given
calcium + water → ?

Required
prediction of products

Analysis
Calcium metal, Ca(s), is one of the very reactive metals.

The metal and hydrogen from the water molecule will switch to give the calcium ion, $Ca^{2+}(aq)$, and hydrogen gas, $H_2(g)$.

Solution
Write the skeleton equation:

$$\text{Ca} + \text{HOH} \rightarrow H_2 + \text{Ca(OH)}_2$$

The atoms are already balanced as required by the law of conservation of matter.

Add the states:

$$\text{Ca}(s) + 2 \text{ HOH}(l) \rightarrow H_2(g) + \text{Ca(OH)}_2(aq)$$

Statement
The products will be hydrogen gas and calcium hydroxide.

PRACTICE PROBLEM

Predict the products formed when lithium metal reacts with water, and write a balanced chemical equation.

Coinage and the Activity Series

Coins have been used as currency (in place of actual commodities) for bartering or trade. In the Western world, the use of coins dates back to about 700 B.C. The metals chosen were those low in the activity series, usually copper, silver, and gold. In fact, it was usual for the common coins to be made from copper or one of its alloys, the higher value coins to be made of silver, and only the premium coins to be made of gold.

In Canada, as in most other countries, the coin with the lowest value (the cent) is made of copper. As the price of copper has risen, the mass of the cent has decreased from 3.24 g in 1964 to 2.8 g in 1980 to 2.5 g in 1982. This decrease in mass has prevented the coin from costing more than one cent to make! In the United States, the current cent contains a zinc core, since zinc is less expensive than copper. If you cut a U.S. penny in half, you can see the zinc metal and dissolve it out using dilute hydrochloric acid.

The metal used most in coin production in Canada is nickel. Although nickel is between iron and tin on the activity scale, its hardness, low cost, and high lustre make it a convenient choice. Nickel was first used in 1922 for the five-cent coin (hence the name, nickel). However, the nickel coin was not always made of nickel. Because of wartime shortages of the metal, a mixture of 88% copper and 12% zinc was used to manufacture nickels in 1942 and 1943. Nickel-chromium plated iron was used to make nickels in 1944 and 1945, and again from 1951 to 1954. The 10¢ and 25¢ coins are also made of nickel while the gold-coloured $1 coin (the loonie) has a nickel core with a coating of a copper-tin alloy. It is this alloy, containing about 12% tin, that gives the optimum combination of colour and resistance to tarnish and wear. The "gold" centre of the $2 coin consists of a similar alloy.

There is also a "silver" dollar for coin collectors, although the chemical composition is 50% silver and 50% copper. For gold collectors, there is the world-renowned $50 maple-leaf coin. This coin is traded worldwide for the value of its gold, the Canadian coin being highly prized for the purity of the gold it contains. These and the other coins produced by the Canadian Mint sell for much more than their face value, so they are not really currency.

FIGURE 3.14 A.F. Cronstedt, a Swedish chemist, first isolated nickel in 1751. Many countries have coins that contain nickel.

FIGURE 3.15 Even today, gold, at the lowest end of the activity series, is a prized coinage metal.

The Halogen Activity Series

Just as a more active metal can displace a less active metallic ion from its compound, so can a more active halogen displace a less active halide ion from its compound. This series, called the **halogen series**, is easy to remember because it is in the same order as the elements in the periodic table, with fluorine as the most reactive halogen:

F   Cl   Br   I

halogen   halide ion

One such reaction that is of great industrial importance is the extraction of bromine. The major industrial source of bromine is seawater, where it is present as sodium bromide. The seawater (brine) is first concentrated by evaporating some of the water, and then chlorine gas is bubbled through the solution. The aqueous chlorine replaces the bromide ion to produce aqueous bromine and a solution of sodium chloride:

$$Cl_2(g) + 2\ NaBr(aq) \rightarrow 2\ NaCl(aq) + Br_2(aq)$$

WEBLINK

Although copper, nickel, silver, and gold have been used for most of the world's currencies, at least 24 elements have been used for coins. Research one of these elements, and write a report that explains the advantages (if any) and disadvantages of using that particular element. Begin your research at **www.pearsoned.ca/chemistry11**.

The bromine produced is then used in the synthesis of bromine compounds. Some of these compounds are used as fire-retardants when applied to clothing, while others are used to extinguish electrical fires in places such as computer rooms.

Double Displacement Reactions

The fourth common category of chemical reactions is that between two soluble ionic compounds. This class is known as a **double displacement reaction**. In these reactions, which always involve two ionic compounds, the cation of one compound changes place with the cation of the other compound. The overall effect is that the positive ions exchange their negative partners. Double displacement reactions have the following general form:

$$AB + CD \rightarrow CB + AD$$

There are three possible outcomes of such a reaction:

- production of a precipitate *or*
- production of a gas *or*
- production of water

Investigation

Refer to page 109, Investigation 1

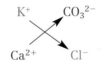

Reactions That Produce a Precipitate

An example of this subcategory is the precipitation of barium carbonate when aqueous solutions of barium chloride and potassium carbonate are mixed. The other product of this reaction, potassium chloride, remains in solution. You can represent the chemical reaction by writing:

$$K_2CO_3(aq) + CaCl_2(aq) \rightarrow 2\ KCl(aq) + CaCO_3(s)$$

The exchange of ions can be seen easily by writing the formulas of the reacting ions in block form, as shown in the margin, and switching partners.

If a precipitate forms, you need to know which ionic compounds are water-soluble and which are not. A set of rules (see Table 3.4) makes such decision-making much easier. Remember that if a substance produced in a reaction is insoluble in water, it will be a precipitate. If it is soluble, it will remain in solution.

TABLE 3.4 Solubility Rules and Exceptions

Rule	Exception
Nitrates (NO_3^-) are soluble.	None
Halides (Cl^-, Br^-, I^-) are soluble.	Ag^+, Hg_2^{2+}, Pb^{2+}
Sulfates (SO_4^{2-}) are soluble.	Ca^{2+}, Ba^{2+}, Pb^{2+}, Hg_2^{2+}, Ag^+
Sulfides (S^{2-}) are insoluble.	NH_4^+ and ions of groups 1 and 2 elements
Carbonates (CO_3^{2-}) are insoluble.	NH_4^+ and ions of group 1 elements
Phosphates (PO_4^{3-}) are insoluble.	NH_4^+ and ions of group 1 elements
Hydroxides (OH^-) are insoluble.	Ba^{2+}, Sr^{2+}, Ca^{2+}, and ions of group 1 elements

If you check the solubilities of the compounds in the previous reaction, you can see that:

- Potassium carbonate is soluble as are all alkali metal salts.
- Calcium chloride is soluble since the only insoluble chlorides are those of Ag^+, Hg_2^{2+}, and Pb^{2+}.
- Potassium chloride is soluble as are all alkali metal salts.
- Calcium carbonate is insoluble since the only soluble carbonates are those of NH_4^+, Cr^{2+}, and the alkali metals.

Many of our household cleansers are sodium compounds. Why do you think this is so? In order to work on grease or other stains, cleansers must themselves be corrosive. It is obvious that sodium hydroxide is very basic, and you will discover in Chapter 6 that sodium phosphate and sodium hypochlorite are also basic. Sodium hydrogen sulfate is very acidic. If you were handling these compounds in the chemistry laboratory, you would be required to wear eye and clothing protection. Why are people at home more casual about how they handle dangerous compounds?

TABLE 3.5 Some Hazardous Household Products

Name	Formula	Use
sodium hydroxide	NaOH	oven and drain cleanser
sodium phosphate	Na_3PO_4	grease remover in kitchen cleansers
sodium hydrogen sulfate	$NaHSO_4$	toilet bowl cleanser
sodium hypochlorite	NaClO	bleach

Corrosive symbol on   WHMIS corrosive symbol
household products   on industrial products

FIGURE 3.16 All the compounds in Table 3.5 are corrosive and must be handled with care.

EXAMPLE 9

When an aqueous solution of lead(II) nitrate is added to an aqueous solution of potassium iodide, a yellow precipitate forms. Write a balanced chemical equation for this reaction.

Given
lead(II) nitrate + potassium iodide → ?

Required
balanced chemical equation

Analysis
This is a double displacement reaction, so there will be a switching of partners.

Pb^{2+} NO_3^-

K^+ I^-

Solution
Write the skeleton equation:

$Pb(NO_3)_2 + KI \rightarrow PbI_2 + KNO_3$

Apply the law of conservation of matter:

$Pb(NO_3)_2 + 2\ KI \rightarrow PbI_2 + 2\ KNO_3$

Add the states. Since lead(II) is one of the insoluble iodides, lead(II) iodide will be a precipitate. Since all nitrates (and all group 1 metals) are soluble, potassium nitrate will remain in solution.

$Pb(NO_3)_2(aq) + 2\ KI(aq) \rightarrow PbI_2(s) + 2\ KNO_3(aq)$

Statement
The balanced chemical equation is:

$Pb(NO_3)_2(aq) + 2\ KI(aq) \rightarrow PbI_2(s) + 2\ KNO_3(aq)$

PRACTICE PROBLEMS

1. When an aqueous solution of copper(II) sulfate is added to an aqueous solution of sodium hydroxide, a blue-green precipitate is obtained. Write a balanced chemical equation for this reaction.

2. When an aqueous solution of calcium chloride is added to an aqueous solution of potassium phosphate, a white precipitate is obtained. Write a balanced chemical equation for this reaction.

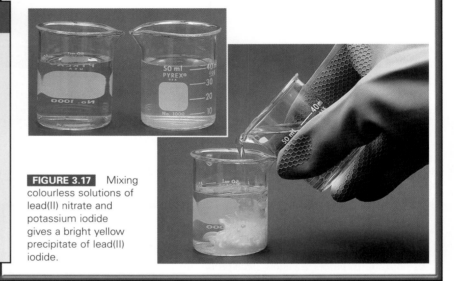

FIGURE 3.17 Mixing colourless solutions of lead(II) nitrate and potassium iodide gives a bright yellow precipitate of lead(II) iodide.

Chemical Reactions and Geochemistry

Where are the metals found that are needed for modern society? The activity series tells you that the only elements that might be found as elements are those to the right of hydrogen—copper, mercury, silver, and gold. Gold is always found as the element, and some deposits of metallic silver, mercury, and copper are known. If any of the metals to the left of hydrogen in the activity series had ever existed as elements, naturally occurring acids would have long ago converted them to metallic ions. Consequently, it is impossible to find elemental deposits of metals such as aluminum, iron, or zinc.

Copper, mercury, and silver are sometimes found as compounds but almost always as the sulfides: silver sulfide, mercury(II) sulfide, and copper(II) sulfide. Recall from the solubility rules that all sulfides (except of groups 1 and 2 metals and ammonium) are insoluble. In fact, most metal sulfides are very insoluble. Many other metals like lead are found as sulfides, for example, lead(II) sulfide.

Where can calcium be found? Again, the solubility rules provide clues. Calcium carbonate is insoluble, and it is very common in Earth's crust as chalk, limestone, and marble. Another insoluble salt of calcium is calcium phosphate, and there are large deposits of this mineral in central Florida. What about sodium, potassium, and magnesium? All of their salts are soluble. So where are they found? The sea has very high concentrations of all three of these metal ions.

So the rules of chemical reactions and solubility are not just of importance in the laboratory. They govern the composition of the surface of our planet.

Reactions That Produce a Gas

If there is a possibility of a gas being formed, a double displacement reaction is also likely to occur. Carbonates are one type of compound that reacts with acids to produce gases. An example is the reaction between an antacid containing calcium carbonate and hydrochloric acid. If the reaction is a double displacement, you would expect the following exchange of ions (as shown in the margin) to take place:

$$CaCO_3(s) + 2\ HCl(aq) \rightarrow CaCl_2(aq) + H_2CO_3(aq)$$

But carbonic acid (H_2CO_3) decomposes into carbon dioxide gas and water.

$$CaCO_3(s) + 2\ HCl(aq) \rightarrow CaCl_2(aq) + H_2CO_3(aq)$$
$$\downarrow$$
$$CO_2(g) + H_2O(l)$$

So the actual chemical equation will be:

$$CaCO_3(s) + 2\ HCl(aq) \rightarrow CaCl_2(aq) + CO_2(g) + H_2O(l)$$

Sulfites also react with acids to produce gases. For example, sodium sulfite reacts with hydrochloric acid to produce the gas that is the major contributor to acid rain, sulfur dioxide. This can be written in a similar way to the carbonate reaction with acid:

$$Na_2SO_3(aq) + 2\ HCl(aq) \rightarrow 2\ NaCl(aq) + H_2SO_3(aq)$$
$$\downarrow$$
$$SO_2(g) + H_2O(l)$$

The reaction can be summarized as:

$$Na_2SO_3(aq) + 2\ HCl(aq) \rightarrow 2\ NaCl(aq) + SO_2(g) + H_2O(l)$$

This is a double displacement reaction, so there will be a switching of partners (as shown in the margin).

Gases are also produced when ammonium salts are mixed with bases. For example, ammonium chloride reacts with sodium hydroxide to produce sodium chloride and ammonium hydroxide. Ammonium hydroxide, in turn, decomposes to produce water and ammonia gas.

$$NH_4Cl(aq) + NaOH(aq) \rightarrow NaCl(aq) + NH_4OH(aq)$$
$$\downarrow$$
$$NH_3(g) + H_2O(l)$$

The reaction can be summarized as:

$$NH_4Cl(aq) + NaOH(aq) \rightarrow NaCl(aq) + NH_3(g) + H_2O(l)$$

This is a double displacement reaction, so there will be a switching of partners (as shown in the margin).

FIGURE 3.18 An antacid tablet reacts with a dilute solution of hydrochloric acid in the same way as the tablet reacts with your stomach acid.

The last group of gas-producing reactions occurs between sulfides and acids. For example, sodium sulfide reacts with hydrochloric acid to produce hydrogen sulfide gas:

$$Na_2S(aq) + 2\ HCl(aq) \rightarrow 2\ NaCl(aq) + H_2S(g)$$

This is a double displacement reaction, so there will be a switching of partners.

TABLE 3.6 Summary of the Reactions That Produce Gases

Compound	Gas Produced	Reaction
carbonates	carbon dioxide	$CO_3^{2-}(aq) (+\ acid) \rightarrow CO_2(g)$
sulfites	sulfur dioxide	$SO_3^{2-}(aq) (+\ acid) \rightarrow SO_2(g)$
ammonium salts	ammonia	$NH_4^+(aq) (+\ base) \rightarrow NH_3(g)$
sulfides	hydrogen sulfide	$S^{2-}(aq) (+\ acid) \rightarrow H_2S(g)$

WEBLINK

SIMULATION

For a simulation to show how chemical reactions work, go to **www.pearsoned.ca/chemistry11**.

EXAMPLE 10

Write a balanced chemical equation for the reaction between solid copper(II) carbonate and nitric acid.

Given
$CuCO_3 + HNO_3 \rightarrow$?

Required
balanced chemical equation

Analysis
This is a double displacement reaction, so there will be a switching of partners:

Solution
Write the skeleton equation:

$$CuCO_3 + HNO_3 \rightarrow Cu(NO_3)_2 + H_2CO_3$$

Apply the law of conservation of matter:

$$CuCO_3 + 2\ HNO_3 \rightarrow Cu(NO_3)_2 + H_2CO_3$$

Add the states. All nitrates are soluble and common acids are soluble, so the complete equation will be:

$$CuCO_3(s) + 2\ HNO_3(aq) \rightarrow Cu(NO_3)_2(aq) + H_2CO_3(aq)$$

However, carbonic acid decomposes into carbon dioxide and water:

$$CuCO_3(s) + 2\ HNO_3(aq) \rightarrow Cu(NO_3)_2(aq) + H_2CO_3(aq)$$
$$\downarrow$$
$$CO_2(g) + H_2O(l)$$

Statement
The balanced chemical equation will be:

$$CuCO_3(s) + 2\ HNO_3(aq) \rightarrow Cu(NO_3)_2(aq) + CO_2(g) + H_2O(l)$$

PRACTICE PROBLEM

Write the balanced chemical equation for the reaction between aqueous potassium sulfite and sulfuric acid.

Reactions That Produce Water

The last type of double displacement reaction involves the formation of covalently bonded water molecules. Because this type of double displacement reaction is so important, it is given the special name of **neutralization reaction**. A neutralization reaction involves the reaction of an acid with a base to produce a salt plus water. For example, the reaction between nitric acid and potassium hydroxide gives aqueous potassium nitrate and water:

$$HNO_3(aq) + KOH(aq) \rightarrow KNO_3(aq) + H_2O(l)$$

This is a double displacement reaction, so there will be a switching of partners.

EXAMPLE 11

Write the balanced chemical equation for the reaction between hydrochloric acid and barium hydroxide solution.

Given
$HCl + Ba(OH)_2 \rightarrow$?

Required
balanced chemical equation

Analysis
This is a double displacement reaction, so there will be a switching of partners:

Solution
Write the skeleton equation:

$$HCl + Ba(OH)_2 \rightarrow BaCl_2 + H_2O$$

Apply the law of conservation of matter:

$$2\ HCl + Ba(OH)_2 \rightarrow BaCl_2 + H_2O$$

Add the states. All chlorides are soluble, and barium is not one of the exceptions. Therefore, barium chloride will be aqueous.

$$2\ HCl(aq) + Ba(OH)_2(aq) \rightarrow BaCl_2(aq) + H_2O(l)$$

Statement
The balanced equation will be:

$$2\ HCl(aq) + Ba(OH)_2(aq) \rightarrow BaCl_2(aq) + H_2O(l)$$

PRACTICE PROBLEM

Write a balanced equation for the reaction between sulfuric acid and aqueous potassium hydroxide.

Investigation
Refer to page 110,
Investigation 2

Summary of the Four Types of Chemical Reactions

You have now seen that there are four main categories of chemical reactions: synthesis, decomposition, single displacement, and double displacement. How can you identify a particular reaction and predict what the products will be? This section will provide you with an overview and some practice in reaction identification.

Synthesis Reactions

FIGURE 3.19 A summary of synthesis reactions

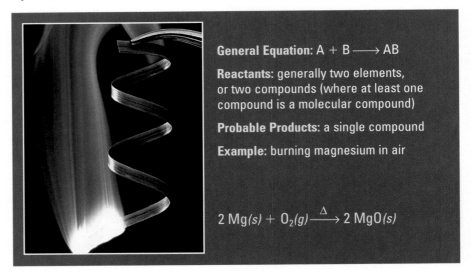

General Equation: $A + B \longrightarrow AB$

Reactants: generally two elements, or two compounds (where at least one compound is a molecular compound)

Probable Products: a single compound

Example: burning magnesium in air

$$2\,Mg(s) + O_2(g) \xrightarrow{\Delta} 2\,MgO(s)$$

a) Combination of two elements
b) Combination of an acidic oxide with water to give an acid
c) Combination of a basic oxide with water to give a base
d) Combination of a basic oxide with an acidic oxide to give a salt

Decomposition Reactions

FIGURE 3.20 A summary of decomposition reactions

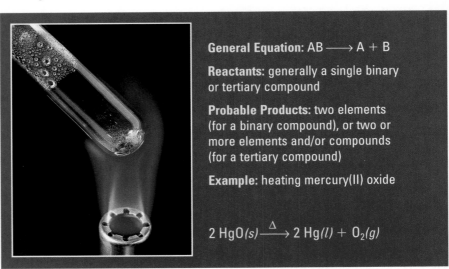

General Equation: $AB \longrightarrow A + B$

Reactants: generally a single binary or tertiary compound

Probable Products: two elements (for a binary compound), or two or more elements and/or compounds (for a tertiary compound)

Example: heating mercury(II) oxide

$$2\,HgO(s) \xrightarrow{\Delta} 2\,Hg(l) + O_2(g)$$

a) Decomposition of a compound into its elements
b) Decomposition of an acid into water and an acidic oxide

c) Decomposition of a base into water and a basic oxide
d) Decomposition of a salt into a basic oxide and an acidic oxide

Note that this is the reverse of synthesis reactions.

Single Displacement Reactions

General Equation: A + BC $\longrightarrow$ AC + B

Reactants: an element and a compound. In a single displacement reaction, an element replaces another element from a compound in aqueous solution. For a single displacement reaction to occur, the element that is displaced must be less active than the element that is doing the displacing.

Probable Products: a different element and a new compound

Example: potassium in water

$$2\,K(s) + 2\,H_2O(l) \longrightarrow 2\,KOH(aq) + H_2(g)$$

FIGURE 3.21 A summary of single displacement reactions

a) Substitution of one metal by another
b) Reaction of a metal with an acid
c) Reaction of a metal with water
d) Substitution of one halogen by another

Double Displacement Reactions

$$K_2CO_3(aq) + BaCl_2(aq) \longrightarrow 2\,KCl(aq) + BaCO_3(s)$$

General Equation:
$$A^+B^- + C^+D^- \longrightarrow C^+B^- + A^+D^-$$

Reactants: two ionic compounds. In a double displacement reaction, two ionic compounds react by exchanging cations to form two different compounds.

Probable Products: two new compounds. Double displacement reactions are driven by the formation of a precipitate, a gaseous product, or water.

Example: reaction of aqueous solutions of barium chloride and potassium carbonate

a) Production of a precipitate
b) Production of a gas
c) Production of water

FIGURE 3.22 A summary of double displacement reactions

EXAMPLE 12

Complete the following equation:

$$Zn(OH)_2(s) \xrightarrow{\Delta}$$

Given

$$Zn(OH)_2(s) \xrightarrow{\Delta}$$

Required
balanced chemical equation for reaction

Analysis
One reactant means it must be a *decomposition* reaction.

The compound is a base, and bases decompose into basic oxides and water.

The products must be ZnO and H_2O.

Solution
Write the skeleton equation:

$$Zn(OH)_2 \xrightarrow{\Delta} ZnO + H_2O$$

Apply the law of conservation of matter:

$$Zn(OH)_2 \xrightarrow{\Delta} ZnO + H_2O$$

Add the states:

$$Zn(OH)_2(s) \xrightarrow{\Delta} ZnO(s) + H_2O(l)$$

Statement
The balanced chemical equation is:

$$Zn(OH)_2(s) \xrightarrow{\Delta} ZnO(s) + H_2O(l)$$

PRACTICE PROBLEM

Identify the reaction below, and then complete and balance the chemical equation.

$$ZnCl_2(aq) + Na_2S(aq) \rightarrow$$

EXAMPLE 13

Complete the following equation:

$$SO_3(s) + H_2O(l) \rightarrow$$

Given
$$SO_3(s) + H_2O(l) \rightarrow$$

Required
balanced chemical equation for reaction

Analysis
A non-metal oxide (an acidic oxide) is reacting with water.

This is a *synthesis* reaction to give an acid.

The product must be H_2SO_4.

Solution
Write the skeleton equation:

$SO_3 + H_2O \rightarrow H_2SO_4$

Apply the law of conservation of matter:

$SO_3 + H_2O \rightarrow H_2SO_4$

Add the states:

$SO_3(s) + H_2O(l) \rightarrow H_2SO_4(aq)$

Statement
The balanced chemical equation is:

$SO_3(s) + H_2O(l) \rightarrow H_2SO_4(aq)$

PRACTICE PROBLEM

Identify the reaction below, and then complete and balance the chemical equation.

$KOH(aq) + H_2SO_4(aq) \rightarrow$

EXAMPLE 14

Complete the following equation:

$KOH(aq) + H_3PO_4(aq) \rightarrow$

Given
$KOH(aq) + H_3PO_4(aq) \rightarrow$

Required
balanced chemical equation for reaction

Analysis
A base is reacting with an acid; therefore, it is a neutralization (double displacement) reaction.

The products must be K_3PO_4 and H_2O.

All potassium salts are soluble, so potassium phosphate will be aqueous.

Solution
Write the skeleton equation:

$KOH + H_3PO_4 \rightarrow K_3PO_4 + H_2O$

Apply the law of conservation of matter:

$3\ KOH + H_3PO_4 \rightarrow K_3PO_4 + 3\ H_2O$

Add the states:

$3\ KOH(aq) + H_3PO_4(aq) \rightarrow K_3PO_4(aq) + 3\ H_2O(l)$

Statement
The balanced chemical equation is:

$3\ KOH(aq) + H_3PO_4(aq) \rightarrow K_3PO_4(aq) + 3\ H_2O(l)$

PRACTICE PROBLEM

Identify the reactions below, and then complete and balance the chemical equations.
a) $Ba(s) + S(s) \rightarrow$
b) $Pb(NO_3)_2(aq) + Mg(s) \rightarrow$

EXAMPLE 15

Complete the following equation:

$$Mg(s) + HCl(aq) \rightarrow$$

Given
$Mg(s) + HCl(aq) \rightarrow$

Required
balanced chemical equation for reaction

Analysis
An element reacting with a compound means that it must be a *single displacement* reaction.

Since it is a metal reacting with an acid, this must be the reaction of a reactive metal to give magnesium chloride ($MgCl_2$) and hydrogen gas (H_2).

Magnesium chloride is soluble, and so it is aqueous.

Solution
Write the skeleton equation:

$$Mg + HCl \rightarrow MgCl_2 + H_2$$

Apply the law of conservation of matter:

$$Mg + 2 \, HCl \rightarrow MgCl_2 + H_2$$

Add the states:

$$Mg(s) + 2 \, HCl(aq) \rightarrow MgCl_2(aq) + H_2(g)$$

Statement
The balanced chemical equation is:

$$Mg(s) + 2 \, HCl(aq) \rightarrow MgCl_2(aq) + H_2(g)$$

PRACTICE PROBLEM

Identify each of the following types of reactions, and then complete and balance each chemical equation.
a) $NaI(aq) + Br_2(aq) \rightarrow$
b) $FeS(s) + HCl(aq) \rightarrow$

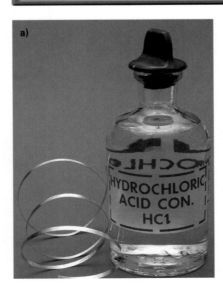

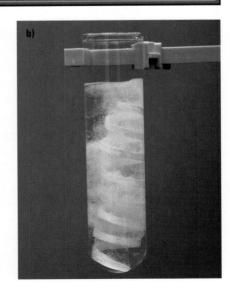

FIGURE 3.23 a) Magnesium is a silver-coloured, malleable metal and hydrochloric acid is a clear colourless liquid. b) When a piece of magnesium is dropped in hydrochloric acid, the reaction produces hydrogen gas and aqueous magnesium chloride.

Understanding Concepts

1. In your own words, explain what is meant by the following terms and give an example of each.
   a) single displacement reaction
   b) double displacement reaction

2. Keep a log of all chemical reactions you observe in a week. Classify each reaction by type. Describe evidence of the reactants, as well as what you think the products were.

3. Explain why the metals used in coins are low in the activity series. Research the metals used in jewellery and the reasons why they are used.

Applying Inquiry/ Communication Skills

4. Complete the following equations by predicting what the products are. If no reaction will take place, write "no reaction."
   a) $Cl_2(aq) + NaI(aq) \rightarrow$
   b) $Ca(s) + H_2O(l) \rightarrow$
   c) $Mg(s) + HCl(aq) \rightarrow$
   d) $Zn(s) + CuCl_2(aq) \rightarrow$
   e) $Br_2(aq) + CaCl_2(aq) \rightarrow$

5. Predict the products of these chemical reactions, and write a balanced chemical equation in each case.
   a) $CaCl_2(aq) + Na_2SO_4(aq) \rightarrow$
   b) $AgNO_3(aq) + NaI(aq) \rightarrow$
   c) $MgSO_4(aq) + NaOH(aq) \rightarrow$
   d) $(NH_4)_2SO_4(aq) + KOH(aq) \rightarrow$
   e) $K_2CO_3(aq) + HNO_3(aq) \rightarrow$
   f) $CaS(s) + H_2SO_4(aq) \rightarrow$
   g) $H_2SO_4(aq) + LiOH(aq) \rightarrow$
   h) $Fe_2O_3(s) + HCl(aq) \rightarrow$
   i) $KOH(aq) + SO_2(g) \rightarrow$

Making Connections

6. Most consumers do not heed or read warning labels on household products. Create a pamphlet educating consumers about the importance of reading and following instructions on products that contain warning labels and describing potential health, economic, and environmental consequences.

3.4 An Introduction to the Canadian Chemical Industry

Key Understandings

When you have completed this section, you will be able to:
- identify some chemical reactions of economic and environmental significance
- use appropriate vocabulary to communicate ideas related to chemical reactions
- recognize the need for safe use and disposal of chemicals

Chemistry is unique among the fundamental sciences in that it is a major contributor to the Canadian economy. Hopefully, many of you will enjoy chemistry so much that you will consider a career in this field. If you do, then it is most probable that you will work in the chemical industry. What is **industrial chemistry**? It is the use of large-scale chemical processes to convert naturally occurring raw materials into desired end products.

How Laboratory and Industrial Reactions Differ

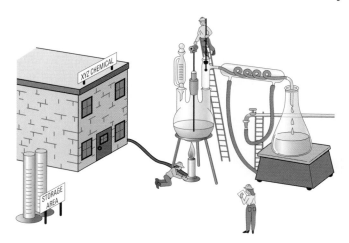

FIGURE 3.24 An erroneous image of an industrial chemical plant

How do you picture an industrial chemical process? Do you think of it as being just like a regular chemistry lab only larger (Figure 3.24)? There are some major differences between small-scale laboratory work and large-scale industrial chemistry.

Cost

In industry, cost is of major importance. In order for any industry to survive, the market value of its product must be more than the total cost of producing it. Production costs include the price of raw materials, transportation, depreciation and maintenance of the plant, labour, and energy. Even then, the selling price of the product is not determined by simply adding a profit margin to the production cost. Consumer demand and competition in the marketplace must also be taken into account.

Why is a chemical plant built in a particular location? There are three main reasons, each of which relates to cost:

- **The availability of an ample supply of raw materials** If impure raw materials are processed near their source of supply, transportation costs can be minimized. This is a major reason why, for example, nickel metal is refined in Sudbury near the local nickel mines. However, the development of large, bulk-cargo ships that can move huge volumes of raw materials at very low cost has reduced the importance of this consideration.

- **The proximity of an inexpensive energy source** Many chemical processes consume vast quantities of energy, often in the form of electricity. The cost of this energy is usually a major factor in determining the cost of the final product. In Canada, there has been an ample supply of hydro-electric power, explaining why energy-intensive aluminum extraction plants are located in British Columbia and Quebec.

- **A large domestic market for the product** Canada has a small domestic market for chemical products, and, therefore, many international or U.S. companies would prefer to locate manufacturing plants in the United States, where there is a much larger domestic market. Without its vast natural resources and relatively abundant low-cost energy, Canada probably could not maintain a viable chemical industry.

Scale

In the laboratory, you mix reactants together in a glass beaker or test tube in order to obtain a small amount of product. In industry, much larger quantities of material are used. Consequently, it is preferable to design an industrial plant so that its product can be prepared on a continual basis. Furthermore, although glass is an excellent material for small laboratory containers, its fragility makes it impractical for the large-scale storage tanks, pipes, and reaction containers required by industry. These are usually constructed of steel.

Some problems that may seem minor when a chemical is produced in a test-tube reaction might be major on a large scale. For example, the release of a small amount of heat or gas in a test-tube reaction could indicate the possibility of a massive buildup of heat or pressure in a large, sealed reaction vessel. To avoid problems of this nature, a pilot plant, which is a scaled-down version of the proposed plant, is usually built before construction begins on the plant itself. Problems can then be identified and any necessary modifications made and tested before hundreds of millions of dollars are spent.

Waste Disposal

Even in your chemistry experiments, the disposal of the products has to be considered. You may think the products from some reactions are harmless. For example, if you react hydrochloric acid with sodium hydroxide solution, the gram or two of sodium chloride can be safely flushed down the sink. But what if your chemical company were producing thousands of tonnes of waste sodium chloride per day? And this is one of the safer chemicals! The process of minimizing waste chemicals is a major concern of responsible chemical industries today. Unfortunately, many chemical plants were built long before environmental pollution became a major concern. It is often both difficult and costly to install anti-pollution devices in these older plants. Sometimes it is more economical to close such plants down and build new ones, frequently in different locations. Such moves often result in social upheaval and the loss of employment in the communities that were home to the older plants.

The three major types of wastes produced by chemical industries are gases, which can cause air pollution; liquids, which can cause water and soil pollution; and solids, which can cause soil pollution. Chemical manufacturers are eager to find uses for these by-products. If a use can be found, the disposal problem can be reduced and the plant can become more cost-effective.

Green Chemistry

Traditionally, industrial chemistry simply involved the synthesis of a chemical product by the lowest cost route. Gaseous waste products would be pumped into the atmosphere, liquid waste products would be poured into rivers, and solid waste products would end up in landfills. During the 20th century, many industries took steps to minimize waste, but it is the beginning of the 21st century that has seen a whole revolution in the philosophy of industrial chemistry. This is called **green chemistry**. Green chemistry is not a separate branch of chemistry but the use of different aspects of chemistry to make chemical industry eco-friendly and energy-efficient. Today, green chemistry is one of the most crucial fields of chemical research. There are several ways in which environmentally friendly chemical processes can be accomplished. Industry can:

- make existing chemical products in a way that minimizes the production of waste chemicals. This may be through the development of a completely new route of synthesis or the improvement of a current method so that only the required product and no waste materials are produced.

- minimize energy consumption. It would be most energy-efficient if the process could be performed at room temperature.

WEBLINK

Green chemistry is the fastest growing branch of chemistry. Research some of the new developments in this important field. Begin your research at **www.pearsoned.ca/chemistry11**.

- develop new chemical products, such as refrigerants, that serve the same function as existing ones, yet are less toxic and less harmful to the environment. These products should break down (degrade) into harmless compounds when their purpose, such as being used in household refrigerators for a certain length of time, is complete.

- use reagents (starting materials) that come from renewable resources rather than non-renewable ones.

The Canadian Iron and Steel Industry

Iron smelting in North America was first practised by the Vikings about a thousand years ago in a place now known as L'Anse aux Meadows, Newfoundland. Smelting is the process of using high temperatures and carbon (charcoal or coke) to convert a metal oxide to a pure metal. This iron production was just for the needs of the tiny Norse community. It was not until 1736 that the first large-scale iron production occurred in Canada at St. Maurice, Quebec. Now the iron and steel industry in Canada is centred in Hamilton, Ontario.

How is iron obtained? There are four raw materials needed: iron ore (mainly iron(III) oxide), coke, oxygen (from air), and limestone (calcium carbonate), together with large quantities of cooling water. Coke, an impure form of carbon, is obtained by heating coal in the absence of air. Unfortunately, the other products from the reaction are highly toxic coal tars. The iron ore, coke, and limestone are placed in a giant smelter (Figure 3.25), and heated air is passed up the tower. The first reaction is that between carbon and oxygen:

$$2\ C(s) + O_2(g) \xrightarrow{\Delta} 2\ CO(g)$$

The carbon monoxide then reacts with the iron(III) oxide to give molten iron metal:

$$Fe_2O_3(s) + 3\ CO(g) \xrightarrow{\Delta} 2\ Fe(l) + 3\ CO_2(g)$$

What is the purpose of adding the limestone? Industrial substances are not pure like those you use in the laboratory. The iron ore contains many other substances other than iron(III) oxide, particularly sand, silicon dioxide. The limestone is used to remove these impurities. The first step is the decomposition of the calcium carbonate:

$$CaCO_3(s) \xrightarrow{\Delta} CaO(s) + CO_2(g)$$

The calcium oxide then reacts with the impurities, such as sand, to give molten calcium silicate, commonly called slag. Calcium silicate is less dense than molten iron, so it can be poured off separately.

$$CaO(s) + SiO_2(s) \xrightarrow{\Delta} CaSiO_3(l)$$

Which of the four equations above does not fit into one of the standard categories of reaction? Identify the type of reaction for the other three equations.

Great iron smelters used to belch enormous clouds of smoke into the sky while pumping out millions of litres of polluted cooling water. Those days are gone. Although scientists have so far been unable to find an alternative route for producing iron, the technology of the smelting process

FIGURE 3.25 The extraction of iron is performed in this enormous tower called a blast furnace.

has improved tremendously. The dust is now separated from the exhaust gases, the heat from the exhaust carbon dioxide gas is recycled, much of the water is recycled, and whatever water is expelled into Lake Ontario must be of high purity. Nevertheless, using the current process, it is impossible to avoid producing large volumes of the greenhouse gas, carbon dioxide. The production of slag is also an inevitable part of the process.

Case *Study*

Is There a Place for Enviro-Industry?

Decision-Making Skills

▷ Defining the Issue
▷ Developing Assessment Criteria
▷ Researching the Issue
▷ Analyzing Data and Information
▷ Proposing a Course of Action
▷ Justifying the Course of Action
▷ Communicating Your Proposal

BACKGROUND INFORMATION

Bowater Inc. is a huge international company that operates pulp and paper mills throughout North America. While environmentalists demonstrate that paper mills pollute and contribute to the destruction of the natural environment, Bowater claims that conservation and replacement of the natural environment and proper disposal of the waste according to certain international standards (ISO 14001) are high priorities for the company. One such Bowater mill is located in Thunder Bay, Ontario, and is ISO 14001 compliant.

ISO, the International Organization for Standards, is a non-governmental body set up in 1947 to facilitate the international exchange of goods and services. ISO standards relate to many different industries and products, from setting the size of phone cards to the size of metric screw threads worldwide. ISO 14000, which includes ISO 14001, is a group of international environmental standards set in 1992 at the United Nations Conference on Environment and Development.

Through the ISO 14000 environmental management system, Bowater tries to limit its impact on the environment. In 1997, the Thunder Bay mill was one of the largest pulp and paper mills in North America to receive the ISO 14001 certification. Bowater did this while increasing productivity. The mill maintains ongoing projects aimed at improving the environment and identifying hazardous waste materials. One initiative is the replacement at the Thunder Bay mill of halon, a fire suppressant containing chlorofluorocarbons (CFCs), which depletes the ozone layer. Another was the replacement of mercury-filled thermometers, which, if broken, would leach mercury into the environment.

The paper industry, while keeping an eye on the costs of these standards, claims that it is changing corporate culture from management to labourers, and is becoming more environmentally aware. Environmentalists claim that the ISO standards are simply a way for industries that have been heavy polluters in the past to avoid cleaning up their act by flashing their ISO 14001 certification, which states they are meeting international standards.

Analyzing the Issue

1. Write a statement that clearly identifies the main issue.

2. Research what is meant by sustainable development.

3. Use the Internet to research the global role of ISO in relation to its influence on sustainable development.

4. People in industry have different perspectives about the important role of environmental chemistry as it relates to sustainable development. Develop a criterion list for the industrial sector that could form the basis of future decision-making about this issue. Consider criteria related to social, economic, and environmental impacts.

5. Describe the short-term and long-term social, economic, and environmental impacts as they relate to Bowater's actions. Use this as your basis to provide a persuasive argument for question 6.

6. Prepare a multimedia presentation to inform industry and government policy makers about the social, economic, and environmental impacts when sustainable development considerations are factored into the development of production technology.

FIGURE 3.26 Four examples of green chemistry. a) The newly built solar-powered biological treatment centre north of Toronto treats domestic sewage by simulating a natural wetland. b) An environmental chemist at a chemical waste treatment facility takes industrial waste samples to test for toxicity. c) Heating water to 374°C at a pressure over 200 times atmospheric pressure causes certain toxic wastes to become soluble. These wastes can then be reacted to form harmless chemicals that can be easily disposed of. d) The last stage of treating industrial wastewater involves filtration through activated charcoal in large tanks. Activated charcoal is used to remove solid particles and compounds such as pesticides.

Section 3.4 Review

Understanding Concepts

1. Explain what green chemistry is in your own words.

2. List three factors that must be considered when locating a chemical plant and the driving factor that determines the ultimate location.

Applying Inquiry/ Communication Skills

3. Create an advertisement for a local newspaper that informs the community about the need for the safe disposal of chemicals.

Making Connections

4. You are a senior executive of a bridge-building company that is considering developing its own iron-making capabilities so that it is no longer dependent on existing steel suppliers. Explore the advantages and disadvantages of buying an existing old smelter complex versus building a new one. Research where you will obtain the raw materials to manufacture iron. Develop a plan taking environmental issues into account.

5. Attempts to establish industrial waste disposal sites frequently meet with public protests of "not in my backyard." Outline the issues involved and potential consequences or solutions.

a)

b)

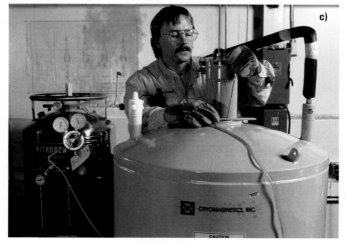
c)

d)

Investigation 1 (Section 3.3)

Inquiry Skills

▶ Initiating and Planning
Applying Technical Skills
▶ Using Tools, Materials, and Equipment
▶ Conducting and Recording
▶ Analyzing and Interpreting
▶ Concluding and Communicating

Solubility of Inorganic Compounds

Certain combinations of ions will form insoluble precipitates in solution while other combinations will remain dissolved in solution. From this information, it is possible to predict whether a reaction between two solutions will produce a precipitate, and what the precipitate would be. Chemists use this knowledge when performing analytical tests. For example, if they know that a certain anion, such as chloride ion, is present in a water sample, they can determine quantitatively how much of it is present by selecting the appropriate cation that will precipitate virtually all the chloride ion out of solution.

Problem

To determine which combinations of cations and anions will form precipitates.

Materials

All solutions are 0.1 mol·L^{-1}.
- barium chloride solution
- copper(II) sulfate solution
- potassium chloride solution
- silver nitrate solution
- sodium carbonate solution
- sodium chloride solution
- sodium nitrate solution
- sodium phosphate solution
- sodium sulfate solution
- zinc sulfate solution
- eye droppers
- spot plate

(Your teacher may substitute a compound in this list. Check before starting the activity.)

CHEMICAL DISPOSAL: Dispose of all solutions in a special container.

Experimental Design

1. Using the above solutions as sources of anions and cations, develop a method to determine which combinations of solutions will form precipitates. Note that the sodium solutions provide the source of the different anions while the rest provide the source of the different cations.

2. Show your procedure to your teacher before performing the activity.

Analyzing and Interpreting

1. List the combinations of solutions in which you saw evidence of a chemical reaction, and note what the evidence was. Indicate the colours of the precipitates.

2. Present all your observations in a chart.

3. Write balanced equations for the combinations you tested.

4. Suggest a classification of precipitates based on colour. Organize your results in a second chart according to this classification scheme.

Concluding and Communicating

5. Report a summary of your findings.

Extending

6. Your factory produces wastewater that is contaminated with a large number of different metal ions. Of the anions you used above, which one would you choose to precipitate the metals from the water so that the water might be run into the nearby river and the metals recycled? What would be the problem if you added too much of that anion to the wastewater?

Inquiry Skills

Initiating and Planning
▶ Applying Technical Skills
▶ Using Tools, Materials, and Equipment
▶ Conducting and Recording
▶ Analyzing and Interpreting
▶ Concluding and Communicating

Investigation 2 (Section 3.3)

Chemical Reactions

This investigation has four stations representing four types of chemical reactions. You and your lab partner(s) will become experts on at least one of these stations. Be prepared, if called upon, to demonstrate the reaction and explain the chemistry to the class. Once you have determined what is happening in your station, you can plan how you will demonstrate the reaction to the rest of the class. You can use the *Handbook of Chemistry and Physics* as a reference.

Problem

To identify the products of the chemical reaction you observe and write the chemical equations to describe it.

Station 1: Heating Copper(II) Carbonate

Materials

- safety goggles
- solid copper(II) carbonate
- calcium hydroxide solution (limewater)
- large and small test tubes
- a delivery tube assembly, consisting of a one-hole rubber stopper to fit the large test tube (A 90° glass tube elbow should be inserted in the rubber stopper with the elbow being connected to some rubber tubing and a short piece of glass tubing.)
- adjustable clamp
- retort stand
- gas burner

> **CHEMICAL DISPOSAL: Place unused copper(II) carbonate into a solid waste container.**

Procedure

1. Place approximately 1-cm depth of copper(II) carbonate in a large, dry test tube.

2. Insert the rubber stopper of the delivery tube into the mouth of the large test tube.

3. Add 2 cm to 3 cm of limewater to the small test tube.

4. Place the glass elbow of the delivery tube into the limewater in the small test tube.

5. Tilt the tube and shake so the copper(II) carbonate spreads about 2 cm up the side of the test tube.

6. Use an adjustable clamp to support the test tube on a retort stand. Place the clamp at the mouth of the test tube. Adjust the clamp so that the test tube is at a 45° angle.

7. Begin heating the tip of the copper(II) carbonate farthest from the base of the test tube, and slowly work the flame toward the base.

8. Describe the changes in the copper(II) carbonate and in the limewater. When no further changes occur in the limewater, remove the delivery tube from the limewater and then turn off the gas burner.

> **CAUTION: Remove the delivery tube from the limewater just *before* you stop heating the test tube. This is to prevent drawback of limewater.**

9. When the test tube has cooled to room temperature, remove the delivery tube assembly and return it to the teacher. Empty the solid in the test tube into the "Solid Waste" container. Return the test tube and all other materials to their appropriate storage tray.

Analyzing and Interpreting

1. Give evidence that suggests that chemical reactions have occurred when:
   a) copper(II) carbonate was heated
   b) the gas produced was bubbled into the limewater

2. Identify the gas produced.

3. Use the *Handbook of Chemistry and Physics* to check your identification of the solid that remains in the large test tube. Write the word equation and balanced chemical equation to describe what happens when copper(II) carbonate is heated.

4. Write the word equation and the balanced chemical equation for the reaction when carbon dioxide reacts with the limewater (a solution of calcium hydroxide).

5. Continued bubbling of carbon dioxide through the limewater should have caused the limewater to become clear again as a result of the formation of a solution of calcium hydrogen carbonate, $Ca(HCO_3)_2$.

▶

(continued)

Write the word equation and balanced chemical equation for the clearing of milky limewater.

Concluding and Communicating

6. Classify each of the chemical reactions.

7. Suppose the activity had been performed using calcium carbonate instead of copper(II) carbonate. What would have been the difference?

Extending

8. The dissolving of the limewater is the same chemical reaction that occurs when caves form in limestone rocks. Research how caves form and how stalagmites and stalactites form in caves.

Station 2: Copper(II) Sulfate and Potassium Hydroxide Solutions

Materials

- safety goggles
- copper(II) sulfate solution (0.2 mol·L^{-1})
- potassium hydroxide solution (0.2 mol·L^{-1})
- stirring rod
- test tubes and rack
- gas burner

> CAUTION: Wear gloves when handling potassium hydroxide solution.

Procedure

1. Place about 2 mL of copper(II) sulfate solution in one test tube and about the same volume of potassium hydroxide solution in another test tube.

2. Pour the potassium hydroxide solution into the copper(II) sulfate solution and stir. Record your observations.

3. Light the gas burner and *gently* warm the mixture, pointing the mouth of the tube away from you and anyone else. Be very careful since the liquid has a tendency to "bump." Note your observations.

4. After making your observations, pour the contents of the test tube into a waste container provided by your teacher.

Analyzing and Interpreting

1. In the first reaction, what evidence suggests that a chemical reaction occurred?

2. Write the word equation and the balanced chemical equation for the reaction.

3. In the second reaction, what evidence suggests that a chemical reaction occurred?

4. Write the word equation and balanced chemical equation for the reaction. (Hint: The only reactant is the insoluble product from the first reaction.)

Concluding and Communicating

5. Classify the reactions.

6. What type of product is the solid compound formed in the first reaction? And in the second reaction?

Extending

7. What would you expect to happen if you added dilute sulfuric acid to the final solid product? Explain your reasoning. Write a chemical equation. What would you expect to observe? Try the activity and see if you are correct.

Station 3: Chlorine and Potassium Iodide Solutions

Materials

- aqueous solution of chlorine (prepared by adding hydrochloric acid to dilute bleach)
- potassium iodide solution (0.2 mol·L^{-1})
- TTE (trichlorotrifluoroethane) in a dispensing bottle
- test tubes and rack

> CAUTION: Wear gloves during this activity. This activity must be performed in a well-ventilated fume hood.
>
> CHEMICAL DISPOSAL: Dispose of TTE in a "TTE Residues" container. Add an excess of sodium sulfite solution to the excess aqueous chlorine, leave overnight, and wash down the sink with copious amounts of water.

Procedure

1. Pour 1-cm depth of an aqueous chlorine solution into a test tube.

(continued)

2. Add 1-cm depth of the potassium iodide solution to the test tube. Swirl the contents of the tube.
3. Add 1-cm depth of TTE, and swirl the contents. Compare the colour of the lower layer with the provided reference solution of TTE and iodine.
4. Dispose of the contents of the test tube into the bottle labelled "TTE Residues."
5. Wash the test tube, and return it and the other materials to the tray.

Analyzing and Interpreting

1. What evidence suggests that there is a chemical reaction between the chlorine and potassium iodide?
2. Write the word equation and the balanced chemical equation for the reaction of chlorine and aqueous potassium iodide.

Concluding and Communicating

3. Classify the reaction.
4. What other potassium halide(s) would have reacted with chlorine?
5. What other potassium halide(s) would not have reacted with chlorine?
6. Explain why the TTE was added to the solution.

Extending

7. To what class of compounds does TTE belong? Why is it important to recycle the TTE?
8. What other compound could be substituted for TTE?

Station 4: Magnesium and Chlorine Solution

Materials

- aqueous chlorine (prepared by adding hydrochloric acid to dilute bleach)
- magnesium ribbon
- test tubes and rack

> **CHEMICAL DISPOSAL: Pour all solutions into special waste containers.**

Procedure

1. Place a piece of magnesium ribbon in a test tube.
2. Collect about 2 mL of the aqueous chlorine, and pour it over the magnesium metal.
3. After making your observations, pour the contents of the test tube into a waste container provided by your teacher.
4. Rinse the test tube, and return it and other materials to the tray. Pour the rinse water into the container marked "Waste."

Analyzing and Interpreting

1. What evidence suggests that a chemical reaction occurred?
2. Write the word equation and balanced chemical equation for the reaction.
3. Classify this reaction.

Concluding and Communicating

4. If the reaction is reversed so that the initial reactants are formed, what type of reaction would it be?
5. If you reacted calcium with chlorine instead of magnesium, would you expect the reaction to be more or less vigorous? Explain your reasoning.
6. If you reacted magnesium with iodine instead of chlorine, would you expect the reaction to be more or less vigorous? Explain your reasoning.

Extending

7. Magnesium is a strong, low-density metal that should be ideal for the manufacture of many items, such as aircraft. Suggest why pure magnesium is so rarely used in our economy.
8. Explain the "fizz" in soda pop using a chemical equation. Identify the type of reaction that represents the formation of the fizz.

CHAPTER SUMMARY

Key Terms

acidic oxide
activity series
basic oxide
biochemical reaction
chemical equation
chemical reaction
decomposition reaction

double displacement
   reaction
geochemical reaction
green chemistry
halogen series
industrial chemistry
neutralization reaction

precipitate
product
reactant
single displacement
   reaction
synthesis reaction
thermal decomposition

thermochemical reaction
word equation

Essential Understandings

■ There are many types of chemical reactions that take place all around us, and by observing certain signs, we know that they occur.

■ Chemical reactions involve the rearrangement of atoms, resulting in the products having different properties from the reactants.

■ Chemical equations concisely describe chemical reactions and reflect the law of conservation of matter.

■ Classifying reactions as synthesis, decomposition, and single and double displacement helps us predict possible products and their properties.

■ Arranging the metals in an activity series helps us predict whether a single displacement reaction will occur, the metal that will be produced by the reaction, and whether a reaction will occur with an acid or water.

■ Double displacement reactions involve the cations exchanging their respective anions to produce a gas, a precipitate, or water.

■ The activity series explains why most metals are found in nature as compounds, not as elements, and the solubility rules indicate where those metals are found.

■ The Canadian chemical industry is important economically and faces the challenge of developing environmentally friendly products and processes.

Consolidate Your Understanding

1. Explain why the properties of a compound can be so different from the properties of its elements.

2. Construct a concept map starting with the word "chemical reactions."

3. Create a mind map illustrating as many careers as you can think of that are related to the chemical industry. Draw connecting lines between the careers that are dependent on each other.

4. Investigation 2 on page 110 required you to become an expert in understanding a particular type of chemical reaction and being able to communicate this information to others. Identify criteria that result in effective communication and conducting an effective demonstration. Explain why.

CHAPTER 3 REVIEW

Understanding Concepts

1. State which one of the following single displacement reactions will not occur.
   a) $2\,NaBr(aq) + Cl_2(aq) \rightarrow 2\,NaCl(aq) + Br_2(aq)$
   b) $2\,NaI(aq) + Br_2(aq) \rightarrow 2\,NaBr(aq) + I_2(aq)$
   c) $2\,NaF(aq) + Cl_2(aq) \rightarrow 2\,NaCl(aq) + F_2(aq)$
   d) $2\,NaI(aq) + Cl_2(aq) \rightarrow 2\,NaCl(aq) + I_2(aq)$

2. List which of the following salts is soluble in water.
   a) PbS
   b) $CuCO_3$
   c) $Ca_3(PO_4)_2$
   d) $MgSO_4$

3. Predict which of the following salts when added to an acid will not produce a gas.
   a) FeS
   b) $CaSO_4$
   c) Na_2CO_3
   d) NH_4Cl

4. List in order the following metals from most to least chemically reactive.
   a) Na, Cu, Fe   b) Cu, Na, Fe
   c) Na, Fe, Cu   d) Fe, Na, Cu

5. Identify the pairs of substances in solution that will form a precipitate.
   a) sodium chloride and potassium nitrate
   b) calcium nitrate and copper(II) bromide
   c) ammonium chloride and potassium phosphate
   d) magnesium sulfide and lead(II) nitrate
   e) barium nitrate and sodium hydroxide

6. Identify the reactants and products in each of the following chemical reactions.
   a) When sodium is dropped into water, hydrogen gas and sodium hydroxide are formed.
   b) In photosynthesis, oxygen gas and glucose are formed when carbon dioxide and water react.

7. Explain why sodium metal is not used for making coins. Indicate the metals that are used, and give reasons for choosing these metals.

8. List the observations that would indicate that a chemical reaction may have occurred. Explain why some of those observations do not definitively indicate the occurrence of a chemical reaction.

9. Explain the meaning of the symbol above the arrow in each of the following examples:

   $$\xrightarrow{\Delta} \qquad \xrightarrow{light} \qquad \xrightarrow{250°C}$$

10. Identify the four main types of chemical reactions. Explain why it is useful to classify reactions by their type, and briefly describe each one.

11. In each of the following cases, identify the category of reaction, and then complete the equation.

    a) $CaSO_3(s) \xrightarrow{\Delta}$
    b) $H_2(g) + Cl_2(g) \rightarrow$
    c) $Cu(s) + AgNO_3(aq) \rightarrow$
    d) $Pb(NO_3)_2(aq) + KI(aq) \rightarrow$

12. In your own words, write a definition for the term "activity series," and explain its significance.

13. Describe three differences between performing a chemical reaction in a laboratory and carrying out the same process on an industrial scale.

14. The following directions are given for cleaning silverware: "Fill an aluminum pie plate with hot water. Add several teaspoons of baking soda. Immerse the tarnished silverware in the solution, making sure the silverware is touching the aluminum pie plate. Keep the water hot on the stove, and let sit for several hours. Remove the silverware and polish with a soft cloth." The following chemical equations describe the process of tarnishing and cleaning:

    Tarnishing: $Ag(s) + H_2S(g) + O_2(g) \rightarrow Ag_2S(s) + H_2O(l)$

    Cleaning: $Al(s) + Ag_2S(s) + H_2O(l) \rightarrow$
    $\qquad\qquad\qquad Ag(s) + Al(OH)_3(aq) + H_2S(g)$

    a) Use the equations to explain first how silver tarnishes and then how it is cleaned.
    b) Identify the kinds of chemical reactions that are involved in the tarnishing and cleaning of silverware.

15. In addition to magnesium, many other elements can be extracted from seawater (brine). The dissolved salts can be removed to produce freshwater for irrigation or for drinking. Write a report for the school newspaper on either the extraction of chemicals from seawater or the production of freshwater from brine, or build a scale model that demonstrates one of these processes.

Applying Inquiry/Communication Skills

16. Design an experiment to test for lead ions in well water. Identify any other ions that, if in the well water, would contaminate your test.

17. **TABLE 3.8**

Metals	Aqueous Solutions of Salts of the Metals				
	V_2SO_4	$W(NO_3)_2$	$X_2(SO_4)_3$	YNO_3	$Z(NO_3)_2$
V	—	R	R	R	R
W	NR	—	R	R	R
X	NR	NR	—	R	R
Y	NR	NR	NR	—	NR
Z	NR	NR	NR	R	—

a) Arrange the elements V, W, X, Y, and Z in an activity series.
b) Write chemical equations to show the relative reactivity of the elements closest together in your activity series. You should have only four equations.

18. Calcium chloride is deliquescent, which means it absorbs water from the air. A group of students wondered if the absorption was a chemical reaction and some new compound was forming or if the calcium chloride was just forming a solution. They tried to answer their question by measuring the maximum mass of water absorbed by given masses of calcium chloride. Their data is given below:

TABLE 3.9

Mass $CaCl_2$(s) (in grams)	17.3	48.8	124	337
Mass H_2O (l) (in grams)	5.62	15.8	40.3	109

a) Suggest a method the students could have used to determine when the maximum mass of water absorbed was reached.
b) Plot the mass of water versus the mass of calcium chloride. Describe the trend in the data. Account for any trend you see.
c) Explain if the data gathered can be used to answer the students' question. Give reasons why or why not.

19. Using the activity series, decide whether the following reactions will occur. If there is no reaction, indicate that in your answer.
a) $Fe(s) + Al_2(SO_4)_3(aq) \rightarrow$
b) $Mg(s) + Zn(NO_3)_2(aq) \rightarrow$
c) $Sn(s) + HCl(aq) \rightarrow$

20. Predict in which one of the following cases a reaction will not occur. For the reactions that you predict will occur, complete and balance the chemical equations.
a) $Al(s) + H_2O(l) \rightarrow$
b) $Cu(s) + Hg(NO_3)_2(aq) \rightarrow$
c) $Br_2(aq) + MgI_2(aq) \rightarrow$

21. For each of the following equations, indicate the physical state of each of the products formed. Identify any products that are precipitates.
a) $Cu(NO_3)_2(aq) + H_2S(aq) \rightarrow$
b) $KOH(aq) + MgCl_2(aq) \rightarrow$
c) $Hg_2(NO_3)_2(aq) + NaCl(aq) \rightarrow$

22. Complete the following synthesis reactions. Identify each product as an acid, a base, a salt, an acidic oxide, or a basic oxide.
a) $S(s) + O_2(g) \rightarrow$
b) $CaO(s) + H_2O(l) \rightarrow$
c) $Li_2O(s) + CO_2(g) \rightarrow$

23. Complete the following reactions. In each case, classify each reaction and indicate if a precipitate will be formed, a gas will be produced, or a neutralization will occur.

a) $Mg(OH)_2(s) + H_2SO_4(aq) \rightarrow$
b) $Na_2CO_3(aq) + H_3PO_4(aq) \rightarrow$
c) $Pb(NO_3)_2(aq) + KCl(aq) \rightarrow$
d) $(NH_4)_2S(aq) + FeSO_4(aq) \rightarrow$

24. Classify each of the following reactions, and predict what the products are.
a) $KOH(aq) + HNO_3(aq) \rightarrow$
b) $Ni(s) + CuSO_4(aq) \rightarrow$
c) $NaNO_3(s) \xrightarrow{\Delta}$
d) $Al(NO_3)_3(aq) + LiOH(aq) \rightarrow$
e) $Zn(s) + O_2(g) \rightarrow$

25. For each of the following reactions, write a balanced chemical equation indicating the physical state of each substance.
a) Ammonia gas and hydrogen chloride gas are mixed.
b) Carbon dioxide gas is bubbled into a solution of calcium hydroxide in water. The other product of the reaction is water.
c) Zinc metal reacts with a solution of lead(II) nitrate.
d) Solid copper(II) nitrate trihydrate is heated. Two of the three gases produced are nitrogen dioxide gas and water vapour.

Making Connections

26. The term "corporate responsibility" implies that industry has a responsibility to provide safe products and to avoid unnecessary pollution of the environment. Select the chemical industry nearest you. Prepare a report that documents ways in which that industry and the various levels of government have worked together to share the burden of costs associated with maintaining a safe and clean environment.

27. Many products today are marketed as "environmentally friendly" because they are biodegradable. Research what biodegradable means. Select a product that is marketed as being biodegradable, and identify the products into which it degrades. Prepare a cost/benefit analysis of the product in terms of factors related to cost, scale, and waste disposal.

28. Like any other industry, the chemical industry exists in order to make profits. As a consequence, most industrial research concentrates on finding new uses for either existing products or waste materials from the manufacturing process. On the other hand, research carried out by universities has not usually been driven by such commercial industries and has been supported by government agencies, such as the National Research Council. Formulate an opinion as to whether research should be funded by industry or government. Write a PMI (plus, minus, interesting) outlining your viewpoint and identifying and raising various issues that can arise from either perspective.

The World's a Lab and We Are All Chemists

Is it? Are we? Yes, in the sense that chemical reactions are taking place all around us, as well as inside our bodies. As for being chemists, the skills you are learning in chemistry labs are those you use every day, from measuring and preparing, to analyzing and communicating. But what about chemistry and your skills in terms of what you might like to do for a career? Does everything grind to a halt at the mere thought? It shouldn't. Chemistry offers a world of possibilities, within which you can choose not only the area that interests you, but the type of work as well.

You can begin finding out about these possibilities right now, because you have more information about chemistry careers than you may realize. You need to look at things just a little differently to find it.

1. Imagine you are starting your first day of a new job working in chemistry. What are you wearing? Where is this job? What are you going to be doing? Write down the first ideas that come to mind.

If you compared your ideas with those of others in your class, chances are you'd have some in common. Many of you might describe yourselves as wearing a lab coat and maybe safety goggles. Many might think of a laboratory setting or a classroom. There could be differences in what's being done, but very likely the answer is measuring or mixing "chemicals."

2. But there are far more careers in chemistry than this. Look at the people pictured on this page. They are all working in chemistry. Match each picture with the career listed below.
   - perfumer
   - environmental scientist
   - technical support consultant
   - soil scientist
   - food chemist

Choices in Chemistry

3. To start your list of possible careers in chemistry, look around your chemistry classroom. Think of everything you do in a typical laboratory investigation. Now, write down all the careers that might be involved. You know more of these than you may realize.

FIGURE 1

FIGURE 2

FIGURE 3

FIGURE 4

FIGURE 5

Here's an example:

You read over the investigation.
Possible chemistry careers? Science writer, photographer, educator, a researcher who develops the inks and paper for printers

You collect and set up your equipment.
Possible chemistry careers? Ceramics engineer, equipment designer, electronics technician, materials engineer. And don't forget scientific equipment salesperson.

Do you need to heat something using a gas flame?
Possible chemistry careers? Gas-line technician, geological engineer, safety inspector

For example: take a look inside your bathroom.

Any medicines? Vitamins?
Possible chemistry careers? Biomedical researcher, analytical chemist, spectroscope operator, measurement specialist, pharmacist, food chemist, nutritionist

Any soaps or shampoos? Toothpaste and brushes?
Possible chemistry careers? Perfumer, chromatographer, cosmetician, production-line designer, industrial chemist, dentist, dental hygienist

How about towels, wallpaper, mirrors, and even the curtain rod?
Possible chemistry careers? Textile chemist, materials engineer, glazier, metallurgist

4. Continue this for the rest of the stages of performing and completing an investigation. Think of as many careers as you can. Compare your list with others and add any new careers to make your list as complete as possible.

■ Now, who trains all of these people? Add those careers.
■ Who provides support and supplies to people in these careers? Add those as well.

Looking Outward

5. Another way to discover career choices in chemistry is to consider how chemistry is involved in our daily lives. You've been exploring this as you learn about matter and chemical reactions. Now, turn it around. Think about the careers involved in that chemistry. As you go through your day, add these ideas to your list.

Keep going, but now begin to focus on things that interest you personally. Do you love music? You could combine that with chemistry and look for a career involving the materials used to make instruments (restorer, materials researcher, inventor). Maybe you'd prefer to design better ways to make headphones, or create new plastics to use in their manufacture.

As you've seen, there are areas of chemistry related to everything we use and everything we do. Within those areas, careers range from research to design to sales to almost anything imaginable. So is the world a lab and are all of us chemists? Perhaps it's more accurate to say that chemistry offers a world of possibilities and you may find that a career in chemistry is exactly right for you.

Calcium Carbonate—A Viable Product?

Background Information

The manufacturing process converts raw materials into products that are more useful and, therefore, more valuable. For example, the naturally occurring compound calcium carbonate ($CaCO_3$), in the form of the mineral calcite, is found in limestone, which is plentiful throughout the world. The calcium carbonate you are used to seeing in the laboratory is in the form of a white powder, but limestone comes out of the ground in rock form. Mining processes extract over 1500 million tonnes of limestone every year and provide an important raw material for the chemical industry.

However, the extraction process does not produce extra value without a cost. There is an economic cost to the production of raw materials. Energy is needed in the extraction process, employees have to be paid, and machinery and buildings need to be maintained. Manufacturing also relies on technology related to engineering. The cost of all of these factors contributes to the economic cost.

But an economic cost is not the only consideration. Manufacturing processes also have an effect on both the natural environment and the working environment. People's health and safety need to be considered, of both those who work in the buildings and factories, and those who live nearby. There are also issues related to pollution and the depletion of resources, especially those that are non-renewable. These factors contribute to the environmental costs.

When a product is manufactured, both its economic and environmental costs must be considered.

SCENARIO

You have been hired as a consultant to a company that is considering manufacturing calcium carbonate products for particular use in the agricultural industry. The company wants to consider all factors so that it can develop a cost-efficient product. You have been asked to prepare a presentation to the company executives that summarizes your research in the following areas:

- mining and manufacturing of the compound
- properties of the compound
- economic and environmental considerations

Part A: Research the Compound Calcium Carbonate

1. Use electronic and print resources to research how and where calcium carbonate is presently being extracted. Identify the technologies that are needed as well as the manufacturing process.

2. Use electronic and print resources to research the different uses of calcium carbonate in the agricultural industry.

Part B: Analyzing the Chemistry of Calcium Carbonate

3. Describe the physical properties of calcium carbonate.

4. Design a set of procedures to synthesize calcium carbonate in the laboratory. Once you have approval from your teacher, carry out your investigation.

5. Design a set of procedures to determine if calcium carbonate reacts with an acid and/or a base. Once you have approval from your teacher, carry out your investigation.

6. Write a balanced equation for any reaction that occurs, and identify the type of reaction.

7. Provide a description of the structure of calcium carbonate by drawing the Lewis structures for the calcium ion and the carbonate ion.

8. Prepare a summary describing the chemistry of calcium carbonate.

Part C: Preparing a Cost-Benefit Analysis

9. Prepare a cost-benefit analysis on the mining process and agricultural uses of calcium carbonate based on your research. Make sure you consider both economic and environmental factors.

10. Create a flowchart showing the steps that lead from the raw materials to possible finished products.

Part D: Communicating Results

11. Prepare a presentation to the company executives that informs them about the chemistry of calcium carbonate and its uses in the agricultural industry. Summarize clearly the economic and environmental factors that will help to inform the company whether or not it should proceed with production.

UNIT 1 REVIEW

Understanding Concepts

1. State which of the following represents the thermal decomposition of lead(II) carbonate.

   a) $PbCO_3(s) \xrightarrow{\Delta} Pb(s) + CO_3(g)$

   b) $PbCO_3(s) \xrightarrow{\Delta} PbO(s) + CO_2(g)$

   c) $PbCO_3(s) \xrightarrow{\Delta} Pb(s) + C(s) + O_3(g)$

   d) $PbCO_3(s) \xrightarrow{\Delta} PbC(s) + O_3(g)$

2. Successive ionization energies in $kJ \cdot mol^{-1}$ for an unknown element are as follows:

   $E_1 = 711 \quad E_2 = 1421 \quad E_3 = 7733 \quad E_4 = 9196$

   Identify to which group of the periodic table the element could belong.
   a) 1
   b) 2
   c) 13
   d) 14
   e) transition metals

3. As the atomic number of the halogens increases, the relative activity:
   a) increases
   b) increases and then decreases
   c) remains the same
   d) decreases
   e) decreases and then increases

4. An unknown white crystalline solid was dissolved in water. The solution was tested with a conductivity apparatus, and the light bulb glowed brightly. Identify which of the following could be the identity of the unknown.
   a) sulfur trioxide, a by-product of heavy industry that is involved in forming acid rain
   b) potassium hydroxide, used in the manufacture of soap and inks
   c) silicon dioxide, found in quartz and sand
   d) nitrogen dioxide, used in the production of explosives
   e) arsenic trioxide, used as a rodent killer

5. The following reaction is characteristic of one group of elements.

   $2 X(s) + 2 H_2O(l) \rightarrow 2 XOH(aq) + H_2(g)$

   The group is:
   a) alkali metals
   b) alkaline-earth metals
   c) noble metals
   d) transition metals

6. The elements fluorine, oxygen, and nitrogen listed in order of increasing electronegativity would be:
   a) oxygen, nitrogen, fluorine
   b) fluorine, nitrogen, oxygen
   c) fluorine, oxygen, nitrogen
   d) nitrogen, oxygen, fluorine
   e) nitrogen, fluorine, oxygen

7. A certain solid consists of ions bound in a crystal lattice. You could expect the solid to have the following property:
   a) a low melting point
   b) a hard and brittle texture
   c) good conductivity when dissolved in water
   d) a low solubility in water
   e) a low boiling point

8. State which of the following substances would involve both ionic and covalent bonds.
   I calcium chloride, used to keep dust down on rural roads
   II sulfur dioxide, a by-product of burning coal that is involved in forming acid rain
   III sodium hydrogen carbonate, commonly known as baking soda
   IV nitric acid, used for making explosives and cauterizing warts

   a) I only
   b) I and II only
   c) III and IV only
   d) I, III, and IV only

9. Crystals of sodium chloride consist of:
   a) molecules of NaCl held together by ionic bonds
   b) ions of Na^+ and Cl^- held together by ionic bonds
   c) atoms of Na and Cl held together by polar covalent bonds
   d) atoms of Na and Cl held together by ionic bonds
   e) ions of Na^+ and Cl^- held together by covalent bonds

10. Identify which pair of reactants will *not* react.
    a) sodium and water
    b) aluminum and copper(II) sulfate
    c) lead and nickel(II) nitrate
    d) copper and mercury(II) chloride
    e) calcium and hydrochloric acid

11. Draw a block diagram of the periodic table, and mark the following on it: main group elements, transition metals, lanthanoids, actinoids, alkali metals, alkaline-earth metals, halogens, noble gases, unstable elements, metals, and non-metals.

12. For each of the following pairs, predict which element will have the larger atomic radius and which will have the higher first ionization energy.
    a) sodium and aluminium
    b) magnesium and barium
    c) hydrogen and helium

13. Explain and give an example of:
    a) an acidic oxide
    b) a basic oxide

14. Describe, in your own words, what is meant by the term "stable octet."

15. Briefly describe the major contribution made by each of the following chemists toward the development of a systematic method for naming compounds:
    a) Guyton de Morveau   b) Alfred Stock

16. Predict the usual ionic charge on the ions of the following atoms:
    a) Rb
    b) Sr
    c) Xe
    d) S
    e) I
    f) H

17. Explain the meaning of the following symbols:
    a) *(aq)*
    b) *(g)*
    c) *(l)*
    d) *(s)*

18. State the periodic law, and use an example to illustrate it.

19. Explain how the electronegativity scale is useful when trying to predict whether the bonds in a compound are ionic or covalent.

20. Explain and give an example of:
    a) a thermochemical reaction
    b) a neutralization reaction

21. Explain why arranging the elements by atomic number is more useful than by atomic mass.

22. In 1827, Friedrich Wöhler, a German chemist, first isolated aluminum by the following reaction:

    $$3\ K(s) + AlCl_3(s) \xrightarrow{\Delta} 3\ KCl(l) + Al(l)$$

    When the reaction mixture was cooled, both the potassium chloride and aluminum solidified. The potassium chloride was dissolved in water exposing the aluminum.
    a) Classify the reaction.
    b) Describe what this reaction implies about potassium and aluminum metals.

23. Describe the least electronegativity difference possible between 2 atoms involved in a bond. Identify the type of bonding that is involved, and give an example.

24. Looking at the two eyes in Figure 1, determine if they are the same. Explain what you would like to know to be certain. The building of the periodic table is all about detecting patterns. Detecting patterns is a skill found in many areas. Iris recognition uses the iris, the coloured region that surrounds the pupil, as the physical characteristic to be measured. Determine which regularity would have to be noted if iris scanning were to be used for identification or for verification. Give reasons for your choice.

 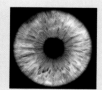

FIGURE 1

Applying Inquiry/ Communication Skills

25. Organize the following 15 elements into a mini-periodic table (see the table below). The mini-periodic table has all the features of the periodic table except it only involves 5 of the 8 representative groups and only periods 2 through 4. The code letters A to O have been assigned to the 15 elements. They do not correlate in any way with the real symbols for these elements. The following are the known properties of these elements.

    Properties:
    - All of the elements combine with element B except G, H, and L.
    - The formulas of the compounds formed with B are AB, BB, EB, FB, JB, MB, CB_2, DB_2, IB_2, KB_2, NB_2, and OB_2.
    - The elements A, D, F, K, M, and O have a silvery lustre and conduct heat and electricity well.
    - The elements B, C, E, J, and N react with I to form compounds that react with water to form acids.
    - J has a lower electron affinity than G.
    - The relative atomic mass of H is greater than that of E but less than that of F.
    - B is a gas, E is a liquid, and J is a solid at room temperature and pressure.
    - L is the lightest gas in its group.
    - I has a smaller atomic radius than either N or C.
    - F has the lowest electronegativity.
    - The melting point of O is greater than D but less than K.
    - The first ionization energy of M is greater than either A or F.
    - C has one more electron than O.

26. Draw Lewis structures for each of the following compounds. Determine whether the compound is ionic or covalent.
    a) NaI
    b) N_2
    c) SO_2
    d) Li_2O
    e) $BaCl_2$
    f) AlF_3
    g) O_3

27. Use the Internet to find the following properties of the alkali metals and the group 17 elements: density, relative atomic mass, formulas of oxides, atomic radius, and first ionization energies. Justify the placement of the elements in either group 1 or 17 based on this data.

28. Describe how the following compounds are named:
   a) a binary ionic compound
   b) a binary covalent compound
   c) a binary ionic compound in which the cation has more than one possible charge (two ways)
   d) a hydrated salt
   e) an acid salt

29. Name each of the following compounds:
   a) Li_2CO_3
   b) $Fe_2(SO_4)_3$
   c) $(NH_4)_2S$
   d) $Sn_3(PO_4)_2$
   e) $Ca(OH)_2$
   f) $AgClO$
   g) $Pb(CO_3)_2$
   h) $AgClO_4$
   i) $FeSO_4$
   j) $Mg(ClO_2)_2$

30. Write a chemical equation for each of the following reactions. Predict what the products will be.
   a) placing solid sodium oxide in a container of carbon dioxide gas
   b) heating solid calcium carbonate

31. Name the following salts, and indicate whether each is an acid salt or a hydrated salt:
   a) $SnCl_2 \cdot 5H_2O$
   b) $BaHPO_4$
   c) $NaHSO_4$
   d) $FePO_4 \cdot 3H_2O$

32. Predict the products for each of the following equations:
   a) $Cu(OH)_2(s) \xrightarrow{\Delta}$
   b) $CuBr_2(aq) + Cl_2(aq) \rightarrow$
   c) $Cu(OH)_2(s) + HNO_3(aq) \rightarrow$
   d) $CuS(s) + HCl(aq) \rightarrow$
   e) $CuCO_3(s) \xrightarrow{\Delta}$

33. Draw the structural formula for each of the following covalent substances:
   a) F_2
   b) OF_2
   c) NCl_3
   d) SiH_4
   e) N_2
   f) SO_2
   g) O_3

34. Draw the structural formulas for the following compounds, and indicate the polar nature of the covalent bonds.
   a) ICl
   b) PCl_3
   c) NH_3

35. Based on the activity series, identify which one of the following reactions will take place.
   a) $Ag(s) + NaNO_3(aq) \rightarrow$
   b) $K(s) + H_2O(l) \rightarrow$
   c) $Cu(s) + HCl(aq) \rightarrow$

36. Look up the crystal structure of some common ionic compounds, such as sodium chloride and cesium chloride. Draw a diagram of the arrangement of ions in the crystal, and construct a model of the structure. Explain why the ions are arranged as they are. Design a display to illustrate your findings.

37. Identify the type of reaction for each of the following equations, and write the formula of the product(s). Classify the products as acids, bases, salts, acidic oxides, or basic oxides.
   a) $Mg(s) + S(s) \rightarrow$
   b) $Na_2O(s) + SO_2(g) \rightarrow$
   c) $MgO(s) + H_2O(l) \rightarrow$

38. Write the formula for each of the following:
   a) potassium sulfate
   b) sodium cyanide
   c) sodium chromate
   d) iron(III) hydroxide
   e) ammonium nitrate
   f) lead(II) perchlorate
   g) ammonium phosphate
   h) zinc perchlorate
   i) iron(II) sulfite
   j) magnesium hypochlorite

39. State the formula and name of the compound formed by the following pairs of ions:
   a) lithium and nitride
   b) tin(IV) and phosphate
   c) copper(II) and phosphide
   d) potassium and dichromate
   e) magnesium and oxide
   f) iron(III) and bromite

40. Write a chemical equation for each of the following reactions, and indicate the physical state of the species involved whenever possible.
   a) Magnesium metal is heated in nitrogen gas.
   b) Hydrogen sulfide gas is bubbled into a solution of copper(II) sulfate in water.
   c) Solid manganese(IV) oxide reacts with hydrochloric acid. One of the other products is water.
   d) Barium metal reacts with water.

Making Connections

41. Many people today rely on buying prepared foods because they have busy lifestyles. Write a persuasive essay that outlines the importance for the food industry to continue itemizing ingredients and their amounts on all food labels. Include supporting evidence for the arguments you present.

42. Atoms that contain odd numbers of protons or neutrons can absorb specific frequencies of radiowaves when they are placed in a magnetic field. The frequency that is absorbed depends on the identity of the surrounding atoms. This is the analytical technique of nuclear magnetic resonance (NMR). It is now possible to study atoms within the human body to gain information about health, disease, and the workings of the human brain. Medical researchers call the technique magnetic resonance imaging (MRI). Identify which elements are most common in the human body and which have odd numbers of protons or neutrons. Suggest why the medical name for the procedure is different from the chemical name. Research how MRI is performed in hospitals, and find out exactly how it is used. Suggest how MRI has improved the ability of medical personnel to diagnose disease. Write a report on your findings.

43. We all use certain products that need to be disposed of in a safe manner. Some examples of waste mismanagement are throwing away toxins, such as pesticide containers, in the garbage and pouring old motor oil and/or paints down the drain or down storm sewers. Design a public service announcement that will inform consumers of their responsibility toward waste management. Include environmental and health consequences that are possible if this responsibility is ignored.

44. Pick a group of elements or a single element. Using the library and the Internet, research the properties and uses of the element(s) you have chosen. In your report, link the uses with the properties, and explain the impact the elements have had on society. Your report can be completed using one of three formats: a newspaper article for the school newspaper, a 5-min to 15-min computer-based presentation, or a 5-min to 15-min skit.

45. Canada has the second-largest deposits of uranium in the world. Uranite is one of the most important sources. The ore is first ground into a fine sand, and then the uranium is separated chemically to form what is called "yellowcake." Heating the yellowcake at the uranium processing plant in Blind River, Ontario, yields U_3O_8, which is dissolved in nitric acid to produce an aqueous solution of $UO_2(NO_3)_2$, uranyl nitrate. Heating the solution leaves uranyl nitrate hexahydrate. It then undergoes the following chemical reaction:

$$2\ UO_2(NO_3)_2 \cdot 6H_2O(s) \xrightarrow{\Delta}$$
$$2\ UO_3(s) + 4\ NO_2(g) + O_2(g) + 6\ H_2O(g)$$

Then the uranium(VI) oxide is transported to Port Hope, Ontario, and the following reaction is carried out:

$$UO_3(s) + H_2(g) \rightarrow UO_2(s) + H_2O(g)$$

Uranium in the form of UO_2 is used in CANDU reactors. However, most of the uranium processed in Canada is for export, so the uranium has to undergo two more processes before it can be exported. They are as follows:

$$UO_2(s) + 4\ HF(aq) \rightarrow UF_4(s) + 2\ H_2O(l)$$

and

$$UF_4(s) + F_2(g) \rightarrow UF_6(s)$$

Rewrite the overview of the uranium industry presented above, but this time, describe the kinds of chemical reactions that are occurring rather than using chemical or word equations. Prepare a risk assessment for each of the processes involved, focussing on health and environmental concerns.

46. "Corporate responsibility" is a term that is used to imply that industry has a responsibility to provide safe products and to avoid unnecessary pollution of the environment. You are part of a consulting firm that is trying to facilitate discussion between industry and various levels of government to work together to share the burden of costs associated with maintaining a safe and clean environment. Brainstorm ideas showing both risks and benefits to both parties, and write a proposal that will persuade all concerned parties to compromise and agree on a joint action plan.

47. Critically examine a television advertisement for a household product that uses chemicals. Identify who you think the target audience is, and make a chart listing the following criteria: use of colour, lighting, camera angles, music, voices, sound effects, models, props, and background setting. Describe how each criterion can affect the purchase of the product. Write a summarizing paragraph analyzing how effective the advertisement is, and note any additional information that would contribute to an informed decision regarding the purchase of the product.

2 Quantities in Chemical Reactions

OVERALL EXPECTATIONS

By the end of this unit, you will be able to:

■ demonstrate an understanding of the mole concept and its significance in the analysis of chemical systems

■ carry out experiments and complete calculations based on quantitative relationships in balanced chemical reactions

■ demonstrate an awareness of the importance of quantitative chemical relationships in the home or in industry

From biological to industrial processes, your life depends on chemical reactions and the compounds they make. As knowledge about the nature of substances and chemical reactions has progressed, we have become able to make substances that do not occur in nature and have just the right properties for our needs. The quantities of substances are as important as using the right kind of substance in producing such products. Manufacturers must produce the right quantity of their products. Making too much could increase storage or disposal costs; making too little could make customers go elsewhere. Products composed of more than one substance, such as paint or cosmetics, must contain exactly the same proportions of components in every batch that is made. Information about the quantities of substances is also necessary to identify unknown substances.

Whether you want to know what a substance is, how much you can make, or if you have the right mix of substances, the tool you need is stoichiometry. **Stoichiometry** refers to the relative proportions in which elements form compounds or in which substances react. In this unit, you will develop an understanding of stoichiometry and how it is used to analyze substances, determine relative proportions, and predict the amounts of products of chemical reactions.

Stoichiometry is about quantities of substances.

Synthetic materials must always have consistent quality.

Europeans Fear Connection between Depleted Uranium and Gulf War Syndrome

Top officials of NATO and the European Union are holding crisis meetings as more countries allege the health of their soldiers was damaged by exposure to weapons made with depleted uranium during conflicts in the Balkans. Depleted uranium is left after fissionable isotopes are removed from natural uranium and made into nuclear fuel. Canada supplies most of the depleted uranium used in the world.

New Ingredient Improves Rare Earth Magnets

Researchers from the Idaho National Engineering and Environmental Laboratory (INEEL), Ames Laboratory, and Brookhaven National Laboratory have added a new ingredient to rare earth magnets. Rare earth magnets (based on the element neodymium) are used in products such as computer hard drives, cordless power tools, and miniature speakers. The secret ingredient in the new recipe is non-metallic crystals of titanium carbide. These crystals make the magnets stronger and more durable.

Poison and the Death of Beethoven

An analysis of a lock of Ludwig van Beethoven's hair suggests that lead poisoning might have caused the early death and maybe even the deafness of the musical genius. A hair sample, snipped from the composer after his death at age 56 in 1827, contained up to 100 times the level commonly found in people today.

ACHIEVEMENT TASK PREVIEW

At the end of the unit, you will demonstrate your learning by completing the task "Oh, My Aching Head." As part of a marketing team for a pain reliever, you will research the qualities of competing products, analyze the efficiency of ASA synthesis, and develop a marketing proposal and advertising campaign. You will then summarize your research and ideas in a two-page paper. See page 212.

Agricultural chemicals have to be used in the correct quantities to be effective.

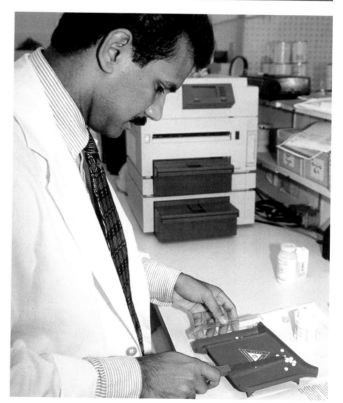

Medicines must have precise quantities of the active ingredient.

CHAPTER 4

SPECIFIC EXPECTATIONS

By the end of this chapter, you will be able to:

- demonstrate an understanding of Avogadro's number, the mole concept, and the relationship between the mole and molar mass (4.1, 4.2)

- explain the relationship between isotopic abundance and relative atomic mass (4.1, Investigation 1)

- distinguish between the empirical formula and the molecular formula of a compound (4.4)

- explain the law of definite proportions (4.3)

- use appropriate scientific vocabulary to communicate ideas related to chemical calculation (4.1, 4.2, 4.3, 4.4)

- determine percent composition of a compound through experimentation, as well as through analysis of the formula and a table of relative atomic masses (4.3, Investigation 2)

- solve problems involving quantity in moles, number of particles, and mass (4.1, 4.2, 4.3)

- determine empirical formulas and molecular formulas, given molar masses and percent composition or mass data (4.4, Investigation 1, Investigation 2)

- give examples of the application of chemical quantities and calculations (4.1, 4.2, 4.3, 4.4)

- explain how different stoichiometric combinations of elements in compounds can produce substances with different properties (4.3)

- identify everyday situations and work-related contexts in which analysis of unknown substances is important (4.1, 4.2, 4.3, 4.4)

Calculations Involving Elements and Compounds

In Unit 1, you used the information in the periodic table to predict the types of chemical reactions in which elements will participate and the products these reactions will form. You should now understand more about how two hydrogen atoms and one oxygen atom react to give you water, or how two oxygen atoms and one carbon atom give you carbon dioxide. But what if you did not know how a substance had formed? How would you figure out exactly what that substance was?

This kind of problem has to be solved by many people in many kinds of careers. A geologist has to identify the minerals in samples of Earth's surface. A medical technician has to identify the substances in a urine sample. An ecologist has to identify the pollutants in a stream. Although the techniques that these people use are probably different, one thing will be common to them all. To find out what is in a sample, you have to take it apart, identify its components, and then determine the quantity of each component.

In order to identify chemical substances, scientists have developed ways of identifying and counting the atoms in a sample. However, since atoms are very small, they cannot be counted directly. Instead, atoms are counted by measuring their mass and then relating their mass to the relative atomic masses on the periodic table. You will learn about the relationships between mass and the number of particles in this chapter, and also how to use this information to determine the chemical formula of an unknown compound.

FIGURE 4.1 Measuring quantities by mass can be easier than counting out a particular number.

Counting Particles by Mass

How do chemists find the number of atoms, ions, or molecules in a sample? These particles are too small to count directly. Chemists use the mass of the sample to estimate the number of particles. In this activity, you will use mass to estimate the number of individual beans in a handful of jellybeans.

Materials

jellybeans
Smarties™
250-mL beaker
centigram balance

1. Place a clean, dry, 250-mL beaker on the centigram balance, and determine its mass. Add 10 jellybeans to the beaker, and record the mass.

2. Calculate the average mass of one jellybean from the mass of ten beans.

3. Repeat step 1 with a handful of jellybeans. Record the mass.

4. Divide the mass of the handful of jellybeans by the average mass of one bean. This will give you an estimate of the number of jellybeans in the handful.

5. Count the number of jellybeans in the handful directly.

6. Repeat steps 1 to 5 using Smarties™.

■ Did you find the same number of beans in the handful of jellybeans or Smarties™ when you estimated from their mass as when you counted them directly?

■ Calculate the expected mass of 15 jellybeans and of 15 Smarties™.

■ How are these masses the same? How are they different? Why?

■ Why did you determine the average mass of one jellybean instead of measuring the mass of one bean directly?

CHECKPOINT

Prepare a mind map using the following words: element, molecule, mole, Avogadro's number, and atomic mass.

4.1 Units for Chemical Quantities

Key Understandings

When you have completed this section, you will be able to:

- explain Avogadro's number and the concept of the mole
- explain how relative atomic mass is related to isotopic abundance
- use appropriate scientific vocabulary when you communicate about chemical calculations
- solve problems involving moles, number of particles, and mass

Each branch of science uses a particular set of scientific units. Astronomers work with light-years to measure distances between stars, while microbiologists use micrometres to measure the size of cells, for example. In order to work with chemicals, you need to understand the units that are used in chemistry.

Chemists study matter and the particles that comprise matter. Matter is measured by its mass. When relatively large quantities of matter are measured, chemists generally use the gram, a unit you are already familiar with. A particular mass might be reported using grams or a derivative of the gram, such as the kilogram or milligram. However, even micrograms are useless for measuring the mass of very small particles like atoms and molecules. The mass of individual atoms and molecules is measured using something called relative atomic mass.

Average Atomic Mass

If atoms were as big as the plastic models used to represent them or even as big as jellybeans, you would easily be able to find the mass of a single atom using a balance. Although you cannot actually place a single atom of an element on a balance to determine its mass, you can find its mass by comparing it with the mass of atoms of another element.

Suppose you have an equal number of small plastic balls and small rubber balls. Because you have equal numbers of both kind of balls, you can find the relationship between the mass of one plastic ball and the mass of one rubber ball by measuring the mass of all of the plastic balls and all of the rubber balls. For example, if the mass of all the plastic balls is one-half the mass of all the rubber balls, then one plastic ball has half the mass of one rubber ball. This type of measurement is called relative mass. **Relative mass** is the mass of any object compared with the mass of another object.

As in the example with balls, instead of trying to measure the mass of one atom, you can determine the atomic mass of one element relative to the atomic mass of another element. **Relative atomic mass** is the mass of any atom compared with the mass of an atom of another element. In science, that other element is always one particular form of carbon. Recall that atoms of the same element sometimes have different numbers of neutrons, even though they have the same number of protons. These different atoms are called isotopes of the element. Relative atomic mass is determined by comparing the mass of an atom against C-12, the most common isotope of carbon. Examine the atomic masses of the elements on the periodic table. You should notice that most of the elements have fractional atomic masses.

Although an atom of carbon-12 has a relative atomic mass of 12, the relative atomic mass of carbon on the periodic table is 12.01. The values on the periodic table have been determined by experiments using naturally occurring carbon. Naturally occurring carbon is actually a mixture of two different carbon isotopes, carbon-12 and carbon-13. **Average atomic mass** is the atomic mass of the mixture of isotopes of an element that is usually found in nature. The values on the periodic table are average atomic masses.

Calculating Average Atomic Mass   You can calculate the average atomic mass of an element if you know both the relative atomic mass and the abundance of every one of its isotopes. Scientists determine these values by analyzing a naturally occurring sample of the element in a mass spectrometer (Figure 4.2). A mass spectrometer creates ions from the particles in a sample and then measures the mass of these ions by how much they are deflected by a magnetic field. A detector then measures the abundance of each type of ion. Table 4.1 shows the abundance of the isotopes of some common elements.

WEBLINK

Models of the changes in Earth's climate and atmosphere over the last few millions of years can be studied by analyzing stable isotopes with a mass spectrometer. Prepare a poster presentation of other analytic tools that are used by scientists for this type of research. Begin your research at **www.pearsoned.ca/chemistry11**.

TABLE 4.1 Natural Percent Abundance of Isotopes of Some Elements

	Symbol	Natural Percent Abundance	Mass	Average Atomic Mass
Hydrogen	$_1^1H$	99.985	1.0078	
	$_1^2H$	0.015	2.0141	1.0079
	$_1^3H$	trace	3.0160	
Carbon	$_6^{12}C$	98.89	12.000	
	$_6^{13}C$	1.11	13.003	12.011
Oxygen	$_8^{16}O$	99.759	15.995	
	$_8^{17}O$	0.037	16.995	15.999
	$_8^{18}O$	0.204	17.999	
Zinc	$_{30}^{64}Zn$	48.89	63.929	
	$_{30}^{66}Zn$	27.81	65.926	
	$_{30}^{67}Zn$	4.11	66.927	65.38
	$_{30}^{68}Zn$	18.57	67.925	
	$_{30}^{70}Zn$	0.62	69.925	

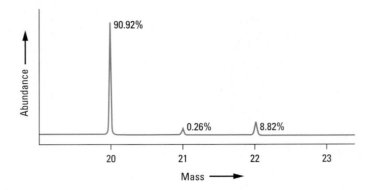

FIGURE 4.2 A typical readout of an analysis of naturally occurring neon using a mass spectrometer. Each peak corresponds to a particular isotope; the height of the peaks can be used to calculate isotopic abundance.

To calculate average atomic mass, first write the abundance of each isotope as a fraction:

$$\text{fraction of an isotope} = \frac{\text{abundance (\%)}}{100\%}$$

If you have two isotopes of an element, A and B, then average atomic mass is calculated by:

$$\text{average atomic mass} = (\text{relative atomic mass A} \times \text{fraction of A})$$
$$+ (\text{relative atomic mass B} \times \text{fraction of B})$$

For example, consider an element with two isotopes. Imagine that in a naturally occurring sample of this element, half of the atoms have a relative atomic mass of 8 and half have a relative atomic mass of 6.

First calculate the fraction of each isotope:

$$\text{fraction of isotope with atomic mass of 8} = \frac{50}{100}$$
$$= 0.5$$

$$\text{fraction of isotope with atomic mass of 6} = \frac{50}{100}$$
$$= 0.5$$

Then use these values in the equation for average atomic mass:

$$\text{average atomic mass} = (8 \times 0.5) + (6 \times 0.5)$$
$$= 7$$

The Mass Spectrometer and Its Applications

The mission of the unmanned *Viking Lander* that touched down on the surface of Mars on July 20, 1976, was to answer one question: Is there life on Mars? During the descent through the Martian atmosphere, an upper-atmosphere mass spectrometer on board the *Viking Lander* tested for the presence of various gases. From this analysis, we know the Martian atmosphere is 95% carbon dioxide, 2.7% nitrogen, and 1.6% argon, with some additional trace gases. Several soil analyses were also conducted on the surface of Mars. A combination gas chromatograph-mass spectrometer apparatus searched for organic (carbon-based) molecules in the soil that would indicate the presence of life. The *Viking Lander* found no such evidence of life on Mars.

Mass spectrometry is used to analyze gas, liquid, and solid samples. It can detect very small amounts of materials. This type of analysis is called trace analysis. Trace analysis is used often in medicine and pharmaceutical manufacturing, where small differences in the amounts of some substances can make dramatic differences to the health of a patient. Mass spectrometry is the most accurate and direct method of determining atomic and molecular masses. It is used in investigating components of flavourings and perfumes, as well as for accurate dating of archaeological remains and works of art.

In Figure 4.4, you will see where a gaseous sample is to be injected into a vacuum chamber, where it will be bombarded by a stream of high-energy electrons. Collisions between the gaseous atoms or molecules in the sample and the high-energy electrons produce positively charged ions. These cations then remove an electron from each atom or molecule in the sample by electrostatic force. Two oppositely charged plates then accelerate the cations through a magnetic field. As the cations pass through this magnetic field, their paths become deflected (curved). The extent of their deflection depends on their masses. Each ion has a unique mass, so each will have a unique deflection path. The path of a heavy ion, like that of a speeding transport truck, is difficult to change. However, like a small car, the path of a lightweight ion is more easily deflected to a greater extent. The magnetic field therefore sorts out the ions in the sample stream based on their mass, giving discrete beams containing only one type of ion. The result is a **mass spectrum**, which is an array of ion streams of discrete masses. Since each ion can be identified by the amount of its deflection, we are therefore able to identify the original atom or molecule it came from. When the ions arrive at the detector, a current is registered for each type of ion. The amount of current generated is directly proportional to the number of ions, so the relative abundance of the components of a sample can also be determined.

The English physicist F.W. Aston, who was awarded the Nobel prize in chemistry in 1922 for this achievement, developed the first mass spectrometer. Aston analyzed a sample of neon with his mass spectrometer and was thus able to provide indisputable evidence of the existence of the neon isotopes neon-20 (relative atomic mass 19.9924 and natural abundance 90.92%) and neon-22 (relative atomic mass 21.9914 and natural abundance 8.82%). When more sensitive mass spectrometers were developed, scientists detected a third isotope of neon (neon-21) that has a natural abundance of only 0.26%.

FIGURE 4.3 When the *Viking Lander* reached Mars after one-and-a-half years of travel, one of its tasks was to analyze Martian soil samples for signs of life with an onboard mass spectrometer.

FIGURE 4.4 Schematic diagram of a mass spectrometer

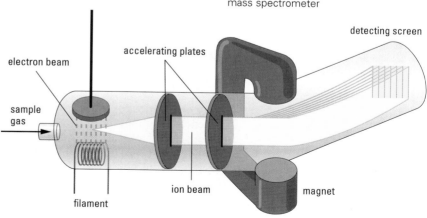

EXAMPLE 1

Calculate the average atomic mass of natural carbon using the following values for relative atomic mass and abundance of each of its isotopes:

TABLE 4.2

Isotope	Relative Atomic Mass	Abundance (%)
C-12	12	98.89
C-13	13.003	1.11

Given

$m_{C\text{-}12}$ = 12
$abundance_{C\text{-}12}$ = 98.89%
$m_{C\text{-}13}$ = 13.003
$abundance_{C\text{-}13}$ = 1.11%

Required

average atomic mass$_{natural\ carbon}$ = ?

Analysis

$$\text{fraction of an isotope} = \frac{\text{abundance (\%)}}{100\%}$$

Therefore

$$\text{fraction}_{C\text{-}12} = \frac{98.89\%}{100\%}$$
$$= 0.9889$$

$$\text{fraction}_{C\text{-}13} = \frac{1.11\%}{100\%}$$
$$= 0.0111$$

Solution

$\text{average atomic mass}_{natural\ C} = (m_{C\text{-}12} \times \text{fraction}_{C\text{-}12})$
$+ (m_{C\text{-}13} \times \text{fraction}_{C\text{-}13})$

$= (12)(0.9889) + (13.003)(0.011)$
$= 11.87 + 0.144$
$= 12.01$

Statement

The average atomic mass of natural carbon is 12.01.

PRACTICE PROBLEM

Chlorine (atomic number 17) has two naturally occurring isotopes. One isotope has mass 34.969 and an abundance of 75.77%. The other has mass 36.966 and an abundance of 24.23%. Calculate the average atomic mass of chlorine.

The Mole

The **mole** (symbol mol) is the unit for the *amount* of a substance (symbol n). In chemistry, "amount" always refers to the number of moles of a substance. **Avogadro's number** (symbol N) is the number of particles in one mole, which is 6.02×10^{23}. The term "mole" describes a particular number of particles, just as the terms "pair" and "dozen" refer to a particular number of things. When you talk about a pair of shoes, for example, the person listening knows that you are talking about two shoes. When chemists talk about a mole of carbon, you know they mean 6.02×10^{23} atoms of carbon.

Just how much is a mole? These analogies may help you to picture the magnitude of 6.02×10^{23} of something.

- If one mole of pennies were distributed equally among the 6 billion people on Earth, then each person would have 1×10^{14} pennies, or 1×10^{12} dollars. In other words, every person on the planet would be a trillionaire.
- If Avogadro's number of sheets of paper were divided into a million equal piles, each pile would be so tall that it would stretch from Earth to the sun and beyond.
- In order to obtain Avogadro's number of grains of sand, you would have to dig the entire surface of the Sahara desert to a depth of 2 m. The Sahara desert has an area of 8×10^6 km²; Canada has an area of about 9 970 610 km² or about 10.0×10^6 km².

Conversion Factors and Units

Through Avogadro's number, you can easily convert from moles to any other unit and vice versa. One way to change from one unit to another is to use **conversion factors**. A conversion factor is a ratio that describes how one unit is related to another unit. Example 2 uses a familiar example, the relationship between dozens and single eggs, to demonstrate how to use conversion factors.

EXAMPLE 2

Calculate the amount of eggs in dozens (doz) in a box containing 432 eggs.

Given
number of eggs = 432

Required
amount of eggs$_{dozen}$ = ? doz

Analysis
There are 12 eggs in a dozen, or 12 eggs·doz^{-1}. From this relationship, you get the conversion factor $\dfrac{12 \text{ eggs}}{1 \text{ doz}}$.

To obtain the number of eggs in dozens, *invert* the conversion factor and multiply the given number of eggs by the inverted factor.

Solution
$$\text{amount of eggs}_{dozen} = 432 \text{ eggs} \times \frac{1 \text{ doz}}{12 \text{ eggs}}$$
$$= 36 \text{ doz}$$

Statement
The box contains 36 dozen eggs.

FIGURE 4.5 "Mole" is a term for a certain quantity, similar to "dozen."

PRACTICE PROBLEM

There are 144 objects in a gross. Use the conversion factor method to determine the number of gross in a case of 864 pencils.

To calculate moles of atoms, you proceed exactly as in Example 2, except that you will use Avogadro's number, or 6.02×10^{23} atoms·mol^{-1}, as the conversion factor.

EXAMPLE 3

Find the amount in a sample containing 3.01×10^{24} atoms of a substance.

Given
number of atoms = 3.01×10^{24} atoms

Required
amount of substance = $n_{substance}$

Analysis
Since you need to determine the amount of the substance, the conversion factor is Avogadro's number:

$$\frac{6.02 \times 10^{23} \text{ atoms}}{1 \text{ mol}}$$

Solution
Invert the conversion factor and multiply by the number of atoms:

$$n_{substance} = 3.01 \times 10^{24} \text{ atoms} \times \frac{1 \text{ mol}}{6.02 \times 10^{23} \text{ atoms}}$$

$$= 5.00 \text{ mol}$$

Statement
The substance contains 5.00 mol of the element.

PRACTICE PROBLEMS

1. Calculate the number of atoms in 3.75 mol of an element.

2. Calculate the number of atoms in 5.5 mol of an element.

Section 4.1 Review

Understanding Concepts

1. Define the term "mole" in your own words.

2. Write a statement that distinguishes between the terms "relative atomic mass" and "average atomic mass."

3. Describe the relationship between one mole of any substance and Avogadro's number.

4. Chemists were able to detect a third isotope of neon using a modern mass spectrometer. Explain why this isotope was so difficult to detect.

Applying Inquiry/ Communication Skills

5. Iron has four naturally occurring isotopes of masses 53.940, 55.935, 56.935, and 57.933 with abundances of 5.84%, 91.68%, 2.17%, and 0.31% respectively. Calculate the average atomic mass of iron.

6. Using Table 4.1, calculate the average atomic mass of zinc.

7. Calculate the number of atoms in 4.15 mol of an element.

8. Calculate the amount of a substance (in moles) in 1.0×10^{22} atoms.

Making Connections

9. Research two applications of mass spectrometry not mentioned in the section. Make a brochure describing these applications. Outline the advantages and disadvantages of each application in your brochure.

10. Describe how gas chromatographs and mass spectrometers have helped chemists to further our understanding of matter.

4.2 Calculating Mass

Key Understandings

When you have completed this section, you will be able to:
- explain how the mole and molar mass are related
- use appropriate scientific vocabulary to communicate ideas related to chemical calculations
- solve problems involving quantity in moles, numbers of particles, and mass

Imagine you are a chemist in a pharmaceutical company. Your research technician has just determined the chemical formula for a new drug. The formula is $A_2B_3C_4$. You know this means that 1 mole of $A_2 B_3 C_4$ contains 2 moles of A, 3 moles of B, and 4 moles of C. But you can't just count out a mole of something! In order to make more of the drug, you need to determine the masses in grams of A, B, and C that you will need. Chemists often use molar mass to convert between moles and mass. **Molar mass** is the mass of one mole of a substance, and is expressed in units of $g \cdot mol^{-1}$. Molar mass can be applied to conversions of elements, covalent compounds, and ionic compounds.

Calculating the Mass of Elements

In section 4.1, you saw how atoms were converted to moles. Now suppose you have one mole (Avogadro's number) of carbon-12 atoms, each of which has a mass of 1.99×10^{-23} g. What is the mass of a mole of carbon atoms?

$$mass_{mole\ C} = 1.99 \times 10^{-23}\ g \times 6.02 \times 10^{23}$$

$$= 12.0\ g$$

The numeric value of the mass of a mole of carbon atoms is the same as that of the relative atomic mass of carbon! That is,

relative mass of one carbon atom $= 12$
mass of one mole of carbon atoms $= 12$ g

The molar mass of an element, expressed in grams, is always numerically the same as the relative atomic mass of that element.

WEBLINK

For a simulation that shows how moles and mass are related, go to **www.pearsoned.ca/chemistry11**.

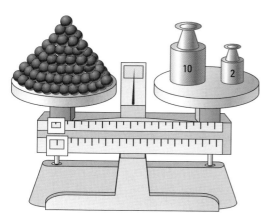

FIGURE 4.6 One mole of carbon-12 atoms (6.02×10^{23} atoms) has a mass of 12 g.

1 mol of carbon atoms = 12.0 g C

1 mol of sulfur atoms = 32.1 g S

1 mol of mercury atoms = 200.6 g Hg

1 mol of iron atoms = 55.8 g Fe

FIGURE 4.7 One molar mass of carbon, sulfur, mercury, and iron. These quantities all contain 6.02×10^{23} atoms of the element, but have different masses.

EXAMPLE 4

Calculate the mass of 0.50 mol of sulfur.

Given
amount of sulfur, n = 0.50 mol

Required
mass of sulfur, m_S = ? g

Analysis
From the periodic table, the relative atomic mass of sulfur is 32.06. Thus, the molar mass of sulfur is 32.06 g·mol^{-1} or, as a conversion factor, is:

$$\frac{32.06 \text{ g S}}{1 \text{ mol S}}$$

Solution

$$m_S = 0.50 \text{ mol S} \times \frac{32.06 \text{ g S}}{1 \text{ mol S}}$$
$$= 16 \text{ g}$$

Statement
The mass of sulfur is 16 g.

PRACTICE PROBLEMS

1. Calculate the mass of 2.75 mol of nickel.

2. Calculate the mass of 2.50 mol of aluminum.

3. Determine the mass of 1.6×10^{23} mol of hydrogen.

EXAMPLE 5

Determine the amount of substance in a mass of 10.0 g of iron.

Given
mass of iron, $m_{Fe} = 10.0$ g

Required
amount of substance, $n = ?$ mol

Analysis
From the periodic table, you can see that the molar mass of iron is 55.85 g·mol^{-1} (corresponding to a relative atomic mass of 55.85). Invert this value to get the conversion factor.

$$\frac{1 \text{ mol Fe}}{55.85 \text{ g Fe}}$$

Solution

$$n_{Fe} = 10.0 \text{ g Fe} \times \frac{1 \text{ mol Fe}}{55.85 \text{ g Fe}}$$

$$= 0.179 \text{ mol Fe}$$

Statement
The amount of iron is 0.179 mol.

PRACTICE PROBLEM

Determine the amount of substance in 8.40 g of copper.

Example 5 illustrates the conversion from mass in grams to moles. However, when reagents are brought together for a chemical reaction, it is important to use the correct amount of each one. This will often require a conversion from moles to mass. Because a mole is 6.02×10^{23} atoms, you can use the mole to relate numbers of atoms to mass, which can then be measured. Relating numbers of atoms to mass has two steps:

Step 1: Convert the number of atoms into moles.

Step 2: Convert the number of moles into grams.

EXAMPLE 6

Calculate the mass of 1.2×10^{23} atoms of aluminum.

Given
number of atoms$_{Al} = 1.2 \times 10^{23}$ atoms

Required
$m_{Al} = ?$ g

Analysis
Convert the number of atoms to moles using Avogadro's number (6.02×10^{23} atoms·mol^{-1}) as the conversion factor. You first need to invert the conversion factor.

$$\frac{1 \text{ mol Al}}{6.02 \times 10^{23} \text{ atoms Al}}$$

Now find the molar mass of aluminum on the periodic table (or a relative atomic mass table). You should obtain the value 26.98 g·mol^{-1}. Write this value as a conversion factor:

$$\frac{26.98 \text{ g Al}}{1 \text{ mol Al}}$$

Solution

$m_{Al} = 1.2 \times 10^{23} \text{ atoms Al} \times \dfrac{1 \text{ mol Al}}{6.02 \times 10^{23} \text{ atoms Al}} \times \dfrac{26.98 \text{ g Al}}{1 \text{ mol Al}}$

$= 5.4 \text{ g Al}$

Statement

The mass of aluminum is 5.4 g.

PRACTICE PROBLEMS

1. Calculate the mass of 3.4×10^{24} atoms of sodium.

2. Determine the mass of 1.5×10^{24} atoms of the following:
   a) potassium
   b) nitrogen

EXAMPLE 7

Determine the number of atoms in 2.30 g of sodium.

Given

$m_{Na} = 2.30 \text{ g}$

Required

number of atoms$_{Na}$ = ? atoms

Analysis

Convert from mass to moles using the molar mass as the conversion factor. Using the periodic table, find the molar mass of sodium (22.99 g·mol^{-1}). Invert the conversion factor:

$$\frac{1 \text{ mol Na}}{22.99 \text{ g Na}}$$

Now use Avogadro's number to convert number of moles to number of atoms. The conversion factor is:

$$\frac{1 \text{ mol Na}}{6.02 \times 10^{23} \text{ atoms Na}}$$

Solution

atoms$_{Na}$ = $2.30 \text{ g Na} \times \dfrac{1 \text{ mol Na}}{22.99 \text{ g Na}} \times \dfrac{6.02 \times 10^{23} \text{ atoms Na}}{1 \text{ mol Na}}$

$= 6.02 \times 10^{22} \text{ atoms Na}$

Statement

There are 6.02×10^{22} atoms of sodium.

PRACTICE PROBLEMS

1. Determine the number of atoms in 4.60 g of boron.

2. Calculate the number of atoms in 55.3 g of zinc.

Calculating the Mass of Covalent Compounds

So far, you have carried out mole calculations using only elements. However, mole calculations can also be performed with compounds. Earlier in this section, you saw that for elements, molar mass is numerically equal to the relative atomic mass of the element. The molar mass of a covalent compound and its molecular mass are related in a similar manner. That is, the molar mass of a covalent compound is numerically equivalent to its molecular mass. For example, glucose ($C_6H_{12}O_6$) is a covalent compound. Its molecular mass is 180.0, so we know its molar mass is 180.0 g·mol^{-1}.

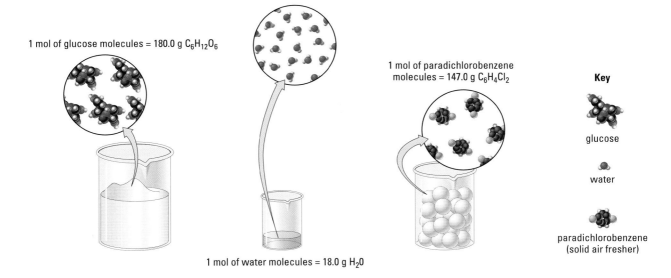

1 mol of glucose molecules = 180.0 g $C_6H_{12}O_6$

1 mol of paradichlorobenzene molecules = 147.0 g $C_6H_4Cl_2$

Key

glucose

water

paradichlorobenzene (solid air fresher)

1 mol of water molecules = 18.0 g H_2O

FIGURE 4.8 Molar masses of three covalent compounds. Each of these masses contains 6.02×10^{23} molecules.

Calculating Molecular Mass and Molar Mass **Molecular mass** is the mass of one molecule of a covalent compound. To calculate the molecular mass of a compound, simply add all the relative atomic masses of the atoms that make up one molecule. To obtain the molar mass of a covalent compound, you simply add the necessary unit (g·mol^{-1}) to the molecular mass.

EXAMPLE 8

Determine the molecular mass and molar mass of water (H_2O).

Given
number of atoms$_H$ = 2 atoms
$m_{\text{atom H}}$ = 1.01
number of atoms$_O$ = 1 atom
$m_{\text{atom O}}$ = 16.00

▶

WEBLINK

For a simulation to show how to determine molecular mass, go to **www.pearsoned.ca/chemistry11**.

Required

molecular mass$_{H_2O}$ = ?

Analysis

$$m_{\text{total atoms H}} = 2 \text{ atoms} \times m_{\text{atom H}}$$
$$= 2 \times 1.01$$
$$= 2.02$$

$$m_{\text{total atoms O}} = 1 \text{ atom} \times m_{\text{atom O}}$$
$$= 1 \times 16.00$$
$$= 16.00$$

Solution

$$\text{molecular mass}_{H_2O} = m_{\text{total atoms H}} + m_{\text{total atoms O}}$$
$$= 2.02 + 16.00$$
$$= 18.02$$

Statement

The molecular mass of water is 18.02. Therefore, the molar mass of water is 18.02 g·mol^{-1}.

PRACTICE PROBLEMS

1. Determine the molecular mass and molar mass of propane, (C_3H_8).

2. Determine the molecular mass and molar mass of BaHPO$_4$.

Calculating the Mass of Ionic Compounds

The smallest unit of an ionic compound is a formula unit; the **formula mass** is the mass of a formula unit. The molar mass of an ionic compound and its formula mass are related. The molar mass of an ionic compound is numerically equivalent to its formula mass. For example, sodium chloride (NaCl) is an ionic compound. It has a formula mass of 58.44 and therefore a molar mass of 58.44 g·mol^{-1}.

Calculating Formula Mass and Molar Mass   Formula mass is the mass of one formula unit of an ionic compound. To calculate the formula mass of an ionic compound, you add all the relative atomic masses of the atoms that make up one formula unit. To obtain the molar mass of an ionic compound, you simply add the necessary unit (g·mol^{-1}) to the formula mass.

EXAMPLE 9

Determine the formula mass and molar mass of sodium sulfate, Na$_2$SO$_4$.

Given

number of atoms$_{Na}$ = 2 atoms

$m_{\text{atom Na}}$ = 22.99

number of atoms$_{S}$ = 1 atom

$m_{\text{atom S}}$ = 32.06

number of atoms$_{O}$ = 4 atoms

$m_{\text{atom O}}$ = 16.00

Required

formula mass$_{Na_2SO_4}$ = ?

Analysis

$$m_{\text{total atoms Na}} = 2 \text{ atoms} \times m_{\text{atom Na}}$$
$$= 2 \times 22.99$$
$$= 45.98$$

$$m_{\text{total atoms S}} = 1 \text{ atom} \times m_{\text{atom S}}$$
$$= 1 \times 32.06$$
$$= 32.06$$

$$m_{\text{total atoms O}} = 4 \text{ atoms} \times m_{\text{atom O}}$$
$$= 4 \times 16.00$$
$$= 64.00$$

Solution

$$\text{formula mass}_{\text{Na}_2\text{SO}_4} = m_{\text{total atoms Na}} + m_{\text{total atoms S}} + m_{\text{total atoms O}}$$
$$= 45.98 + 32.06 + 64.00$$
$$= 142.04$$

Statement

The formula mass of sodium sulfate is 142.04. Therefore, the molar mass is 142.04 $g \cdot mol^{-1}$.

PRACTICE PROBLEMS

1. Calculate the formula mass of barium carbonate, $BaCO_3$.

2. Calculate the formula mass and molar mass of $AgClO_4$.

EXAMPLE 10

Determine the formula mass and molar mass of calcium nitrate, $Ca(NO_3)_2$.

Given

number of atoms$_{\text{Ca}}$ = 1 atom

$m_{\text{atom Ca}}$ = 40.08

number of atoms$_{\text{N}}$ = 2 atoms

$m_{\text{atom N}}$ = 14.01

number of atoms$_{\text{O}}$ = 6 atoms

$m_{\text{atom O}}$ = 16.00

Required

formula mass$_{Ca(NO_3)_2}$ = ?

Analysis

$$m_{\text{total atoms Ca}} = 1 \text{ atom} \times m_{\text{atom Ca}}$$
$$= 1 \times 40.08$$
$$= 40.08$$

$$m_{\text{total atoms N}} = 2 \text{ atoms} \times m_{\text{atom N}}$$
$$= 2 \times 14.01$$
$$= 28.02$$

$$m_{\text{total atoms O}} = 6 \text{ atoms} \times m_{\text{atom O}}$$
$$= 6 \times 16.00$$
$$= 96.00$$

INFO BIT

Large-scale laboratories and manufacturers cannot afford to make errors when converting between units or calculating mass. The chemists at this kind of facility often make use of software programs that can store formulas and recipes and then automatically perform the appropriate stoichiometric calculations. Some even allow the chemist to input molecular mass directly from a barcode on the reagent bottle!

PRACTICE PROBLEMS

1. Determine the formula mass and molar mass of magnesium phosphate, $Mg_3(PO_4)_2$.

2. Determine the formula mass and molar mass of $(NH_4)_2S$.

Solution

$$\text{formula mass}_{Ca(NO_3)_2} = m_{\text{total atoms Ca}} + m_{\text{total atoms N}} + m_{\text{total atoms O}}$$
$$= 40.08 + 28.02 + 96.00$$
$$= 164.10$$

Statement
The formula mass of calcium nitrate is 164.10. Therefore, the molar mass is 164.10 g·mol^{-1}.

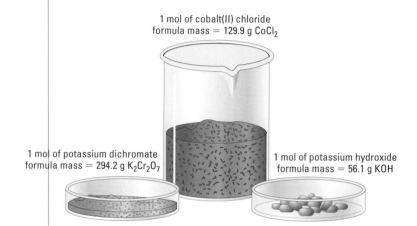

FIGURE 4.9 Each of these ionic compounds contains 6.02×10^{23} formula units.

Calculating Mass of a Hydrate Recall that some ionic compounds are found in the hydrated state. When this occurs, you must add the mass of the atoms in the associated water molecules as well as the formula mass of the ionic compound. Example 11 illustrates this.

EXAMPLE 11

Calculate the molar mass of calcium chloride dihydrate, $CaCl_2 \cdot 2H_2O$.

Given
This is a hydrated ionic compound in which 2 molecules of water are associated with each formula unit. Therefore:

number of atoms$_{Ca}$ = 1 atom

$m_{\text{mole Ca}}$ = 40.08 g

number of atoms$_{Cl}$ = 2 atoms

$m_{\text{mole Cl}}$ = 35.45 g

number of atoms$_H$ = 4 atoms

$m_{\text{mole H}}$ = 1.01 g

number of atoms$_O$ = 2 atoms

$m_{\text{mole O}}$ = 16.00 g

Required

molar mass$_{CaCl_2 \cdot 2H_2O}$ = ?

Analysis

$m_{\text{total miles Ca}}$ = $1 \times m_{\text{mole Ca}}$
$= 1 \times 40.08$ g
$= 40.08$ g

$m_{\text{total moles Cl}}$ = $2 \times m_{\text{mole Cl}}$
$= 2 \times 35.45$ g
$= 70.90$ g

$m_{\text{total moles H}}$ = $4 \times m_{\text{mole H}}$
$= 4 \times 1.01$ g
$= 4.04$ g

$m_{\text{total moles O}}$ = $2 \times m_{\text{mole O}}$
$= 2 \times 16.00$ g
$= 32.00$ g

Solution

molar mass$_{CaCl_2 \cdot 2H_2O}$ = $m_{\text{total atoms Ca}} + m_{\text{total atoms Cl}} + m_{\text{total atoms H}} + m_{\text{total atoms O}}$
$= 40.08$ g $+ 70.90$ g $+ 4.04$ g $+ 32.00$ g
$= 147.02$ g

Statement

The molar mass of calcium chloride dihydrate, $CaCl_2 \cdot 2H_2O$, is 147.02 g·mol^{-1}.

PRACTICE PROBLEMS

1. Calculate the molar mass of cobalt(II) chloride hexahydrate, $CoCl_2 \cdot 6H_2O$.

2. Calculate the molar mass of $FePO_4 \cdot 3H_2O$.

From the preceding examples in this section, you can see that molar mass allows you to convert between moles and mass for three types of substances—elements, covalent compounds, and ionic compounds.

Section 4.2 Review

Understanding Concepts

1. Describe the relationship between the mole and molar mass.

2. Write a statement that distinguishes between atomic mass, molecular mass, and formula mass.

Applying Inquiry/ Communication Skills

3. Calculate the mass of the following:
   a) 4.2 mol of helium
   b) 8.11×10^{-2} mol of lead
   c) 3.01×10^{22} atoms of helium

4. Determine the amount of carbon (in moles) in a mass of 63.0 g.

5. Determine the amount of sodium (in moles) in a mass of 0.115 g.

6. Calculate the amount of lead (in moles) in 2.6×10^{-3} g of lead.

7. Determine the number of atoms present in 6.20 g of phosphorus.

8. Calculate the following:
   a) the molecular mass of CF_2Cl_2
   b) the formula mass of $MgCO_3$
   c) the molar mass of $(NH_4)_2SO_4$
   d) the molar mass of $C_{12}H_{22}O_{11}$
   e) the molar mass of $Ba(OH)_2 \cdot 8H_2O$.

4.3 Calculating Amount of a Substance

Key Understandings

When you have completed this section, you will be able to:

- explain the law of definite proportions
- determine percent composition of a pure compound through analysis of the formula and other relevant data
- use appropriate scientific vocabulary to communicate ideas related to chemical calculations
- solve problems involving quantity in moles, number of particles, and mass
- explain how some pairs of elements can combine to form more than one compound
- give examples of the application of chemical quantities and calculations
- identify situations and careers involving analysis of unknown substances

Toxicologists are scientists who study poisonous substances. A toxicologist might work in a government testing laboratory, a medical facility, or even a police unit. Toxicologists are often asked to find out if an unknown sample contains any poisonous chemicals. Since many substances are only toxic above certain concentrations, a toxicologist must also determine how much of each substance is in a sample. In this section, you will learn about some of the calculations that are needed to identify and quantify unknown samples.

Converting Moles to Mass

Mole calculations for compounds are the same as those for elements, except that you must first find the molar mass of the compound. After you do this, you can then determine the number of moles present in a specific mass of the compound. You can also calculate the mass that contains a particular number of moles of the compound.

EXAMPLE 12

A chemist decides to conduct an experiment with 0.200 mol of calcium carbonate ($CaCO_3$). Determine the mass of calcium carbonate that must be used.

Given
amount of calcium carbonate, $n_{CaCO_3} = 0.200$ mol

Required
$m_{CaCO_3} = ?$ g

Analysis
Using the method shown in Example 11, calculate the mass of 1 mole of $CaCO_3$.

$m_{\text{mole } CaCO_3} = 40.08 \text{ g} + 12.01 \text{ g} + 3(16.00 \text{ g})$
$= 100.09 \text{ g}$

Now use the molar mass of $CaCO_3$, or 100.09 g·mol^{-1}, as the conversion factor.

Solution

$$m_{CaCO_3} = 0.200 \; \text{mol } CaCO_3 \times \frac{100.09 \text{ g } CaCO_3}{1 \text{ mol } CaCO_3}$$

$$= 20.0 \text{ g } CaCO_3$$

Statement

The chemist must use 20.0 g of calcium carbonate.

Example 12 illustrated the calculations for an ionic compound. You can also determine the number of molecules in a given mass of a covalent compound in a similar manner.

EXAMPLE 13

Determine the number of molecules of water in an ice cube of mass 12.6 g.

Given

$m_{H_2O} = 12.6$ g

Required

number of molecules$_{H_2O}$ = ? molecules

Analysis

First determine the molar mass of water.

$$m_{\text{mole } H_2O} = 2(1.01 \text{ g}) + 16.00 \text{ g}$$
$$= 18.02 \text{ g}$$

Use the reciprocal of this value as the first conversion factor. Then, since each mole of water contains Avogadro's number of water molecules, the second conversion factor is 6.02×10^{23} molecules·mol^{-1}.

Solution

$$\text{molecules}_{H_2O} = 12.6 \; \text{g } H_2O \times \frac{1 \; \text{mol } H_2O}{18.02 \; \text{g } H_2O} \times \frac{6.02 \times 10^{23} \text{ molecules } H_2O}{1 \; \text{mol } H_2O}$$

$$= 4.21 \times 10^{23} \text{ molecules } H_2O$$

Statement

There are 4.21×10^{23} molecules of water in the ice cube.

PRACTICE PROBLEMS

1. You want to do an experiment with 0.034 mol of magnesium sulfate ($MgSO_4$). Determine the mass of magnesium sulfate you will require.

2. Calculate the mass of each of the following:
   a) 0.500 mol of calcium carbonate
   b) 6.47×10^{-2} mol of nitrogen dioxide

PRACTICE PROBLEMS

1. Calculate the number of molecules of methanol (CH_3OH) in 8.75 g.

2. Calculate the number of molecules in 1.00 g of each of the following:
   a) UF_6
   b) $FeSO_4$

You can also determine the number of hydrogen and oxygen atoms in the ice cube by adding one more step to the calculation carried out in Example 13. Each molecule of water contains two atoms of hydrogen and one atom of oxygen. Therefore, to derive the number of hydrogen atoms, you multiply the answer to Example 13 by a factor of two. There is only one oxygen atom in a water molecule, so the number of atoms of oxygen in the ice cube is the same as the number of water molecules. Example 14 shows a similar calculation.

EXAMPLE 14

Nitrogen is the most common gas in the atmosphere. Calculate the number of atoms in 1.00 g of nitrogen.

Given
$m_N = 1.00$ g

Required
number of atoms$_N$ = ? atoms

Analysis
Nitrogen forms diatomic molecules. Therefore, calculate the mass of 1 mole of nitrogen gas by multiplying the atomic mass of nitrogen by two.

$$m_{\text{mole } N_2} = 2(14.01 \text{ g})$$
$$= 28.02 \text{ g·mol}^{-1}$$

Use the reciprocal of this value as the first conversion factor. Since 1 mole of nitrogen has Avogadro's number of molecules, the second conversion factor is 6.02×10^{23} molecules·mol^{-1}.

Finally, because each nitrogen molecule contains two atoms, the third conversion factor is:

$$\frac{2 \text{ atoms N}}{1 \text{ molecule } N_2}$$

Solution
atoms$_N$
$$= 1.00 \text{ g } N_2 \times \frac{1 \text{ mol } N_2}{28.02 \text{ g } N_2} \times \frac{6.02 \times 10^{23} \text{ molecules } N_2}{1 \text{ mol } N_2} \times \frac{2 \text{ atoms N}}{1 \text{ molecule } N_2}$$
$$= 4.30 \times 10^{22} \text{ atoms N}$$

Statement
There are 4.30×10^{22} atoms of nitrogen.

PRACTICE PROBLEM

Calculate the number of atoms present in 1.00 g of oxygen.

EXAMPLE 15

Calcium chloride ($CaCl_2$) is used as a desiccant (to absorb moisture in the air) and as road salt. Calculate the number of chloride ions in 22.2 g of calcium chloride.

Given
$m_{CaCl_2} = 22.2$ g

Required
number of ions$_{Cl^-}$ = ? ions

Analysis
Determine the molar mass of calcium chloride.

$$m_{mole\ CaCl_2} = 40.08\ g + 2(35.45\ g)$$
$$= 110.98\ g\cdot mol^{-1}$$

Use the reciprocal of the molar mass as the first conversion factor. One mole of calcium chloride has Avogadro's number of calcium chloride formula units, so the second conversion factor is 6.02×10^{23} formula units$\cdot mol^{-1}$.

Finally, since each calcium chloride formula unit contains 2 chloride ions, the third conversion factor is:

$$\frac{2\ ions\ Cl^-}{1\ formula\ unit\ CaCl_2}$$

Solution

$$ions_{Cl^-} = 22.2\ g\ CaCl_2 \times \frac{1\ mol\ CaCl_2}{110.98\ g\ CaCl_2}$$

$$\times\ \frac{6.02 \times 10^{23}\ formula\ units\ CaCl_2}{1\ mol\ CaCl_2} \times \frac{2\ ions\ Cl^-}{1\ formula\ unit\ CaCl_2}$$

$$= 2.40 \times 10^{22}\ ions\ Cl^-$$

Statement

There are 2.40×10^{22} chloride ions.

PRACTICE PROBLEM

Iodine is required by the thyroid gland. When iodine is lacking from the diet, the thyroid gland swells to become a visible lump on the throat, a condition known as goitre. To prevent iodine deficiency, potassium iodide (KI) is added to table salt (NaCl). Calculate the number of iodide ions in 5.35 g of potassium iodide.

Discovering Chemistry   *A Mouthful of Water*

Can you think of a way to determine the number of moles and molecules contained in one mouthful of water? Here's a hint: you will need water, a paper cup, and a balance.

■ What is the mass of the mouthful of water you drank?

■ Calculate the amount of water (in moles) that you drank.

■ Determine the number of molecules of water you swallowed.

The Law of Definite Proportions

In some communities, sodium fluoride (NaF) is added to the water supply in small quantities to prevent dental decay. This compound can be prepared by reacting sodium hydroxide (NaOH) and hydrogen fluoride (HF), or by reacting sodium carbonate (Na_2CO_3) and hydrogen fluoride. Sodium fluoride also occurs naturally. If you were a manager at a water treatment plant, which source of NaF would you choose? Do all three sources of sodium fluoride give exactly the same compound?

The law of definite proportions tells you that the answer is yes; the sodium fluoride from all three sources will be the same. The **law of definite proportions** states the following:

The composition of a specific compound is constant.

For example, a molecule of water will always contain two hydrogen atoms and one oxygen atom. This is true anywhere on Earth, on another planet, or indeed in any location in the universe.

Then &NOW

Collaboration and Chemistry

When Proust proposed the law of definite proportions, his ideas were challenged by another prominent French chemist, Claude Berthollet. Berthollet believed that the composition of a compound depended on how it was made and on the proportions of the reactants used to make it. Proust took up the challenge, and for the next 8 years these two scientists engaged in a brilliant, vigorous, yet always gentlemanly debate through scientific journals. Their argument held chemists around the world in fascination. It also helped to clarify the difference between a mixture, a solution, and a compound.

Finally, Proust repeated Berthollet's experiments using the purest chemicals, and the best balances and other laboratory equipment available. Proust was thus able to show that what Berthollet had classified as compounds were in fact solutions or mixtures of two different compounds of the same element. As a good scientist should, Berthollet considered Proust's results carefully and then agreed that he had made errors. Proust had proven that his idea was right—the composition of a compound does not change.

The story of Proust and Berthellot illustrates a point that most non-scientists do not realize—science is a collaborative and competitive endeavour. It is as true today as it was 200 years ago. Now chemists use conferences and e-mail in addition to scientific journals to exchange information about discoveries and to debate one another's findings. Conferences are particularly important since they enable scientists to meet in person and develop collaborative research projects. Often, new ideas and friendships develop over coffee during lecture breaks or social events. Socialization is as big a part of science as it is in any other career.

FIGURE 4.10 a) Joseph Proust and b) Claude Berthollet initially disagreed on the principle of the law of definite proportions.

FIGURE 4.11 Water and hydrogen peroxide both contain hydrogen and oxygen atoms, but in different proportions.

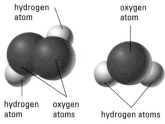

hydrogen atom

oxygen atom

hydrogen atom   oxygen atoms   hydrogen atoms

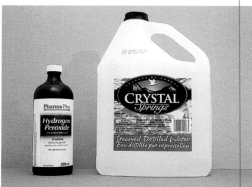

This law was first proposed in 1799 by the French chemist Joseph Proust. Proust produced copper(II) carbonate in various ways and then showed it always had the same chemical composition, no matter how it was prepared. The law of definite proportions, sometimes also called the law of constant composition, is now a fundamental principle of chemistry.

The law of definite proportions can also be expressed in terms of mass ratios; i.e., a specific compound will always contain the same elements in the same fixed mass ratio. For example, water will always contains 8 g of oxygen for every 1 g of hydrogen.

Some pairs of elements, however, can combine to form more than one compound. For example, hydrogen and oxygen can form either water (H_2O) or hydrogen peroxide (H_2O_2). Water always contains 8 g of oxygen for every 1 g of hydrogen. Hydrogen peroxide always contains 16 g of oxygen for every 1 g of hydrogen. The difference between these two compounds is that hydrogen peroxide contains twice the mass of oxygen.

Although both water and hydrogen peroxide are clear, colourless liquids, the difference in their proportions of oxygen and hydrogen results in very different properties. While water will extinguish a fire, a 90% solution of hydrogen peroxide is so combustible that it can be used to propel a rocket! You may be familiar with a 3% hydrogen peroxide solution, which is sold in pharmacies for use as a topical antiseptic. Dilute hydrogen peroxide can also be found in antiseptic products like mouthwash. Unlike water, hydrogen peroxide is unstable, especially in light. Hydrogen peroxide solutions are sold in dark plastic bottles to slow down this process.

Another such pair of compounds (Table 4.3) is carbon monoxide (CO) and carbon dioxide (CO_2). Carbon monoxide is formed by incomplete combustion of carbon-containing compounds and is extremely poisonous. Carbon dioxide is a product of respiration and is essential to life. Plants require carbon dioxide to photosynthesize, a process that provides the planet with food and oxygen.

A third example is that of two oxides of nitrogen, dinitrogen oxide (N_2O) and nitrogen dioxide (NO_2). Dinitrogen oxide is sometimes used as an anesthetic; it smells sweet and can be addictive. Its common name is nitrous oxide or laughing gas. Like oxygen, dinitrogen oxide will support combustion, and so it is sometimes used to boost acceleration in high-performance racing cars. Nitrogen dioxide, in contrast, is a red-brown toxic gas that is a major pollutant.

TABLE 4.3 Compounds Composed of Different Proportions of the Same Atoms

Formula	Properties	Formula	Properties
Compounds containing C and O atoms			
carbon monoxide CO	colourless, odourless gas	carbon dioxide CO_2	colourless, odourless, dense gas
	very poisonous		product of respiration; required for photosynthesis
	melting point: $-205°C$; boiling point: $-192°C$		sublimes at $-78°C$
	burns in air		does not support combustion or burn
Compounds containing N and O atoms			
dinitrogen oxide N_2O	colourless, sweet-smelling gas	nitrogen dioxide NO_2	red-brown, choking, dense gas
	can be used as an anesthetic gas		poisonous
	melting point: $-91°C$; boiling point: $-88°C$		melting point: $-11°C$; boiling point: $21°C$
	supports combustion		reacts with water to form an acidic solution

Percent Composition

Percent values are used in many aspects of everyday life. For example, food companies are required to provide the percent of ingredients, such as protein, carbohydrate, fat, and salt, on the label of their products. Manufacturers often determine the percents of various components in a product to ensure that it is of sufficient quality. When chemists analyze a sample, they often need to know the proportions of elements in the sample expressed as percents. For example, a sample of pure salt should contain 39.3% sodium and 60.7% chlorine. A sample that does not contain these precise percents is not pure. How can the percent composition of a chemical compound be found? The calculation is very simple using the molar masses.

Instead of stating the actual mass of each element in a compound, it is often more useful to express the composition of a compound as **percent composition** by mass. The percent composition of a sample of a compound is always the same, regardless of the actual amount of the sample.

FIGURE 4.12 Percent composition is often used to tell a consumer exactly what is in a product.

FIGURE 4.13 Water from any source is composed of 11.1% hydrogen and 88.9% oxygen by mass.

K₂CrO₄

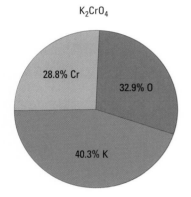

potassium chromate, K₂CrO₄

K₂Cr₂O₇

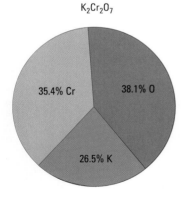

potassium dichromate, K₂Cr₂O₇

FIGURE 4.14 Potassium chromate (K_2CrO_4) is composed of 40.3% potassium, 26.8% chromium, and 32.9% oxygen. Potassium dichromate ($K_2Cr_2O_7$) is composed of these same three elements, but has a different percent composition.

Consider this simple analogy. Let's say you have an apple of mass 90.0 g and an orange of mass 60.0 g for your lunch. You could say that since your lunch consists of one apple and one orange, the percent composition of your lunch is 50% oranges and 50% apples. However, if you consider the mass, then the total mass of your lunch is 90.0 g + 60.0 g = 150.0 g. Therefore, the percent composition by mass of your lunch is calculated by:

$$\text{percent of orange by mass} = \frac{60.0 \text{ g}}{150.0 \text{ g}} \times 100\%$$
$$= 40.0\%$$
$$\text{percent of apple by mass} = \frac{90.0 \text{ g}}{150.0 \text{ g}} \times 100\%$$
$$= 60.0\%$$

Now consider a chemical example. You know that 1.00 mol of carbon monoxide contains 6.02×10^{23} molecules, and that each of these molecules is composed of 1 carbon atom and 1 oxygen atom. Therefore, in 6.02×10^{23} molecules of CO, there are 6.02×10^{23} atoms of carbon and 6.02×10^{23} atoms of oxygen. In other words, 1.00 mol of CO contains of 1.00 mol of carbon atoms and 1.00 mol of oxygen atoms. The mass of a mole of CO is therefore:

$$\text{mass of 1.00 mol of CO} = 12.01 \text{ g} + 16.00 \text{ g}$$
$$= 28.01 \text{ g}$$

Thus, for 1.00 mol of carbon monoxide, you can calculate the following:

$$\text{percent of element A} = \frac{\text{mass of element A in compound}}{\text{molar mass of compound}} \times 100\%$$

$$\text{percent of carbon by mass} = \frac{12.01 \text{ g}}{28.01 \text{ g}} \times 100\%$$
$$= 42.88\%$$

$$\text{percent of oxygen by mass} = \frac{16.00 \text{ g}}{28.01 \text{ g}} \times 100\%$$
$$= 57.14\%$$

EXAMPLE 16

Determine the percent composition by mass of table sugar (sucrose), which has the formula $C_{12}H_{22}O_{11}$.

Given
$C_{12}H_{22}O_{11}$

Required
percent composition

Analysis
From the chemical formula, you know that sucrose has 12 carbon atoms, 22 hydrogen atoms, and 11 oxygen atoms. Use the relative atomic mass of these elements to calculate the molar mass of sucrose. Then calculate the percent composition of each element.

Solution
$$\text{molar mass of } C_{12}H_{22}O_{11} = 12(12.01 \text{ g}) + 22(1.01 \text{ g}) + 11(16.00 \text{ g})$$
$$= 144.12 \text{ g} + 22.22 \text{ g} + 176.00 \text{ g}$$
$$= 342.34 \text{ g}$$

For 1.00 mol of sugar, you can write:

$$\text{percent of carbon} = \frac{144.12 \text{ g}}{342.34 \text{ g}} \times 100\%$$
$$= 42.09\%$$

$$\text{percent of hydrogen} = \frac{22.22 \text{ g}}{342.34 \text{ g}} \times 100\%$$
$$= 6.49\%$$

$$\text{percent of oxygen} = \frac{176.00 \text{ g}}{342.34 \text{ g}} \times 100\%$$
$$= 51.41\%$$

Statement
Sucrose consists of 51.41% oxygen, 42.09% carbon, and 6.49% hydrogen. Note that although the sum of the percentages should be 100%, the errors introduced by rounding give us an actual total of 99.99%.

WEBLINK

SIMULATION

For a simulation to show how percent composition works, go to **www.pearsoned.ca/chemistry11**.

PRACTICE PROBLEMS

1. Silver nitrate is commonly used in photography and in manufacturing mirrors. Determine the percent composition (by mass) of silver nitrate, $AgNO_3$.

2. A ceramic artist uses the following chemicals that are used as colourants for ceramic glazes. Determine the percent composition of each.

   a) cobalt(II) carbonate ($CoCO_3$), which produces a blue glaze colour
   b) barium chromate ($BaCrO_4$), which produces colours in the yellow to light-green range
   c) iron(III) chloride hexahydrate ($FeCl_3 \cdot 6H_2O$), which produces an iridescent gold colour

Decision-Making Skills

▶ Defining the Issue
▶ Developing Assessment Criteria
▶ Researching the Issue
▶ Analyzing Data and Information
▶ Proposing a Course of Action
▶ Justifying the Course of Action
▶ Communicating Your Proposal

Playing by the Rules: Controlling Drug Use in Sports

BACKGROUND INFORMATION

Before the 2000 Summer Olympic Games were even half over, a cynical press had already dubbed them the "Shame Games." An alarming number of the world's elite athletes had tested positive for use of banned performance-enhancing drugs, and were sent home in disgrace. Is the use of performance-enhancing drugs cheating? Many athletes believe it is, and feel frustrated when they lose out to a known user of these substances. Others argue that using these drugs is no different than using a special diet to enhance body functioning during training. However, these drugs can also pose significant health risks, especially when used long-term. The athletic community has therefore attempted to stop the use of performance-enhancing drugs by regularly testing competitors for the use of specific substances. Although the purpose of this testing has a laudable purpose, its practical use has caused a lot of controversy by "catching" athletes who had no intention of using anything but hard work to achieve their athletic goals.

Take the case of Canada's Silken Laumann. In 1995, this much-admired rower was stripped of a gold medal at the Pan-American Games. The positive test came from an over-the-counter cold remedy, Benadryl, which contains the banned substance pseudoephedrine, a synthetic match to the stimulant ephedrine. Silken had taken the cold medicine with the full knowledge of her coach and the team physician. Benadryl was also approved for use by the drug-monitoring arm of the athletic community. They were unaware, however, that there are two formulations for Benadryl; Silken innocently had taken the wrong one.

Athletic organizations from most countries readily agree that the use of performance-enhancing drugs should be prohibited. However, as the case of Silken Laumann demonstrates, these policies do not take into account the individual circumstances of drug use. Furthermore, many tests cannot determine when drugs were taken and, therefore, if they are active. The practice of random testing also suggests that all athletes are under suspicion solely for their choice of occupation.

Analyzing the Issue

1. Write a statement that clearly defines the issue related to drug testing in athletes.

2. Create a consequences map related to this issue.

3. Research the following questions and summarize your findings in a chart.
   a) How is drug testing carried out at major sports events like the Pan American Games?
   b) What kinds of drugs are banned? Why?
   c) Who decides whether a substance enhances athletic performance?

4. In your opinion, was it necessary to take away Silken Laumann's gold medal at the Pan American Games? Explain your reasons and justify your position on this issue.

5. Outline the impact of the consequences you identified in question 2 from the perspective of one of the following:
   • a member of the Canadian Olympic Association
   • an elite athlete
   • a technician in an accredited laboratory for drug testing of athletes
   • an athlete banned from competition for positive test results

6. Prepare to debate the following question from the perspective you have chosen in question 4:

   • Is Canada's policy on banned substances in athletic competition fair?
   • At the conclusion of the debate, reflect on whether other perspectives influenced your opinion about the issue. Explain why or why not.

Section 4.3 Review

Understanding Concepts

1. In your own words, describe the law of definite proportions and its importance in analyzing chemical compounds.

2. Describe in your own words the meaning of the term "percent composition" and how percent composition is calculated.

Applying Inquiry/ Communication Skills

3. If a spoonful of sugar (sucrose, $C_{12}H_{22}O_{11}$) holds 4.87 g of sugar, find:
   a) the number of sugar molecules in each spoonful
   b) the number of carbon atoms in each spoonful

4. In each of the following examples, determine which contains the larger number of atoms or molecules:
   a) 11.5 g sodium or 8.1 g of boron
   b) 4.40 g of carbon dioxide or 0.200 mol of sulfur dioxide
   c) 186 g of water or 1.00 kg of urea, $(NH_2)_2CO$

5. Calculate the mass of the following:
   a) 2 mol of HNO_3
   b) 0.05 mol of P_2O_5
   c) 10 mol of NaCl

6. Determine the number of sodium ions in 6.81 g of sodium sulfate.

7. Calculate the percent by mass of nitrogen in each of the following compounds:
   a) N_2O_5
   b) $Ca(NO_3)_2$
   c) NH_4NO_2

8. Calculate how many molecules are present in 0.015 mol of carbon dioxide.

9. Calculate the amount of substance in each of the following:
   a) 200 g of CO_2
   b) 40 g of CH_4
   c) 100 g of P_2O_5

10. Calculate the number of molecules in 10 g of chlorine gas, Cl_2.

11. A sample of chloroform gas, $CHCl_3$, has a mass of 300 g. Calculate the amount of substance in the sample. Determine the total number of atoms in the sample.

12. Element A combines with element B in the ratio 9:5 by mass. In a different experiment, it is found that 1 g of B reacts with 1.8 g of A. Use these figures to show whether these compounds support the law of definite proportions.

13. Obtain a piece of chalk. Assume that the chalk is composed of calcium carbonate only. Write a procedure for how you would determine the number of moles of calcium carbonate in your piece of chalk. Write your name on the board with your piece of chalk, and then calculate the number of molecules it took to write your name.

Making Connections

14. Research and describe briefly three methods that some athletes use to enhance their performance. In your description, include how these methods work and how they can be detected.

15. Select one of the following analytical technologies: gas chromatography, liquid chromatography, or immuno-assay. Using electronic and print sources, research and write a brief description of it, and list the types of substances that are analyzed using this technology.

16. Lawn-care fertilizers are sold with the percent concentrations of nitrogen, potassium, and phosphorus on the label. Identify the importance of these three compounds to the growth of plants. Prepare an information flyer that will inform consumers about which fertilizer is appropriate to purchase for the different seasons.

4.4 Determining Chemical Formulas

Key Understandings

When you have completed this section, you will be able to:

- distinguish between the empirical formula and the molecular formula of a compound
- use appropriate scientific language to communicate ideas related to chemical calculations
- determine the percent composition of an unknown compound by experimentation
- solve problems involving quantities in moles, numbers of particles, and mass
- determine empirical and molecular formulas from data given
- give examples of the application of chemical quantities and calculations
- identify situations and careers that involve analysis of an unknown substance

In section 4.3, you learned to determine the percent composition of a compound from its formula. However, chemists must often determine the chemical formula of a compound from its percent composition. For example, metals rarely occur as pure compounds; they are usually found as metal ore, which contains metal combined with oxygen, sulfur, or silica. By determining the percent composition of an ore sample, a geochemist can determine whether the ore is sufficiently rich in the desired metal. Percent composition is also used to determine the formula of unknown compounds. Identifying such compounds is commonly carried out in toxicology labs and in pharmaceutical research.

Empirical and Molecular Formulas

Establishing the chemical formula of a compound from experimental data involves several steps. One important step is to determine the empirical formula from the percent composition. The **empirical formula** of a compound is the simplest whole-number ratio of the atoms (or ions) in the compound. The **molecular formula** gives the actual number of atoms of each element in one molecule of the compound.

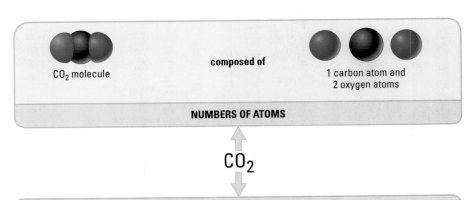

FIGURE 4.15 A chemical formula provides information about numbers of atoms and about numbers of moles of atoms.

Calculating Empirical Formula To calculate the empirical formula of a compound, you need to know which atoms are in a compound and the percent composition of each. To get this information, samples to be identified must first be analyzed by a technique such as mass spectrometry.

EXAMPLE 17

By mass spectrometry, an unknown compound is found to consist of 40.1% sulfur and 59.9% oxygen by mass. Determine the empirical formula of the unknown compound.

Given
sulfur   = 40.1%
oxygen = 59.9%

Required
empirical formula for the sulfur- and oxygen-containing compound

Analysis and Solution
Assume that you have 100.0 g of the compound. First determine the mass of each element present:

$$m_S = 100.0 \text{ g} \times \frac{40.1 \text{ g}}{100.0 \text{ g}}$$
$$= 40.1 \text{ g}$$
$$m_O = 100.0 \text{ g} \times \frac{59.9 \text{ g}}{100.0 \text{ g}}$$
$$= 59.0 \text{ g}$$

The next step is to convert mass to moles:

$$n_S = 40.1 \text{ g S} \times \frac{1 \text{ mol S}}{32.06 \text{ g S}}$$
$$= 1.25 \text{ mol S}$$
$$n_O = 59.9 \text{ g O} \times \frac{1 \text{ mol O}}{16.00 \text{ g O}}$$
$$= 3.74 \text{ mol O}$$

The mole ratio of sulfur to oxygen is therefore 1.25 : 3.74. Therefore, the ratio of sulfur atoms to oxygen atoms is also 1.25 : 3.74. However, this is not a whole-number ratio. To find the whole-number ratio, divide both numbers by the smaller number.

$$S : O = 1.25 : 3.74$$
$$= \frac{1.25}{1.25} : \frac{3.74}{1.25}$$
$$= 1.00 : 2.99$$
$$= 1 : 3$$

Since the percent composition of sulfur and oxygen has been determined by experiment, you are justified in rounding off this ratio to 1 : 3.

Statement
The empirical formula of the compound is SO_3.

PRACTICE PROBLEM

The substance that gives sour milk its taste is lactic acid. It consists of 40.0% carbon and 6.71% hydrogen, with the rest being oxygen. Determine its empirical formula.

Calculating Molecular Formula Although the empirical formula of a compound can be useful, it does not provide you with complete information about the composition of the compound. To identify a compound, you need to identify its molecular formula; that is, the actual number of atoms of each element in the compound.

For example, consider the compounds acetylene and benzene. Acetylene is the gas used in welders' torches. Benzene is a liquid used to make many other compounds in the chemical industry. The empirical formula of both acetylene and benzene is CH (Table 4.4). However, these are very different compounds with very different properties. Acetylene is an odourless gas at room temperature. Benzene is a liquid at room temperature and has a very characteristic smell. The molecular formula of acetylene is C_2H_2; therefore, each acetylene molecule contains 2 carbon atoms and 2 hydrogen atoms. The molecular formula of benzene is C_6H_6. Each molecule of benzene contains six carbon and six hydrogen atoms.

a)

b)

FIGURE 4.16 Although a) styrene, which is used to make polystyrene, and b) acetylene have the same empirical formula (CH), these substances have very different properties.

TABLE 4.4 Comparison of Empirical and Molecular Formulas

Empirical Formula	Molecular Formula	Molar Mass
CH	none	13
	C_2H_2 (ethyne or acetylene)	$2 \times 13 = 26$
	C_6H_6 (benzene)	$6 \times 13 = 78$
	C_8H_8 (styrene)	$8 \times 13 = 104$
CH_2O	CH_2O (methanol)	30
	$C_2H_4O_2$ (ethanoic acid)	$2 \times 30 = 60$
	$C_6H_{12}O_6$ (glucose)	$6 \times 30 = 180$

To determine the molecular formula of a compound, you must know both its empirical formula and its molar mass. When that data is available, the molecular formula can be deduced by the method shown in Example 18.

EXAMPLE 18

A student has determined that the empirical formula for a compound of sulfur and chlorine is SCl. The known molar mass of this compound is 135 $g \cdot mol^{-1}$. Determine the molecular formula of the compound.

Given
molar mass = 135 $g \cdot mol^{-1}$

Required
molecular formula of SCl

Analysis
First calculate the empirical formula mass. The **empirical formula mass** is the mass of one mole of the empirical formula of the substance, in this case SCl.

empirical formula mass of SCl = 32.06 g + 35.45 g

$$= 67.51 \text{ g}$$

The molar mass was given, so you know that the mass of 1 mol of the substance is actually 135 g. Since the molecular formula is always a multiple of the empirical formula, you can divide the molar mass by the empirical formula mass. Therefore:

$$\frac{\text{molar mass}}{\text{empirical formula mass}} = \frac{135 \text{ g}}{67.51 \text{ g}}$$

$$= 2.00$$

Solution
molecular formula = 2 × empirical formula
= 2 × SCl
= S_2Cl_2

Statement
The molecular formula is S_2Cl_2.

PRACTICE PROBLEM

The empirical formula of paradichlorobenzene, a moth repellant, is C_3H_2Cl. The molar mass of this compound is 147 $g \cdot mol^{-1}$. Determine the molecular formula of paradichlorobenzene.

Of course, a chemist will not usually have the empirical formula and the molar mass of an unknown compound. It is far more likely that the data will include percent composition values. The first step then becomes to deduce the empirical formula, as was shown in Example 17, and then use this information to determine the molecular formula. This second step is the same calculation performed in Example 18.

EXAMPLE 19

A compound contains 40.0% carbon, 6.70% hydrogen, and 53.3% oxygen by mass. The mass of 1 mol of the compound is 90.1 g. Determine the molecular formula of the compound.

Given

m_{mole} = 90.1 g
C = 40.0%
H = 6.70%
O = 53.3%

Required

molecular formula of the compound

Analysis

Determine the empirical formula of the compound. Assume you have 100.0 g of the compound. From the percent composition data, a 100.0 g sample therefore contains 40.0 g of carbon, 6.70 g of hydrogen, and 53.3 g of oxygen.

Use the reciprocal of the molar mass to determine the amount of each element:

$$n_C = 40.0 \text{ g C} \times \frac{1 \text{ mol C}}{12.01 \text{ g C}}$$

$$= 3.33 \text{ mol C}$$

$$n_H = 6.70 \text{ g H} \times \frac{1 \text{ mol H}}{1.01 \text{ g H}}$$

$$= 6.63 \text{ mol H}$$

$$n_O = 53.3 \text{ g O} \times \frac{1 \text{ mol O}}{16.00 \text{ g O}}$$

$$= 3.33 \text{ mol O}$$

Therefore,

$$\text{ratio of C : H : O} = 3.33 : 6.63 : 3.33$$

$$= \frac{3.33}{3.33} : \frac{6.63}{3.33} : \frac{3.33}{3.33}$$

$$= 1.00 : 1.99 : 1.00$$

$$= 1 : 2 : 1$$

Thus, the empirical formula is CH_2O.

To find the molecular formula, first calculate the empirical formula mass:

$$\text{empirical formula mass} = 12.01 \text{ g} + 2(1.01) \text{ g} + 16.00 \text{ g}$$

$$= 30.03 \text{ g}$$

Now divide the molar mass of the substance by the empirical formula mass:

$$\frac{\text{molar mass}}{\text{empirical formula mass}} = \frac{90.1 \text{ g}}{30.03 \text{ g}}$$

$$= 3.00$$

Solution

Molecular formula = 3 × empirical formula

= 3 × CH₂O

$= 3 \times CH_2O$

$= C_3H_6O_3$

Statement

The molecular formula of this compound is $C_3H_6O_3$.

PRACTICE PROBLEM

Resorcinol, a compound used to manufacture resins and drugs, is 65.44% C, 5.49% H, and 29.06% O by mass. The mass of 1 mol of this compound is 110 g. Determine the molecular formula of the compound.

Decomposition Reactions and Determination of Chemical Formulas

Previously, you explored the calculations involved in determining molecular formulas. In all the examples, either the percent composition or the empirical formula was given. However, if you are trying to identify an unknown sample, no one is going to supply you with this information. Instead, you will have to find a way to get this data for yourself.

Most analyses of unknown substances start with finding what atoms are present in a sample and their percent compositions. You have already read about one of the ways this information is found, the mass spectrometer. Alternatively, one of the simplest ways of determining the composition of a compound is to decompose (or break down) a known mass of the unknown compound. After breaking the compound down, the component elements must be identified and their amounts determined. The procedure used for decomposition will vary for different compounds.

Analysis of Oxides Metals and oxygen often combine to form oxide compounds. You are probably familiar with rust, an oxide of iron. Chemists have found that heating some metal oxides releases the oxygen as oxygen gas and leaves the pure metal. To determine the formula of a metal oxide, chemists take a known mass of the compound and heat it strongly to decompose it. You can do this in a laboratory by heating the metal oxide in a crucible over a Bunsen burner. Decomposition releases the oxygen in the compound and leaves the metal in the reaction vessel. You can then measure the mass of metal directly, using a balance. Subtracting this value from the mass of the original compound gives the mass of oxygen that was released. These data are then used to determine the empirical formula.

WEBLINK

SIMULATION

For a simulation of an experiment to show how unknown samples are identified, go to **www.pearsoned.ca/chemistry11**.

Investigation

Refer to page 166, Investigation 1

Refer to page 166, Investigation 1

EXAMPLE 20

After a 4.626-g sample of silver oxide is heated, 4.306 g of silver metal remains. What is the empirical formula of silver oxide?

Given

$m_{\text{silver oxide}} = 4.626$ g

$m_{\text{silver}} = 4.306$ g

Required

empirical formula of silver oxide

Analysis

$m_{oxygen} = m_{silver\ oxide} - m_{silver}$

$\qquad = 4.626\ g - 4.306\ g$

$\qquad = 0.320\ g$

$n_{Ag} \quad = 4.306\ g\ Ag \times \dfrac{1\ mol\ Ag}{107.87\ g\ Ag}$

$\qquad = 3.991 \times 10^{-2}\ mol\ Ag$

$n_O \quad = 0.320\ g\ O \times \dfrac{1\ mol\ O}{16.00\ g\ O}$

$\qquad = 2.00 \times 10^{-2}\ mol\ O$

Solution

$Ag : O = 3.991 \times 10^{-2} : 2.00 \times 10^{-2}$

$\qquad = \dfrac{3.991 \times 10^{-2}}{2.00 \times 10^{-2}} : \dfrac{2.00 \times 10^{-2}}{2.00 \times 10^{-2}}$

$\qquad = 2 : 1$

Statement

The empirical formula of silver oxide is Ag_2O.

PRACTICE PROBLEM

When a 3.862-g sample of silver oxide is heated, the remaining silver has a mass of 3.363 g. Determine the empirical formula of this compound. Is it the same compound as in Example 20? Explain your answer.

Instead of using a calculation as in the last example, you can analyze your data graphically if you have several sets of experimental data. Using graphical analysis of several sets of data can be more accurate, because experimental error will have less of an effect on your analysis. **Experimental error** is the variation that occurs between repeated trials of an experiment.

Experimental error occurs for a number of possible reasons. For example, there is always some inaccuracy whenever a measurement is made. Compounds are not usually 100% pure, and so will contain some impurities. There will also always be differences in how different people carry out an experiment, no matter how careful they are. For example, one person may stir a reaction more vigorously than another, or spread out a chemical being heated more than someone else. Even small variations like these can affect the data.

Most sources of experimental error cannot be completely eliminated. To account for this, scientists usually repeat an experiment a number of times and then use the average value of their data. The average value of data from repeated trials of an experiment is more accurate than data from one experiment.

When working out the empirical formula of a compound, one way to determine the average of several experiments is to plot the values on a graph. If you then draw a straight line where it best fits your data, the slope of this line will give you a more reliable value for determining the empirical formula. Figure 4.17 presents an example of this graphing method.

On the graph in Figure 4.17, six sets of data from the silver oxide experiment described in Example 20 have been plotted. Within experimental error, all the points lie on a straight line; therefore, there is a fixed relationship between the number of moles of silver and the number of moles of oxygen,

WEBLINK

Dr. Jed Harrison of the Department of Chemistry, University of Alberta, has developed an analytical device he calls a "lab-on-a-chip." This micro device is capable of detecting and analyzing chemical substances, performing many of the functions of large, complex instruments. Not only is a lab-on-a-chip easy to transport, but it can analyze a sample of about only 1-billionth of a mL! Prepare a model that explains Dr. Harrison's lab-on-a-chip. Begin your research at **www.pearsoned.ca/chemistry11**.

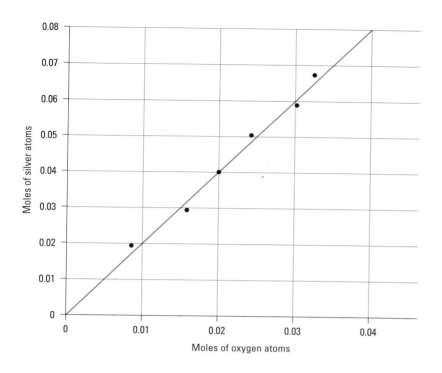

FIGURE 4.17 Data from repeated trials of the analysis of silver oxide were plotted on a graph. Graphical analysis can reduce the effect of experimental error.

WEBLINK

SIMULATION

For a simulation to show sources of experimental error, go to **www.pearsoned.ca/chemistry11**.

and hence between the numbers of atoms of each element. This is evidence for the law of definite proportions.

If you determine the slope of the line, you will find it has a value of 2.00. This result is the same as that calculated in Example 20. For every mole of oxygen there are 2 moles of silver, which gives you the formula Ag_2O.

Analysis of Hydrated Salts Hydrated compounds have water molecules associated with them. People working with compounds that can form hydrates need to know how much water they contain. For example, calcium chloride ($CaCl_2$) can be associated with 1, 2, or 6 moles of water for every mole of calcium chloride. Suppose you were conducting an experiment that required 10 g of chloride ions. You would have to use a larger mass of $CaCl_2 \cdot 6H_2O$ than of $CaCl_2 \cdot H_2O$ to add the 10 g of chloride ions. Without the formula of the specific hydrate you were using, you would not be able to calculate the correct mass to use.

You can determine the amount of water in hydrates by heating a known mass to release the water. If you then determine the mass of the anhydrous salt that remains, you can use this information to calculate the formula of the hydrate.

FIGURE 4.18 Hydrated copper sulfate ($CuSO_4 \cdot 5H_2O$) is a blue solid. When it is heated to form anhydrous copper sulfate ($CuSO_4$), the product is a white solid.

Investigation

Refer to page 167,
Investigation 2

EXAMPLE 21

When 5.742 g of hydrated magnesium sulfate (Epsom salts) is heated until all the water has been released, 2.801 g of anhydrous magnesium sulfate remains. Determine the formula of hydrated magnesium sulfate.

Given

$m_{\text{hydrated magnesium sulfate}} = 5.742$ g
$m_{\text{anhydrous magnesium sulfate}} = 2.801$ g

Required
formula of hydrated magnesium sulfate

Analysis

$m_{\text{H}_2\text{O released}} = m_{\text{hydrated salt}} - m_{\text{anhydrous salt}}$

$\qquad\qquad = 5.742 \text{ g} - 2.801 \text{ g}$

$\qquad\qquad = 2.941 \text{ g}$

Using the periodic table, you can determine the following molar masses:

molar mass$_{\text{MgSO}_4}$ = 120.36 g·mol^{-1}

molar mass$_{\text{H}_2\text{O}}$ = 18.02 g·mol^{-1}

These can be used as conversion factors to find the amount of water (in moles) released and the amount of anhydrous magnesium sulfate remaining, as follows:

$n_{\text{anhydrous MgSO}_4} = 2.801 \text{ g MgSO}_4 \times \dfrac{1 \text{ mol MgSO}_4}{120.36 \text{ g MgSO}_4}$

$\qquad\qquad\qquad = 0.02327 \text{ mol MgSO}_4$

$n_{\text{H}_2\text{O}} \qquad\quad = 2.941 \text{ g H}_2\text{O} \times \dfrac{1 \text{ mol H}_2\text{O}}{18.02 \text{ g H}_2\text{O}}$

$\qquad\qquad\qquad = 0.1632 \text{ mol H}_2\text{O}$

Solution

$\text{MgSO}_4 : \text{H}_2\text{O} = n_{\text{anhydrous MgSO}_4} : n_{\text{H}_2\text{O}}$

$\qquad\qquad\quad = 0.02327 : 0.1632$

$\qquad\qquad\quad = \dfrac{0.02327}{0.02327} : \dfrac{0.1632}{0.02327}$

$\qquad\qquad\quad = 1 : 7$

Statement
Therefore, the formula of the hydrate is MgSO$_4$·7H$_2$O.

PRACTICE PROBLEM

When 3.62 g of anhydrous calcium chloride, CaCl$_2$, is left open to the air, 1.17 g of water is absorbed. Determine the formula of the hydrated compound that is formed.

Carbon-Hydrogen Analysis To determine the empirical formula of a compound containing carbon and hydrogen, chemists use a technique called combustion analysis. A known mass of the compound is burned, and the water and carbon dioxide produced are collected. From the mass of each of these elements, you can calculate the mass of carbon and hydrogen in the original compound and so determine the empirical formula.

Figure 4.19 is a simplified diagram of the interior of a carbon-hydrogen analyzer. Dry oxygen gas is passed over a heated sample of the compound. As the compound burns, the oxygen combines with the carbon to form carbon dioxide, and with the hydrogen to form water vapour. The resulting carbon dioxide–water vapour mixture is passed through a tube that contains anhydrous magnesium perchlorate, which absorbs the water vapour from the mixture. The remaining carbon dioxide is then passed through a second tube that contains sodium hydroxide to absorb the carbon dioxide. The increase in mass of the first tube is equal to the mass of water produced, and the increase in mass of the second tube is equal to the mass of carbon dioxide that was formed.

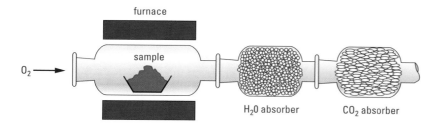

furnace

$O_2 \longrightarrow$

sample

H_2O absorber

CO_2 absorber

FIGURE 4.19 A simplified diagram of a carbon-hydrogen analyzer

EXAMPLE 22

A sample of an unknown compound containing only carbon and hydrogen is burned in a carbon-hydrogen analyzer; 3.94 g of water and 9.62 g of carbon dioxide are produced. The measured molar mass is 84.0 g·mol⁻¹. Determine the molecular formula of the compound.

Given
m_{H_2O} = 3.94 g
m_{CO_2} = 9.62 g
molar mass = 84.0 g·mol⁻¹

Required
molecular formula

Analysis
First calculate the amount of the products of combustion, water and carbon dioxide:

$$n_{H_2O} = 3.94 \text{ g } H_2O \times \frac{1 \text{ mol } H_2O}{18.02 \text{ g } H_2O}$$

$$= 0.219 \text{ mol } H_2O$$

$$n_{CO_2} = 9.62 \text{ g } CO_2 \times \frac{1 \text{ mol } CO_2}{44.01 \text{ g } CO_2}$$

$$= 0.219 \text{ mol } CO_2$$

From these values, calculate the amount of carbon and hydrogen in the products of combustion.

From the molecular formula of H_2O, you know that each molecule of water has 2 atoms of hydrogen and 1 atom of oxygen. Therefore:

$$n_H = 0.219 \text{ mol } H_2O \times \frac{2 \text{ mol } H}{1 \text{ mol } H_2O}$$

$$= 0.438 \text{ mol } H$$

Carbon dioxide molecules consist of 1 carbon atom and 2 oxygen atoms.

$$n_C = 0.219 \text{ mol } CO_2 \times \frac{1 \text{ mol } C}{1 \text{ mol } CO_2}$$

$$= 0.219 \text{ mol } C$$

Solution

$$C : H = n : n_H$$

$$= 0.219 : 0.438$$

$$= \frac{0.219}{0.219} : \frac{0.438}{0.219}$$

$$= 1 : 2$$

The empirical formula of the unknown compound is therefore CH_2.

Solution

Using the periodic table, you can calculate the empirical formula mass of CH_2 to be 14.03 g.

Therefore,

$$\frac{\text{molar mass}}{\text{empirical formula mass}} = \frac{84.0 \text{ g}}{14.03 \text{ g}}$$

$$= 6.00$$

$$\text{molecular formula} = 6 \times \text{empirical formula}$$
$$= 6 \times CH_2$$
$$= C_6H_{12}$$

Statement

The molecular formula of the unknown compound is C_6H_{12}.

PRACTICE PROBLEMS

1. By combustion analysis, a 10.68-mg sample of a compound that contains only carbon, hydrogen, and oxygen is found to produce 16.01 mg of carbon dioxide and 4.37 mg of water. The compound has a molar mass of 176.1 g·mol^{-1}. Determine the molecular formula of the unknown compound.

2. Determine the empirical formula of a compound that contains 24.0 g of carbon and 8.00 g of hydrogen.

3. A sample of a compound containing only carbon and hydrogen was burned to produce 1.36 g of water and 5.22 g of carbon dioxide. Calculate the empirical formula of the compound.

Understanding Concepts

1. Write a statement distinguishing the term "empirical formula" from "molecular formula."

2. Methyl hydrate is a solid compound that is sometimes found with natural gas. Methyl hydrate is composed of methane molecules and water molecules, and can be burned as a fuel. Would heating this hydrate be a good way to determine its formula? Explain your answer.

3. Chemists working in the pharmaceutical industry are often required to identify an unknown substance. Explain why a pharmaceutical chemist must determine the molecular formula of unknown compounds and not the empirical formula.

4. The supervisor in a chemical plant is responsible for ensuring that the plant produces high quality chemicals. Explain how analysis of percent composition might be used to measure the quality of the chemicals.

Applying Inquiry/ Communication Skills

5. Calculate the empirical formula for compounds with the following percent compositions:
   a) 59.3% lead, 40.6% chlorine
   b) 50.1% sulfur, 49.9% oxygen
   c) 44.9% potassium, 18.4% sulfur, 36.7% oxygen

6. Determine the molecular formula of a compound with the empirical formula P_2O_3 and a molar mass of 220.0 g·mol^{-1}.

7. Determine the molecular formula of a compound containing 85.7% carbon and 14.3% hydrogen by mass. The molar mass of the compound is 84.0 g·mol^{-1}.

8. The combustion of a sample of an unknown compound gives only two products, 6.29 g of carbon dioxide and 3.86 g of water. The unknown therefore contains only carbon and hydrogen. The molar mass of the compound is found to be 30.0 g·mol^{-1}. Determine the molecular formula of the compound.

9. A sample of a compound containing carbon, hydrogen, and lead is burned at a high temperature. As a result, 37.8 g of carbon dioxide, 23.2 g of water, and 44.5 g of lead are produced. Determine the empirical formula of the compound.

10. You have been asked to determine the empirical formula of an oxide of calcium. Outline the laboratory procedure you would use.

11. Boron and hydrogen form a series of compounds called boranes, some of which have been used as rocket fuels. A fuel chemist has determined the percent composition and molar mass of a number of these compounds. The values are given in Table 4.5 below. Find the empirical formula and molecular formula of each compound.

TABLE 4.5 Percent Composition of Unknown Borane Samples

Compound	Boron (% by mass)	Hydrogen (% by mass)	Molar Mass (g·mol⁻¹)
1	78.3	21.7	27.7
2	81.2	18.8	53.3
3	85.7	14.3	63.1
4	88.5	11.5	122

200 500

Investigation 1 (Section 4.4)

Inquiry Skills

Initiating and Planning
▶ Applying Technical Skills
▶ Using Tools, Materials, and Equipment
▶ Conducting and Recording
▶ Analyzing and Interpreting
▶ Concluding and Communicating

Empirical Formula of a Compound

Problem

A manufacturer of high-heat furnaces uses magnesium oxide to line the furnace components. The company has been buying magnesium oxide from an outside supplier, but the CEO has directed the research department to investigate the feasibility of manufacturing the magnesium oxide on site. You are the chief chemist in charge of research. As a first step in developing a process for production of magnesium oxide, you are carrying out small test reactions to determine the empirical formula of magnesium oxide.

Materials

- magnesium ribbon
- steel wool
- centigram balance
- clay triangle
- crucible and lid
- crucible tongs
- retort stand
- ring clamp
- gas burner

CAUTION: Wear your safety goggles throughout the experiment.

Do not look directly at the burning magnesium.

Do not inhale the toxic smoke.

Always use crucible tongs to avoid burns.

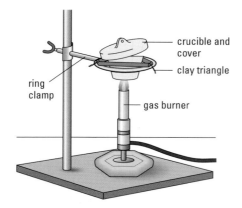

FIGURE 4.20 Experimental set-up

Procedure

1. Wash a crucible and its lid, then set up your equipment as shown in Figure 4.20. Heat the crucible and lid in the hottest part of the flame for about 5 min. Allow them to cool completely (approximately 10 min), then measure and record the combined mass of the crucible and lid to the nearest 0.01 g.

2. Clean the surface of a 20-cm strip of magnesium ribbon with steel wool. Loosely coil the magnesium ribbon and place it in the crucible. Measure and record the combined mass of the magnesium, crucible, and lid.

3. Heat the magnesium over a high flame in the uncovered crucible until the magnesium ignites. Using the crucible tongs, immediately place the lid over the crucible at an angle. Remove the burner from under the apparatus.

4. When the smoke stops, replace the burner under the crucible and continue to apply heat. Every 2 to 3 min, remove the burner and lift the lid to check the reaction. Continue heating until the crucible contains only a light grey powder (about 10 min).

5. When you no longer have any magnesium ribbon, turn off the burner and allow the crucible to cool completely (at least 10 min). Measure and record the combined mass of the product (magnesium oxide) and the crucible and lid.

6. Dispose of the magnesium oxide according to your teacher's instructions.

Analyzing and Interpreting

1. Prepare a chart to record your observations like the one below:

TABLE 4.6 Observed Masses

Material	Mass (grams)
crucible and lid	
crucible, lid, and magnesium strip before heating	
crucible, lid, and crucible contents after heating	

(continued)

2. Use your observations to calculate the following:

    a) the amount of magnesium used in both grams and moles

    b) the mass of magnesium oxide produced

    c) the amount of oxygen that reacted with the magnesium in both grams and moles

    Show all your calculations.

3. Determine the simplest whole-number ratio between the moles of magnesium and moles of oxygen that you used.

4. Write the empirical formula for magnesium oxide.

5. Calculate the percent composition of magnesium oxide.

Concluding and Communicating

6. Determine and describe the major sources of error in your investigation.

7. Suggest at least one way that you might improve the investigation to obtain greater precision.

8. Why could you assume that the magnesium reacted with oxygen in this investigation? Explain why it is unlikely that the magnesium reacted with the nitrogen in the air.

Extending

9. Caffeine is a stimulant and an enzyme inhibitor commonly found in coffee, tea, chocolates, and colas. Chemical analysis of coffee showed the following percent composition:

oxygen	16.5%
carbon	49.5%
nitrogen	29.0%
hydrogen	5.0%

    Determine the empirical formula of caffeine from this data.

---

200   500

Investigation 2 (Section 4.4)

Formula of an Unknown Hydrate

Inquiry Skills

▶ Initiating and Planning
▶ Applying Technical Skills
▶ Using Tools, Materials, and Equipment
▶ Conducting and Recording
▶ Analyzing and Interpreting
▶ Concluding and Communicating

Problem

You are the chief forensic toxicologist for the Cityville Police Crime Investigation Unit. Three days ago, a raid on a suspected drug-making operation uncovered a makeshift laboratory stocked with bottles of unknown chemicals. In order to make the case, the Crown Prosecutor has to know exactly what is in those bottles. You have already been able to identify one of these as a hydrate. All that's left is for you to determine the percent by mass of water in the hydrate, then to determine the empirical formula.

Heating a hydrate will remove the water molecules from the compound, making it anhydrous. Your teacher will demonstrate the procedure for this.

Based on this demonstration, design an experiment to determine the empirical formula of a hydrate.

CAUTION: Wear your safety goggles throughout the experiment.

Always use crucible tongs to handle the crucible and lid (Figure 4.21).

FIGURE 4.21 Use crucible tongs as shown here to handle the crucible and lid.

(continued)

Experimental Design

1. Observe and record the reaction that takes place during the demonstration. Record all the changes you observe.

2. During the demonstration and as you plan your own procedure, think about the following points:

   a) What safety procedures do you need to be aware of in carrying out this procedure? What would you need to do in the case of an emergency?

   b) Will the mass of the compound change during heating? Why or why not?

   c) What data would you need to be able to determine the mass of water in the hydrate before it was heated?

   d) What data will you need to be able to determine the number of molecules of water in each molecule of the compound?

3. Write a laboratory procedure that describes how you intend to determine the mass of water in the hydrate and the empirical formula of the hydrate. Use the reaction that your teacher demonstrated in your procedure.

4. Write a list of the materials you need, and include it in your procedure.

5. Prepare a T-chart or table that lists all the data you will need to record. You will need to record the mass of the hydrate and the mass of the dry crucible and lid, for example.

6. Read over your procedure and look for any steps where you might need to take safety precautions. Include these in your procedure.

7. Hand your procedure to your teacher for approval. You are not to proceed before your procedure has been approved.

8. Carry out your procedure. Ensure you record your results in an organized way.

9. Clean up your work area. Dispose of your chemicals as directed by your teacher.

Analyzing and Interpreting

1. Your teacher will give you the molar mass of the anhydrous salt. Calculate the amount of anhydrous salt (in moles) that you prepared.

2. Calculate the amount of water (in moles) that was removed by heat from your hydrate sample.

3. Determine the moles of water per mole of the anhydrous salt.

4. Calculate the percent of water in the hydrate.

5. Using the term "anhydrous salt" in place of the formula of the salt, write the empirical formula for the hydrate.

Concluding and Communicating

6. Look back over your data and identify the major sources of experimental error.

7. Write a report to the Police of Cityville of your analysis. Remember that the police might not understand chemistry as well as you. Make sure your report is written using appropriate language. Explain in everyday language any scientific terms that you use.

Extending

8. Your data might be used in court to convict someone of a crime. How sure are you that your results are correct? In a short paragraph, outline how you might increase the accuracy of your data.

CHAPTER SUMMARY

Key Terms

average atomic mass
Avogadro's number
empirical formula
formula mass

formula unit
hydrate
law of definite proportions
molar mass

mole
molecular formula
molecular mass
percent composition

relative atomic mass

Key Equations

$$\text{fraction of an isotope} = \frac{\text{abundance (\%)}}{100\%}$$

$$\text{average atomic mass} = (\text{relative atomic mass A} \times \text{fraction of A}) + (\text{relative atomic mass B} \times \text{fraction of B})$$

$$\text{percent composition of element A} = \frac{\text{mass of element A in compound}}{\text{molar mass of compound}} \times 100\%$$

Essential Understandings

■ The average atomic mass of an element can be calculated from the relative atomic mass and the abundance of each isotope.

■ The amount of substance and the number of particles of a substance can be calculated using Avogadro's number of particle·mol^{-1} as a conversion factor.

■ The law of definite proportions states that the chemical composition of a compound is constant.

■ The mass of an element in a compound can be expressed as percent composition of that compound.

■ The empirical formula of a compound indicates the simplest whole-number ratio of the elements in that compound. The molecular formula indicates the actual number of atoms of each element in that compound.

■ The empirical formula and the molecular formula of a compound can be determined from its percent composition and molar mass.

■ The formula of a compound or a hydrate can be determined from mass data.

Consolidate Your Understanding

1. Explain how a large number of particles can be "counted" by weighing.

2. Construct a concept map that starts with the word "mole."

3. Describe situations where it is important to keep close control and accurate records on the "quantity" of things. Explain why.

4. A "formula" is not always a chemical representation. Describe circumstances where you would encounter "formulas" and explain their function.

Understanding Concepts

1. Identify which one of the following represents the number of moles of nitrogen molecules in 56.0 g of $N_2(g)$.
   a) 11.2 mol   b) 2.00 mol
   c) 22.4 mol   d) 4.00 mol
   e) 2.24 mol

2. When iron rusts in air, iron(III) oxide is produced. Determine which one of the following represents the number of moles of oxygen that reacts with 2.4 mol of iron in the reaction:
   $4 Fe(s) + 3 O_2(g) \rightarrow 2 Fe_2O_3(s)$
   a) 1.2 mol   b) 1.8 mol   c) 2.4 mol
   d) 3.2 mol   e) 4.8 mol

3. Identify which one of the following represents the number of molecules in 2.0 mol of carbon dioxide, CO_2.
   a) 1.8×10^{24} molecules   b) 6.0×10^{23} molecules
   c) 1.2×10^{24} molecules   d) 3.6×10^{24} molecules
   e) 4.0×10^{23} molecules

4. Determine which one of the following is the percent composition by mass of oxygen in MgO (magnesium oxide).
   a) 16%   b) 24%   c) 30%
   d) 40%   e) 60%

5. A substance is found to contain 40% carbon, 6.67% hydrogen, and 53.33% oxygen by mass. Identify which one of the following represents the empirical formula of the substance,
   a) CHO   b) C_2HO
   c) CH_2O d) CH_3O
   e) none of the above

6. List three common ways that matter is measured, and provide an example of each.

7. Describe how the molecular mass of a covalent compound is calculated. Compare this to how the formula mass of an ionic compound is calculated.

8. State the law of definite proportions in your own words.

9. Summarize the steps that need to be followed in determining the empirical formula of a compound from its percent composition.

10. State what additional information is necessary to find the molecular formula if the empirical formula is known.

11. State which of the following contains more molecules: 1.00 mol N_2O_4, 1.00 mol C_3H_8, or 1.00 mol CO. Explain your reasoning.

12. The average atomic mass of a compound is the same as the average of the isotopic masses. Do you agree or disagree with this statement? Explain your reason why.

13. Give an example of two different compounds made from the same two elements. Compare the properties of the compounds in your example.

14. The percent composition of water is always 11.1% H and 88.9% O by mass. Explain this statement.

15. Describe a situation in chemistry class that would require you to use the molecular formula of a compound and not its empirical formula.

16. Empirical formulas are used only for ionic compounds. State whether you agree or disagree with this statement. Explain your answer.

17. Decide whether the molecular mass and the molar mass of a compound are always the same number. Explain your decision.

18. Name the representative particle (i.e., atom, molecule, or formula unit) of each of the following substances:
    a) nitrogen gas   b) potassium iodide
    c) carbon dioxide   d) magnesium metal

19. Classify each formula below as an empirical or molecular formula.
    a) S_2Cl_2 b) Na_2SO_3
    c) $C_6H_{10}O_4$ d) $Cl_7H_{19}NO_3$
    e) $C_5H_{10}O_5$ f) $(NH_4)_2CO_3$

20. Copy and complete Table 4.7 below.

21. Mercury and chlorine can react to form more than one product, depending on the reaction conditions. One product contains 73.8 g of mercury and 26.2 g of chlorine. Under different conditions, the product is composed of 84.9 g of mercury and 15.1 g of chlorine. State whether these two products will have similar or different properties.

TABLE 4.7 Quantities of Substances

Element or Compound	Symbol	Molar Mass	Mass	Amount of Substance	Number of Particles
	He				3.01×10^{23} atoms
copper			30 g		
	H_2O			0.15 mol	
carbon dioxide					1.8×10^{24} molecules

Applying Inquiry/Communication Skills

22. A chemical analyst wants to determine the molar mass of a gaseous compound but does not know its molecular formula. Outline the procedure the analyst would need to follow.

23. CH_2O is the empirical formula for a series of compounds. Figure 4.22 shows the relationship between the molar mass of the compounds and the mass of carbon in each compound.

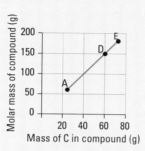

FIGURE 4.22 Molar mass versus mass of carbon

a) Determine the molecular formulas for the compounds represented by points A, D, and E.
b) Find the slope of the line. Determine whether this value is consistent with the empirical formula.
c) There are two other valid data points that fall on the line between points A and D. Identify the x and y values for these data points.

24. Design an investigation to measure the percent by mass of water in soil. After your teacher approves the design, collect some soil samples and perform the experiment. Prepare a report of your results.

25. Determine the mass of 0.200 mol of ASA ($C_9H_8O_4$).

26. Calculate the mass of nitrogen in 24.0 g N_2O_5.

27. Determine the number of oxygen atoms in 0.725 g of $HClO_4$.

28. Determine the amount of sulfur (in grams) in 1.24 mol of H_2SO_4.

29. Calculate the percent by mass of oxygen in ethanol (CH_3CH_2OH).

30. A 128.0-g sample contains 0.5516 mol of a highly radioactive element. Identify the element.

31. State the number of hydrogen atoms found in one particle of each of the following substances. Identify the type of particle (i.e., element, covalent molecule, ionic compound) in your answer.
a) $Ca(OH)_2$
b) H_2SO_4
c) $(NH_4)_2HPO_4$
d) $C_4H_{10}O$

32. A bag of sugar ($C_{12}H_{22}O_{11}$) has a mass of 1.0 kg. Calculate the amount of sugar it contains (in moles).

33. Determine the amount of salt (in moles) that is present in a 1.0-kg box of table salt (sodium chloride).

34. Silver nitrate, $AgNO_3$, costs $99.50 for a 100-g bottle. Calculate the cost per mole of this chemical.

35. A Canadian maple leaf gold coin with a mass of 28.0 g costs $450. Calculate the cost of purchasing 1 mol of gold in these coins.

36. Water and acetone (CH_3COCH_3) can be mixed in any proportion to give a solution. You are asked to prepare 20.0 g of a mixture containing equal numbers of moles of water and acetone. Calculate the mass of each substance you would need to use.

37. When 7.59 g of an oxide of manganese is heated, 3.76 g of manganese metal is obtained. Determine the empirical formula of this compound.

38. When 8.72 g of iron is heated in an atmosphere of chlorine gas, 25.36 g of a compound of iron and chlorine is formed. Determine the empirical formula of this compound.

39. Calculate the amount of substance (in moles) in each of the following:
a) 27 mg of $FeSO_4$
b) 1.24×10^3 g of $AgNO_3$
c) 90.0 g of H_2O

40. Calculate the amount of substance (in moles) in each of the following:
a) 3.00×10^{23} atoms of magnesium
b) 8.72×10^{15} molecules of carbon dioxide
c) 5.0×10^{24} formula units of sodium chloride

41. Calculate the mass in grams of one formula unit of each of the following:
a) $KClO_2$
b) $(NH_4)_2SO_3$

Making Connections

42. Research the history of the development of Avogadro's number. Identify what elements other than carbon have been used to define a mole. Write a short summary report on the validity of Avogadro's number.

43. In mining, the composition of an ore is an important factor in determining whether mining operations would be economical. The analysis of an ore's composition is called an assay. Write a report on how an assay is done for at least one type of ore. Describe how technological developments have contributed to this process.

44. Water (H_2O) and hydrogen peroxide (H_2O_2) are compounds made from different proportions of the same two elements. Make a poster illustrating a comparison of their properties and uses.

45. Conduct a consumer survey comparing the quality of different ice creams and the actual percentages of fat in each. Write a summary of your results including visuals.

46. Lawn fertilizers show the elements essential for plant growth as percent by mass of nitrogen, phosphorus, and potassium. Visit your local garden centre to find examples of fertilizers that are designed for certain types of plants. Create a poster display of the requirements of these plants.

*By the end of this chapter,
you will be able to:*

- state the quantitative relationships expressed in a chemical equation (5.3)

- use appropriate scientific vocabulary to communicate ideas related to chemical calculations (5.1, 5.2, 5.3, 5.4)

- solve problems involving quantity in moles, number of particles, and mass (5.2, 5.3, Investigation 1, Investigation 2)

- balance chemical equations by inspection (5.1, Investigation 1)

- balance simple nuclear equations (5.4)

- calculate, for any given reactant or product in a chemical equation, the corresponding mass or quantity in moles or molecules of any other reactant or product (5.2, 5.3)

- solve problems involving percentage yield and limiting reagents (5.3)

- compare, using laboratory results, the theoretical yield of a reaction to the actual yield, calculate the percentage yield, and suggest sources of experimental error (5.3, Investigation 1, Investigation 2)

- give examples of the application of chemical quantities and calculations (5.2, 5.3)

Calculations Involving Reactions

Determining quantities is an important part of any science. In chemistry, the quantities of the reactants and products of chemical reactions are measured to give us greater understanding of the chemical processes that occur. In fact, it was by measuring the masses of substances in chemical reactions that chemists were first able to determine the atomic masses of the elements. This work provided Mendeléev with the data he used to plot his periodic table, which is the key to chemistry even today.

In this chapter, you will learn some of the calculations that can be carried out using the information in a balanced chemical equation. A balanced chemical equation provides a lot of information about the reactants and products. By performing specific calculations, chemists can make accurate predictions

FIGURE 5.1   Careful determination of quantities is an everyday part of all science.

about the masses and numbers of particles of all the substances involved in a reaction. These kinds of calculations are used in many occupations to determine concentrations of particular substances, such as toxin levels in blood samples. Quantitative chemical analysis is one of the primary tasks of many chemical laboratories, particularly industrial and government laboratories.

Determining quantities in chemical reactions is also important outside of the laboratory. Chemical companies need to accurately measure chemical quantities in order to determine the amount of raw material needed to produce a specific quantity of a product, for example. Determining quantities can also be used to find the efficiency of a process, which can help to reduce waste and increase profitability.

Discovering Chemistry

Predicting a Reaction Outcome

How do chemists predict the amount of product a chemical reaction will yield? Using paper clip "atoms," you can investigate what information a chemist needs about quantities in chemical reactions to be able to make this prediction.

Assume that two molecules, A_2 and B_2, react to form a product, AB_3, according to the following balanced equation:

$A_2 + 3 B_2 \rightarrow 2 AB_3$

Materials

    20 metal paper clips
    20 plastic-coated paper clips
    plastic bag

1. You have been given 20 metal paper clips (A atoms), 20 plastic-coated paper clips (B atoms), all the same colour, and one plastic bag. Link pairs of A atoms and pairs of B atoms.

2. You should now have models of 10 A_2 and 10 B_2 diatomic molecules. Place the 20 molecules in your plastic bag, mix the contents, and then select 15 without looking.

3. Record how many of each type of molecule you have.

4. Using only the quantities of A_2 and B_2 molecules you selected from your bag, model the given chemical reaction by disassembling the reactant molecules and forming product molecules. Continue this process until you run out of one of the reactants.

5. Count and record how many product molecules you were able to form.

■ Which reactant molecule did you run out of first?

■ Predict what would happen if you repeated the activity. Would your results be the same? Why or why not?

> CHECK**POINT**
>
> Describe the steps and calculations that you would take to measure out 0.1 moles of potassium nitrate. Calculate the mass of oxygen that is present in this sample.

5.1 Stoichiometry

Key Understandings

When you have completed this section, you will be able to:

- balance chemical equations by inspection
- use appropriate scientific vocabulary to communicate ideas about chemical calculations

WORDORIGIN

Stoichiometry (stoi-kee'om-i-tree) is formed from a Greek work, *stoicheion*, meaning "element" and the suffix *-metry*, which means "to measure."

Have you ever noticed that every tube of your brand of toothpaste always tastes the same? Or that the dish detergent you use always works the same? This is because the manufacturers of these products work carefully to make sure their products are always made exactly the same way. Every product is made using accurately measured amounts of particular chemicals, which are reacted in a specific way every time. In other words, manufacturers work from a *recipe* that spells out the exact amount of every substance that is needed. The recipe also tells the manufacturer how much of the product will be made. If a company were to produce only 100 tubes of toothpaste when 200 were needed, that company would not stay in business very long!

Stoichiometry Is Determining Quantities

In chemistry, balanced chemical equations are the recipes that chemists use to make particular chemical compounds. Like a good recipe to manufacture tubes of toothpaste, balanced equations tell you not only the amount of reactants to mix, but also the amount of product to expect.

INFOBIT

German chemist Jeremias Benjamin Richter (1762–1807) established the principles of stoichiometry in 1792. Richter was studying the amounts of different acids and bases that were needed to produce a specific known product. By making very careful measurements, Richter showed that fixed and definite amounts were necessary. His work began the study of amounts in chemical reactions.

Stoichiometry is the science of determining the relative proportions, or quantity ratios, in which substances react. Stoichiometry involves calculating these quantities using balanced chemical equations. You will have already worked with relative proportions in some part of your daily life. For example, when you cook something, you mix ingredients (reactants) in the proportions given in a recipe (balanced equation) in order to get a specific quantity of the finished food (product). For example, you could use the recipe in Figure 5.2 to make brownies.

125 mL BUTTER
150 mL COCOA
500 mL BROWN SUGAR
5 mL VANILLA
2 EGGS, BEATEN
3 mL SALT
250 mL FLOUR
150 mL NUTS

MIX THE INGREDIENTS TOGETHER,
AND SPREAD THE MIXTURE IN A PAN.
BAKE AT 180° FOR 20 MINUTES.
MAKES 24 BROWNIES.

FIGURE 5.2 You have to follow the recipe for your brownies to taste their best.

If you wrote this recipe like a chemical equation, it might look like this:

125 mL butter + 500 mL brown sugar
+ 2 eggs + 250 mL flour + 150 mL cocoa $\xrightarrow{180°C}$ 24 brownies
+ 5 mL vanilla + 3 mL salt

The "equation" gives the quantity of each ingredient (or reactant) you would need for 24 brownies (the product). But what if you wanted to make 48 brownies for a bake sale, or twice the amount of product? You would also need twice as much of each ingredient, so you would multiply each amount in the equation by two.

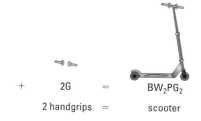

B + 2W + P + 2G = BW$_2$PG$_2$

board + 2 wheels + post + 2 handgrips = scooter

FIGURE 5.3 Balanced chemical equations give the relative proportions of reactants needed to "build" a product. Many consumer products are also manufactured using relative proportions. In the example shown here, the construction of a scooter is written as a balanced equation. The scooter parts are the reactants and the assembled scooter is the product. How many handgrips would you need to make four scooters?

EXAMPLE 1

A company constructs 580 scooters in one week. To build 1 scooter (the product), you would need the following major components (reactants): 1 board (B), 2 wheels (W), 1 post (P), and 2 handgrips (G). The "formula" for a finished scooter (the product) is BW$_2$PG$_2$. You could write the following balanced equation to describe the production of a scooter:

B + 2W + P + 2G = BW$_2$PG$_2$

How many wheels does the plant require per week to make 580 scooters?

Given
number of scooters = 580
1 scooter   = 1 BW$_2$PG$_2$

Required
number of wheels = ? W

Analysis
Two wheels are required for one scooter, or
2 wheels : 1 scooter.

From this relationship, you can obtain the following conversion factor:

$$\frac{2 \text{ wheels}}{1 \text{ scooter}} \text{ or } \frac{2 \text{ W}}{1 \text{ BW}_2\text{PG}_2}$$

Solution
number of wheels = total number of scooters per week

$$\times \frac{\text{wheels for 1 scooter}}{1 \text{ scooter}}$$

number of wheels = 580 BW$_2$PG$_2$ × $\dfrac{2 \text{ W}}{1 \text{ BW}_2\text{PG}_2}$
= 1160 W

Statement
The scooter plant requires 1160 wheels weekly.

PRACTICE PROBLEMS

1. The company has just received an order for 145 scooters. Calculate how many wheels, boards, and handgrips are required to fill this order.

2. Your neighbour made a felt animal for a toy drive at your school. He sewed together four legs, one body, one head, two eyes, and one nose to make the toy. Write an equation for the felt animal.

WEBLINK

For a simulation to show how
stoichiometry works, go to
www.pearsoned.ca/chemistry11.

Balanced Chemical Equations

You have learned that a balanced chemical equation tells you the proportion
of reactants you need in relation to the amount of products you can expect.
Remember that in chemistry, the unit for amount is always the mole. In a
balanced equation, you always write the number of moles of each reactant
and product in front of the chemical it refers to. These numbers are called
coefficients. **Coefficients** are numbers that show the proportions of reactants and products in a reaction in moles.

When a chemical equation is balanced, the number of atoms of all the
elements that occur in the reactants is equal to the number that occurs in
the products. This reflects the **law of conservation of mass**, which states:

Matter is neither created nor destroyed in a chemical reaction.

When you write a balanced chemical equation, you can gain valuable information about the exact amounts of reactants required to produce the exact
amounts of products. See if you can determine which atoms are unbalanced
in the first equation below.

$$A_2 + B_2 \rightarrow AB_3 \text{ (unbalanced)}$$

$$A_2 + 3 B_2 \rightarrow 2 AB_3 \text{ (balanced)}$$

Guidelines for Writing Balanced Chemical Equations

You can balance an equation by inspection using the following three steps:

Step 1. Write the skeleton or unbalanced equation.

Determine the correct symbol or formula for each substance in the reaction.
Write the reactants on the left side of the arrow and the products on the
right. If it is known, indicate the state of the substance in parentheses after
the symbol or formula.

Step 2. Balance the equation using coefficients.

Place coefficients in front of the symbols or formulas such that there is the
same number of each type of atom on both sides of the equation. You may
not change the symbols or formulas you determined in the first step to complete the second, since doing so would describe substances other than those
you had intended. Although there are no firm rules to determine the coefficients that will balance a chemical equation by inspection, the following
guidelines can assist you:

- First balance elements other than H and O.

- As a group, balance any polyatomic ions that appear unchanged on both
  sides of the arrow.

- Balance H.

- Balance O.

Step 3. Check that the coefficients are in the lowest ratio possible.

EXAMPLE 2

Aluminum reacts with oxygen in the air to form a thin layer of aluminum oxide. Write the balanced chemical equation for this reaction.

Given

reactants: aluminum (Al) and oxygen (O_2)

product: aluminum oxide (Al_2O_3)

Analysis and Solution

Apply the rules for balancing chemical equations.

Step 1. Write the correct symbols and formulas to give the skeleton equation.

$Al(s) + O_2(g) \rightarrow Al_2O_3(s)$ (unbalanced)

Step 2. Balance the aluminum first, by placing a coefficient of 2 in front of Al.

$2\ Al(s) + O_2(g) \rightarrow Al_2O_3(s)$ (unbalanced)

You now have a common problem in balancing equations, the "even-odd" problem. Since there are two oxygen atoms per molecule of oxygen gas, any coefficient you assign to O_2 will still result in an even number of oxygen atoms in the reactants. However, you have an odd number of oxygen atoms in the product.

To solve this problem, multiply the chemical formula that has an odd number of atoms by an even number. Start by trying the number 2:

$2\ Al(s) + O_2(g) \rightarrow 2\ Al_2O_3(s)$ (unbalanced)

You now have six oxygen atoms on the right-hand side, so you can balance the oxygen atoms on the left side with a coefficient of 3.

$2\ Al(s) + 3\ O_2(g) \rightarrow 2\ Al_2O_3(s)$ (unbalanced)

Next, balance the aluminum atoms by changing the coefficient of the reactant to 4:

$4\ Al(s) + 3\ O_2(g) \rightarrow 2\ Al_2O_3(g)$ (balanced)

The equation is now balanced; there are 4 Al and 6 O on each side.

Step 3. Check the coefficients to confirm they are in the lowest ratio possible.

Statement

The balanced chemical equation for the reaction of aluminum with oxygen is:

$4\ Al(s) + 3\ O_2(g) \rightarrow 2\ Al_2O_3(s)$

PRACTICE PROBLEM

Balance the following equations:

a) $CO(g) + Fe_2O_3(s) \rightarrow$
$Fe(s) + CO_2(g)$

b) $CS_2(l) + Cl_2(g) \rightarrow$
$CCl_4(l) + S_2Cl_2(l)$

c) $Al_4C_3(s) + H_2O(l) \rightarrow$
$Al(OH)_3(aq) + CH_4(g)$

EXAMPLE 3

Aqueous solutions of potassium hydroxide (KOH) and sulfuric acid (H_2SO_4) will react to form potassium sulfate (K_2SO_4) and water. The potassium sulfate remains in solution. Write the balanced chemical equation for this reaction.

Given

reactants: KOH*(aq)* and H_2SO_4*(aq)*

products: K_2SO_4*(aq)* and H_2O*(l)*

Analysis and Solution

Apply the rules for balancing chemical equations.

Step 1. Write the correct symbols and formulas to give the skeleton equation.

KOH*(aq)* + H_2SO_4*(aq)* → K_2SO_4*(aq)* + H_2O*(l)*   (unbalanced)

Step 2. Following the guidelines for balancing equations, first balance the potassium. Since there are 2 K in K_2SO_4, give KOH a coefficient of 2 as a first try:

2 KOH*(aq)* + H_2SO_4*(aq)* → K_2SO_4*(aq)* + H_2O*(l)*   (unbalanced)

The polyatomic ion sulfate (SO_4) appears on both sides of the equation, so you can consider this as a unit of atoms; these units are also balanced in the above equation. That leaves two atoms of oxygen in the reactants but only one in the products. To balance these, give H_2O a coefficient of 2.

2 KOH*(aq)* + H_2SO_4*(aq)* → K_2SO_4*(aq)* + 2 H_2O*(l)*   (balanced)

Adding this last coefficient also balances the number of hydrogen atoms. The chemical equation is therefore balanced; there are 2 K, 6 O, 4 H, and 1 S on each side.

Step 3. Check the coefficients and confirm that they are in the lowest ratio possible.

Statement

The balanced chemical equation for the reaction is:

2 KOH*(aq)* + H_2SO_4*(aq)* → K_2SO_4*(aq)* + 2 H_2O*(l)*

PRACTICE PROBLEMS

1. Write the balanced chemical equations for the following reactions:

   a) calcium hydroxide + nitric acid → calcium nitrate + water

   b) magnesium carabonate + aluminum bromide → aluminum carbonate + magnesium bromide

2. Balance the equations that describe the processes of photosynthesis, in which plants produce simple sugars that may then be converted to starch or cellulose:

$$CO_2(g) + H_2O(l) \xrightarrow[\text{sunlight}]{\text{chlorophyll}}$$
$$C_6H_{12}O_6(s) + O_2(g)$$

3. The neutralization reaction between stomach acid (HCl) and sodium aluminum dihydroxide carbonate, the active ingredient in some antacids, proceeds as follows:

$$NaAl(OH)_2CO_3(s) + HCl(aq) \rightarrow$$
$$AlCl_3(aq) + H_2O(l) + CO_2(g)$$

Balance this equation.

Section 5.1 Review

Understanding Concepts

1. Define stoichiometry in your own words.

2. Write a statement comparing a chemical equation to a cooking recipe.

3. Balance the following equations:

   a) Fe*(s)* + H_2O*(l)* → Fe_3O_4*(s)* + H_2*(g)*

   b) C_4H_{10}*(g)* + O_2*(g)* → CO_2*(g)* + H_2O*(l)*

4. Explain how the law of conservation of mass is related to balancing a chemical equation.

5. Balance the following equation describing the extraction of phosphorus from the ore apatite.

$$Ca_3(PO_4)_2(s) + SiO_2(s) + C(s) \rightarrow$$
$$P_4(s) + CaSiO_3(s) + CO_2(g)$$

6. The students' council in your school has adopted a local daycare centre. This month, they are putting together gift packages for the children. Each package will contain 1 towel (T), 2 washcloths (W), 1 teddy bear (B), and 3 picture books (P).

   a) Write a balanced equation for the gift package (TW$_2$BP$_3$).

   b) Calculate the number of each item needed for 35 packages.

7. Baking soda (sodium hydrogen carbonate) can be used to put out stovetop fires because when it is heated, it decomposes into solid sodium carbonate, carbon dioxide gas, and water vapour. Write a balanced chemical equation for this reaction.

8. Pure copper can be produced by heating solid copper(II) sulfide in oxygen from the air. Sulfur dioxide gas is also produced in this reaction. Write a balanced equation for this reaction.

5.2 Calculating Quantities from Balanced Equations

Key Understandings

At the end of this section, you will be able to:

- use appropriate scientific vocabulary to communicate ideas about chemical calculations
- state the qualitative relationships expressed in a chemical equation
- solve problems involving quantity in moles, number of particles, and mass
- calculate the quantity of any reactant or product in a chemical equation when you know the quantity of one reactant or product
- give examples of how chemical quantities and calculations are used

FIGURE 5.4 Gardeners apply ammonium salts to provide plants with nitrogen, which is essential for plant growth.

Every balanced chemical equation contains both qualitative and quantitative information. Let's investigate this by looking at the production of ammonia, a common component in plant fertilizer in the form of ammonia salts. Plants need nitrogen to manufacture the proteins in all their cells; without enough nitrogen, plant growth is reduced. Most agricultural soils become deficient in nitrogen over time, so chemical fertilizers are applied to keep the nutrient level high enough for growers to get good yields and quality from their crops. Salts of ammonia are used because they dissolve quickly in the soil water. The first step in making ammonia salts is production of ammonia gas by reacting nitrogen gas with hydrogen gas. The balanced equation for this reaction is:

$$N_2(g) + 3\ H_2(g) \rightarrow 2\ NH_3(g)$$

To ensure that enough ammonia is made to fill all the orders, a manufacturer needs to know how much reactant to buy. Buying too much reactant would mean the company would have to spend money on storing the unused chemicals; buying too little might mean losing customers from late or unfilled orders. What quantitative information can be derived from the balanced equation?

Interpreting Chemical Equations

A balanced chemical equation contains information about the following:

- the number of particles
- the number of moles
- the masses of the components of the reaction

FIGURE 5.5 The balanced chemical equation for the formation of ammonia can be interpreted in several ways. How many molecules of NH_3 could be made from 4 molecules N_2 and 12 molecules H_2?

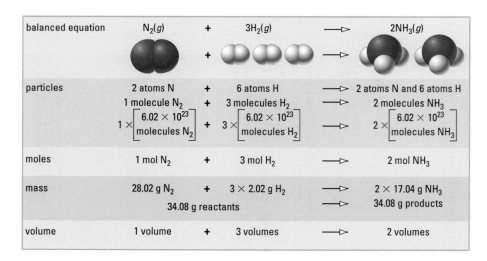

balanced equation	$N_2(g)$	+	$3H_2(g)$	$\longrightarrow$	$2NH_3(g)$
particles	2 atoms N	+	6 atoms H	$\longrightarrow$	2 atoms N and 6 atoms H
	1 molecule N_2	+	3 molecules H_2	$\longrightarrow$	2 molecules NH_3
	$1 \times \begin{bmatrix} 6.02 \times 10^{23} \\ \text{molecules } N_2 \end{bmatrix}$	+	$3 \times \begin{bmatrix} 6.02 \times 10^{23} \\ \text{molecules } H_2 \end{bmatrix}$	$\longrightarrow$	$2 \times \begin{bmatrix} 6.02 \times 10^{23} \\ \text{molecules } NH_3 \end{bmatrix}$
moles	1 mol N_2	+	3 mol H_2	$\longrightarrow$	2 mol NH_3
mass	28.02 g N_2	+	3×2.02 g H_2	$\longrightarrow$	2×17.04 g NH_3
		34.08 g reactants		$\longrightarrow$	34.08 g products
volume	1 volume	+	3 volumes	$\longrightarrow$	2 volumes

Particles   The balanced equation for the production of ammonia tells you that 1 molecule of nitrogen reacts with 3 molecules of hydrogen to produce 2 molecules of ammonia (Figure 5.5). This reaction will always have this 1 : 3 : 2 ratio of molecules. Therefore, if you were to take 10 molecules of nitrogen and react them with 30 molecules of hydrogen, you know you would produce 20 molecules of ammonia. Of course, you can't count such small numbers of molecules. However, if you multiply this ratio by Avogadro's number (6.02×10^{23}), then you see that $1 \times 6.02 \times 10^{23}$ of nitrogen molecules will react with $3 \times 6.02 \times 10^{23}$ of hydrogen molecules and produce $2 \times 6.02 \times 10^{23}$ of ammonia molecules.

Moles Applying the particle interpretation above and knowing that Avogadro's number represents 1 mole of a substance, the coefficients of a balanced chemical equation also can tell you the relative number of moles of reactants and products. Staying with the example of the reaction of nitrogen and hydrogen gas to form ammonia, 1 mole of nitrogen molecules reacts with 3 moles of hydrogen molecules to produce 2 moles of ammonia molecules.

$$N_2(g) \quad + \quad 3\,H_2(g) \quad \rightarrow \quad 2\,NH_3(g)$$

1 mol	3 mol		2 mol

Mass As you saw earlier, the law of conservation of mass states that matter is not created or destroyed in a chemical reaction. That is, the total mass of the products is always equal to the total mass of the reactants. Therefore, you can determine the amounts of reactants and products using molar masses and the mole interpretation of the balanced chemical equation. For the example of the production of ammonia, use the molar mass of each reaction component and you will find that 28.02 g of nitrogen will react with 6.06 g of hydrogen to produce 34.08 g of ammonia.

$$N_2(g) \quad + \quad 3\,H_2(g) \quad \rightarrow \quad 2\,NH_3(g)$$

1 mol	3 mol		2 mol
28.02 g	3×2.02 g		2×17.04 g

Investigation

Refer to page 205, Investigation 1

Although the total number of moles of reactants is not equal to the total number of moles of the product, the total number of *grams* of reactants is equal to the total number of *grams* of product. Check this yourself using the values above. You will see that mass is conserved.

Volume A balanced equation also provides information about the volumes of gases under the same conditions. Therefore, 1 volume of nitrogen gas reacts with 3 volumes of hydrogen gas to form 2 volumes of ammonia gas. You will learn more about gases in Chapter 9, Gases and Chemical Reactions.

Mass and atoms are conserved in every chemical reaction. Molecules, formula units, moles, and volumes of gases are not usually conserved. You should be aware, however, that there are some reactions in which these factors appear to be conserved as well. For example, consider the formation of hydrogen iodide:

$$H_2(g) + I_2(g) \rightarrow 2\,HI(g)$$

In this reaction, molecules, moles, and volume are the same on both sides of the equation. However, such reactions are rare.

FIGURE 5.6 Hydrogen sulfide (H_2S), a gas that smells like rotten eggs, occurs in volcanic areas.

INFO BIT

Hydrogen sulfide is extremely poisonous to human beings. However, some kinds of bacteria found deep in the ocean depend on hydrogen sulfide to produce their food, in a process similar to photosynthesis in plants.

PRACTICE PROBLEM

Interpret the following equation in terms of the number of representative particles, number of moles, and mass of reactants and product.

$$4\ Fe(s) + 3\ O_2(g) \rightarrow 2\ Fe_2O_3(s)$$

EXAMPLE 4

Hydrogen sulfide is a foul-smelling gas that can be found in volcanic areas. Using the balanced chemical equation given below, interpret the reaction of hydrogen sulfide and oxygen gas in terms of the number of particles, the number of moles, and the mass of reactants and products.

$$2\ H_2S(g) + 3\ O_2(g) \rightarrow 2\ SO_2(g) + 2\ H_2O(g)$$

Given
$$2\ H_2S(g) + 3\ O_2(g) \rightarrow 2\ SO_2(g) + 2\ H_2O(g)$$

Required
a) number of particles
b) number of moles
c) masses of reactants and products

Analysis
a) The coefficients in the balanced equation give the relative number of particles (in this case, molecules) of reactants and products.
b) The number of moles of reactants and products is also given by the coefficients in the balanced equation.
c) The total mass of each reactant and product is obtained by multiplying the number of moles of each reaction component by its molar mass.

Solution
a) 2 molecules H_2S react with 3 molecules O_2 to form 2 molecules SO_2 and 2 molecules H_2O.
b) 2 mol H_2S react with 3 mol O_2 to form 2 mol SO_2 and 2 mol H_2O.
c)

$2\ H_2S(g)$	$+$	$3\ O_2(g)$	$\rightarrow$	$2\ SO_2(g)$	$+$	$2\ H_2O(g)$
$2\ mol \times 34.08\ g{\cdot}mol^{-1}$	$+$	$3\ mol \times 32.0\ g{\cdot}mol^{-1}$	$\rightarrow$	$2\ mol \times 64.06\ g{\cdot}mol^{-1}$	$+$	$2\ mol \times 18.02\ g{\cdot}mol^{-1}$
$68.16\ g\ H_2S(g)$	$+$	$96.00\ g\ O_2(g)$	$\rightarrow$	$128.12\ g\ SO_2(g)$	$+$	$36.04\ g\ H_2O(g)$

$$164.16\ g \qquad = \qquad 164.16\ g$$

Statement
In the reaction of hydrogen sulfide gas with oxygen gas to produce sulfur dioxide gas and water vapour:

a) 2 molecules H_2S react with 3 molecules O_2 to form 2 molecules SO_2 and 2 molecules H_2O
b) 2 moles H_2S react with 3 moles O_2 to form 2 moles SO_2 and 2 moles H_2O
c) 68.16 g of H_2S reacts with 96.00 g of O_2 to form 128.12 g SO_2 and 36.04 g of water

Mole–Mole Calculations A balanced chemical equation gives you the *ratios by moles* of the reactants and products. Therefore, if you know the amount of one substance in moles, you can determine the amounts of all other substances from the balanced equation.

Figure 5.7 shows the decomposition of water by electrolysis. The balanced equation for this reaction is:

$$2\ H_2O(l) \xrightarrow{\text{electricity}} 2\ H_2(g) + O_2(g)$$

In this reaction, 2 mol of water decompose to produce 2 mol of hydrogen and 1 mol of oxygen. The reaction can be carried out with any amount of water, but the coefficients tell you the proportions in which the reaction will always occur. You can use these coefficients to write conversion factors called mole ratios.

Mole ratios can be used to calculate the amount of product (in moles) from a given amount of reactant (in moles), or to calculate the amount of reactant (in moles) from a given amount of product (in moles). Three mole ratios for the electrolysis of water are:

$$\frac{2\ \text{mol}\ H_2O}{2\ \text{mol}\ H_2} \qquad \frac{2\ \text{mol}\ H_2O}{1\ \text{mol}\ O_2} \qquad \frac{2\ \text{mol}\ H_2}{1\ \text{mol}\ O_2}$$

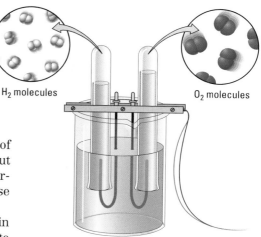

FIGURE 5.7 Electrolysis causes water to decompose into hydrogen and oxygen.

H_2 molecules

O_2 molecules

EXAMPLE 5

Determine how many moles of oxygen are produced when 3.50 mol water decompose.

Given
$$2\ H_2O(l) \quad \rightarrow \quad 2\ H_2(g) \quad + \quad O_2(g)$$
$$\text{2 mol} \qquad\qquad\qquad \text{1 mol}$$
$n_{H_2O} = 3.50$ mol

Required
$n_{O_2} = ?$ mol

Analysis
According to the balanced equation, 2 mol H_2O produce 1 mol O_2 and hydrogen. Therefore, the mole ratio is:
$$\frac{2\ \text{mol}\ H_2O}{1\ \text{mol}\ O_2}$$

Invert the mole ratio (conversion factor) and use it to multiply the number of moles of water.

Solution
$$n_{O_2} = 3.50\ \text{mol}\ H_2O \times \frac{1\ \text{mol}\ O_2}{2\ \text{mol}\ H_2O}$$
$$= 1.75\ \text{mol}\ O_2$$

Statement
The reaction produces 1.75 mol oxygen.

PRACTICE PROBLEM

Acetylene (C_2H_2) is a gas used in welding. Acetylene is produced by adding water to calcium carbide (CaC_2). The balanced equation for this reaction is

$$CaC_2(s) + 2\ H_2O(l) \rightarrow$$
$$Ca(OH)_2(aq) + C_2H_2(g)$$

Determine how many moles of water are used when 15 mol of acetylene are produced.

Mass–Mass Calculations In mass–mass calculations, you have the mass of one substance and must determine the mass of another substance in the same reaction. To do this, you use the mole interpretation of a balanced equation to convert the mass of a reactant or product to the mass of any other reactant or product.

Take another look at the production of ammonia from nitrogen and hydrogen. The balanced equation for this reaction is:

$$N_2(g) + 3 H_2(g) \rightarrow 2 NH_3(g)$$

The coefficients in the balanced equation give you the relative amounts of reactants and products in moles. You use these values to calculate the masses of the reactants and products.

FIGURE 5.8 To determine the number of moles in a sample of a compound, first measure the mass of the sample. Then use the molar mass to calculate the number of moles in that mass.

EXAMPLE 6

Calculate the mass of hydrogen needed to produce 15.5 g of ammonia in the presence of an abundant amount of nitrogen.

Given

$$N_2(g) \quad + \quad 3 H_2(g) \quad \rightarrow \quad 2 NH_3(g)$$
$$ 3 \text{ mol} 2 \text{ mol}$$
$$m_{NH_3} = 15.5 \text{ g}$$

Required

$m_{H_2} = ?g$

Analysis

Use the mass of ammonia to determine the mass of hydrogen:

$$m_{NH_3} \rightarrow m_{H_2}$$

From the coefficients in the balanced equation, you can see that 2 mol of ammonia are produced when 2 mol of hydrogen react with nitrogen.

You need to make the following calculations:

$m_{NH_3} \rightarrow n_{NH_3}$	The ratio is 1 mol NH_3 : 17.04 g NH_3
$n_{NH_3} \rightarrow n_{H_2}$	The mole ratio is 3 mol H_2 : 2 mol NH_3
$n_{H_2} \rightarrow m_{H_2}$	The ratio is 2.02 g H_2 : 1 mol H_2

Solution

$$m_{H_2} = 15.5 \text{ g } \cancel{NH_3} \times \frac{1 \text{ mol } \cancel{NH_3}}{17.04 \text{ g } \cancel{NH_3}} \times \frac{3 \text{ mol } \cancel{H_2}}{2 \text{ mol } \cancel{NH_3}} \times \frac{2.02 \text{ g } H_2}{1 \text{ mol } \cancel{H_2}}$$
$$= 2.76 \text{ g } H_2$$

Statement

This reaction requires 2.76 g of hydrogen.

PRACTICE PROBLEM

When iron rusts, iron metal and oxygen gas combine to form iron (III) oxide. The balanced equation for this reaction is:

$$4 Fe + 3 O_2 \rightarrow 2 Fe_2O_3$$

If a 745-g iron gate hinge turned completely to rust, how many grams of iron(III) oxide would be formed?

Other Stoichiometric Calculations

In the previous chapter, you saw how Avogadro's number is used to convert moles and particles. Stoichiometric calculations can involve any unit of measurement related to the mole, including numbers of particles, units of mass, or volumes. In addition to the mole–mole and mass–mass problems you have seen, problems can involve mole–mass, particle–mole, particle–mass, mass–volume, and volume–volume conversions. Stoichiometry calculations using volume will be developed in Chapter 7, Reactions in Solutions, and in Chapter 9, Gases and Chemical Reactions.

In all problems you encounter involving conversion between two units, follow the steps shown in Figure 5.9:

WEBLINK

One workplace that requires daily use of stoichiometric calculations is the Canadian Centre for Occupational Health and Safety (CCOHS). The scientists at CCOHS must provide chemical data in units that their users can understand. For example, exposure thresholds of toxic substances may be determined in mg·mL^{-1}, but be communicated in ppm (parts per million). Prepare a summary chart of the services that CCOHS provides Canadian industries and how stoichiometry is used in these services. Begin your research at **www.pearsoned.ca/chemistry11**.

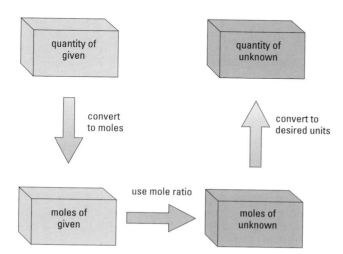

FIGURE 5.9 Use this general solution diagram for working through all types of stoichiometry problems.

EXAMPLE 7

Determine the number of molecules of ammonia that are produced when 43.5 g of nitrogen reacts with an excess of hydrogen. The balanced equation for this reaction is:

$$N_2(g) + 3\ H_2(g) \rightarrow 2\ NH_3(g)$$

Given

$$\begin{array}{cccc} N_2(g) & + & 3\ H_2(g) & \rightarrow & 2\ NH_3(g) \\ 1\ mol & & & & 2\ mol \end{array}$$

$m_{N_2} = 43.5$ g

Required

molecules$_{NH_3}$ = ? molecules

Analysis

$m_{N_2} \rightarrow n_{N_2}$ The ratio is 28.02 g N_2 : 1 mol N_2

$n_{N_2} \rightarrow n_{NH_3}$ The mole ratio is 1 mol N_2 : 2 mol NH_3

$n_{NH_3} \rightarrow$ molecules$_{NH_3}$ The ratio is 1 mol NH_3 : 6.02 × 10^{23} molecules NH_3

The reaction between ammonia and oxygen is one step in the industrial preparation of nitric acid:

$$4 NH_3(g) + 5 O_2(g) \rightarrow 4 NO(g) + 6 H_2O(g)$$

a) Determine the number of molecules of oxygen that are required to completely react 23.2 g of ammonia.

b) Calculate the mass of ammonia that must react with oxygen to produce 8.00×10^{24} molecules of nitrogen monoxide (NO).

Solution

$$molecules_{NH_3} = 43.5 \ g \ N_2 \times \frac{1 \ mol \ N_2}{28.02 \ g \ N_2} \times \frac{2 \ mol \ NH_3}{1 \ mol \ N_2} \times$$

$$\frac{6.02 \times 10^{23} \ molecules \ NH_3}{1 \ mol \ NH_3}$$

$$= 1.87 \times 10^{24} \ molecules \ NH_3$$

Statement

The reaction produces 1.87×10^{24} molecules of ammonia.

Section 5.2 Review

Understanding Concepts

1. Interpret the following equation in terms of relative numbers of representative particles, numbers of moles, and masses of reactants and products.
   $$2 Na(s) + 2 H_2O(l) \rightarrow 2 NaOH(aq) + H_2(g)$$

2. Balance this equation for the combustion of octane in gasoline.
   $$C_8H_{18}(g) + O_2(g) \rightarrow CO_2(g) + H_2O(g)$$
   Interpret the equation in terms of numbers of molecules and moles.

3. Balance the equations that describe the following processes:
   a) the reaction that occurs when dynamite explodes
   $$C_7H_5N_3O_6(s) + O_2(g) \rightarrow CO_2(g) + H_2O(l) + N_2(g)$$
   b) the reaction that produces energy in a nickel-cadmium rechargeable dry cell
   $$NiO(OH)(s) + H_2O(l) + Cd(s) \rightarrow Ni(OH)_2(s) + Cd(OH)_2(s)$$

4. Interpret the following equations in terms of relative numbers of representative particles, numbers of moles, and masses of reactants and products:
   a) $2 Zn(s) + 4 HCl(aq) \rightarrow 2 ZnCl_2(aq) + 2 H_2(g)$
   b) $3 Mg(s) + 2 H_3PO_4(aq) \rightarrow Mg_3(PO_4)_2(aq) + 3 H_2(g)$
   c) $2 KIO_3(s) \rightarrow 2 KI(s) + 3 O_2(g)$

5. Explain how a balanced equation obeys the law of conservation of mass.

Applying Inquiry/Communication Skills

6. The following equation shows the formation of phosphorus(V) oxide:
   $$4 P(s) + 5 O_2(g) \rightarrow 2 P_2O_5(s)$$
   a) Write the mole ratios that can be derived from this equation.
   b) Calculate the amount of phosphorus that is needed to form 4.5 mol P_2O_5.

7. Using the equation in question 5:
   a) Determine the amount of phosphorus(V) oxide that is formed when 7.2 mol of oxygen reacts with phosphorus.
   b) Calculate the amount of oxygen that is required to react completely with 13.3 mol phosphorus.

8. The combustion of acetylene gas is represented by:
   $$2 C_2H_2(g) + 5 O_2(g) \rightarrow 4 CO_2(g) + 2 H_2O(g)$$
   During one job, a welder burns 38.0 g of acetylene. Using this balanced equation, calculate the following:
   a) the mass of oxygen used
   b) the mass of CO_2 produced
   c) the mass of H_2O produced
   d) Use your answers from a), b), and c) to show that this equation obeys the law of conservation of mass.

9. Oxygen gas can be produced by the decomposition of potassium chlorate. Determine the number of molecules of oxygen produced when 7.5 mol of potassium chlorate ($KClO_3$) decomposes according to this balanced equation:
   $$2 KClO_3(s) \rightarrow 2 KCl(s) + 3 O_2(g)$$

5.3 Yield of Products in Chemical Reactions

Key Understandings

When you have completed this section, you will be able to:

- solve problems involving percent yield and limiting reagents
- compare the theoretical yield to the actual yield of chemical reaction in an experiment
- calculate percent yield of an experiment and suggest sources of experimental error
- give examples of how chemical quantities and calculations are used
- solve problems involving quantity in moles, number of particles, and mass
- calculate the quantity of any reactant or product in a chemical equation when you know the quantity of one reactant or product
- use appropriate scientific language to communicate about chemical calculations

Imagine you want to make cheese sandwiches for you and your friend, and you discover that only one slice of cheese is left. You have lots of bread, tomatoes, lettuce, and mayonnaise, but you can't make more than one cheese sandwich with only one slice of cheese. The amount of cheese limits the amount of sandwiches, even though you have an excess of the other ingredients.

FIGURE 5.10 No matter how much of the other ingredients you have, with two rolls you can make only two sandwiches.

Limiting and Excess Reagents

A situation similar to the example of the cheese sandwiches can occur in a chemical reaction. Sometimes the amount of one reagent is less than is needed to convert the entire amount of the other reagents into the reaction product. This reagent is called the limiting reagent. The **limiting reagent** limits the amount of product that can be formed in a reaction. Just as you determined how many sandwiches you could make from the number of rolls, when a chemical reaction has a limiting reagent, you can use the amount of the limiting reagent to determine how much product will be made.

FIGURE 5.11 In this chemical reaction, there are three molecules of H_2 for every one molecule of N_2. Compare the experimental conditions before and after the reaction: H_2 is the limiting reagent and N_2 is in excess. Would the amount of products formed be different if we started with four molecules of N_2 and three molecules of H_2?

Consider the production of ammonia from nitrogen and hydrogen:

$$N_2(g) + 3\ H_2(g) \rightarrow 2\ NH_3(g)$$

The equation tells you that when 1 molecule (or 1 mole) of N_2 reacts with 3 molecules (3 moles) of H_2, 2 molecules (2 moles) of NH_3 are produced. What would happen if 2 molecules (2 moles) of N_2 reacted with 3 molecules (3 moles) of H_2? How many molecules (3 moles) of NH_3 would be formed then?

Before the reaction begins, nitrogen and hydrogen are present in a 2:3 molecule (mole) ratio. When the reaction begins, it proceeds according to the balanced chemical equation: 1 molecule (1 mole) of N_2 reacts with 3 molecules (3 moles) of H_2 and produces 2 molecules (2 moles) of NH_3. However, now all 3 molecules (3 moles) of hydrogen have been used up. At this point, the reaction cannot continue, so no more ammonia will be produced.

In this example, hydrogen is the limiting reagent (Figure 5.11). All the hydrogen is consumed in the reaction. However, there is still 1 molecule (1 mole) of nitrogen left that has nothing to react with. The nitrogen is therefore the excess reagent. An **excess reagent** is any reactant that is not completely consumed in a reaction.

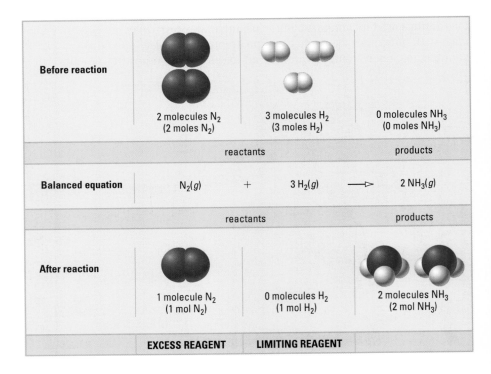

Before reaction	2 molecules N_2 (2 moles N_2)	3 molecules H_2 (3 moles H_2)	0 molecules NH_3 (0 moles NH_3)
	reactants		products
Balanced equation	$N_2(g)$ $+$	$3\ H_2(g)$ $\longrightarrow$	$2\ NH_3(g)$
	reactants		products
After reaction	1 molecule N_2 (1 mol N_2)	0 molecules H_2 (1 mol H_2)	2 molecules NH_3 (2 mol NH_3)
	EXCESS REAGENT	LIMITING REAGENT	

If the quantities in a chemical reaction are not given in moles, you must first convert the quantities of each reactant to the amount in moles. Then you can identify the limiting reagent and determine the amount of product that will be produced.

EXAMPLE 8

Sodium metal reacts with chlorine gas to form solid sodium chloride according to the following balanced equation:

$$2 \text{ Na}(s) + \text{Cl}_2(g) \rightarrow 2 \text{ NaCl}(s)$$

If 4.80 mol Na reacts with 2.70 mol Cl_2, determine the following:
a) the limiting reagent
b) the amount of NaCl that is produced

Given

$$2 \text{ Na}(s) \qquad + \qquad \text{Cl}_2(g) \qquad \rightarrow \qquad 2 \text{ NaCl}(s)$$

$$\quad 2 \text{ mol} \qquad\qquad\qquad 1 \text{ mol} \qquad\qquad\qquad 2 \text{ mol}$$

$$n_{\text{Na}} = 4.80 \text{ mol} \qquad\qquad n_{\text{Cl}_2} = 2.70 \text{ mol}$$

Required
a) limiting reagent
b) $n_{\text{NaCl}} = ?$ mol

Analysis (part a)
First, since the reactants are given in moles, you know you do not need to convert any units. Therefore, you can start by arbitrarily choosing one of the reactants and then using the mole ratio from the balanced equation to calculate the required amount of the other reactant.

Solution (part a)

$$n_{\text{Cl}_2} = 4.80 \text{ mol Na} \times \frac{1 \text{ mol Cl}_2}{2 \text{ mol Na}}$$

$$= 2.40 \text{ mol Cl}_2$$

From this calculation, you can see that you need 2.40 mol Cl_2 to react completely with 4.80 mol Na. Since you have 2.70 mol Cl_2, more than is required, then sodium is the limiting reagent.

Analysis (part b)
Use the quantity of the limiting reagent (Na) to calculate the amount of product (NaCl) that can be produced.

Solution (part b)

$$n_{\text{NaCl}} = 4.80 \text{ mol Na} \times \frac{2 \text{ mol NaCl}}{2 \text{ mol Na}}$$

$$= 4.80 \text{ mol NaCl}$$

Statement
a) Sodium is the limiting reagent.
b) The reaction will produce 4.80 mol NaCl.

FIGURE 5.12 Igniting sodium metal in chlorine gas produces a white smoke of NaCl and a bright yellow flame.

PRACTICE PROBLEM

Copper(I) sulfide is produced as shown in the following balanced equation.

$$2 \text{ Cu}(s) + \text{S}(s) \rightarrow \text{Cu}_2\text{S}(s)$$

a) Determine the limiting reagent when 85.0 g Cu reacts with 30.0 g S.
b) Calculate the maximum mass of Cu_2S that can be produced.

0.6 g Mg

1.2 g Mg

2.4 g Mg

FIGURE 5.13 Predict which balloon will change the most.

FIGURE 5.14 The productivity of a farm is measured in yield. Since growing conditions vary every year, the actual yield often differs from the theoretical yield.

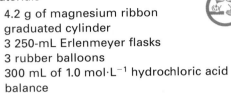

Discovering Chemistry   *Limiting Reagent*

Magnesium reacts with hydrochloric acid to form hydrogen gas. Predict the relative volume of hydrogen produced by 0.6 g, 1.2 g, and 2.4 g of magnesium in an excess of HCl. You or your teacher will carry out the reaction according to the following procedure and test your prediction.

CAUTION: Wear goggles and gloves throughout the procedure.

Materials
    4.2 g of magnesium ribbon
    graduated cylinder
    3 250-mL Erlenmeyer flasks
    3 rubber balloons
    300 mL of 1.0 mol·L⁻¹ hydrochloric acid
    balance

1. Add 100 mL of hydrochloric acid to each Erlenmeyer flask. This is about 0.10 mol HCl in each flask.

2. Label the three balloons 0.6 1.2, and 2.4. Weigh out 0.6 g, 1.2 g, and 2.4 g of magnesium ribbon, and then place each sample into the appropriate balloon.

3. Stretch the end of each balloon over the mouth of a flask, as shown in the Figure 5.13. Don't allow the magnesium ribbon in the balloon to fall into the flask.

4. Lift each balloon and shake the magnesium metal into the flasks. Observe the reaction in each flask. Record the maximum size that each balloon gets relative to the other balloons.

5. When the reaction is complete, take your apparatus apart and dispose of all materials safely, as directed by your teacher. Clean up your work area.

■ From your observation of the relative sizes of the balloons, compare the volumes of hydrogen gas produced by each reaction. Did the actual results agree with your prediction?

■ Write a balanced chemical equation for the reaction between magnesium metal and hydrochloric acid. Using a calculation, explain what happened in each flask. Identify the limiting reagent in your answer.

Percent Yield

You have learned how to determine the amount of product you can expect to produce in a chemical reaction. However, as for farmers and their farms, it is rare for the actual amount of product to equal the expected amount that you calculate. The amount of product calculated from a balanced equation is called the expected or theoretical yield. The **theoretical yield** is the maximum amount of product that could be formed from the given amounts of the reactants. The **actual yield** is the amount of product that actually forms when the reaction is carried out. Actual yield is usually less than theoretical yield.

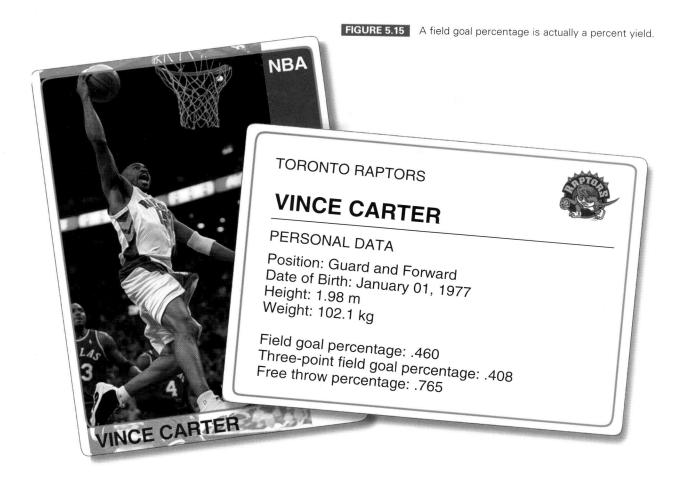

FIGURE 5.15 A field goal percentage is actually a percent yield.

NBA

TORONTO RAPTORS

VINCE CARTER

PERSONAL DATA

Position: Guard and Forward
Date of Birth: January 01, 1977
Height: 1.98 m
Weight: 102.1 kg

Field goal percentage: .460
Three-point field goal percentage: .408
Free throw percentage: .765

VINCE CARTER

There are several possible reasons why the yield of a reaction might be reduced. Reactions do not always go to completion. Some reactants may be impure. Competing side reactions can use up reactants in the formation of unwanted products. There is always some loss of product when it is recovered or transferred between containers.

The **percent yield** is the ratio of the actual yield to the theoretical yield, expressed as a percent. The percent yield indicates the efficiency of the reaction.

$$\text{percent yield} = \frac{\text{actual yield}}{\text{theoretical yield}} \times 100\%$$

Actual yield is *always* an experimental value. You can only get an actual yield if you have done an experiment yourself, or if someone else does an experiment and gives you the results.

Percent yield is often used to keep track of how well an industrial process is running. For example, one step in the commercial production of aluminum metal is the decomposition of aluminum oxide by electrolysis. If the percent yield of this step decreases, a manager of an aluminum extraction plant knows there is a problem. Checks of equipment and reactants can then be made to find and correct the problem. In processes with a number of steps, usually percent yield is monitored regularly at each step to help isolate the cause of any problems.

Investigation

Refer to page 206, Investigation 2

EXAMPLE 9

Calcium carbonate is decomposed by heating, as shown in the following balanced equation:

$$CaCO_3(g) \xrightarrow{\Delta} CaO(s) + CO_2(g)$$

If 20.4 g $CaCO_3$ are heated, determine the following:

a) theoretical yield of CaO
b) percent yield if 10.6 g are actually produced

Given

$$CaCO_3(s) \xrightarrow{\Delta} CaO(s) + CO_2(g)$$

| 1 mol | | 1 mol | |

$m_{CaCO_3} = 20.4$ g $\qquad\qquad m_{CaO} = 11.6$ g

Required

a) theoretical yield of CaO
b) percent yield of CaO

Analysis (part a)

$$m_{CaCO_3} \rightarrow n_{CaCO_3} \rightarrow n_{CaO} \rightarrow m_{CaO}$$

Solution (part a)

$$m_{CaO} = 20.4 \text{ g } \cancel{CaCO_3} \times \frac{1 \text{ mol } \cancel{CaCO_3}}{100.09 \text{ g } \cancel{CaCO_3}} \times \frac{1 \text{ mol } \cancel{CaO}}{1 \text{ mol } \cancel{CaCO_3}} \times \frac{56.08 \text{ g CaO}}{1 \text{ mol } \cancel{CaO}}$$

$$= 11.4 \text{ g CaO}$$

Analysis (part b)

actual yield$_{CaO}$ $\quad = 10.6$ g
theoretical yield$_{CaO} = 11.4$ g

$$\text{percent yield} \quad = \frac{\text{actual yield}}{\text{theoretical yield}} \times 100\%$$

Solution (part b)

$$\text{percent yield}_{CaO} = \frac{10.6 \text{ g } \cancel{CaO}}{11.4 \text{ g } \cancel{CaO}} \times 100\%$$

$$= 93.0\%$$

Statement

a) The theoretical yield is 11.4 g CaO.
b) The percent yield when 10.6 g CaO is produced is 93.0%.

PRACTICE PROBLEM

Lead(II) nitrate decomposes on heating to produce solid lead(II) oxide, nitrogen dioxide gas, and oxygen, according to the following balanced equation:

2 Pb(NO$_3$)$_2$(s) →
2 PbO(s) + 4 NO$_2$(g) + O$_2$(g)

When 3.31 g of lead(II) nitrate were heated in an experiment, the yield of lead(II) oxide obtained was 1.75 g. Calculate the percent yield for the reaction.

Understanding Concepts

1. Define limiting reagent in your own words.

2. Compare actual yield to theoretical yield. For any given reaction, predict whether the actual yield or the theoretical yield would be the larger. Explain your answer.

Applying Inquiry/ Communication Skills

3. Identify the limiting reagent for the given combination of reactants in the following balanced equations:

   a) $4 P_{(s)} + 5 O_{2(g)} \rightarrow 2 P_2O_{5(s)}$
      14.5 mol   18.0 mol

   b) $2 Al_{(s)} + 3 C_{2(g)} \rightarrow 2 AlCl_{3(s)}$
      3.6 mol   5.3 mol

   c) $2 H_{2(s)} + O_{2(g)} \rightarrow 2 H_2O_{(l)}$
      6.4 mol   3.4 mol

   d) $2 P_2O_{5(s)} + 6 H_2O_{(l)} \rightarrow 4 H_3PO_{4(aq)}$
      0.48 mol   1.52 mol

4. Calculate the amount of product formed (in moles) for each reaction in question 3.

5. Calculate the amount of the excess reagent (in moles) remaining after the reaction for each reaction in question 3.

6. A double replacement reaction occurs when barium nitrate solution reacts with potassium sulfate solution:

   $Ba(NO_3)_{2(aq)} + K_2SO_{4(aq)} \rightarrow$
   $BaSO_{4(s)} + 2 KNO_{3(aq)}$

   a) Identify the limiting reagent when 12.0 g barium nitrate reacts with 16.0 g of potassium sulfate.

   b) Calculate the mass of barium sulfate that will be produced by this reaction.

7. Design an experiment to measure the percent yield for the following reaction:

   $NaOH_{(aq)} + HCl_{(aq)} \rightarrow$
   $NaCl_{(aq)} + H_2O_{(l)}$

8. Acetylene (C_2H_2) will burn in the presence of oxygen. The balanced equation for this reaction is:

   $C_2H_{2(g)} + 5 O_{2(g)} \rightarrow$
   $4 CO_{2(g)} + 2 H_2O_{(g)}$

   a) Identify the limiting reagent when 3.20 mol C_2H_2 reacts with 8.50 mol O_2.

   b) Calculate the mass of carbon dioxide that will be produced by this reaction.

9. Hydrogen gas can be produced in the laboratory by the reaction of magnesium metal with hydrochloric acid. The reaction occurs according to the following balanced equation:

   $Mg_{(s)} + 2 HCl_{(aq)} \rightarrow$
   $MgCl_{2(aq)} + H_{2(g)}$

   a) Identify the limiting reagent when 9.00 g HCl reacts with 7.00 g Mg.

   b) Calculate the mass of grams of hydrogen that can be produced by this reaction.

10. Lead(II) nitrate decomposes on heating to produce solid lead(II) oxide, nitrogen dioxide gas, and oxygen according to the following balanced equation:

    $2 Pb(NO_3)_{2(s)} \rightarrow$
    $2 PbO_{(s)} + 4 NO_{2(g)} + O_{2(g)}$

    When 3.31 g of lead(II) nitrate was heated in an experiment, the yield of lead(II) oxide was found to be 1.75 g. Calculate the percentage yield that was obtained.

11. The pain reliever acetylsalicylic acid ($C_9H_8O_4$) can be prepared by reacting salicylic acid ($C_7H_6O_3$) with acetic anhydride ($C_4H_6O_3$) in the presence of sulfuric acid according to the following balanced equation:

    $C_7H_6O_3 + C_4H_6O_3 \rightarrow$
    $C_9H_8O_4 + C_2H_4O_2$

    When this reaction was carried out using 10.0 g salicylic acid and 15.3 g of acetic anhydride, a yield of 9.20 g acetylsalicylic acid was obtained. Calculate the percent yield of the reaction.

5.4 Nuclear Reactions

Key Understandings

When you have completed this section, you will be able to:

- balance simple nuclear equations
- use appropriate scientific vocabulary to communicate ideas related to nuclear reactions

You saw in Unit 1 that chemical reactions involve breaking and forming bonds between substances. Bonding only involves the electrons, so the atomic nuclei of the reactants remain unchanged in chemical reactions. A **nuclear reaction**, however, is a reaction that involves changes in the atomic nuclei of the reactants. Only radioisotopes (substances with unstable atomic nuclei) can participate in nuclear reactions.

Both chemical reactions and nuclear reactions produce new substances with new and different properties. Chemical reactions always involve a change in energy, but this change can be either an endothermic reaction (a net gain) or an exothermic reaction (a net loss) of energy. In contrast, nuclear reactions are always exothermic.

Unlike chemical reactions, nuclear reactions are unaffected by changes in temperature, pressure, or by the presence of catalysts. A radioactive atom will have the same nuclear reaction no matter what compound that atom occurs in. Finally, the rate of a nuclear reaction cannot be decreased or increased, and the reaction cannot be stopped once it has started.

Radioactivity Involves Disintegration of Atomic Nuclei

In Chapter 1, you were introduced to the concept of radioactivity. **Radioactive decay** is the process by which certain isotopes of elements are transformed atom-by-atom into other isotopes over time. The newly formed atoms may be of the same element or of a different element.

Why are some isotopes radioactive (unstable) and others stable? The stability of an atom is mainly determined by the ratio of protons to neutrons in its nucleus. As more protons are added to the nucleus, an atom requires more neutrons to hold the positively charged protons together. Beyond bismuth (element 83) on the periodic table, it is impossible to hold any more protons together in a stable atom. Therefore, polonium and all subsequent elements occur only as radioactive isotopes.

Other factors also help determine the stability of a nucleus. Elements with odd numbers of protons tend to have only one or two stable isotopes. Elements with even numbers of protons, however, tend to have a large number of stable isotopes. In fact, only 4 of the 273 stable isotopes contain an odd number of protons and an odd number of neutrons. Therefore, it seems that nuclei with pairs of protons and/or pairs of neutron are more stable.

Types of Radiation

When a nucleus decays, radiation and energy are released in the process. There are several types of radiation, and these are listed in Table 5.1. Three of the forms are of particular importance, and will be described in detail.

TABLE 5.1 Common Forms of Radiation and their Symbols

Name	Symbol
alpha particle (helium nucleus)	^4_2He
beta particle (electron)	$^0_{-1}\text{e}$
gamma ray	$^0_0\gamma$ or γ
proton	^1_1p or ^1_1H
neutron	^1_0n
positron (positive electron)	$^0_{+1}\text{e}$

Alpha Radiation **Alpha radiation** is a stream of helium nuclei that is emitted from a radioactive source. The emitted particles, **alpha particles**, consist of two protons and so have a charge of $+2$. In nuclear equations, an alpha particle is written as ^4_2He. The electric charge is generally omitted. Alpha radiation has a low penetrating power and can be stopped by paper or clothing (Figure 5.17).

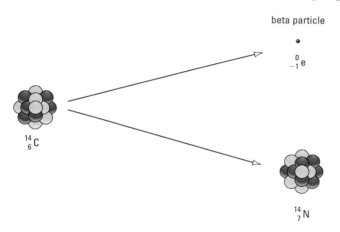

beta particle

$^0_{-1}\text{e}$

$^{14}_6\text{C}$

$^{14}_7\text{N}$

FIGURE 5.16 Carbon–14 is shown undergoing beta decay to form nitrogen-14. What particle is emitted during this decay process?

Beta Radiation **Beta radiation** consists of fast-moving electrons. The beta ray or **beta particle** is written as $^0_{-1}\text{e}$ to indicate that it has a mass close to zero (compared with the proton and neutron) and that it has a charge of -1. Beta particles are more penetrating than those of alpha particles (Figure 5.17). Typically, beta particles will penetrate about 4 mm into body tissue. Beta particles can be stopped by a metal foil.

INFOBIT

X-radiation, or **X-rays**, like gamma rays, consists of high-energy electromagnetic radiation. X-rays are not emitted during radioactive decay, but when excited electrons in certain metals lose their energy. X-rays pass easily through paper, wood, and the human body. They can be partially stopped by materials such as several metres of concrete or several centimetres of lead.

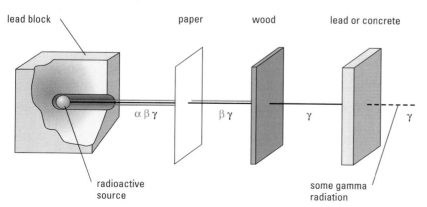

lead block   paper   wood   lead or concrete

$\alpha\ \beta\ \gamma$ $\beta\ \gamma$ γ γ

radioactive source

some gamma radiation

FIGURE 5.17 Due to their large mass and charge, alpha particles have the least penetrating power of the three main types of radiation. Gamma rays have no mass or charge and are the most penetrating.

Gamma Radiation   **Gamma radiation** is high-energy electromagnetic radiation given off by a radioisotope. Visible light, or the light your eyes can detect, is also electromagnetic radiation but of much lower energy. **Gamma rays** are often emitted along with alpha or beta radiation by the nuclei of disintegrating radioactive atoms. Gamma rays have no mass and no electrical charge and are written as $_0^0\gamma$. Gamma rays are by far the most penetrating kind of radiation (Figure 5.17). Gamma rays pass through the body, and a lead or concrete shield is required to reduce their intensity. Cobalt-60 is an important gamma-ray emitter because it is used for some kinds of cancer therapy. Cobolt-60 decays to form nickel-60 and both a gamma and a beta particle.

$$_{27}^{60}\text{Co} \rightarrow\ _{28}^{60}\text{Ni} +\ _{-1}^{0}\text{e} +\ _{0}^{0}\gamma$$

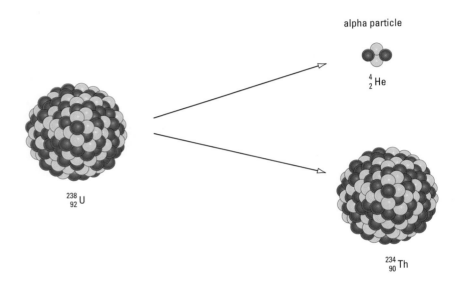

FIGURE 5.18   Uranium-238 is shown undergoing alpha decay to form thorium-234. What particle is emitted during this decay process?

alpha particle

$_2^4$ He

$_{92}^{238}$ U

$_{90}^{234}$ Th

Writing and Balancing Nuclear Equations

WEBLINK

For a simulation to show how nuclear reactions work, go to **www.pearsoned.ca/chemistry11**.

To balance a chemical equation, you make sure that the same number of each type of atom occurs on both sides of the equation. You do this because mass is conserved in all chemical reactions. In nuclear reactions, both mass and charge are conserved. A nuclear equation is written using the atomic symbols of the nuclei. As for chemical equations, reactants are placed on the left side of an arrow and products on the right side. A nuclear equation is balanced when the following two conditions are met:

• The sums of the mass numbers on both sides of the equation are equal. The equation is said to be "mass balanced."
• The sums of the atomic numbers on both sides of the equation are equal. The equation is said to be "charge balanced."

Uranium is the most abundant radioactive element in Earth's crust. Most uranium occurs as the uranium-238, which transforms into the radioisotope thorium-234 in the following reaction:

$$_{92}^{238}\text{U} \xrightarrow{\text{radioactive decay}}\ _{90}^{234}\text{Th}\ +\ _2^4\text{He} \quad (\alpha \text{ emission})$$

uranium–238   thorium–234   alpha particle

In this equation, both the mass numbers (superscripts) and the atomic numbers (subscripts) are balanced ($238 = 234 + 4$; $92 = 90 + 2$). Therefore you have mass balance and charge balance.

EXAMPLE 10

One radioisotope of radon, radon-222, releases one alpha particle per nucleus as it decays. Determine the element that is formed in this reaction, and calculate its mass number.

Given

$$^{222}_{86}\text{Rn} \rightarrow {}^{4}_{2}\text{He} + \text{?}$$

Required
element formed and its mass number

Analysis
Mass and charge are conserved; i.e., mass numbers on both sides are equal and atomic numbers on both sides are equal.

Calculate the mass number and the atomic number of the unknown element. Then use the periodic table to identify the element with the calculated atomic number.

Solution
$$\text{mass number}_{\text{unknown}} = 222 - 4$$
$$= 218$$

$$\text{atomic number}_{\text{unknown}} = 86 - 2$$
$$= 84$$

The element with atomic number 84 is polonium (Po).

Statement
The element formed is polonium, with mass number 218.

WEBLINK

Radioactivity from radon can be a naturally occurring environmental hazard. Radioactive radon gas can accumulate in homes and other buildings if they are built in a uranium-rich area. Compare the health risk of radon exposure to the health risks of air pollution. Summarize your findings in a brief paper. Begin your research at **www.pearsoned.ca/chemistry11**.

PRACTICE PROBLEMS

1. Determine the element formed by the following reaction, and calculate its mass number.

$$^{18}_{10}\text{Ne} \rightarrow {}^{0}_{+1}\text{e} + \text{?}$$

2. State the name of the element formed by the following nuclear reaction, and then calculate its mass number.

$$^{214}_{83}\text{Bi} \rightarrow {}^{4}_{2}\text{He} + \text{?}$$

EXAMPLE 11

A radioactive isotope of oxygen, oxygen-15, undergoes radioactive decay to form nitrogen-15. Determine the type of radiation released during this process.

Given
$$^{15}_{8}\text{O} \rightarrow {}^{15}_{7}\text{N} + \text{?}$$

Required
type of radiation released

Analysis
Mass numbers on both sides are equal and atomic numbers on both sides must be equal. Again, calculate the mass number and the atomic number of the unknown radiation. Then refer to Table 5.1 to determine the type of radiation released.

Determine the type of radiation released during the following reactions:

a) $^{234}_{90}\text{Th} \rightarrow ^{234}_{91}\text{Pa} + ?$

b) $^{54}_{26}\text{Fe} + ^{1}_{1}\text{H} \rightarrow ^{54}_{27}\text{Co} + ?$

c) $^{10}_{5}\text{B} + ^{1}_{0}\text{n} \rightarrow ^{3}_{1}\text{H} + 2?$

Solution

Mass number$_{\text{unknown}}$ $= 15 - 15$
$= 0$

Atomic number$_{\text{unknown}}$ $= 8 - 7$
$= 1$

Statement

The unknown type of radiation is a positron $\left(^{0}_{+1}\text{e}\right)$

Types of Nuclear Reactions

Nuclear reactions are not always the result of decay of radioactive isotopes, but can also be caused by colliding nuclei together.

Nuclear fusion occurs when nuclei combine to produce a nucleus of greater mass. In **solar fusion**, hydrogen nuclei (protons) fuse to make helium nuclei. This reaction also requires two electrons (beta particles).

$$4^{1}_{1}\text{H} + 2^{\ 0}_{-1}\text{e} \rightarrow ^{4}_{2}\text{He} + \text{energy}$$

FIGURE 5.19 Thermonuclear fusion reactions occurring in the sun have provided earth with energy for billions of years.

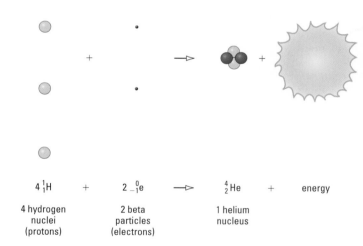

$$4^{1}_{1}\text{H} + 2^{\ 0}_{-1}\text{e} \longrightarrow ^{4}_{2}\text{He} + \text{energy}$$

4 hydrogen nuclei (protons)   2 beta particles (electrons)   1 helium nucleus

Fusion reactions occur only at extremely high temperatures. A hydrogen bomb is an uncontrolled fusion reaction.

Scientists are currently investigating whether controlled nuclear fusion could be used for an energy source. Their work involves combining a deuterium (hydrogen-2) nucleus and a tritium (hydrogen-3) nucleus to form a helium nucleus.

$$^{2}_{1}\text{H} + ^{3}_{1}\text{H} \rightarrow ^{4}_{2}\text{He} + ^{1}_{0}\text{n} + \text{energy}$$

Isotopes and Dating

Geologists and archaeologists take advantage of the fact that the percent abundance of radioactive isotopes of an element decreases over time. Since the rate of radioactive decay is known very precisely, rocks or historical artifacts can be dated by measuring the amounts of certain isotopes. For example, rocks brought back from the moon were shown to be about 3.8 billion years old by uranium isotope measurements. Rocks beside the skeleton of one of the early human ancestors found in Africa were dated at 1.75 million years old using potassium-40 dat-

ing, and wood from an Egyptian tomb was dated at 4000 years old using carbon-14 dating.

Even the abundance of stable isotopes can vary slightly. This is particularly important in the case of oxygen-18. The percent abundance of this oxygen-18 is an indication of the temperature at which a mineral formed. Oxygen-18 percent abundance therefore tells geologists the temperature that existed at sites from different geological periods.

Measuring abundance of oxygen-18 has also become very important in archaeology. For example, a skeleton of a young woman was found during an excavation in central London, England, in 1999. The items included with the burial indicated that the woman was Roman and was buried about 1700 years ago. Some of her

clothing, made of silk with gold thread, was still preserved. To the archeologists' surprise, chemical analysis of the impurities in the gold thread indicated that the gold had been mined at a particular site in Syria, far from Rome or Britain. How did a woman end up in Britain wearing silk from China and gold from the Middle East?

A study of the oxygen-18 percent abundance in her teeth showed that the woman had grown up not in the cold climate of Britain, but somewhere around the Mediterranean Sea. She likely brought her clothes with her when she moved to Britain. Through careful study of the composition of these artifacts, including isotopic abundance, the archaeologists were able to piece together some of the life history of this long-dead woman.

FIGURE 5.20 This experimental reactor is a fusion reactor. A magnetic field holds the hot (approximately 40 000 000°C) corrosive plasma away from the walls of the vacuum vessel.

INFOBIT

In a nuclear fission reaction, the production of neutrons induces reactions in nearby uranium atoms. This produces more neutrons, which in turn react with other uranium atoms. This chain reaction is the important mechanism in the design of nuclear weapons.

Nuclear fission occurs when the nucleus of an atom is bombarded with a slow-moving neutron and split into two smaller fragments of nearly equal mass. Small particles such as neutrons may also be given off. Some materials, such as uranium-235 and plutonium-239, are **fissionable**; that is, they undergo fission spontaneously in nature. When uranium-235 is bombarded by a neutron, atoms of barium-142 and krypton-91 and three neutrons are formed.

$$^{235}_{92}\text{U} + ^{1}_{0}\text{n} \rightarrow ^{142}_{56}\text{Ba} + ^{91}_{36}\text{Kr} + 3\ ^{1}_{0}\text{n}$$

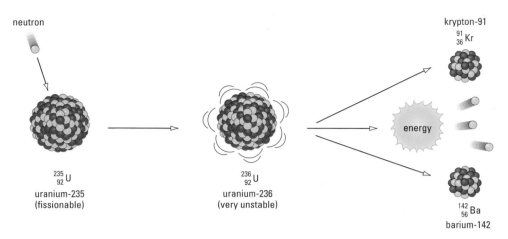

neutron

krypton-91
$^{91}_{36}$Kr

$^{235}_{92}$U
uranium-235
(fissionable)

$^{236}_{92}$U
uranium-236
(very unstable)

energy

$^{142}_{56}$Ba
barium-142

FIGURE 5.21 In nuclear fission, uranium-235 breaks into two fragments. What is produced? The released neutrons can split other uranium-235 atoms, creating a chain reaction similar to toppling dominoes.

Nuclear fission can release enormous quantities of energy, although not as much as a fusion reaction. Fission is controlled in nuclear reactors to produce energy we can use. Nuclear fusion weapons contain a fission device to generate the immense temperatures needed for a fusion.

Transmutation reactions are reactions in which an atom of an element is changed to an atom of a different element. Transmutation occurs when high-energy particles bombard the nucleus of an atom; these particles are absorbed by the nucleus and a different particle is emitted. The high-energy particles are protons, neutrons, or alpha particles. Many transmutations occur in nature, such as the production of carbon-14 from nitrogen-14.

FIGURE 5.22 In 1919, Ernest Rutherford carried out the first experimental transmutation when he bombarded nitrogen gas with alpha particles.

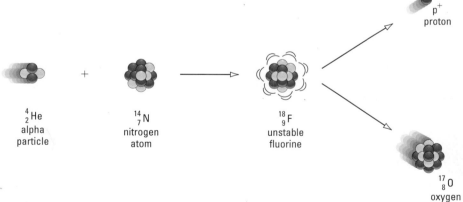

$^{4}_{2}$He
alpha
particle

$+$

$^{14}_{7}$N
nitrogen
atom

$^{18}_{9}$F
unstable
fluorine

p^{+}
proton

$^{17}_{8}$O
oxygen

Nuclear Energy

Where does the energy come from in a nuclear reaction? Recall that in a chemical reaction, the reactants and products form according to the law of conservation of mass. That is, to the limit of our measurements, the mass of the reactants is the same as the mass of the products. In nuclear reactions, however, a measurable proportion of the mass is converted into energy. It is the sum of mass and energy that is conserved. In other words, it is actually the law of conservation of mass/energy. Consider the predominant nuclear reaction that occurs in the sun:

$$4\,_1^1\text{H} + 2\,_{-1}^{0}\text{e} \rightarrow\,_2^4\text{He} + \text{energy}$$

Each proton has a mass of 1.00727. Each electron has a mass of 0.00055. The helium nucleus has a mass of 4.00260. The sum of the reactant masses is 4.03018. That gives a difference in mass of 0.02758. Where has this mass gone?

The mass lost appears in the form of energy, as is described in Albert Einstein's famous equation, $E = mc^2$. This equation enables scientists to calculate how much energy corresponds to the loss of a specific mass, and is the key to nuclear energy.

Using Nuclear Reactions: The CANDU Reactor

Nuclear reactions release large amounts of energy. Engineers have designed generating stations that can convert the heat energy released by a nuclear fission reaction into electrical energy. The nuclear reactor in the generating station splits uranium atoms, which release heat energy that is used to convert water into steam. The steam spins large turbines that drive generators that produce electricity.

In the reactor, slow-moving neutrons strike the nuclei of uranium-235 atoms and split them into fragments that rapidly separate and generate heat. This fission reaction also produces a few new neutrons. To sustain continuous nuclear fission, the speed of these neutrons must be slowed down. In Canadian nuclear reactors, heavy water is used to slow the neutrons. **Heavy water** is water molecules in which the hydrogen-1 atoms ($_1^1\text{H}$) have been replaced by deuterium atoms ($_1^2\text{H}$). Since the chemical name of heavy water is deuterium oxide, the Canadian-engineered reactor was named the Canada Deuterium Uranium (CANDU) reactor.

FIGURE 5.23 The Darlington nuclear generating station on Lake Ontario.

Because they use deuterium oxide instead of water or graphite, CANDU reactors can use natural uranium. Natural uranium contains only 0.7% uranium-235 and so is safer. The reactor core is contained in a large cylindrical tank called the calandria. A series of tubes runs from one end of the calandria to the other. Inside these tubes are smaller tubes that house fuel bundles containing natural uranium in the form of ceramic uranium oxide pellets. The heavy water moderator surrounds these tubes. Heavy water is also pumped through the tubes, and is heated by the energy of the fission reaction. The heated heavy water then travels to heat exchangers, which use the heat energy to produce steam from ordinary water. The cooled heavy water from the heat exchanger is recycled back to the reactor, while the steam is piped to turbines and generators to produce electricity.

Our increasing world population and industrialization create a continuous need for a greater supply of energy. Nuclear energy is sustainable and can meet large electrical demands safely and reliably. Nuclear generating stations do not produce greenhouse gases, so nuclear energy also has less environmental impact than other energy forms.

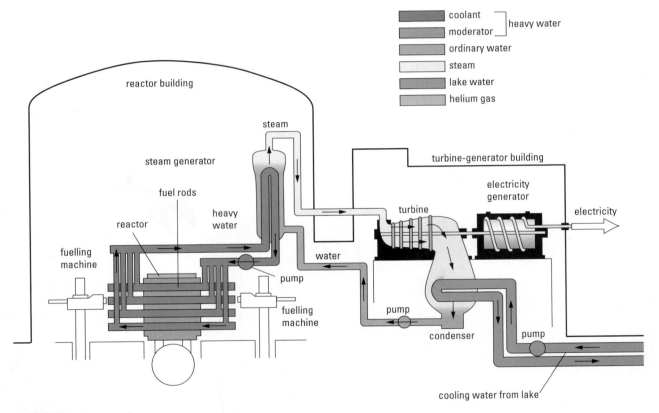

FIGURE 5.24 A schematic of the CANDU system

Case Study

Safety and the CANDU Reactor

Decision-Making Skills

Defining the Issue

Developing Assessment Criteria

▷ Researching the Issue

▷ Analyzing Data and Information

▷ Proposing a Course of Action

▷ Justifying the Course of Action

▷ Communicating Your Proposal

Nuclear energy has the potential to reduce the use of fossil fuels and the environmental costs this brings. The design of the CANDU reactor has been hailed as significantly safer than other reactors, including those that operate in the United States. CANDU reactors have three distinguishing features that contribute to improved safety:

- They use naturally occurring uranium as fuel, not fuel enriched in the highly radioactive isotope uranium-235.
- They employ pressure tubes rather than a large pressure vessel to hold the fuel, which limits the amount of fuel that would be released in the event of a leak.
- They use heavy water as a coolant and moderator, which controls the rate of the nuclear reactions far more efficiently than ordinary water.

There has been no serious breakdown of a CANDU reactor, so many Canadians have grown complacent about the safety of operating these reactors. However, Canadian nuclear energy plants are now decades old, and many now need costly maintenance to keep running safely. Those that are no longer safe are shut down, but shutting down a nuclear power station takes more than throwing a switch. The leftover fuel and heavy waste needs to be safely removed, and then stored somewhere until the radiation has dissipated.

The CANDU reactor offers the opportunity to produce power in a way that will not contribute to such problems as air pollution and global warming. However, running a reactor requires costly maintenance and a well-planned system for taking old reactors off-line before they become unsafe.

Analyzing the Issue

1. Research information about nuclear reactors in Canada. How many reactors are in operation? What is the average age of power plants? Who is responsible for ensuring that Canada's nuclear plants are kept in safe running order? Who is responsible for reactor safety?

2. Complete a risk-benefit table to summarize the positive and negative factors that relate to the operation of nuclear reactors.

3. Identify the short-term and long-term social, economic, and environmental consequences of potential radiation leakage from a nuclear reactor.

4. Write a letter to the editor of your local paper that expresses your point of view on the environmental impact of using nuclear reactors. Do you support their continued use? Why? Why not?

Section 5.4 Review

Understanding Concepts

1. Explain how the process of balancing nuclear equations is different from balancing chemical equations.

2. Define in your own words the terms "radioactivity" and "radioactive decay."

3. Describe why you would expect the chemical properties of carbon-14 to be the same as those of carbon-12.

4. Distinguish between alpha, beta, and gamma radiation on the basis of the following:
   a) mass
   b) charge
   c) penetrating power

5. Describe the nuclear reaction that takes place in a nuclear reactor.

6. Describe the two functions of heavy water in the CANDU reactor.

Applying Inquiry/ Communication Skills

7. Complete and balance the following nuclear equations:

   a) $^{190}_{75}\text{Re} \rightarrow {}^{190}_{76}\text{Os} + ?$

   b) $^{214}_{83}\text{Bi} \rightarrow {}^{4}_{2}\text{He} + ?$

   c) $^{120}_{49}\text{In} \rightarrow {}^{0}_{-1}\text{e} + ?$

   d) $^{162}_{69}\text{Tm} \rightarrow {}^{0}_{+1}\text{e} + ?$

   e) $^{9}_{3}\text{Li} \rightarrow {}^{8}_{3}\text{Li} + ?$

8. Complete the following nuclear equations:

   a) $^{27}_{13}\text{Al} + {}^{4}_{2}\text{He} \rightarrow {}^{1}_{1}\text{H} + ?$

   b) $4\,{}^{1}_{1}\text{H} \rightarrow 2\,{}^{0}_{+1}\text{e} + ?$

   c) $^{235}_{92}\text{U} + {}^{1}_{0}\text{n} \rightarrow {}^{87}_{35}\text{Br} + ? + 3\,{}^{1}_{0}\text{n}$

   d) $^{249}_{98}\text{Cf} + {}^{11}_{5}\text{B} \rightarrow 6\,{}^{1}_{0}\text{n} + ?$

9. Identify the type of nuclear reaction represented by each of following equations, and name the type of particle emitted:

   a) $^{234}_{90}\text{Th} \rightarrow {}^{234}_{91}\text{Pa} + {}^{0}_{1}\text{e}$

   b) $^{54}_{26}\text{Fe} + {}^{1}_{1}\text{H} \rightarrow {}^{54}_{27}\text{Co} + {}^{1}_{0}\text{n}$

10. Technetium-99, a major by-product of nuclear weapons manufacturing, has a half-life of 210,000 years. Neutron bombardment converts it to technetium-100, which decays with a 16-second half-life to ruthenium-100. Write the two nuclear equations for these reactions.

Making Connections

11. Consider the following possible scenario:

    We are in an energy crisis and the price of oil has skyrocketed. The citizens in your community are outraged. A consultant has demonstrated to the community that the cost of nuclear energy is much less, and advises that a nuclear site be introduced into your community. However, doing so will also require that a nuclear waste disposal site be created.

    Analyze this situation using a PMI organizer. Based on your analysis, write a summary report to distribute to the citizens to help them make an informed decision.

Investigation 1 (Section 5.2)

Inquiry Skills

Initiating and Planning
► Applying Technical Skills
► Using Tools, Materials, and Equipment
► Conducting and Recording
► Analyzing and Interpreting
► Concluding and Communicating

Identifying a Reaction Product by Stoichiometry

Problem

You are a chemist in a company that supplies dyes to the textile industry. One of the steps in making one of the dyes you are developing is to decompose sodium hydrogen carbonate by heating. You need to determine the products of decomposition of sodium hydrogen carbonate.

Materials

- sodium hydrogen carbonate
- test tube (25 × 150 mm)
- centigram balance
- retort stand
- utility clamp
- gas burner

> CAUTION: Wear safety goggles throughout the procedure.
> Make sure the opening of test tube is always facing away from you.
> Be alert to the open flame.

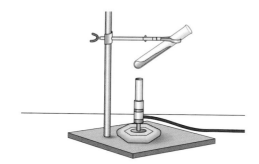

FIGURE 5.25

Procedure

1. Write a balanced equation for each of the two different reactions that can occur when sodium hydrogen carbonate decomposes. State which reaction you predict will take place.

2. Measure and record the mass of a clean, dry test tube. Add approximately 2 g of sodium hydrogen carbonate to the test tube. Measure and record the combined mass of the test tube and reactant.

3. Set up the equipment as shown in Figure 5.25. Clamp the test tube at a 45° angle.

4. Heat the sodium hydrogen carbonate evenly for 5 min. Increase the heat and continue for another 8 min.

5. Allow the test tube to cool completely, then remove the test tube from the clamp. Measure and record the combined mass of the cooled test tube and product.

6. Dispose of the product according to your teacher's instructions.

Analyzing and Interpreting

1. Determine the mass of sodium hydrogen carbonate used, and the actual mass of product that formed.

2. Using the balanced equations you wrote in step 1, carry out stoichiometric calculations to obtain the theoretical mass of the sodium products in the two possible decomposition reactions.

3. Compare the actual mass of the product with the calculated product masses.

Concluding and Communicating

4. Identify the actual product in the test tube and write the balanced equation for the reaction that occurred. Was it the reaction you predicted? Explain any uncertainty you may have about your prediction. Give a reason for your final choice.

5. Outline a procedure that would demonstrate that water and carbon dioxide were also products of this reaction.

Extending

6. A blue dye requires sodium hydrosulfite, sodium hydroxide, and indigo. However, you must determine the correct combination of these chemicals to produce the shade you need. If sodium hydrosulfite costs $35.00 per kg, sodium hydroxide costs $25.00 per kg, and indigo costs $90.00 per kg, which reagent will you make the limiting reagent in your tests? Explain your choice.

Investigation 2 (Section 5.3)

Inquiry Skills

▶ Initiating and Planning
Applying Technical Skills
▶ Using Tools, Materials, and Equipment
▶ Conducting and Recording
▶ Analyzing and Interpreting
▶ Concluding and Communicating

Determining Percent Yield

Problem

You are a metallurgical chemist working with a large mining company. You are developing a procedure for extracting copper metal from copper salts. In order for the copper extraction to be profitable, the mass of copper recovered from the process has to be quite high. You must therefore determine the percent yield of each procedure you try out. Today, you are going to establish the percent yield of copper recovered from a solution of copper(II) sulfate.

Your teacher will demonstrate the reaction of copper(II) sulfate with iron in the form of steel wool and describe how to retrieve the copper product in a pure and dry form for weighing. You will then develop and carry out a procedure to estimate the percent yield of copper from this reaction.

Experimental Design

1. Observe and record the reaction that takes place during the demonstration. As the reaction proceeds, think about the following points:

   a) What information do you need about the reactants or products of the reaction to determine the percent yield of copper?

   b) What data could you collect about the reactants and products that would help you to determine this information?

   c) What equipment would you need to collect this data?

   d) What safety precautions will you need to use with this equipment and these materials?

2. Using a flow-chart, write a detailed procedure that describes how you intend to determine the percent yield of copper in the reaction that your teacher demonstrated.

3. Write a list of the materials you will need, and include it in your procedure.

4. Read over your procedure and look for any steps where you might need to take safety precautions. Include these in your procedure. If you are not sure about the safety of any chemicals, check them using the MSDS data available in your classroom.

5. Hand your procedure to your teacher for approval. You are not to proceed before your procedure has been approved.

6. Carry out your approved procedure. Ensure you record your results in an organized way.

7. Clean up your work area. Dispose of any chemical waste safely, according to your teacher's instructions.

Analyzing and Interpreting

1. Determine the mass of iron (steel wool) used.

2. Determine the mass of copper produced.

3. What type of reaction has occurred?

4. Write a balanced equation for the reaction.

5. Calculate the theoretical yield of copper in this reaction using the balanced equation and the mass of iron used.

6. Determine the actual yield of copper in this reaction.

Concluding and Communicating

7. Suggest how you could improve the investigation to obtain greater precision.

8. Examine a sample of the reaction product under a magnifying glass. Is there evidence of more than one substance present? Explain how this could have affected the percent yield of copper.

Extending

9. Ethanol is used as an alternative fuel in some countries. Ethanol can be obtained from sugar, according to the following balanced equation:

$$C_{12}H_{22}O_{11} + H_2O \rightarrow 4\ C_2H_6O + 4\ CO_2$$

Determine the theoretical yield of ethanol that could be made from 1 kg of sugar. Is this a worthwhile alternative? Explain your answer.

CHAPTER SUMMARY

Key Terms

actual yield
alpha particle
beta particle
excess reagent

gamma ray
heavy water
law of conservation of mass
limiting reagent

nuclear fission
nuclear fusion
nuclear reaction
percent yield

radioactive decay
stoichiometry
theoretical yield

Key Equations

$$\text{percent yield} = \frac{\text{actual yield}}{\text{theoretical yield}} \times 100\%$$

Essential Understandings

■ A balanced chemical equation can be used to calculate the quantities of substances in the reaction and contains both quantitative and qualitative information.

■ The quantitative relationships in a chemical equation can be expressed in particles, moles, mass, or volume.

■ The percent yield compares the actual amount of product formed with the maximum theoretical amount that could be obtained.

■ The limiting reagent determines the amount of product that can be formed.

■ Both mass and charge are conserved in both chemical and nuclear reactions.

■ Fusion and fission are the main kinds of nuclear reactions, in which matter is converted into energy according to Einstein's equation $E = mc^2$.

Consolidate Your Understanding

1. Explain why you must first balance a chemical equation before you can use it to perform a stoichiometric calculation.

2. Construct a concept map that starts with the word "stoichiometry."

3. The concept of using a mole ratio to calculate a new value is also known as "proportional reasoning." Describe other situations that require thinking in manner a similar to proportional reasoning.

4. The solution diagram on page 185 is a visual way of explaining how a stoichiometric problem can be solved. Describe examples of other diagrams or flowcharts that are designed to help to visualize a process, structure, or problem.

CHAPTER 5 REVIEW

Understanding Concepts

1. Propane, C_3H_8, is used as a fuel in gas barbeques and in some automobiles. Identify which one of the following represents the mass of propane that contains exactly 25.0 g of carbon.
   a) 30.6 g   b) 46.2 g
   c) 35.4 g   d) 20.5 g
   e) 91.7 g

2. Identify which one of the following is the percentage, by mass, of oxygen in CO_2:
   a) 27.3%   b) 36.4%
   c) 57.1%   d) 72.7%
   e) none of the above

3. Identify which one of the following is *not* a reason why actual yield is less than theoretical yield:
   a) impure reactants present
   b) competing side reactions
   c) loss of product during purification
   d) conservation of mass
   e) none of the above

4. In a particular reaction between copper metal and silver nitrate, 12.7 g Cu produced 38.1 g Ag. Identify which one of the following is the percent yield of silver in this reaction:

   $Cu(s) + 2\ AgNO_3(aq) \rightarrow Cu(NO_3)_2(aq) + 2\ Ag(s)$

   a) 29.4%   b) 56.7%
   c) 77.3%   d) 88.2%
   e) 176%

5. Identify which one of the following particles is the unknown product in this nuclear equation:

   $^{222}_{86}Rn \rightarrow\ ^{4}_{2}He + ?$

   a) $^{56}_{27}Co$ b) $^{57}_{25}Mn$ c) $^{55}_{26}Fe$

   d) $^{58}_{24}Cr$ e) none of these

6. Explain what information the coefficients in a balanced equation provide about the chemical reaction.

7. Draw a diagram illustrating the atoms and molecules involved in the chemical reaction between 2.30 moles of solid sulfur and oxygen gas to produce sulfur trioxide. Include the mole and mass values for each reactant and product in your model.

8. Explain the significance of a limiting reagent in a chemical process.

9. Describe two situations in everyday life in which percent yield is important.

10. State four variables that affect chemical reactions but have no effect on nuclear reactions.

11. Make a poster comparing and contrasting nuclear fission and nuclear fusion. Your poster should include reactants and products for both types of reactions.

12. For each of the reactions described below, write a balanced chemical equation that indicates the physical state of each substance.
    a) When magnesium metal is heated in nitrogen gas, magnesium nitride is formed.
    b) Bubbling hydrogen sulfide gas into a solution of copper(II) sulfate in water produces a precipitate of copper(II) sulfide and a solution of sulfuric acid.
    c) Chlorine gas can be made by reacting solid manganese(IV) oxide with hydrochloric acid. The other products are water and manganese(II) chloride.
    d) Barium metal reacts with water to produce barium hydroxide solution and hydrogen gas.

13. For each of the reactions described below, write a balanced chemical equation that indicates the physical state of each substance:
    a) When ammonia gas and hydrogen chloride gas are mixed, a white solid, ammonium chloride, is formed.
    b) If carbon dioxide gas is passed into a solution of calcium hydroxide in water, a precipitate of calcium carbonate is obtained. The other product of the reaction is water.
    c) Metallic zinc reacts with a solution of lead(II) nitrate. Solid lead metal is formed together with a solution of zinc nitrate.
    d) Heating solid copper(II) nitrate trihydrate produces solid copper(II) oxide, nitrogen dioxide gas, oxygen gas, and water vapour.

14. Write the mole ratios that can be derived from this equation:

    $2\ KClO_3(s) \rightarrow 2\ KCl(s) + 3\ O_2(g)$

15. Oxygen gas is commonly prepared on a small scale by heating potassium chlorate with a manganese(IV) oxide catalyst:

    $2\ KClO_3(s) \rightarrow 2\ KCl(s) + 3\ O_2(g)$

    a) Calculate the amount of oxygen (in moles) that will be produced from 12.4 mol of potassium chlorate.
    b) Determine the mass of oxygen gas that can be prepared from 5.12 g of potassium chlorate.

16. Sulfuric acid is formed when sulfur trioxide combines with water:

    $SO_3(g) + H_2O(l) \rightarrow H_2SO_4(aq)$

    a) Calculate the minimum mass of water that is required to convert 35.0 g of sulfur trioxide to sulfuric acid.
    b) Calculate the mass of sulfur trioxide that is needed in order to produce 80.0 g of sulfuric acid.

17. Sodium and water react according to the equation
    $2\ Na(s) + 2\ H_2O(l) \rightarrow 2\ NaOH(aq) + H_2(g)$

    If 10.0 g of sodium is placed in 50.0 g of water, calculate the mass of hydrogen gas that will be produced.

18. Equal masses of phosphorus and chlorine react according to the following equation:

$$2 \ P(s) + 3 \ Cl_2(g) \rightarrow 2 \ PCl_3(l)$$

Identify which reagent is in excess. Calculate the percent that will remain at the end of the reaction.

19. A certain reaction is calculated to give a theoretical yield of 4.214 g of product. Calculate the following:
    a) the percent yield if only 3.615 g of product is obtained.
    b) the actual yield obtained if the percentage yield is only 63.5%.

Applying Inquiry/ Communication Skills

20. Design an experiment to measure the percent yield for one of these reactions.
    a) $Zn(s) + 2 \ HCl(aq) \rightarrow ZnCl_2(aq) + H_2(g)$
    b) $CaCl_2(aq) + Na_2CO_3(aq) \rightarrow CaCO_3(s) + 2 \ NaCl(aq)$

21. One of the reactions involved in the smelting of copper sulfide ores involves copper(I) oxide and copper(I) sulfide

    $$2 \ Cu_2O(s) + Cu_2S(s) \rightarrow 6 \ Cu(g) + SO_2(g)$$

    Assume that 50.0 g of copper(I) oxide is heated with 25.8 g of copper(I) sulfide.

    a) Determine which reagent, if any, is in excess.
    b) Calculate the theoretical yield of copper.
    c) Determine the percentage yield if 58.0 g of copper is actually isolated.

22. In an experiment, varying masses of sodium metal are reacted with a fixed initial mass of chlorine gas. The amounts of sodium used and the amounts of sodium chloride formed are shown on the following graph.

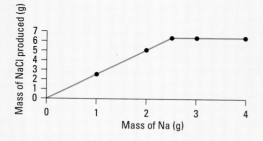

FIGURE 5.26

a) Explain the general shape of the graph.
b) Estimate the amount of chlorine gas (in grams) used in this experiment at the point where the curve becomes horizontal.

23. Complete each of the following nuclear equations.
    a) $^{18}_{10}Ne \rightarrow \ ^{0}_{-1}e \ + \ ?$

    b) $^{212}_{86}Rn \rightarrow \ ^{208}_{84}Po \ + \ ?$

    c) $^{6}_{2}He \rightarrow \ ^{6}_{3}Li \ + \ ?$

24. The following equations each represent a fusion reaction that can occur in the sun and other stars. Identify the missing particle in each equation.
    a) $^{12}_{6}C \ + \ ^{12}_{6}C \rightarrow \ ^{23}_{12}Mg \ + \ ?$

    b) $^{18}_{8}O \ + \ ? \rightarrow \ ^{15}_{7}N \ + \ ^{4}_{2}He$

    c) $^{3}_{2}He \ + \ ^{4}_{2}He \rightarrow \ ? \ + \ ^{0}_{0}\gamma$

Making Connections

25. An organizer of a major event needs to purchase 5000 grapes for a large gathering. Counting them by hand is a long and tedious process. Describe an alternative method for "counting" the grapes. Describe a situation in which chemists would use the same method when counting atoms or molecules.

26. Antacid tablets react with the hydrochloric acid in the stomach to ease indigestion. Baking soda ($NaHCO_3$) is often used as an antacid because it takes part in the following reaction:

    $$NaHCO_3(s) + HCl(aq) \rightarrow NaCl(aq) + H_2O(l) + CO_2(g)$$

    Milk of magnesia ($Mg(OH)_2$) is also used as an antacid because it takes part in the following reaction:

    $$Mg(OH)_2(aq) + 2 \ HCl(aq) \rightarrow 2 \ H_2O(l) + MgCl_2(aq)$$

    Prepare a consumer information sheet that describes which antacid is more effective (reacts with more HCl per gram).

27. Using electronic and print resources research nuclear power as an energy source. Write an essay describing whether or not we should use nuclear power as an energy source. Provide supporting evidence for your perspective from your research.

28. Supermarkets are beginning to carry irradiated foods, the safety of which is a controversial topic. Research the issue of irradiated foods, and then write a newspaper-style article that presents your opinion. Include facts to support your opinion.

29. Research the penetrating power of four types of radiation discussed in this chapter on the human body. Compare the word "radiation" with its use in the term "electromagnetic radiation." Design and make a poster display to inform the public on these different types of radiation.

Skills: From the Classroom to Your Future

You've been hearing about the importance of skills, especially those that can help you no matter which career you eventually choose. Fortunately, you are developing all of these skills and more as part of your classroom work, especially in science. But how can you tell if you are developing these skills? How can you identify your strengths as well as any weak areas that you need to improve? You need to know, if you are to take these skills from the classroom to your future.

In sports, you assess your skills by measuring your own improvement as well as by the results you obtain during competition. For example, if you play hockey, you can measure your skating speed and shooting accuracy. In games, you can keep track of several factors, including success in passing plays, goals against statistics, and points from assists and goals. In your science class, you will get information about your skill development from your teacher, but you can qualitatively assess those skills for yourself.

Assessing Your Skills

1. Assess your skills right at this moment. Take two sheets of paper. At the top of the first, write "My Strengths." A strength would be any skill you use with confidence. You don't need help with it and you can help others with it. At the top of the second, write "Could Improve." These would be any skills you don't feel confident using by yourself or without instructions. Complete these two sheets by writing the skills listed on the next page, and any others you can think of, on the appropriate sheet. Think about the following as you decide.

   - Be honest with yourself. Many students underestimate their skills because they don't wish to appear boastful, but it is important to be aware of your strengths and be able to express them to others.

   - If you aren't sure about your ability in a particular skill, ask your lab partner or teacher. Their opinion may surprise you.

   - Use your experience in class to help you sort your skills. What

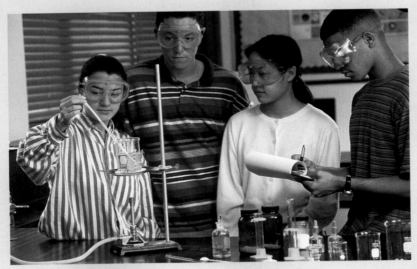

FIGURE 1 Some skills you develop in the chemistry lab may be applicable in a future career. *Participate!* You develop a skill by using that skill, so make sure you participate in the laboratory portion of your chemistry class. It isn't always easy, but there are some ways to help make sure you learn as much as you can. Is it a demonstration by the teacher? Volunteer to help or ask if you can try the same experiment after class. Are you working with a partner or in a group? Be very clear that work is divided so everyone gains experience handling the apparatus and performing tasks, as well as recording observations. If necessary, you can alternate. If you feel you haven't learned a skill well enough, don't hesitate to approach your teacher and ask to repeat the experiment. Learning these skills is your responsibility.

kinds of laboratory activities do you like the most? Which seem easier than others? What kinds do you dislike or find difficult?

2. Take your list of "Could Improve" skills. Circle or highlight those in which you feel you need the most improvement. These should be your priority. Make plans to work on these skills. Here are some ideas to get you started.

   ■ Arrange a meeting with your teacher to discuss how you can improve these particular skills. Try to identify exactly where you are having difficulty. For example, did you miss a class in which a particular technique was practised? Do you have a lab partner who rushes in to use the equipment, so you haven't had much chance to try it?

   ■ Compare your list with those of other students. Is there someone who wants to improve the same skill(s)? If so, you may want to work together. Is there someone especially strong in those skills? If so, you could ask this person for help.

   ■ You can work on these skills in other classes and at home as well. For example, if you need to improve your graphing skills, go to the math department and ask if there is a peer assistant or tutor available. If you need to improve your teamwork or communication skills, join a club or sports team, or volunteer. Be active in your approach to improving your skills.

3. Keep your skills sheets handy. Make it a personal goal to move all of the skills from "Could Improve" to "Strengths."

List of Skills

- assembling and using apparatus
- communicating procedures and results
- compiling and organizing data
- coordinating tasks
- decision-making
- designing procedures
- identifying variables
- interpreting patterns and trends in data
- lab safety
- measuring
- problem-solving
- recording observations
- researching topics under study
- using instruments effectively and accurately
- using the appropriate graphing technique
- time management
- using appropriate techniques for handling, storing, and disposing of laboratory materials
- working independently
- working with others

Looking Outward

Practice really does make perfect, as the saying goes. One way to improve your skills in science class is to repeat an activity at least twice.

4. Choose an experiment that involves using equipment or a technique that you found difficult. With your teacher's permission, repeat this experiment. Compare the results you obtain the second time with those from the first. Repeat a third time, if possible.

   ■ What trend do you see?
   ■ What other advantage to improving your skills is there?
   ■ Why would this matter to someone working in chemistry or another science?

Oh My Aching Head!

Background Information

Many people take a pain reliever when they have a headache. Many pain relievers are available over the counter and consumers have a wide choice. But how do they decide which one to use? How different are the products that are available to relieve headaches? What factors contribute to market success?

Acetylsalicylic acid (ASA) is a common drug that relieves pain, fever, and inflammation. The benefits of ASA were first observed by the Chinese in 500 B.C. and by the Greeks in 400 B.C. The ASA they took was not in the form of a pill, but came from willow tree bark. Native Canadians also knew of the pain-relieving qualities of willow bark. In the early 1800s scientists discovered the active ingredient in willow bark—a compound called salicin. Several modern pain relievers contain a salicin derivative called acetylsalicylic acid, ASA.

SCENARIO

You are a consultant for a pharmaceutical company that produces ASA headache medication. Since the product is not selling well, the company is unsure about continuing to manufacture it. You are responsible for presenting a report to the Board of Directors that will advise on how to increase the product's sales. Your presentation must include:

■ a report by the research department outlining its current manufacturing process and the percent yield

■ a report comparing features and costs of competitors' products

■ a redesigned package to attract consumers

Part A: Conducting Market Research

1. Visit a pharmacy and examine the labels of several over-the-counter headache medications. Take note of the following:
   - active ingredients
   - percent mass per tablet of the pain-relieving ingredient(s)
   - dosage directions and cautions
   - advertising statements on the package

2. Use electronic and print resources to research the function of each active ingredient and its side effects.

3. Summarize your results in an appropriate format.

Part B: Synthesis of ASA

ASA is synthesized by reacting salicylic acid with acetic acid anhydride:

$$HC_7H_5O_3 + C_4H_6O_3 \rightarrow HC_9H_7O_4 + HC_2H_3O_2$$

Prepare an ASA tablet using the following procedure.

Materials

safety goggles
salicylic acid
125-ml Erlenmeyer flask
acetic acid anhydride
thermometer
concentrated phosphoric acid or sulfuric acid
hot water bath
water
ice bath
ice
funnel
watch glass
filter paper

Procedure

- Mix 5 g of salicylic acid with 10 mL of acetic acid anhydride in the flask.
- Add 3 to 5 drops of either sulfuric acid or phosphoric acid (preferred) to the flask and swirl to mix.
- Place a thermometer in the flask and heat the mixture in a hot water bath (between 50°C and 60°C) for 10 min. Do not let the temperature exceed 60°C.
- Allow the flask to cool to room temperature.
- Add 40 mL of water and 10 g of crushed ice to the flask. Stir the mixture until crystals begin to form.
- Place the flask in an ice bath for approximately 5 min to complete the crystallization.
- Filter the crystals and wash them with 10 mL of ice water.
- Allow the crystals to air-dry on a watch glass before determining their mass.
- Hand in your crystals to the teacher for evaluation.

Analysis

- Calculate the percent yield of ASA.
- Determine the limiting reagent in this reaction. (Note: The density of acetic acid anhydride is 1.0820 g·mL^{-1}.)

Conclusions and Evaluation

- Identify the major sources of error, and suggest how you could increase the percent yield.

4. Write a report summarizing the current synthesizing process and suggestions to increase the percent yield.

Part C: Improving Sales

5. Design a new package for the product that will help promote sales.

6. Your new designed package should include:
   - name of medication
   - the active ingredients and their quantities
   - dosage directions and cautions

Part D: Presenting Solutions

7. Prepare a presentation for the Board of Directors summarizing your research. Your presentation should include:
   - self-standing poster board advertisement for the medication
   - 3-dimensional prototype of the package
   - recommendations on how to increase sales

Understanding Concepts

1. Identify which quantity is conserved in the reaction:
$H_2(g) + Cl_2(g) \rightarrow 2\ HCl(g)$
   a) only moles
   b) only mass
   c) only mass and moles
   d) only mass, moles, and molecules
   e) only mass, moles, molecules, and volume

2. Identify which interpretation of this balanced equation is *incorrect*:
$2\ Al(s) + 3\ Cl_2(g) \rightarrow 2\ AlCl_3(s)$
   a) 2 atoms Al + 3 molecules Cl_2 → 2 molecules $AlCl_3$
   b) 2 g Al + 3 g Cl_2 → 2 g $AlCl_3$
   c) 2 mol Al + 3 mol Cl_2 → 2 mol $AlCl_3$
   d) 54 g Al + 210 g Cl_2 → 264 g $AlCl_3$
   e) none of the above

3. Identify which quantity represents the number of moles in 0.66 g of CO_2:
   a) 0.015 moles
   b) 0.12 moles
   c) 0.22 moles
   d) 0.44 moles
   e) 2.2 moles

4. Determine the ratio of moles of oxygen consumed to moles of CO_2 produced in this reaction:
$2\ CO(g) + O_2(g) \rightarrow 2\ CO_2(g)$
   a) 1 : 1
   b) 2 : 1
   c) 1 : 2
   d) 2 : 2
   e) 3 : 2

5. Oxides of sulfur are common air pollutants. If a compound is found to be 50.0% sulfur and 50% oxygen by mass, identify the empirical formula of the compound:
   a) SO_4
   b) SO_2
   c) S_2O
   d) SO
   e) SO_3

6. In an experiment, 3.48 g of methane (CH_4) gas reacted with oxygen and produced 8.44 g of carbon dioxide, as described in the following equation:
$CH_4(g) + 2\ O_2(g) \rightarrow CO_2(g) + 2\ H_2O(g)$
Identify the correct percent yield of carbon dioxide:
   a) 96.3%
   b) 81.4%
   c) 75.3%
   d) 88.2%
   e) 100%

7. Pyrite, FeS_2, or "fools gold," reacts with oxygen as shown in the equation below:
$4\ FeS_2(s) + 11\ O_2(g) \rightarrow 2\ Fe_2O_3(s) + 8\ SO_2(g)$
Identify which quantity represents the number of moles of O_2 that have reacted if 3.25 mol of SO_2 are produced by this reaction.
   a) 35.8 mol
   b) .25 mol
   c) 4.47 mol
   d) 0.406 mol
   e) 2.36 mol

8. The data below was obtained in an electrochemical reaction:

mass of cadmium strip before reaction	15.27 g
mass of cadmium strip after reaction	13.02 g
mass of silver formed	4.32 g

The relative atomic masses of Ag and Cd are 107.9 and 112.4 respectively. Identify the correct value for the number of moles of silver that formed in the reaction:
   a) 0.0100 mol
   b) 0.0200 mol
   c) 2.00 mol
   d) 0.0400 mol
   e) 0.400 mol

9. Identify which particle is emitted when uranium-239 decays to neptunium-239:
   a) proton
   b) beta particle
   c) neutron
   d) positron
   e) alpha particle

10. Identify which particle is needed to complete this equation:
$$^{253}_{99}\text{Es} + ^{4}_{2}\text{He} \rightarrow\ ? + ^{1}_{0}\text{n}$$
   a) $^{256}_{101}\text{Md}$
   b) $^{257}_{101}\text{Md}$
   c) $^{256}_{100}\text{Fm}$
   d) $^{248}_{97}\text{Bk}$
   e) none of the above

11. Explain this statement: "Mass and number of atoms are conserved in every chemical reaction, but moles will not necessarily be conserved."

12. Explain the relationship between the mass of a single atom in an element, the mass of one mole of atoms of that element, and Avogadro's number.

13. Interpret the following chemical equation in terms of relative numbers of representative particles, numbers of moles, and masses of reactants and products.
$2\ K(s) + 2\ H_2O(l) \rightarrow 2\ KOH(aq) + H_2(g)$

14. Butane is a component of camping gas. The burning of butane is represented below first as a word equation and then as balanced equation:

butane + oxygen → carbon dioxide + water
$2\ C_4H_{10}(g) + 13\ O_2(g) \rightarrow 8\ CO_2(g) + 10\ H_2O(g)$

State three things that the balanced equation tells you that you cannot learn from the word equation.

15. Given the truth of the law of conservation of matter, explain why it is possible to make 30.6 g NH_3 from only 5.40 g H_2.

16. Describe the difference between the empirical formula and the molecular formula of a compound.

17. Although the coefficients in a balanced chemical equation represent the ratio of moles and particles, they do not represent the ratio of the masses of reactants or products. Explain this statement.

18. In one experiment, element A combines with element B in the ratio 9:5 by weight. In a different experiment, 1 g of B reacts with 1.8 g of A. Explain whether these values support the law of definite proportions.

19. Define the term "mole ratio" and explain how mole ratios are used.

20. Based on the following general reaction, identify the limiting reagent if 1 mol of A is allowed to react with 2 moles of B. Describe how you would determine the amount of A_2B_3 that can be produced.
$$2\ A + 3\ B \rightarrow A_2B_3$$

21. Explain what happens to the atomic structure of reactants in a nuclear reaction. Compare this to what happens in a chemical reaction.

22. For each of the following, identify the type of nuclear reaction and name the type of particle emitted:

a) $^{101}_{46}\text{Pd} \rightarrow\ ^{101}_{45}\text{Rh} +\ ^{0}_{+1}\text{e}$

b) $^{238}_{92}\text{U} +\ ^{14}_{7}\text{N} \rightarrow\ ^{247}_{99}\text{Es} +\ ^{1}_{0}\text{n}$

c) $^{10}_{5}\text{B} +\ ^{1}_{0}\text{n} \rightarrow\ ^{3}_{1}\text{H} + 2\ ^{4}_{2}\text{He}$

Applying Inquiry/ Communication Skills

23. Aluminum is one of the most common materials to recycle. Using the concept of the mole, write a procedure that will allow you to determine the number of aluminum atoms in a typical aluminum can. Include the calculation steps. Will your results be valid for all aluminum cans?

24. A mixture of iron filings and salt contains exactly 1 mol of particles. Design an experiment that would allow you to determine the percent of iron and of salt in the mixture.

25. Design a procedure involving the decomposition of a weighed sample of $CuSO_4 \cdot 5H_2O$ that would allow you to determine its percent composition. Show your teacher your procedure and carry out your experiment. Calculate the percent of ash of your original sample and compare this to a classmate's data. Summarize your findings and make a conclusion based on them.

26. A research chemist prepares a compound believed to be $Co(NH_3)_5NO_2Cl_2 \cdot H_2O$. The analysis is shown in Table 1:

TABLE 1

	Sample 1	Sample 2
% N	30.12	30.22
% Co	21.2	21.2
% Cl	25.52	25.59

a) Discuss whether these results are consistent with the given formula.
b) Before the analysis was received, the chemist performed a test that indicated the compound may be $Co(NH_3)_5NO_3Cl_2$. State if it is possible to distinguish between these two products from the analytical results. Explain.
c) Suggest how one might distinguish clearly between these two products.

27. Mercuric oxide, HgO, was heated until it decomposed as follows:

$$2\ \text{HgO} \xrightarrow{\Delta} 2\ \text{Hg} + O_2$$

a) Use the experimental data below to calculate the percent of mercury in mercuric oxide;

mass of test tube	22.32 g
mass of test tube and HgO	22.99 g
mass of test tube and Hg	22.93 g

b) Calculate the % error in this experiment.

28. Alkanes are a group of compounds containing only carbon and hydrogen. Some alkanes form the main constituents of natural gas and gasoline. The percent composition and molar mass data for the alkanes is shown in Table 2:

TABLE 2

Compound	Carbon (% by mass)	Hydrogen (% by mass)	Molar Mass (g·mol^{-1})
1	74.87	25.13	16.0
2	79.89	20.11	30.1
3	81.71	18.29	44.1
4	84.12	15.88	114.2

Using this data, perform the necessary calculations in order to:
a) derive the empirical formula and the molecular formula of each compound
b) calculate the number of atoms in 2.56 mol of hydrogen gas
c) determine the number of chloride ions in 0.41 mol of calcium chloride
d) calculate the number of atoms of oxygen in 22.5 g of aluminum nitrate

29. Calculate the number of:
a) molecules in 1.00 g of oxygen
b) atoms of sulfur in 3.08 mol of sulfur dioxide
c) nitrite ions in 3.99 g of aluminum nitrite

30. Balance the following equations:
a) the reaction that occurs when dynamite explodes
$$C_7H_5N_3O_6(s) + O_2(g) \rightarrow CO_2(g) + H_2O(l) + N_2(g)$$
b) the reaction that occurs to produce energy in a nickel-cadmium rechargeable dry cell
$$NiO(OH)(s) + H_2O(l) + Cd(s) \rightarrow Ni(OH)_2(s) + Cd(OH)_2(s)$$

31. For each of the reactions described below, write a balanced chemical equation. Indicate the physical state of each substance:
    a) When ammonia gas and hydrogen chloride gas are mixed, a white solid, ammonium chloride, is formed.
    b) If carbon dioxide gas is passed into a solution of calcium hydroxide in water, a precipitate of calcium carbonate is obtained. The other product of the reaction is water.
    c) Metallic zinc reacts with a solution of lead(II) nitrate. Solid lead metal is formed together with a solution of zinc nitrate.
    d) Heating solid copper(II) nitrate trihydrate produces solid copper(II) oxide, nitrogen dioxide gas, oxygen gas, and water vapour.

32. Calculate the molar mass of the following compounds:
    a) P_2O_5
    b) LiH_2PO_4
    c) $Cu(CH_3CO_2)_2$
    d) IF_5
    e) $SnCl_2 \cdot 5H_2O$

33. Chlorophyll, which is essential to photosynthesis in plant cells, contains 2.72% Mg by mass. Assuming one magnesium atom per chlorophyll molecule, calculate the molecular mass of chlorophyll.

34. Calculate the mass of each of the following:
    a) 1.15×10^{20} formula units $LiNO_3$
    b) 6.02×10^{30} atoms of mercury
    c) 10×10^{10} molecules of iodine pentachloride

35. Calculate the amount of substance (in moles) in each of the following:
    a) 1×10^2 g Cl_2
    b) 284 g Na_2SO_4
    c) 0.100 mg NaF
    d) 10 g CO_2
    e) 262 g UO_3

36. Calculate the amount of substance in each of the following:
    a) 7.08×10^{24} molecules of sugar
    b) 1.59×10^{22} atoms of sulfur
    c) 8.82×10^{10} formula units of calcium phosphate
    d) 3.00×10^{23} atoms of magnesium
    e) 8.72×10^{15} molecules of carbon dioxide
    f) 5.0×10^{24} formula units of sodium chloride

37. A chemist needs to carry out a chemical reaction in which potassium bromide (KBr) and silver nitrate ($AgNO_3$) are used.
    a) Calculate the molar mass of each of these substances.
    b) Determine the mass of each that would be required if the chemist wanted to use 6×10^{-2} moles of each compound.
    c) How many moles of KBr would be required to have the same total number of particles as there are in one mole of $AgNO_3$?

38. A sugar found in grapes has a molar mass of 180.2 g and an empirical formula of CH_2O. Determine the molecular formula of this sugar.

39. Diethyl ether, a medical anesthetic, contains 64.9% carbon, 13.5% hydrogen, and 21.6% oxygen by mass. Find the molecular formula of diethyl ether, given that its molar mass is 74.1 $g \cdot mol^{-1}$.

40. Acetylsalicylic acid has a molar mass of 180 $g \cdot mol^{-1}$ and contains 60.02% carbon, 4.44% hydrogen, and 35.54% oxygen by mass. Find the molecular formula of this substance.

41. A compound containing only carbon and hydrogen was burned. The water produced was condensed and collected. From a 0.436 g sample of the compound, 0.478 g of water and an undetermined amount of carbon dioxide was obtained. Determine the empirical formula of the compound. If the molar mass of the compound is 82.1 $g \cdot mol^{-1}$, determine its molecular formula.

42. Magnetite (Fe_3O_4) is a commonly occurring iron ore.
    a) Calculate the percentage composition of magnetite.
    b) Calculate how many iron atoms are present in 1.0 mg of Fe_3O_4.

43. Find the percent composition of the following commonly used laboratory chemicals:
    a) sodium dichromate ($Na_2Cr_2O_7$)
    b) potassium permanganate ($KMnO_4$)
    c) magnesium sulfate ($MgSO_4$)

44. Determine the empirical formula of the compounds with the following percent compositions:
    a) 48.0% zinc, 52% chlorine
    b) 25.9% iron, 74.1% bromine
    c) 62.6% lead, 8.5% nitrogen, 29.0% oxygen
    d) 7.2% phosphorus, 92.8% bromine
    e) 19.0% tin, 81.0% iodine

45. The percentage composition of a polymer used for the non-stick surfaces of cooking utensils is 24.0% C and 76.0% F by mass. Determine the empirical formula of the polymer.

46. Sulfuric acid is formed when sulfur trioxide combines with water:

    $SO_3(g) + H_2O(l) \rightarrow H_2SO_4(aq)$

    a) Determine the minimum mass of water that is required to convert 35.0 g of sulfur trioxide to sulfuric acid.
    b) Calculate the mass of sulfur trioxide that is needed in order to produce 80.0 g of sulfuric acid.

47. Naval vessels generate smoke screens using a compound of silicon and chlorine. In one experiment, 1.652 g silicon was combined with 8.348 g chlorine to produce this compound. Determine the mass of chlorine required if 15.25 g of silicon are to be used in the next experiment.

48. Spacecrafts use solid lithium hydroxide (LiOH) to remove exhaled carbon dioxide gas from the air. The carbon dioxide gas reacts with lithium hydroxide to form lithium carbonate (Li_2CO_3) and water. Calculate the mass of carbon dioxide that can be absorbed by each gram of lithium hydroxide.

49. One method used to prevent the ends of wooden fence posts from rotting while they are stuck in the ground is to soak them in an aqueous solution of zinc chloride, $ZnCl_2$. If 720 g zinc chloride are dissolved in 3.00 L of water, determine the amount of zinc chloride (in moles) that is used.

50. When 3.76 g of hydrated iron(III) phosphate was heated, 2.77 g of anhydrous salt remained. Determine the formula of the hydrated salt.

51. A student places a 3.45 g iron nail into a beaker containing a copper(II) sulfate ($CuSO_4$) solution. After the nail has completely reacted, a quantity of copper metal remains at the bottom of the beaker. The student finds the mass of the recovered copper to be 3.73 g. The equation for this reaction is:

    $Fe(s) + CuSO_4(aq) \rightarrow FeSO_4(aq) + Cu(s)$

    Determine the expected yield and the percent yield.

52. You calculate that a particular reaction should produce 67 g of product for a given mass of reactant. When you do the experiment, you find that you have produced 76 g of product.
    a) Calculate the percent yield.
    b) Explain what could have caused a percent yield greater than 100%.

53. Pure iron can be produced by this reaction between magnetite (Fe3O4) and hydrogen:

    $Fe_3O_4(s) + 4\ H_2(g) \rightarrow 3\ Fe(s) + 4\ H_2O(l)$

    a) If 100.0 g of both magnetite and hydrogen are initially present, identify which reagent, if any, is in excess.
    b) Calculate the percent yield if 32.0 g iron was actually isolated.

54. The white limestone cliffs of Dover in England contain a large percentage of calcium carbonate ($CaCO_3$). An 84.4 g sample of this limestone reacts with an excess of hydrochloric acid to form 81.8 g calcium chloride.

    $CaCO_3(s) + 2\ HCl(aq) \rightarrow CaCl_2(aq) + H_2O(l) + CO_2(g)$

    Determine the percentage of calcium carbonate in the limestone.

55. Gold-188 decays by positron emission. Write a balanced nuclear equation to describe this process.

56. The disintegration of the radioisotope radium-226 produces an isotope of the element radon and alpha radiation. The atomic number of radium (Ra) is 33; the atomic number of radon (Rn) is 86. Write a balanced nuclear equation for this transformation.

57. The radioisotope lead-210 decays to an isotope of bismuth (Bi) by emission of a beta particle. Write a balanced nuclear equation for this decay process.

Making Connections

58. Urea is a popular fertilizer in many tropical countries. Use electronic and print resources to research the formula for urea, and how it is manufactured. Write a summary report outlining the advantages of using urea over other nitrogen-supplying fertilizers.

59. Use electronic and print resources to research how radioisotopes of C, N, and O could be harmful to living organisms. Prepare a visual display of the results of your research.

60. Pregnant women often take 325-mg ferrous sulfate ($FeSO_4$) tablets as an iron (Fe^{2+}) supplement. Iron tablets are also one of the leading causes of poisoning deaths in children. As little as 550 mg of Fe^{2+} can be fatal to a 10-kg child. Calculate how many 325-mg ferrous sulfate tablets it would take to make a lethal dose for a 10-kg child. Design a warning label for this product based on your findings.

61. Record the foods you eat for 1 week. From a nutritional reference book, calculate your caloric intake. Determine the percent of your calories coming from fat and from carbohydrates. Summarize the recommended daily intakes for fats and carbohydrates.

62. In Canada, we rely on cars mainly for personal transportation. A 50-L tank of gasoline typically weighs 34 kg. Gasoline is a complex mixture of hydrocarbons, but assume for this question that the gasoline is 60% octane and 40% cyclopropane.
    a) Calculate the mass of CO_2 that is produced by the complete combustion of a tank of gasoline.
    b) Based on your calculations, write a summary of the environmental effects of our reliance on cars. Include a discussion about using alternative forms of transportation or alternative fuels.

63. Using electronic and print resources, research the use of nuclear power as an energy source. Write an essay that explains your view as to whether we should use nuclear power as an energy source. Provide supporting evidence for your perspective from your research.

3

Solutions and Solubility

OVERALL EXPECTATIONS

By the end of this unit, you will be able to:

- demonstrate an understanding of the properties of solutions, the concept of concentration, and the importance of water as a solvent

- carry out experiments and other laboratory procedures involving solutions, and solve quantitative problems involving solutions

- relate scientific knowledge of solutions and solubility to everyday applications, and explain how environmental water quality depends on the concentrations of a variety of dissolved substances

Water is an essential commodity. Picture yourself going through an average day without water—no water (or soft drinks) to drink, no showers, no flushing toilets. Or perhaps, like inhabitants of many countries, you must decide each day the top priority for the one bucket of water that you fetch from some distant water source. In fact, the ownership of water supplies will probably become the most contentious issue of this century. Underground water supplies, such as the world's largest, the Ogalalla aquifer in the central United States, are being pumped up at a far greater rate than they are being replenished. As the level in the underground supply diminishes, where will the U.S. find replacement water for cities such as Denver and the enormous farmlands of the Midwest?

There are also many problems with surface water. Rivers, such as the Rhine and Danube in Europe, are polluted by nearby countries. The countries downstream are faced with contaminated water over which they have no control. The demands on rivers for irrigation are particularly acute in North America. There is one case where environmental impact has produced a site of natural beauty—Mono Lake, California. This lake is unique in the world with its amazing crystal formations. The crystals are formed because the water in the lake has been evaporating faster than replacement water has run in from rivers. As a result, the salts in the lake have started to crystallize. Why has the water flow decreased? The beauty is misleading; it has come at the price of the former inhabitants of the lake. The fish and other freshwater organisms died as the water evaporated since the salt concentration became too high for their survival.

One of the most important properties of water is also a curse—its ability to dissolve compounds, particularly ionic compounds. As water evaporates on the surface of farmland, the dissolved salts become increasingly concentrated, just as the crystals formed in Mono Lake. The crop yields diminish and ultimately farming becomes impossible. But the subject of water raises many chemical questions. Why is water such a good solvent? What are the molecular properties of water that determine which substances dissolve in it and which do not? How and why do compounds react when they are dissolved in water? This is the topic of aquatic chemistry.

Are Water Wars Imminent?

Increasing human populations and the growing need from agriculture have been pushing our water supplies toward the breaking point. The discrepancy between our need for and supply of fresh water may lead to slow economic progress, violence, and the devastation of populations. Even to this day, 50% of the world's population has water services that are worse than those available to the ancient Romans and Greeks.

Chlorine Dioxide May Be the Water Disinfectant of the Future

In North America, chlorine is most commonly used for the disinfection of water supplies. But is it the best choice? There are increasing concerns about the reaction of chlorine with organic material in the water to produce chlorinated organic compounds, including THMs (trihalomethanes). One alternative that has been gaining in popularity is chlorine dioxide because it does not react with organic matter to form THMs, yet is as good as chlorine for destroying water-borne diseases.

Agricultural Run-off Linked to Growth of Harmful Algae Blooms

Twenty years ago, harmful algae blooms were a rare occurrence in coastal marine environments. Now, these toxic organisms are a problem throughout the world's coastal waters. Why are these organisms proliferating? At the moment, scientists do not have definite answers. One strong possibility is the nutrient enrichment resulting from high concentrations of nitrates and phosphates (mostly from agricultural run-off) flowing from rivers into the seas.

ACHIEVEMENT TASK (PREVIEW)

At the end of this unit, you will demonstrate your learning by completing the task "What Am I Drinking?" As a member of a student newspaper, you will prepare a report on the type and amount of dissolved substances in various bottled waters compared to municipal water, identify the effects of these substances on health, research the Health Canada regulations for bottled and municipal water, test the water samples for chloride ions and measure the pH, and make recommendations to better inform consumers about the quality of bottled and municipal water. See page 316.

The crystal formations in Mono Lake, California, are the result of the lake water evaporating faster than it can be replaced by rivers flowing into it.

Properties of Solutions

If you have ever been in a hospital, you will be aware of the importance of intravenous drips. Why do we need them? What is in them? The human body is mainly water, and each of us needs a regular supply of water. But a drip contains dissolved substances, not just water. Typically, a drip will con-

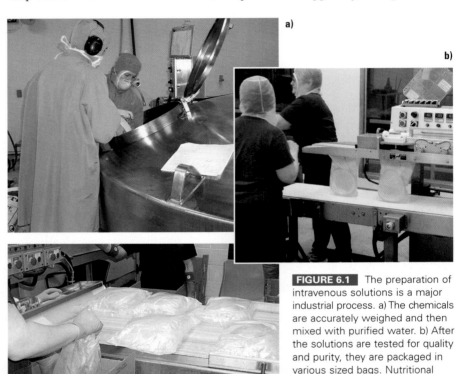

FIGURE 6.1 The preparation of intravenous solutions is a major industrial process. a) The chemicals are accurately weighed and then mixed with purified water. b) After the solutions are tested for quality and purity, they are packaged in various sized bags. Nutritional and other intravenous solutions are wrapped in an over-pouch to prevent possible contamination before use. c) The bags are then taken to an area where they are steam sterilized and, finally, packed in boxes.

tain dissolved salts, such as sodium chloride and potassium chloride. These compounds are added so that the drip fluid has a similar ion composition to human blood. Without the ions, cells such as red blood cells could not function properly. A drip might contain glucose to provide an energy source and possibly any required pharmaceutical drugs, such as painkillers or muscle relaxants. All of these substances—ionic, covalent, and polar covalent—have been dissolved in the one solvent, water. Water is a unique substance in terms of the range of compounds that will dissolve in it.

How are intravenous solutions made? The first requirement is to use very pure water. The water must be free of biological contamination, such as bacteria and viruses, but also free of dissolved salts. The second requirement is that the required salts must be purified to a far greater extent than the grade you would use in the chemistry laboratory. Next, the solids must be dissolved in water to give exactly the right concentrations of ions and molecules. This requires careful calculation. Then, samples of the solution must be checked to make sure the composition is exactly what is required and that no mistakes have been made. Finally, the solution must be sealed in a sterile bag whose chemical components will not leach (dissolve) into the solution.

The chemistry of intravenous drips encompasses almost the whole field of solution chemistry: the ubiquity of water as a solvent, the preparation of aqueous solutions, and the determination of precise concentrations. These are the topics of this chapter.

Discovering Chemistry

Do Ink and Water Mix?

How do different inks mix with water?

Materials

two different types of black overhead pens
water
50-mL beaker
3 cm by 12 cm rectangular piece of filter paper

1. Using one pen, place a tiny spot on the filter paper about 1 cm from the bottom 1 cm away from the side of the paper. Repeat using the other pen.

2. Place 10 mL of water in a 50-mL beaker.

3. Place the paper upright in the beaker, making sure that the ink spots are not making any contact with the water.

4. Hold the paper until the water is about two-thirds of the way up. Record your observations.

■ Considering both types of ink, describe the ability that they have to adhere to water. Explain how this adhesion occurs. Explain the reasoning behind the name "non-permanent."

> **CHECKPOINT**
>
> Explain each of the following terms as they apply to solutions:
>
> a) solute
> b) solvent
> c) saturated
> d) unsaturated
> e) supersaturated
>
> Draw a diagram of a water molecule showing its covalent bonds.

6.1 The Nature of Solutions

Key Understandings

When you have completed this section, you will be able to:

- define solution, solvent, solute, and solubility
- give everyday examples of solutions involving all three states
- describe the effect of temperature on solubility
- explain how ionic compounds dissolve in water
- understand how non-polar solutes dissolve in non-polar solvents
- explain how water's polarity and ability to form hydrogen bonds affect the solubility of ionic compounds

You know you need water to live, but do you ever think about what you drink? Water is such a ubiquitous solvent that it is easy to forget the different components of your drinks. Soft drinks typically contain compounds that contribute flavour; dissolved carbon dioxide to give the "fizz" and add to the sharpness of the flavour; sugar or a sugar substitute to give sweetness; and acids, such as ascorbic acid (vitamin C), citric acid, and often phosphoric acid (Figure 6.2). Cola drinks also contain caffeine, a stimulant drug.

FIGURE 6.2   In the photo, the can of diet cola is floating, while the can containing the regular cola has sunk to the bottom. Why is there a difference? (Hint: How does the sweetness of an artificial sweetener compare with that of sugar?)

Components of a Solution

What is a solution? A **solution** is defined as a homogeneous mixture of two or more substances. It is typically composed of a **solvent**, the liquid in which substances are dissolved, and the **solutes**, the substances being dissolved. For example, when instant coffee is dissolved in hot water, a solution is formed—the water being the solvent and the coffee the solute. If sugar is added to the coffee solution, the sugar will also dissolve in the water and give a solution composed of one solvent and two solutes. When water is used as a solvent, the solutions are given the specific name of **aqueous solutions**.

WORD**ORIGIN**

Aqueous comes from the Latin word *aqua*, meaning "water."

Types of Solutions

The solute and the solvent can be in any of the three states of matter: solid, liquid, or gas. Therefore, there are nine possible solute-solvent combinations, shown in Table 6.1. In this text, we will focus on the six most common combinations.

TABLE 6.1 The Nine Possible Solution Combinations

Solvent / Solute	Solid	Liquid	Gas
Solid	copper in zinc (a brass alloy)	salt in water (brine)	naphthalene in air (a moth repellent)
Liquid	mercury in gold or silver (a dental amalgam)	ethylene glycol in water (automotive antifreeze mixture)	water in air (humidity)
Gas	hydrogen in platinum	carbon dioxide in water (carbonated water)	oxygen in nitrogen (the main components of air)

Solids Dissolved in Liquids   The majority of solutions encountered tend to have a solid as the solute and a liquid as the solvent. When a solid solute such as sodium chloride dissolves in a liquid solvent such as water, we say that sodium chloride is **soluble** in water. Seawater is a solution because it contains many dissolved salts. When a solid solute does not substantially dissolve in a given liquid, we say the solute as **insoluble**.

Liquids Dissolved in Liquids   When two liquids dissolve in each other, we say that they are **miscible**. Usually the liquid present in the smaller quantity is regarded as the solute. **Immiscible** liquids will not dissolve in each other when they are mixed together (Figure 6.3). Water and ethanol are miscible in any proportion, but water and gasoline are immiscible. If these last two liquids are mixed, the less dense gasoline will form a layer on top of the denser water.

Gases Dissolved in Liquids   Solutions formed by dissolving gases in liquids are the basis of the soft-drink industry. Carbonated drinks consist of a flavoured liquid, the solvent, containing dissolved carbon dioxide gas, the solute.

Gases Dissolved in Gases   The air we breathe is an example of a solution. Nitrogen, the main component of air (78%), can be considered as the solvent and oxygen as the solute (21%). A number of other gases, such as carbon dioxide and argon, are also present as very minor components of this solution. Gases *always* mix with one another.

Liquids Dissolved in Solids   Mercury is the most common liquid component in these types of solutions. These kinds of mercury solutions are called amalgams. Dental amalgams, which were used as tooth fillings, are prepared by mixing liquid mercury with one or more solid metallic elements, such as gold, silver, tin, or copper.

FIGURE 6.3   Immiscible liquids of different densities. The liquids from top to bottom are corn oil, water, shampoo, dish detergent, antifreeze, and maple syrup. What physical property is being demonstrated in this photo?

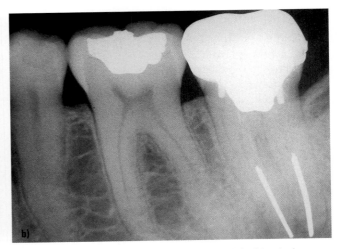

FIGURE 6.4 There are many types of alloys, each with a different use. a) Chrome-moly is a steel alloy usually used for bicycle frames. b) Dental amalgams are a mercury alloy, which was used to fill cavities in teeth.

Solids Dissolved in Solid Solutions formed by dissolving one solid in another are usually referred to as alloys (Figure 6.4). Steel is an alloy containing iron, carbon, and other elements, such as manganese, nickel, and chromium, which are added to improve its durability.

Solubility—the Relationship between Solute and Solvent

The erosion of rocks is one aspect of the science of geology. It is erosion that has turned the mighty mountains that once existed along the eastern side of North America into the lower, rounded Appalachian chain. Although erosion was to a large extent a result of the fragmentation of rocks into tiny grains, some of the rock components dissolved in the rainwater and were carried down to the sea. In fact, the ions in the sea have all been dissolved (leached) out of rocks over billions of years. That rocks can dissolve is an indication that substances you may think of as totally insoluble do, in fact, dissolve to a very tiny extent. For this reason, a compound cannot be regarded simply as soluble or insoluble. Experimental data has to be used to determine how soluble or how insoluble a substance is.

The physical property of a substance that describes how soluble or insoluble it is is called **solubility**. It is defined as the mass of a solute that will dissolve in a given volume or mass of a solvent. If more of one substance dissolves in a solvent than another, the first substance is said to be more soluble than the second. When the maximum amount of a solid or gaseous solute has been dissolved in a given volume of solvent at a given temperature, a **saturated solution** is obtained. If more solute is added to a saturated solution, the excess will remain undissolved. In the case of a gas, the excess gas will escape into the atmosphere; for a solid solute, it will remain at the bottom as a solid; and for a liquid, a separate layer becomes visible.

There is an enormous range of solubility of compounds. For example, it is possible to dissolve over 2 kg of silver nitrate in 1 L of water, but only 0.002 g of silver chloride in 1 L of water. Silver nitrate would be described as being very soluble in water, while silver chloride, which dissolves to such a small extent, would be described as insoluble. The ranges of solubility for which these and other terms are used are listed in Table 6.2.

TABLE 6.2	Terms Used When Discussing Solubility			
Solubility (per litre of water)	greater than 100 g	between 10 g and 100 g	between 1 g and 10 g	less than 1 g
Term Used	very soluble	soluble	slightly soluble	insoluble

The Potash Industry—One of Canada's Major Resources

Salt water contains many ions besides sodium ions, Na^+, and chloride ions, Cl^-, including magnesium, Mg^{2+}, calcium, Ca^{2+}, potassium, K^+, hydrogen carbonate, HCO_3^-, bromide, Br^-, and sulfate, SO_4^{2-}. A few hundred million years ago, most of the prairie province areas formed part of a large inland sea (Figure 6.5). Over millions of years, this sea dried up, and the ionic compounds that were dissolved in it gradually crystallized, but not at the same time and not in the same place. As the water evaporated, the least soluble, calcium sulfate ($CaSO_4$), crystallized first, as the mineral *anhydrite*, then sodium chloride as the mineral *halite*. The last ones to crystallize, near the southeasterly portion of the basin, were the more soluble salts of potassium and magnesium. These settled out as the minerals *sylvite* (KCl) and *carnallite* ($KCl \cdot MgCl_2 \cdot 6H_2O$). Over time, these mineral beds, which are over 200 m thick in places, became covered with several hundred metres of sediment and erosion products. The potassium-containing minerals, collectively known as potash, lie in beds up to 7 m thick.

Canada is one of the world's major potash producers and has more than half of the world's total reserves. The world's largest deposits occur in Saskatchewan, though New Brunswick also contributes to the Canadian output. Only 5% is used in the domestic market. In fact, the United States is heavily reliant on Canadian potash for its needs, buying more than half of the potash produced in this country. Approximately 95% of all the potash produced is used in agriculture; the remainder is used by industry for making other potassium compounds, such as potassium hydroxide and potassium nitrate. To make other compounds, a pure potassium compound is needed as a starting material, and potassium chloride from these underground deposits is one of the few pure potassium minerals to be found.

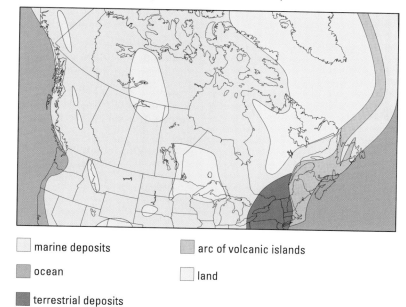

FIGURE 6.5 Four hundred forty million years ago, central Canada was covered by an enormous lake that later dried up. The deposited minerals subsequently became buried, and it is those mineral resources that are valuable today.

- ☐ marine deposits
- ☐ ocean
- ☐ terrestrial deposits
- ☐ arc of volcanic islands
- ☐ land

FIGURE 6.6 Conventional mechanical mining techniques are used to extract potash deposits at depths of approximately 1000 m using the Marietta Miner.

Effect of Temperature on Solubility

Solid Solutes If you cannot dissolve something, such as a lot of sugar, in water what do you do? Most people warm the water, because generally solids dissolve to a greater extent in hot than in cold water. However, as shown in Figure 6.7, there are exceptions. Although the solubility of potassium nitrate increases rapidly with increasing temperature, the solubility of sodium chloride remains approximately the same, and sodium sulfate is actually less soluble in hot water than it is in cold water.

The difference in solubility at different temperatures can be used to your advantage if you want to purify a solid substance. In this process, called **recrystallization**, a solvent is needed in which the substance has a low solubility at 0°C but a greater solubility at the boiling point of the solvent. The impure solid is then dissolved in the minimum amount of hot solvent (Figure 6.8). Any insoluble impurities are removed by filtration. The solution is then cooled slowly in an ice bath, which causes the dissolved solid to crystallize in a very pure form. For example, looking at Figure 6.7, you can see that potassium nitrate can be purified by recrystallization from water. Suggest one compound shown in Figure 6.7 that cannot be purified by this method.

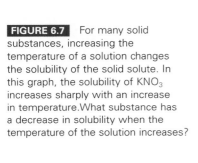

Investigation

Refer to page 277, Investigation 1

FIGURE 6.7 For many solid substances, increasing the temperature of a solution changes the solubility of the solid solute. In this graph, the solubility of KNO_3 increases sharply with an increase in temperature. What substance has a decrease in solubility when the temperature of the solution increases?

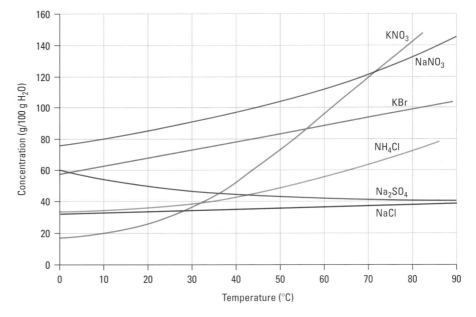

FIGURE 6.8 You can purify many solids by a) dissolving them in a hot solvent, b) filtering off any insoluble impurities, and then c) cooling the solution slowly in ice to give pure crystals.

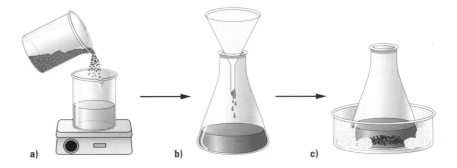

a)   b)   c)

FIGURE 6.9 The edges around hot springs contain crystallized minerals. As the hot water of the spring cools at the surface, some of the dissolved minerals crystallize because they are less soluble in cool water.

Gas Solutes For most gases, the solubility decreases on heating (Figure 6.10). For example, a lake is generally saturated with oxygen gas, which is necessary for the survival of fish and other aquatic life. A small temperature increase can prove beneficial, but a major increase in temperature would cause a decrease in the amount of dissolved oxygen and threaten the survival of life in the lake. This thermal pollution occurs when industries use water from lakes and rivers for cooling and the warm, oxygen-depleted water is then returned, asphyxiating the fish.

To explain the trend in gas solubility, you can picture the gas molecules being trapped in the spaces between the water molecules. According to the kinetic-molecular theory of matter, as the temperature rises, the water molecules will move more vigorously. As they do, spaces will open between the water molecules, providing a greater opportunity for the gas molecules to escape.

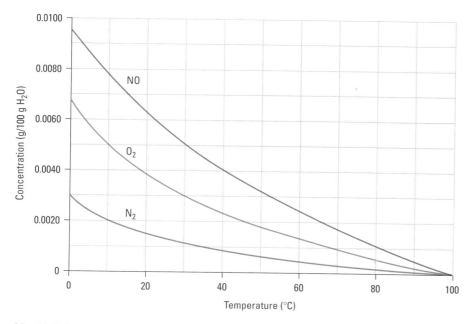

FIGURE 6.10 The solubility of gases varies with temperature. In nearly every case, the solubility decreases as the temperature of the solution increases. Gases such as N_2, O_2, and NO are very insoluble near 100°C. Using the kinetic-molecular theory, how would you explain this decrease in solubility?

Liquid Solutes In general, solids increase in solubility in water while gases decrease in solubility as the temperature of water increases. What about liquids? There is no general trend; some liquid solutes increase in solubility with an increase in temperature, while other liquid solutes decrease in solubility with an increase in temperature.

Are there any patterns in the solubility of ionic compounds?

Materials

sodium chloride, copper(II) chloride, sodium carbonate, copper(II) carbonate, calcium carbonate, calcium phosphate, calcium sulfate, copper(II) sulfate

water

five 10-cm long small test tubes, each with a rubber stopper

spatula

test-tube rack

1. Place a small amount of sodium chloride (the size of a matchstick head) in a test tube. Add 5 mL of distilled water and shake. Note if the substance dissolves in water.

2. Record your observations.

3. Repeat using copper(II) chloride, sodium carbonate, and copper(II) carbonate.

- Identify the substances that dissolved in water and those that did not.

- Develop a hypothesis about the solubility of substances in water.

- Test your hypothesis by repeating the experiment with calcium carbonate and calcium sulfate. Note if these compounds support the hypothesis.

- Test your hypothesis with copper(II) sulfate. Observe if this compound supports your hypothesis. (Patterns in chemistry are rarely as precise as you may like them to be.)

- Predict whether calcium phosphate is likely to be soluble. Check with data tables for the answer.

Why Do Many Ionic Compounds Dissolve in Water?

Water dissolves such a wide variety of compounds that we sometimes (though not quite correctly) refer to it as a "universal solvent." It is such a good solvent because it can dissolve a high proportion of ionic compounds and a large number of covalent compounds. To understand why this is the case, you need to look closely at the structure of the water molecule.

The water molecule contains covalent bonds between the hydrogen and oxygen atoms. However, the bonding electrons are not shared equally. Since the electronegativity of oxygen is greater than that of hydrogen, the bonding electrons are attracted more toward the oxygen atom than the 2 hydrogen atoms. As a result of the electron shift, the hydrogen atoms have a partial positive charge and the oxygen atom has a partial negative charge (Figure 6.11).

If the water molecule had been linear, then the partial charges would cancel each other out. However, the water molecule is V-shaped, and this bent shape has an important result. The partial charges do not cancel each other out; instead, the partially negative oxygen atom will be attracted toward other positive charges, while each of the partially positive hydrogen atoms will be attracted toward other negative charges. This molecule is said to be **polar**. It is, in fact, the polar characteristic of the water molecule that enables it to dissolve many ionic compounds.

The process of dissolving an ionic solid, such as lithium chloride, can be pictured as follows. In the lithium chloride crystal, the lithium ions and chloride

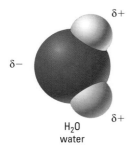

$\delta+$

$\delta-$

$\delta+$

H_2O
water

FIGURE 6.11 A representation of a water molecule. The 2 hydrogen atoms have a partial positive charge ($\delta+$), and the oxygen atom has a partial negative charge ($\delta-$).

ions are packed in a regular array or lattice and are held together by electrostatic attractive forces. When the crystal is placed in water, the water molecules immediately surround the ions on the surface of the crystal. The partially positive hydrogen atoms of some of the water molecules are attracted to the negative chloride ions (anions), and the partially negative oxygen atoms of other water molecules are attracted to the positive lithium ions (cations). The electrostatic attractive forces between the water molecules and the individual ions is greater than the attraction between the ions in the crystal. The result is that the water molecules pull these ions away from the crystal lattice into solution. **Solvation** is the process by which ions are attracted to and surrounded by solvent molecules. The term **hydration** is used if the solvent is water.

When the formula of lithium chloride is written as LiCl*(s)*, it is important to realize that the solid contains the ions. So the formula is actually Li^+Cl^-*(s)*. The process of dissolving lithium chloride in water can be represented as:

$$Li^+Cl^-\text{\textit{(s)}} \xrightarrow[\text{in water}]{\text{dissolve}} Li^+\text{\textit{(aq)}} + Cl^-\text{\textit{(aq)}}$$

where the ions become attracted to, and surrounded by, water molecules rather than one another (Figure 6.12). Ionic compounds are usually written without their ionic charges.

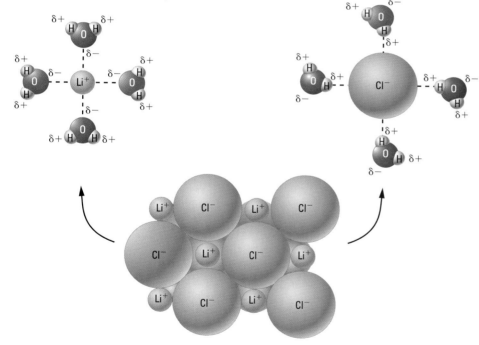

FIGURE 6.12 The solution process for an ionic compound. In a crystal of lithium chloride, each lithium ion has a positive charge and each chloride ion has a negative charge. When an ionic solid dissolves, the ions become solvated. Why do the water molecules orient themselves differently around the anions and cations?

Ionic calcium chloride dissolves in water by a similar process to give hydrated calcium ions and chloride ions. The calcium chloride crystal lattice contains calcium ions (Ca^{2+}) and chloride ions (Cl^-) in the ratio of 1:2 (1 Ca^{2+} : 2 Cl^-). Therefore, 2 hydrated chloride ions will be produced for each hydrated calcium ion:

$$CaCl_2\text{\textit{(s)}} \xrightarrow[\text{in water}]{\text{dissolve}} Ca^{2+}\text{\textit{(aq)}} + 2\ Cl^-\text{\textit{(aq)}}$$

WEBLINK

SIMULATION

For a simulation to show how
dissolving works, go to
www.pearsoned.ca/chemistry11.

Similarly, when magnesium sulfate ($MgSO_4(s)$) is dissolved in water, hydrated magnesium ions and sulfate ions are produced. The polyatomic sulfate ion remains as a single unit because the atoms within SO_4^{2-} are held together by covalent bonds.

$$MgSO_4(s) \xrightarrow[\text{in water}]{\text{dissolve}} Mg^{2+}(aq) + SO_4^{2-}(aq)$$

From this description, you might expect all ionic compounds to be water-soluble. However, some ionic compounds are insoluble in water. Why is this? What determines whether an ionic compound will dissolve in water? The solubility of a compound in water is largely dependent on the strength of the ionic bonds within the crystal compared to the strength of the attraction between the ions and the water molecules.

In general, ionic compounds with low ion charges are likely to be soluble, while those with high ion charges tend to be insoluble. For example, the alkali metal ions (1+ charge) form soluble salts as does the nitrate ion (1− charge) and most (but not all!) compounds of the halide ions. On the other hand, all compounds of the phosphate ion (3− charge) are insoluble (except those of the alkali metal ions and ammonium ion).

You should always be aware of the difference between the physical dissolving process and chemical reactions that cause a solid to "disappear." For example, if you add solid barium oxide to water, the solid will appear to dissolve. However, what has happened is actually a chemical reaction to give a solution of barium hydroxide:

$$BaO(s) + H_2O(l) \rightarrow Ba^{2+}(aq) + 2\ OH^-(aq)$$

Why Do Some Covalent Compounds Dissolve in Water?

Why does alcohol (ethanol) mix with water, but gasoline does not? Ethanol, CH_3CH_2OH, belongs to a family of compounds known as alcohols. All alcohol molecules contain carbon and hydrogen atoms together with an oxygen and a hydrogen atom bonded together. The carbon and hydrogen atoms have very little difference in electronegativity, so the carbon–hydrogen bonds are essentially non-polar. However, like water, the presence of an oxygen atom bonded to a hydrogen atom results in a polar bond. Consequently, the terminal hydrogen atom has a partial positive charge, and the oxygen atom has a partial negative charge (Figure 6.13).

In liquid water, the partially positive hydrogen atom of one molecule is attracted to the partially negative oxygen of a neighbouring molecule. This attraction is known as **hydrogen bonding**. It is this network of hydrogen bonds throughout liquid water that is responsible for its comparatively high boiling point. In other words, a lot of energy is required to break the hydrogen bonds and allow the molecules to escape as a gas. The hydrogen bonds also hold the water molecules rigidly in place when water freezes solid to form ice.

Similarly, in pure ethanol, neighbouring ethanol molecules are attracted to each other by the polar –OH part of the molecule. The $\delta-$ on the oxygen in one molecule is attracted to the $\delta+$ on the hydrogen of another molecule. When ethanol and water are mixed, the oxygen of an ethanol molecule can be attracted to the hydrogen of a water molecule, while the oxygen of a water molecule can be attracted to the hydrogen of an ethanol molecule. These attractions of molecules of one compound for the other cause the components to mix.

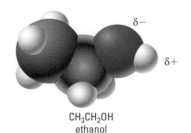

$\delta-$

$\delta+$

CH_3CH_2OH
ethanol

FIGURE 6.13 A space-filling representation of the ethanol molecule. The oxygen atom will have a partial negative charge, while its neighbouring hydrogen atom will have a partial positive charge.

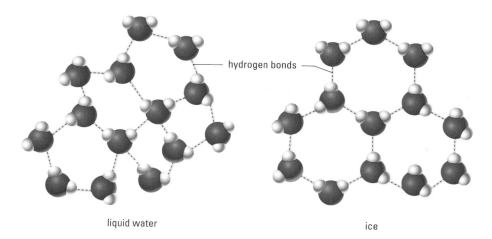

liquid water   ice

FIGURE 6.14 Hydrogen bonds create the hexagonal arrangement of water molecules in ice.

Gasoline contains a mixture of molecules containing only carbon and hydrogen atoms, such as octane (Figure 6.15). These molecules are essentially non-polar. As a result, such molecules are attracted toward other non-polar molecules rather than toward the polar water molecules. The result is that water and gasoline will not mix. On the other hand, octane will mix with other non-polar substances. It is for this reason that gasoline will dissolve non-polar grease stains. A useful but not always accurate saying is "Like dissolves like."

If most polar compounds mix with water and non-polar compounds do not, what about molecules that are part polar and part non-polar? As the non-polar part increases in size, the solubility decreases. For example, methanol, CH_3OH, and ethanol, CH_3CH_2OH, mix with water in any proportion. For octanol, $CH_3CH_2CH_2CH_2CH_2CH_2CH_2CH_2OH$, only 0.5 g of octanol will dissolve in a litre of water.

$CH_3(CH_2)_6CH_3$
octane

FIGURE 6.15 Octane, a component of gasoline, is non-polar. It does not mix with water.

FIGURE 6.16 Common detergents such as these contain molecules with polar "heads" and long, non-polar "tails."

Soaps and Detergents: Non-polar and Ionic Groups Join Forces

Soaps and detergents are compounds whose molecules contain two characteristic features: a long non-polar chain of carbon and hydrogen atoms attached to a very polar end group, which is usually ionic. Both features play an important role in cleansing.

For more than 2000 years, soaps have been prepared from animal fats and vegetable oils; they are the sodium or potassium salts of acids having long non-polar chains. Detergents (Figure 6.16) are synthetic soaps that are synthesized mainly from petroleum products, having either an ionic group (like a sulfate ion) or a non-ionic but polar group.

Calcium ions and magnesium ions, which are present in relatively large amounts in some water supplies (known as "hard" water), form a precipitate with soaps in water. This precipitate, commonly called scum, is the cause of bathtub rings. As a result, soap is often ineffective and inefficient for washing laundry. Detergents are more effective in hard water because calcium and magnesium salts of sulfates are soluble in water.

Discovering Chemistry — *What Does a Detergent Do?*

Materials

  liquid detergent
  vegetable oil
  water
  2 test tubes, stoppers, and a test-tube rack

1. Place a 2-cm depth of water in each tube.

2. Add 10 drops of vegetable oil to each tube.

3. Then add 5 drops of liquid detergent to the second tube.

4. Stopper both tubes, and then shake vigorously. Note your observations.

■ Explain your observations.

■ Many salad dressings contain detergent-like molecules. Explain why dressings may contain such compounds.

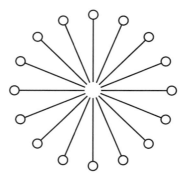

FIGURE 6.17 A detergent micelle in water. Each detergent molecule is shown as a "matchstick."

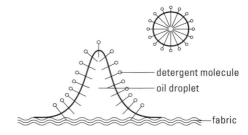

FIGURE 6.18 Detergent molecules "attack" an oil droplet on a fabric and pull the oil away, into the water solution.

Although soaps and detergents are water-soluble, they do not form true solutions. The non-polar chains are hydrophobic ("water-fearing") and are attracted to one another. The polar ends, however, are hydrophilic ("water-loving") and tend to dissolve in water. The result is that as many as a hundred molecules form a water-soluble spherical particle known as a micelle (Figure 6.17). The non-polar chains form the inside of the micelle, while the negative ions form the outside. The large amount of negative charge, which is compensated for by the sodium ions of the soap, keeps the micelles away from one another and dissolved in solution.

Water by itself will not remove dirt mixed with oil and grease on clothing or skin, but a solution of soap or detergent will. The non-polar chains that form micelles will dissolve the non-polar oil or grease, while the polar end groups will be attracted to the water molecules. This allows the dirt particles to be washed away (Figure 6.18).

The detergent industry is a major consumer of chemicals. In fact, about half a million tonnes of detergent are used in Canada every year. A commercial detergent contains much more than a single type of detergent molecule. It contains builders that make the washing solution basic (and so it is more effective at cleaning), anti-redeposition agents to prevent the dirt from sticking back onto the clothes, and optical brighteners to make white appear whiter. Small quantities of other substances, such as anticorrosion agents and perfumes, are also added.

Section 6.1 Review

Understanding Concepts

1. Describe the difference between a solute and a solvent, and give an example that is not in this book.
2. Classify the following in terms of the types of solutions they represent:
   a) air
   b) seawater
   c) an alloy
   d) an amalgam
3. Write a paragraph that supports the statement that water is considered a universal solvent.
4. Explain how water is able to dissolve an ionic solid such as calcium chloride.
5. Explain why a non-polar solute, such as grease, dissolves in a non-polar solvent, such as gasoline.
6. Describe the effect of increasing temperature on:
   a) the solubility of a solid in a liquid
   b) the solubility of a gas in a liquid

Making Connections

7. Investigate the changing supply and demand for Canadian potash. Write a PMI (plus, minus, interesting) essay outlining whether Canada should consider developing its own secondary-level industry related to this resource or should continue to export the raw material.
8. Check the labels of the products in your home that are used for cleaning. Make a chart of the chemicals that are part of each product. Research if any of these have harmful environmental or health effects. Suggest ways that labels should be designed so that consumers can make informed choices about the products they buy.

6.2 Water Quality

Key Understandings

When you have completed this section, you will be able to:

- explain where pollutants in natural waters come from
- identify the allowable concentrations of metallic and organic pollutants in drinking water
- describe the technology used in water purification and sewage treatment
- outline the process of water purification and sewage treatment

Approximately three-quarters of Earth's surface is covered by water with the world's oceans containing most of it (97.3% by mass). This leaves only 2.7% of water on this planet as fresh water. Over three-quarters of this fresh water is in the form of ice and is not readily available for use. More than one-fifth of the fresh water is found as ground water, and only a tiny fraction is readily available in lakes and rivers as surface water (Figure 6.19). This proportion—about 0.015% of the total—is readily recyclable as part of the water (hydrologic) cycle. The sun's energy evaporates the water; as the water vapour rises, it cools, and if the concentration is sufficient, it returns to Earth in the form of rain or snow to repeat the cycle again (Figure 6.20).

INFOBIT

Surface water is found in lakes, rivers, and reservoirs. **Ground water** lies below the surface of the land. Some precipitation and surface water seeps down into the ground, filling pores and cracks in the rocks.

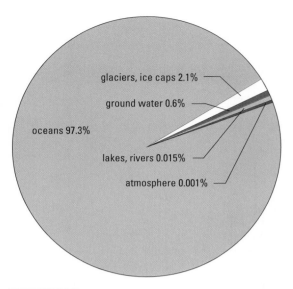

glaciers, ice caps 2.1%

ground water 0.6%

oceans 97.3%

lakes, rivers 0.015%

atmosphere 0.001%

Fresh Water from Salt Water

Many scientists predict that by the year 2025, two-thirds of Earth's population will suffer from water shortages. Can salt water be used for the growing water crisis? In some places, such as parts of Florida and the Middle Eastern gulf states, the fresh water shortage is so acute that drinking water must be obtained from salt water supplies. There are several ways to accomplish this, including large-scale distillation. Distillation uses enormous quantities of energy. A more efficient alternative is reverse osmosis. Osmosis, a common term in biology, is the natural tendency of a solvent such as water to move from a region of low solute concentration (purer water) to one of higher solute concentration (less pure water) through a semipermeable membrane. Such a membrane is a material with tiny pores in it through which water can pass, but not ions or large molecules. The process of osmosis will continue until the solute concentrations are equal on both sides of the membrane.

FIGURE 6.20. The water cycle on Earth involves the evaporation of water from oceans and the soil, as well as from plants (transpiration). The water vapour then condenses and falls back to Earth as rain or snow (precipitation). Some of this precipitation percolates through the soil to form ground water. The process of water being evaporated, condensing, and falling as precipitation occurs continuously.

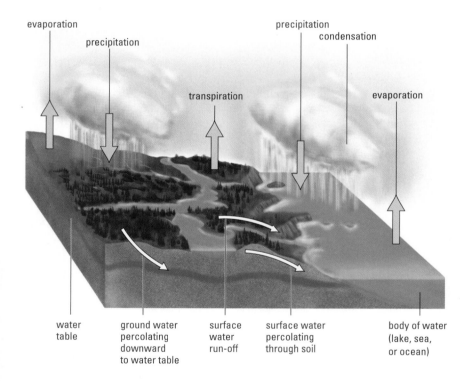

evaporation

precipitation

transpiration

precipitation

condensation

evaporation

water table

ground water percolating downward to water table

surface water run-off

surface water percolating through soil

body of water (lake, sea, or ocean)

FIGURE 6.21 When the Apollo astronauts first saw Earth from thousands of kilometres away, they affectionately called it the "big blue marble."

Reverse Osmosis Reverse osmosis involves the application of pressure to reverse the flow of water molecules. A salt water solution is placed on one side of the membrane and fresh water on the other. Very high pressures applied to the salt water side force the water molecules through the semipermeable membrane, leaving a more concentrated salt solution behind. The water that has passed through the membrane will be of high chemical and biological purity. Though the process is more economical than distillation, it is still a much more expensive process than the extraction of fresh ground water (Figure 6.22).

Reverse osmosis units are used for many other water purification purposes in addition to desalination. There are many biomedical uses, such as providing very pure water for kidney dialysis and hemodialysis. Commercial car washes use reverse osmosis to reclaim the dirty wash water. Astronauts rely on this technique to recycle water in spacecraft. These are only some of the different applications of reverse osmosis water purification.

The most energy-efficient way of desalinating water is **solar distillation**. This process relies on the sun's energy to evaporate the water for subsequent condensation. The method is economical only in geographical regions that experience intense sunlight for most of the year.

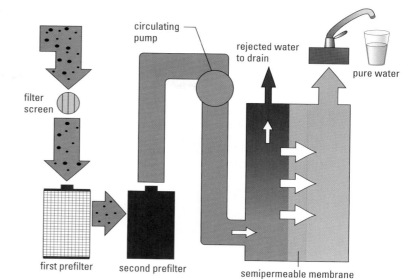

How Water Becomes Polluted

In the previous section, you saw that water is a unique solvent capable of dissolving many ionic and covalent compounds. This has advantages but also disadvantages since water can dissolve many undesirable toxic substances (pollutants). Water can also contain micro-organisms, such as bacteria and viruses. The definition of polluted water is complicated by the fact that water has so many different uses. Water suitable for some uses may be unsuitable for others. The quality of water depends on several factors including:

- oxygen-demanding wastes, such as phosphate-containing detergents and animal farm wastes, that lead to excessive growth of oxygen-consuming algae blooms.
- disease-causing pathogens—for example, cholera and *E. coli*, or micro-organisms, such as giardia ("beaver fever")—that can affect health and can be life-threatening. These enter the water supply when animal or human sewage contaminates the water source and when there is inadequate chemical treatment of water supplies.
- suspended solids (insoluble substances) causing turbidity (cloudiness). This is most common following severe flooding where soil is washed away.
- toxic pollutants—such as benzene, chromium, and mercury—which are all poisonous to aquatic life. These originate from industrial manufacturing plants or from leaking industrial landfill sites. Pesticides, herbicides, and fungicides used for domestic, commercial, and agricultural use are other classes of toxic substances that pollute water systems.
- dissolved salts, such as sodium chloride used on ice-covered roads and ammonium nitrate from fertilizers used on farms.
- oil and gasoline contamination, on the small scale (but cumulatively important) by people dumping old engine oil in sewers and on the large scale from leaking tanks at gas stations or from road, rail, or water tanker accidents.
- thermal pollution, particularly from power plants, pumping hot water into lakes and rivers.

FIGURE 6.22 Visual representation of a small-scale reverse osmosis water purification system. The incoming water is passed through a filter screen to remove large particles, then through a filter to remove smaller particles. A second filter made of carbon particles absorbs many dissolved compounds, particularly organic molecules and chlorine. The water is pressurized to force the pure water through the membrane. Although simple reverse osmosis systems typically waste about 80% of the incoming water, the system shown recycles wastewater several times, decreasing the proportion of wastewater to about 25%.

FIGURE 6.23 The pulp and paper industry is an industry that has contributed to the pollution of many water systems.

The Treatment of Drinking Water

The main reasons for treating drinking water are to kill any disease-causing micro-organisms and to remove suspended particles, objectionable odours, and colours. Two bacteriocidal agents (substances that kill bacteria) commonly used to disinfect water are chlorine gas, Cl_2, and ozone gas, O_3. Both of these compounds are added in very small amounts and kill micro-organisms during water purification.

Chlorination Chlorination is effective in preventing water-borne diseases, such as typhoid fever. One advantage of using chlorine is that it remains in the water supply (has a high retention time) and therefore provides greater protection against disease-causing bacteria. Disadvantages of chlorine include its ineffectiveness against hepatitis and polio-causing viruses. Chlorine also reacts with some compounds present in water, forming chlorinated compounds, particularly the family of compounds known as trihalomethanes, THMs. THMs such as chloroform (trichloromethane, $CHCl_3$) are established health hazards (see Case Study in Chapter 2). The effectiveness of chlorination is usually determined by measuring the concentration of the coliform (bacteria found in the feces of vertebrates) group of bacteria in the water supply. High levels of these bacteria indicate insufficient chlorination.

FIGURE 6.24 How would you know if this tap water were fit for consumption?

Ozonation Ozone's advantage is that it is more effective than chlorine against viruses and that it is needed in lesser concentration. The products formed when it reacts with organic compounds are less toxic than those formed from chlorinated organic compounds. In addition, unlike chlorine, ozone does not leave a chemical taste to water. Because it is more reactive than chlorine, it has to be produced on site, so it is more expensive to use. Unlike chlorine, ozone does not provide additional protection against pathogens since it has a very short retention time, decomposing to give ordinary oxygen, O_2, so the water has to be used soon after purification. An ideal water treatment system is to use ozone for killing bacteria and viruses, and then to add a much smaller amount of chlorine to provide protection until the water is consumed.

Using Chlorine Dioxide Chlorine dioxide, ClO_2, is becoming an increasingly popular alternative to chlorine for water purification. It is effective at killing micro-organisms at very low concentrations and disinfects water differently than chlorine or ozone: it penetrates the cell walls of bacteria, reacts with amino acids in the cytoplasm of the cells, and thereby destroys the micro-organism. It is converted into the chlorite ion, which poses no significant adverse health risks.

Some Common Pollutants

Among the many substances that can pollute water supplies, there are some pollutants that have maximum limits called MACs (Maximum Acceptable Concentrations) allowed in water. If these limits are exceeded, known or suspected adverse health effects may occur.

TABLE 6.3 Maximum Acceptable Concentrations of Some Pollutants in the Drinking Water of Ontario

Pollutant	MAC (mg·L^{-1})	Source
Volatile Organic Compounds		
benzene, C_6H_6	0.005	vehicle emissions, cigarette smoke
carbon tetrachloride, CCl_4	0.005	industrial solvent leaks
dichloromethane, CH_2Cl_2	0.005	solvent, fumigant
toluene (methyl benzene), $C_6H_5CH_3$	0.024	in manufacture of dyes, paints, resins, and medicines
Inorganic Ions		
cadmium, Cd^{2+}	0.005	emissions from zinc-refining plants
copper, Cu^{2+}	1.0	industrial and natural sources
lead, Pb^{2+}	0.01	old plumbing, lead paints, lead-based industries
mercury, Hg_2^{2+} and Hg^{2+}	0.001	variety of low-level sources
nitrates, NO_3^-	10	run-off from use of agricultural fertilizers
Pesticides and PCBs		
DDT	0.03	used in some countries against the spread of malarial mosquitoes
PCBs (polychlorinated biphenyls)	0.003	fluid leaks from electrical transformers

DDT has been banned in many countries due to its biological magnification through the food chain. In the reproductive systems of birds, DDT interferes with the formation of eggshells. The weakened shells often break or crack, killing the embryo. As a result, the past heavy use of DDT caused catastrophic declines in many bird populations, including eagle and osprey populations. On the other hand, malaria continues to be one of the most deadly diseases on the planet, and DDT is one of the few ways of killing malaria-carrying mosquitoes in tropical regions. Many countries in the tropics are opposed to a total ban, arguing that lives can be saved through the prudent use of DDT in their fight against malaria.

Ammonium nitrate, NH_4NO_3, used extensively as a fertilizer, is a source of nitrate ions in water. Nitrate ions are highly water-soluble, so they end up in the water system. In agricultural areas, nitrate concentrations, particularly in well water, can exceed the maximum safe level established by the World Health Organization of 50 mg·L^{-1}. Once the nitrates are dissolved in water, they are converted into toxic nitrites by bacteria present in the human digestive system. In addition, nitrates and phosphates are plant nutrients that, in water, produce the growth of surface plants such as algae. This excess growth is the first stage in the process of eutrophication. In this process, the rapid growth of organisms reduces the oxygen level in the body of water, killing fish and other organisms.

Three Stages of Sewage Treatment

Sewage is the used water that flows away from any community. It can be more than 99.9% pure water, but it also contains wastes from industry, business, household, and sanitation sources. Such sewage contains disease-causing

TABLE 6.4 Sources, Health Effects, and Environmental Effects of Cadmium, Mercury, and Lead

Heavy Metal	Sources	Health Effects	Environmental Effects
cadmium	by-product of zinc refining; rechargeable Ni-Cd batteries; metal plating and pigments	Itai-Itai disease; makes bones brittle and easily broken; kidney and lung cancer in humans	toxic to fish; produces birth defects in mice, inducing abortions
mercury	Hg batteries; Hg amalgams for dental filling and Hg salts as fungicides; mercury cell in chlor-alkali industry	Minamata disease; paralysis and mental disorders	reproductive system failure in fish; inhibits growth and kills fish; biological magnification in the food chain
lead	lead paints; TEL (tetraethyl lead) in gasoline as anti-knocking agent (banned in many countries)	low birth weight, still birth, brain damage	toxic to plants and domestic animals; biological magnification in the food chain

micro-organisms, organic materials, and other toxic substances such as heavy metal ions. Sewage treatment removes hazardous materials, reduces the amount of oxygen-demanding organic substances, and kills micro-organisms prior to discharge.

Different types of sewage treatment with different degrees of effectiveness are carried out depending on the availability of resources; the cost increases with more advanced treatment. These are classified as *primary*, *secondary*, and *tertiary* treatment. Each brings about a more complete reduction of contaminants, with the tertiary treatment being much more expensive to build and operate.

FIGURE 6.25 Aeration tanks in a typical sewage treatment plant

Primary Sewage Treatment   The sewage is first passed through screens to filter out larger objects, such as trash and debris. Floating objects including grease are also removed. The wastewater then passes through settling tanks where smaller, heavier objects (rocks, stones) settle and are removed. It is then channelled through holding or sedimentation tanks, where smaller particles settle; the resulting sludge is removed from the bottom of the tanks. The mechanical process of sedimentation is speeded up by adding chemicals, such as aluminum sulfate. The chemical works as follows: The particles tend to have the same electric charge, so they repel one another. If a highly charged ionic compound, such as aluminum sulfate, is added, the ions with a charge opposite to that on the particle stick to its surface. With the charge neutralized, the particles will clump together, a process known as flocculation. The large clumps, called flocs, settle at the bottom with the suspended particles and are filtered off.

Primary treatment is generally not sufficient to improve the quality of water to safe levels, even if it is treated with chlorine, ozone, or chlorine dioxide to kill pathogens. A typical primary treatment domestic sewage plant can remove about 30% to 40% of oxygen-demanding wastes.

Secondary Sewage Treatment This process involves microbial activity and requires aeration (Figure 6.25). Air or air enriched with oxygen is bubbled through the sewage mixed with bacteria-laden sludge using large blowers. This allows aerobic bacteria to mix thoroughly with the sewage to break down most of the organic matter. The process is biological in nature and is called an activated sludge process. The water containing decomposed suspended particles is passed through a sedimentation tank where large quantities of biologically active sludge collect. Part of the sludge is recycled and the rest is disposed of.

This biological process is then followed by treatment with chlorine gas or ozone gas to kill pathogenic bacteria before it is released into lakes or rivers or to a tertiary plant for further treatment. Secondary sewage treatment can remove about 90% of the organic wastes and suspended particles. However, primary and secondary treatments cannot remove dissolved inorganic substances such as heavy metal ions, which require further treatment (Figure 6.26).

WEBLINK

How pure is the water from Ontario's sewage plants? What are the maximum allowable levels of inorganic ions? How do the ion levels in your local sewage treatment plant compare with the maximum allowable values? Write a report on your findings. Begin your research at **www.pearsoned.ca/chemistry11**.

FIGURE 6.26 An illustration of a typical sewage treatment process

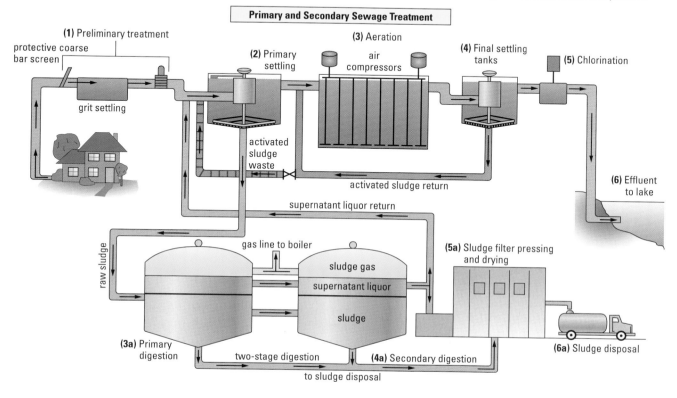

CHAPTER 6 Properties of Solutions **239**

Case *Study*

Don't Drink the Water— the Walkerton Outbreak

Decision-Making Skills

▷ Defining the Issue
▷ Developing Assessment Criteria
▷ Researching the Issue
▷ Analyzing Data and Information
▷ Proposing a Course of Action
▷ Justifying the Course of Action
▷ Communicating Your Proposal

BACKGROUND INFORMATION

The community of Walkerton experienced an outbreak of illness that was linked to the municipal water supply. On Sunday May 21, 2000, the Medical Officer of Health issued a "boil water" advisory to the residents of Walkerton, and the advisory was lifted on December 5, 2000. According to the Executive Summary issued by the Bruce–Grey–Owen Sound Health Unit (BGOSHU), intensive case-finding for the descriptive study ultimately led to the identification of 1346 reported cases of gastroenteritis with exposure to Walkerton municipal water. The number of Walkerton residents that became ill was approximately 1286. The overall estimated number of cases associated with the outbreak was over 2300. Newspaper reports have suggested that several deaths have occurred as a result of the outbreak.

Analysis of Walkerton households conducted in June 2000 confirmed that people residing in homes consuming water from the municipal water supply were 11.7 times more likely to develop gastroenteritis than those not exposed to Walkerton water. Testing of water samples from the distribution system on May 21 and of water from Well 5 on May 23 demonstrated significant contamination with coliform and *E. coli* bacteria. Subsequent DNA analysis of these samples confirmed the presence of *E. coli* in the water samples. Within 5 days of issuing the "boil water" advisory, the number of new cases dropped substantially.

Analyzing the Issue

1. Describe the chemical processes involved in the monitoring of a community's water supply, and identify who is responsible for this monitoring.

2. Construct a list of stakeholders who were connected to the Walkerton crisis. For each group, write a statement that defines the issue from its perspective.

3. Classify the issue as it relates to environmental, economic, political, social, and health consequences. Identify the criteria you used for your classification system. Create a consequence map showing how the consequences are related to each other.

4. Research information on the recommendations from the Walkerton inquiries.

5. Design a communication plan that you would expect to be implemented with citizens if a water crisis were to occur in your community.

Tertiary Sewage Treatment This stage involves specialized chemical and/or physical processes that further treat water after it has undergone primary and secondary treatments. This process removes the remaining organic materials, nutrients, and substances not removed by the biological processes in the secondary treatment, such as toxic metal ions. Examples of tertiary processes include carbon bed, reverse osmosis (mentioned earlier), chemical precipitation, electrodialysis, and ion exchange. The carbon bed method will be discussed here and the latter three in the next chapter.

The **carbon bed** method uses activated black carbon, which consists of tiny carbon granules having large surface areas that have been treated and activated by high temperatures. The activated carbon has the ability to readily **adsorb** organic chemicals from wastewater. Carbon beds are effective against many toxic organic materials, and charcoal filters are often used to purify tap water further for drinking purposes.

Section 6.2 Review

Understanding Concepts

1. List five different origins of pollutants in water, and give a brief explanation of the consequences of each.

2. Describe the main purification methods used by water treatment plants. State the pros and cons of each method.

3. Explain how secondary sewage treatment differs from tertiary treatment.

4. Explain why it is important to identify Maximum Acceptable Concentrations (MACs) in drinking water and the possible consequences if there are no limits.

Making Connections

5. Research the current effectiveness of DDT at combatting malaria, and complete a risk/benefit analysis on whether the environmental and biological costs outweigh the risks. Prioritize the factors that you think should affect the decision a country should make regarding using DDT, and justify your priorities.

6. A major industry (Industry X) is known to have dumped a particularly deadly toxin that can affect the water system. The clean-up will cost billions of dollars. The industry continues operation since it is a major economic source for employment and revenue to Canada. However, it cannot pay the cost of the clean-up, and if it shuts down, thousands of people will lose their jobs. Provide an informed argument supporting one of the following points of view:

   a) The industry should shut down immediately if it cannot pay for the clean-up, regardless of the social and economic effects.

   b) The industry is a valuable source of employment and revenue for Canada, and an alternative solution must be found so that it can continue to operate.

6.3 Calculating the Concentration of a Solution

Key Understandings

When you have completed this section, you will be able to:
- define volume percent, mass percent, mass-volume percent, parts per million, and parts per billion
- calculate the concentration of a solution using different units
- determine the concentration of ions present in a solution

How much sugar is in your soft drink? How many sodium ions are in your blood? What is the ozone level in the city air? To answer these questions, you use the concept of **concentration** of a solution. The more solute that is dissolved in a solvent, the higher the concentration of that solution. But there are various ways of expressing the concentration of a solution. In the previous section, the solubilities of various substances were expressed using units of grams of solute per litre of water (the solvent). But there are different units used depending on the circumstances. In this section, the most common units and the method to calculate concentrations in those units will be given.

Calculating Concentration in Moles per Litre

In chemistry, **moles per litre** ($mol \cdot L^{-1}$) is the most common way of representing how much solute is present in a solution. To determine the concentration of a solution in moles per litre, you must know the number of moles of solute present in a given volume of the solution, not a given volume of solvent. The relationship used to calculate the concentration of a solution is:

$$\text{concentration} = \frac{\text{amount of solute (moles)}}{\text{volume of solution (L)}} \quad \text{or} \quad c = \frac{n}{V}$$

There are, in fact, two ways of representing concentration: you can use the symbol c, as shown above, or you can put square brackets around the chemical formula of the solute. For example, to describe the concentration of a solution of sodium chloride, you can write c_{NaCl} or [NaCl].

In the following examples, you will see how any of the three variables (moles of solute, volume of solution, and concentration) can be calculated if the other two are known.

EXAMPLE 1

A solution contains 5.85 g sodium chloride dissolved in 5.00×10^3 mL of solution. Calculate the concentration of the sodium chloride in $mol \cdot L^{-1}$.

Given
mass of solute = 5.85 g

volume of solution, $V = 5.00 \times 10^3$ mL
$$= (5.00 \times 10^3 \, \text{mL}) \times \frac{1 \, \text{L}}{1000 \, \text{mL}}$$
$$= 5.00 \, \text{L}$$

formula of solute is NaCl

Required
concentration of the sodium chloride = ? $mol \cdot L^{-1}$

Analysis
$m_{NaCl} \rightarrow n_{NaCl}$ (using $M_{NaCl} = 58.44 \, g \cdot mol^{-1}$)

$n_{NaCl}, V \rightarrow c$ (using $c = n/V$)

Solution
$$n_{NaCl} = 5.85 \, \text{g NaCl} \times \frac{1 \, \text{mol NaCl}}{58.44 \, \text{g NaCl}} = 0.100 \, \text{mol NaCl}$$

$$c = \frac{0.100 \, \text{mol NaCl}}{5.00 \, \text{L}} = 2.00 \times 10^{-2} \, mol \cdot L^{-1} \, NaCl$$

Statement
The concentration of the sodium chloride solution is $2.00 \times 10^{-2} \, mol \cdot L^{-1}$.

PRACTICE PROBLEM

A solution contains 12.0 g sodium hydroxide in 2.50×10^2 mL of solution. Calculate the concentration of the sodium hydroxide solution.

EXAMPLE 2

What mass of potassium hydroxide is required to prepare 6.00×10^2 mL of a solution with a concentration of 0.225 mol·L^{-1}?

Given

molecular formula of solute, potassium hydroxide, is KOH

$$V = 6.00 \times 10^2 \text{ mL} = (6.00 \times 10^2 \text{ mL}) \times \frac{1 \text{ L}}{1000 \text{ mL}} = 0.600 \text{ L}$$

$c_{\text{solution}} = 0.225$ mol·L^{-1}

Required

mass of potassium hydroxide to produce specified solution = ? g

Analysis

$c_{\text{solution}} \rightarrow n_{\text{KOH}}$ (using $n = c \times V$)

$n_{\text{KOH}} \rightarrow m_{\text{KOH}}$ (using $M_{\text{KOH}} = 56.11$ g·mol^{-1})

Solution

$$n_{\text{KOH}} = \frac{0.225 \text{ mol KOH}}{1 \text{ L}} \times 0.600 \text{ L} = 0.135 \text{ mol KOH}$$

$$m_{\text{KOH}} = 0.135 \text{ mol KOH} \times \frac{56.11 \text{ KOH}}{1 \text{ mol KOH}} = 7.57 \text{ g KOH}$$

Statement

7.57 g of KOH are required to prepare the solution.

PRACTICE PROBLEM

A saturated solution of calcium sulfate contains 0.209 g of solute in 100.0 mL of solution. Calculate the concentration of the calcium sulfate solution.

EXAMPLE 3

A solution containing 0.125 mol·L^{-1} magnesium chloride is required for an experiment. What is the maximum volume of solution that can be prepared if only 87.8 g solid magnesium chloride are available?

Given

name of solute, magnesium chloride

$c_{\text{solution}} = 0.125$ mol·L^{-1}

mass of solute = 87.8 g

Required

$V = ?$ L

Analysis

$m_{\text{MgCl}_2} \rightarrow n_{\text{MgCl}_2}$ (using $M_{\text{MgCl}_2} = 95.20$ g·mol^{-1})

$n_{\text{MgCl}_2}, c \rightarrow V$ (using $V = n/c$)

PRACTICE PROBLEM

A solution containing 1.25×10^{-1} mol·L^{-1} silver nitrate is required for an experiment. Calculate the volume of solution that can be prepared if only 8.78 g solid silver nitrate is available.

Solution

$$n_{\text{MgCl}_2} = 87.8 \text{ g MgCl}_2 \times \frac{1 \text{ mol MgCl}_2}{95.20 \text{ g MgCl}_2} = 0.922 \text{ mol MgCl}_2$$

$$V = \frac{0.922 \text{ mol MgCl}_2}{0.125 \text{ mol·L}^{-1} \text{ MgCl}_2} = 7.38 \text{ L}$$

Statement

The maximum volume of solution is 7.38 L.

Then & NOW

Claude Litre: Canadian Humour That Became "Fact"

You will have noticed that some symbols of units are written in upper-case letters while others are written in lower-case. The rules outlined by the Conférence Générale des Poids et Mesures require that upper-case letters be used only when the unit is named after a person. Some examples are listed in Table 6.5.

In 1977, while stuck in a blizzard in Ottawa, two science professors from the University of Waterloo, Reg Friesen and Ken Woolner, started discussing the American proposal that the symbol for litre should be changed from "*l*" to "L." The italic el had been used in the first place to distinguish el from the symbol for

"one." But the simple typewriters of the time did not have an italic el, and the sophisticated ones required the typist to stop and change the type ball every time they encountered the litre symbol. The capital el seemed to be the best solution.

Recalling the rules, Friesen suggested that they should invent a scientist by the name of Litre and that Woolner could write a fictitious biography of Litre. Woolner did this, and the account of imaginary Claude Émile Jean-Baptiste Litre (1716–1778) appeared in the April issue of the magazine *Chem13 News* as an April Fools' joke. One reader then invented a biography of a daughter for Litre, Milli Litre.

This humorous article would have faded into obscurity but for one thing. The prestigous journal *Chemistry International* published a shortened version of the article, leaving out the clues that the biography was a hoax. People started believing there really had been a sci-

entist called Litre! The biography was broadcast on CBC Radio, and the account appeared in a Canadian high school textbook. Letters came from people as far away as California, who were eager for more details on this "famous and forgotten scientist." Even today, many people believe Litre was a real person rather than the product of the active imaginations of two Canadian scientists!

FIGURE 6.27 Ken Woolner (left) and Reg Friesen wearing their Claude Litre T-shirts. Friesen (1937–1998), one of Canada's most famous chemical educators, suggested that a fictitious Professor Litre be invented to justify the use of an upper-case "L" as a symbol for the litre.

TABLE 6.5 A Selection of Units Named after Famous Scientists

Unit	Symbol	Named For
celsius	°C	Anders Celsius
curie	C	Marie Curie
kelvin	K	Lord Kelvin
pascal	Pa	Blaise Pascal

Calculating Percent Concentrations

Although chemists usually express concentrations in moles per litre, if you look at household products, you will see that other units are used. These involve the determination of the proportion of a solute using mass and/or volume.

Volume Percent   When two liquids are mixed to form a solution, it is often convenient to express the composition of the solution in terms of volume percent of solute. Vinegar is typically 5% acetic acid by volume and can be represented as 5% (v/v). This means that 5 mL of acetic acid are present in 100 mL of vinegar solution. You will find that the alcohol content of beers, wines, and spirits is usually given in this way. The **volume percent** of the solute is calculated as follows:

$$\% \text{ solute (by volume)} = \frac{\text{volume of solute}}{\text{volume of solution}} \times 100\%$$

EXAMPLE 4

The concentration of acetic acid, CH_3COOH, in a sample of vinegar is determined to be 0.878 mol·L^{-1}. If the density of acetic acid is 1.045 g·mL^{-1}, calculate the volume percent of acetic acid in the vinegar sample.

Given
molecular formula for acetic acid is CH_3COOH
$[CH_3COOH]$ in vinegar $= 0.878$ mol·L^{-1}
density of acetic acid, $d = 1.045$ g·mL^{-1} or $d = \dfrac{1.045 \text{ g}}{1 \text{ mL}} \times \dfrac{1000 \text{ mL}}{1 \text{ L}}$
$$= 1045 \text{ g·L}^{-1}$$

Required
volume % of acetic acid in vinegar $= ?\%$

Analysis
First, calculate the amount of acetic acid in 1 L of solution.
$c_{CH_3COOH}, V_{\text{solution}} \rightarrow n_{CH_3COOH}$ (using $n = c \times V$)
$n_{CH_3COOH} \rightarrow m_{CH_3COOH}$ (using $M_{CH_3COOH} = 60.06$ g·mol^{-1})
$m_{CH_3COOH} \rightarrow V_{CH_3COOH}$ $\left(\text{using } d = \dfrac{m}{V} \right)$

volume % of $CH_3COOH = \dfrac{\text{volume of } CH_3COOH}{\text{volume of solution}} \times 100\%$

Solution
$n_{CH_3COOH} = 0.878$ mol·L^{-1} $CH_3COOH \times 1.00$ L $= 0.878$ mol CH_3COOH
$m_{CH_3COOH} = 0.878$ mol $CH_3COOH \times \dfrac{60.06 \text{ g } CH_3COOH}{1 \text{ mol } CH_3COOH} = 52.73$ g CH_3COOH
$V_{CH_3COOH} = 52.73$ g $\times \dfrac{1 \text{ L}}{1045 \text{ g}} = 5.05 \times 10^{-2}$ L
volume % of $CH_3COOH = \dfrac{5.05 \times 10^{-2} \text{ L}}{1 \text{ L}} \times 100\%$
$$= 5.05\%$$

Statement
The volume percent of acetic acid in vinegar is 5.05%.

PRACTICE PROBLEMS

1. The concentration of hydrochloric acid in a sample is 9.47 mol·L^{-1}. If the density of hydrochloric acid is 1.15 g·mL^{-1}, calculate the volume percent of hydrochloric acid in the sample.

2. The concentration of nitric acid in a sample is 15.4 mol·L^{-1}. If the density of nitric acid is 1.41 g·mL^{-1}, calculate the volume percent of nitric acid in the sample.

Mass Percent You are familiar with the purity of gold expressed in karats, with 24 karats being the highest purity. The scale is actually based on mass percent, where 24 karats is 100% gold by mass. Consequently, 18-karat gold is an alloy and is 75% gold by mass. Alloys consist of two or more metals that have been melted together and then cooled to the solid state, and as such are solid solutions. An alloy can also be obtained by forming a solid solution from a metal (or metals) and a small proportion of a non-metal, such as carbon, silicon, or phosphorus. The composition of an alloy is usually expressed as mass percent. The properties of an alloy can be very different from those of the metals from which it is formed. Why is a gold alloy often used in jewellery rather than pure gold?

TABLE 6.6 Composition of Some Common Alloys

Alloy	Composition (mass %)
brass	Cu (85), Zn (15)
stainless steel	Fe (74), Cr (18), Ni (8)
nickel coinage	Cu (75), Ni (25)
sterling silver	Ag (92.5), Cu (7.5)
18-karat gold	Au (75), Ag (10–20), Cu (1–15)
pewter	Sn (85), Cu (7), Bi (6), Sb (2)
plumber's solder	Pb (67), Sn (33)

Mass percent calculations are similar to those of volume percent. That is, **mass percent** is the percentage of solute (by mass) in a given mass of solution.

$$\% \text{ solute (by mass)} = \frac{\text{mass of solute}}{\text{(mass of solution)}} \times 100\%$$

FIGURE 6.28 An 8th century B.C. Chinese bronze ritual wine vessel. The earliest useful alloy was bronze (about 80% copper, 20% tin by mass). Even 3000 years ago, beautiful objects were cast from this versatile alloy.

FIGURE 6.29 Many food products list the amounts of some ingredients using percentages. Without units, you can't be certain how these concentrations were calculated.

EXAMPLE 5

Electrician's solder consists of 60% tin and 40% lead mass percent. It has a sharp melting point lower than either constituent metal, which minimizes damage to electrical circuits. What is the mole ratio of the two elements?

Given
Sn = 60%; Pb = 40%

Required
mole ratio

Analysis
Assume 100 g of solder.

This would contain 60 g Sn and 40 g Pb.

Mass can then be converted to moles and the ratio calculated.

Solution

$$n_{Sn} = 60 \text{ g Sn} \times \frac{1 \text{ mol Sn}}{118.69 \text{ g Sn}} = 0.51 \text{ mol Sn}$$

$$n_{Pb} = 40 \text{ g Pb} \times \frac{1 \text{ mol Pb}}{207.19 \text{ g Pb}} = 0.19 \text{ mol Pb}$$

$$\text{ratio} = \frac{0.51 \text{ mol Sn}}{0.19 \text{ mol}} : \frac{0.19 \text{ mol Pb}}{0.19 \text{ mol}} = 2.6 \text{ Sn} : 1 \text{ Pb}$$

Statement
For every 1 mol of lead, the solder contains 2.6 mol of tin (i.e., there are over $2\frac{1}{2}$ times as many tin atoms as lead atoms in the alloy).

PRACTICE PROBLEMS

1. A solution contains 5.3 g potassium chloride in 255.5 g water. Calculate the mass percent of solute in this solution.

2. A bottle of hydrochloric acid has a label saying that the solution is 37.0% HCl by mass. If the density of the solution is 1.18 $g \cdot mL^{-1}$, determine the concentration of the solution in moles per litre.

Mass-Volume Percent   There is a third type of concentration unit that you may discover on household products: **mass-volume percent** (% m/v). This concentration is used when the solute is a solid and the solvent is a liquid. It is given by the formula:

$$\% \text{ m/v} = \frac{\text{mass solute (g)}}{\text{volume solution (mL)}} \times 100\%$$

For example, a 3% solution of iodine (called a "tincture of iodine") means that 3 g of iodine are dissolved in 100 mL of solution. The solvent in this case is alcohol. The concentration is written as 3% m/v and the units are $g \cdot mL^{-1}$%.

This unit has been used to debunk the myth that sugar added to the gas tank of an automobile engine will dissolve in the gasoline and that the solution will cause the engine to seize up. Since "like dissolves like," the polar sugar will dissolve in polar water, but it is unlikely to dissolve to any significant extent in non-polar gasoline. Measurements have shown that, in fact, sugar only dissolves in gasoline to the extent of 0.15% m/v (1.5 $g \cdot L^{-1}$). Therefore, the most sugar that would dissolve in an average-sized tank (60 L) of pure gasoline would be about 90 g.

EXAMPLE 6

Ordinary tea typically contains 3.3% m/v caffeine. What mass of caffeine (in mg) will there be in a 150-mL cup of tea? Assume the tea is essentially 100% water.

Given
concentration of caffeine = 3.3% m/v = 0.033 g·mL^{-1}%

volume = 150 mL

Required
mass of caffeine

Analysis
$$\% \text{ m/v} = \frac{\text{mass solute (g)}}{\text{volume solution (mL)}} \times 100\%$$

Solution
$$\text{mass solute (g)} = \left(\frac{0.033 \text{ g}}{1 \text{ mL}}\right)\% \times \frac{150 \text{ mL}}{100\%} = 0.049 \text{ g} = 49 \text{ mg}$$

Statement
The mass of caffeine is 49 mg.

A basic solution contains 4.00% m/v sodium hydroxide. Calculate the mass of sodium hydroxide (in mg) that would be present in 250 mL of the solution.

Calculating Concentrations in Parts Per Million and Parts Per Billion

Electronic instrumentation has enabled chemists to measure ever lower concentrations of trace pollutants. Years ago, parts per thousands were the limits, then **parts per million** (1 part in 10^6), and now **parts per billion** (1 part in 10^9) and even parts per trillion (1 part in 10^{12}). But what do the numbers mean? For example, if you read that a sample of your favourite food contained 0.2 ppm of toxic cadmium, you might give it up in panic. However, 0.2 ppm is the average concentration of cadmium in soil. So there is nothing to worry about. On the other hand, a concentration of 20 ppm would be a major concern.

The two most common concentrations, ppm and ppb, are calculated using the following formulas:

$$\text{ppm} = \frac{\text{mass of solute}}{\text{mass of solution}} \times 10^6$$

$$\text{ppb} = \frac{\text{mass of solute}}{\text{mass of solution}} \times 10^9$$

How would you calculate parts per trillion?

EXAMPLE 7

Biological magnification, that is, the increase of concentration of a substance up the food chain, is a particular environmental problem. A scientific study reported that seabirds living on a particular lagoon contained 25 ppb of DDT, although the DDT-sprayed water contained only 3 ppb of the insecticide. What mass of DDT would be present in a 4.0-kg seabird containing this concentration of DDT?

Given
concentration of DDT in bird = 25 ppb
mass of bird = 4.0 kg

Required
$m_{DDT} = ?$

Analysis
$$c_{DDT} \rightarrow m_{DDT} \left(\text{using ppb} = \frac{\text{mass solute}}{\text{total mass}} \times 10^9 \text{ or } m_{DDT} = m_{bird} \times \frac{\text{ppb}}{10^9} \right)$$

Solution
$$m_{DDT} = (4.0 \times 10^3 \text{ g}) \times \frac{25 \text{ ppb}}{10^9}$$

$$m_{DDT} = 1.0 \times 10^{-4} \text{ g} = 0.10 \text{ mg}$$

Statement
The mass of DDT in the 4.0-kg seabird is 0.10 mg.

PRACTICE PROBLEM

Ammonium nitrate, NH_4NO_3, used extensively as a fertilizer, is a source of nitrate ions in water. The World Health Organization set the maximum nitrate ion concentration at 10 ppm for infants and 50 ppm for adults.
a) If an infant has a mass of 4.0 kg, calculate the maximum allowed mass of nitrate ions that would be present in the infant's body.
b) Compare your answer in a) with an adult's maximum allowed limit if the mass of the adult is 62 kg.

Calculating Ionic Concentrations

In many solutions, such as water supplies, chemists are less interested in the concentration of compounds than in individual ions. There is a myth that water from a well is always good quality drinking water. However, the composition of well water reflects the elements and compounds present in the rocks through which the water has travelled. Without knowing the precise geological structure of the rocks, it is always recommended to have well water analyzed for its chemical (and biological) composition.

Arsenic is one element that can be found in well-water supplies. The World Health Organization recommends that people should not drink water containing more than $1 \times 10^{-7} \text{ mol·L}^{-1}$ of arsenic. There are sites in Canada where this maximum level is exceeded, but there is a bigger problem in India and Bangladesh. In those countries, millions of people depend on their local well water as the only available source of water (Figure 6.30). The level of water in wells has dropped over recent times as a result of the increasing need by agriculture and the requirements of a growing population. As the levels of water have dropped, the arsenic concentrations have increased dramatically. Values as high as 900 times the maximum recommended levels have been recorded. Millions of people, particularly children, are faced with serious health conditions as a result of their arsenic intake.

How do you calculate the concentration of ions in solution if you know the concentration of the compound? The calculation involves one additional step beyond the standard concentration calculations.

FIGURE 6.30 Water being pumped from wells in Bangladesh. Much of the well water contains toxic levels of arsenic.

EXAMPLE 8

In a solution containing 15.6 g magnesium chloride, $MgCl_2$, in 1.25 L of solution, what is the concentration of chloride ions?

Given
mass of solute, $MgCl_2$ = 15.6 g

volume of solution = 1.25 L

Required
$[Cl^-]$ = ? $mol \cdot L^{-1}$

Analysis
$m_{MgCl_2} \rightarrow n_{MgCl_2}$ (using M_{MgCl_2} = 95.20 $g \cdot mol^{-1}$)

$n_{MgCl_2} \rightarrow n_{Cl^-}$ (using mole ratio, 1 mol $MgCl_2$: 2 mol Cl^-)

$n_{Cl^-} \rightarrow [Cl^-]$ $\left(using \ c_{Cl^-} = \dfrac{n_{Cl^-}}{V_{solution}}\right)$

Solution
n_{MgCl_2} = 15.6 g $\overline{MgCl_2}$ $\times \dfrac{1 \ mol \ MgCl_2}{95.20 \ g \ \overline{MgCl_2}}$ = 0.164 mol $MgCl_2$

n_{Cl^-} = 0.164 mol $\overline{MgCl_2}$ $\times \dfrac{2 \ mol \ Cl^-}{1 \ mol \ \overline{MgCl_2}}$ = 0.328 mol Cl^-

$[Cl^-]$ = $\dfrac{0.328 \ mol \ Cl^-}{1.25 \ L}$ = 0.262 $mol \cdot L^{-1}$ Cl^-

Statement
The concentration of Cl^- is 0.262 $mol \cdot L^{-1}$.

PRACTICE PROBLEM

In a solution containing 21.2 g sodium carbonate in 1.50 L of solution, calculate the concentration of the sodium and carbonate ions.

EXAMPLE 9

If 525 mL of a solution containing 6.78 g calcium bromide ($CaBr_2$) is mixed with 325 mL of a solution containing 11.4 g potassium bromide (KBr), what is the bromide ion concentration in the resulting solution? Assume that the volumes are additive; that is, the final volume is the sum of the two initial volumes.

Given
volume of $CaBr_2$ solution = 525 mL

mass of $CaBr_2$ = 6.78 g

volume of KBr solution = 325 mL

mass of KBr = 11.4 g

Required
$[Br^-]$ = ? $mol \cdot L^{-1}$

▶

Analysis

$m_{CaBr_2} \rightarrow n_{CaBr_2}$ (using $M_{CaBr_2} = 199.88$ g·mol^{-1})

$m_{KBr} \rightarrow n_{KBr}$ (using $M_{KBr} = 119.00$ g·mol^{-1})

$n_{CaBr_2} \rightarrow n_{Br^-}$ (using mole ratio, 1 mol Ca^{2+} : 2 mol Br$^-$)

$n_{KBr} \rightarrow n_{Br^-}$ (using mole ratio, 1 mol K$^+$: 1 mol Br$^-$)

total n_{Br^-} = (n_{Br^-} from CaBr$_2$ solution) + (n_{Br^-} from KBr solution)

total V = (V of CaBr$_2$ solution) + (V of KBr solution)

$c_{Br^-} = \dfrac{n_{Br^-}}{V_{solution}}$

Solution

$n_{CaBr_2} = 6.78 \text{ g CaBr}_2 \times \dfrac{1 \text{ mol CaBr}_2}{199.88 \text{ g CaBr}_2} = 3.39 \times 10^{-2}$ mol CaBr$_2$

$n_{KBr} = 11.4 \text{ g KBr} \times \dfrac{1 \text{ mol KBr}}{119.00 \text{ g KBr}} = 9.58 \times 10^{-2}$ mol KBr

n_{Br^-} from CaBr$_2$ = 3.39×10^{-2} mol CaBr$_2$ $\times \dfrac{2 \text{ mol Br}^-}{1 \text{ mol CaBr}_2}$

$\qquad = 6.78 \times 10^{-2}$ mol Br$^-$

n_{Br^-} from KBr = 9.58×10^{-2} mol KBr $\times \dfrac{1 \text{ mol Br}^-}{1 \text{ mol KBr}}$

$\qquad = 9.58 \times 10^{-2}$ mol Br$^-$

Therefore,

total n_{Br^-} = (6.78×10^{-2}) mol + (9.58×10^{-2}) mol = 0.164 mol

total V = $(525 \text{ mL} + 325 \text{ mL})\left(\dfrac{1 \text{ L}}{1000 \text{ mL}}\right)$ = 0.850 L

$[Br^-] = \dfrac{0.164 \text{ mol Br}^-}{0.850 \text{ L}} = 0.192$ mol·L^{-1} Br$^-$

Statement

The bromide ion concentration in the resulting solution is 0.192 mol·L^{-1}.

PRACTICE PROBLEMS

1. In a solution containing 34.2 g aluminum sulfate in 125 mL of solution, calculate the concentration of the aluminum and sulfate ions.

2. 265 mL of a solution containing 5.93 g magnesium chloride is mixed with 135 mL of a solution containing 3.13 g sodium chloride. Calculate the concentration of chloride ions in the resulting solution. Assume that the volumes are additive.

FIGURE 6.31 Seawater is a solution that contains many dissolved minerals, such as chlorine, sodium, magnesium, sulfur, calcium, potassium, bromine, and even silver and gold.

The Fluoridation
of Drinking Water

Decision-Making Skills

Defining the Issue

Developing Assessment Criteria

▶ Researching the Issue

▶ Analyzing Data and Information

▶ Proposing a Course of Action

▶ Justifying the Course of Action

Communicating Your Proposal

BACKGROUND INFORMATION

Ever since fluoride was first added to the water supplies of Grand Rapids, Michigan, in 1945, the controversy over the fluoridation of drinking water has raged, with scientific facts becoming confused with political agendas. Proponents of fluoridation claim that it prevents the incidence of tooth decay and presents minimal health risks. Groups such as the American Dental Association contend that fluoridation of water reduces the incidence of tooth decay by 40% to 65%. Detractors claim that it may cause serious health problems in some individuals. Some question its effectiveness in preventing cavities. Furthermore, many critics see fluoridation as a violation of individual choice, saying it is a form of medication imposed on the public. Others believe that the effects of fluoride should be investigated using the same criteria as for other environmental pollutants.

The data to support the fluoridation campaign were strengthened by a study comparing Sarnia, Brantford, and Stratford. In that study, tooth decay in Brantford dropped from a rate of over 90% for 9–11 year olds to about 55% following the addition of 1 ppm fluoride ion to the water. The low rate matched that in Stratford where the water naturally contained 1.6 ppm fluoride ion. However, tooth decay is a complicated process, influenced by diet, oral hygiene, dental care, genetic predisposition, geochemical factors, and the presence of naturally occurring fluoride in drinking water.

Currently, fluoride is added to water supplies in parts of Canada, the United States, Australia, Russia, and some other countries. In developing countries where only small amounts of sugar and processed foods are consumed, the rates of tooth decay are often lower than in developed nations. Because people in low-fluoride areas are consuming foods processed in fluoridated regions, cavity rates in those areas have fallen too. Medical authorities around the world such as Health Canada, the Canadian Medical Association, the Canadian Dental Association, and the Canadian Public Health Association continue to support fluoridation.

Analyzing the Issue

1. From the information provided, prepare a PMI chart about the addition of fluoride to water supplies.

2. Research the use of fluoride in toothpaste. Identify the fluoride-containing compounds used in different brands of toothpaste. The tubes have labels warning that young children should use very small amounts of toothpaste to prevent excessive fluoride intake. Perform a study to discover what percent of parents are aware of this warning.

3. Identify the reasons behind the controversies related to the fluoride campaigns.

4. Develop a criteria list that citizens need to consider to make an informed decision. Identify potential biases and sources of misinformation.

5. Design an information brochure that will inform citizens on how to make informed decisions for controversial issues that affect them.

Section 6.3 Review

Understanding Concepts

1. In your own words, distinguish between volume percent, mass percent, and mass-volume percent.

Applying Inquiry/ Communication Skills

2. Calculate the concentration, in moles per litre, of each of the following aqueous solutions:
   a) 1.06 g sodium carbonate dissolved in 100.0 mL of solution
   b) 111.0 g calcium chloride dissolved in 20.0 L of solution
   c) 1.70×10^2 g silver nitrate dissolved in 5.00 L of solution

3. Calculate the mass of copper(II) sulfate pentahydrate required to prepare 1.50 L of aqueous copper sulfate solution with a concentration of 0.500 $mol \cdot L^{-1}$.

4. A laboratory technician wishes to prepare a large volume of sodium hydroxide solution with a concentration of 3.00 $mol \cdot L^{-1}$. In the stockroom, there is one unopened bottle containing 5.00 kg sodium hydroxide pellets. Determine the volume of solution that can be prepared.

5. A saline drip used in a hospital has a sodium chloride concentration of 0.154 $mol \cdot L^{-1}$. Calculate the mass of sodium chloride required to prepare a 250-mL solution of this concentration.

6. An oral rinse sample consists of a 5.76×10^{-2} $mol \cdot L^{-1}$ sodium fluoride solution. Calculate the mass of sodium fluoride required to prepare a 750-mL solution of this concentration.

7. Estimate what the total mass of uranium in all the oceans would be if 1 L of seawater contained 3.2 μg (micrograms) of uranium. The approximate total volume of the oceans is 1.3×10^{24} L.

8. Calculate the concentration of each ion present in the following solutions:
   a) 1.50 $mol \cdot L^{-1}$ NaCl
   b) 0.225 $mol \cdot L^{-1}$ $(NH_4)_2CO_3$
   c) 1.1 $mol \cdot L^{-1}$ $Al_2(SO_4)_3$
   d) 1.00 g KNO_3 is dissolved to give 250.0 mL of solution
   e) 35.4 g $Pb(NO_3)_2$ is dissolved to give 2.50 L of solution

9. If 25.0 mL of sodium nitrate solution (0.100 $mol \cdot L^{-1}$) is added to 10.0 mL of sodium carbonate solution (0.150 $mol \cdot L^{-1}$), calculate the concentration of sodium ions in the resulting mixture. Assume that the volumes are additive.

Making Connections

10. Given that the concentration of gold in seawater is 4 $ng \cdot L^{-1}$ (nanograms per litre) and that the estimated volume of the oceans is 1.3×10^{24} L, calculate the total mass of gold present in seawater. Discuss the economic feasibility of extracting this gold and the effect it would have on the environment.

11. A water sample is found to contain 8 ppb of lead. Calculate the number of lead ions in a glass of water containing 240 mL of water (the density of water is 1.0 $g \cdot mL^{-1}$). Explain why the number of ions is very large. Describe the effect these ions would have on your health and the process you could use to remove them from the water. Compare the health benefits and the economic and environmental costs.

6.4 Preparing Standard Solutions

Key Understandings

When you have completed this section, you will be able to:

- prepare a solution of a specific concentration
- provide examples of solutions for which precise concentrations need to be known
- describe how to dilute a solution
- explain the effect of dilution on concentration

Standard solutions are essential in the chemistry laboratory. Special glassware, called **volumetric flasks**, is used for preparing these solutions. The flasks range in size from 10.00 mL to 2.00 L. The sizes that you are most likely to use in your school laboratory are 100.0 mL and 250.0 mL. These volumes are usually written as whole numbers, that is, as 100 mL and 250 mL. However, the line (graduation mark) on the neck of a flask indicates a volume that is more precise than this. When a 100.0-mL flask is filled to the graduation mark, it contains a volume of 100.0 ± 0.1 mL. This means that the volume is known to the nearest one-tenth of a millilitre. Standard solutions can be prepared using many different solvents, but aqueous solutions, those in which the solvent is water, are the most common.

A practical application of knowing the exact concentration of a substance is the testing of drinking water. Allowed levels of pollutants in freshwater supplies must be measured exactly, since serious health consequences would result if those levels were to exceed government regulations. In most cases, very small quantities of contaminants produce adverse health effects, usually in the parts per million range.

If a solute is known to dissolve very slowly in cool water, you place the solute in a beaker and add about half of the total volume of solvent that you need. The solvent is then heated and stirred until the solute dissolves. Solutions are never heated in volumetric flasks because the flasks are expensive, calibrated pieces of glassware and heating may crack them. As soon as all the solute has dissolved, the solution is poured into the volumetric flask using a funnel. Then you rinse the beaker several times with the solvent to ensure that all the solution is removed from it, each time adding the rinses to the solution in the flask. You can also transfer very carefully all the solute into the volumetric flask, add distilled water to half fill the flask, and shake it until all the solid dissolves. After shaking, you add enough solvent to bring the level of the solution in the flask up to the mark. Then you stopper the flask and shake to mix thoroughly (Figure 6.32).

 Investigation

Refer to page 279, Investigation 2

FIGURE 6.32 Preparation of a standard solution of potassium chromate: a) A known mass of the solute is placed in the volumetric flask. b) Distilled water is added until the flask is about half full, and the flask is shaken until the solid has completely dissolved. c) Distilled water is again added until the flask is full to the mark.

How to Dilute a Standard Solution

You may occasionally find that your laboratory work calls for the use of a solution with a lower concentration than that of the available standard solution. In this situation, you will need to add water to the standard solution. This process is called **dilution** (Figure 6.33). When you have two solutions of the same compound at different concentrations, the solution with the higher concentration is referred to as a **concentrated solution**, and the solution with the lower concentration is referred to as a **dilute solution**. Note that the terms "concentrated" and "dilute" are relative.

Shipping costs are a major factor in distributing solutions. Consequently, it is always cheaper to ship concentrated solutions and dilute them where they are to be used. This applies to chemicals and to soft drinks. The ingredients of your favourite canned or bottled drink were probably shipped from a central blending plant, mixed with specially treated local water supplies, and canned or bottled locally.

To prepare a dilute solution of known concentration from a concentrated solution whose concentration is also known, you will need to use, in addition to a volumetric flask, a **volumetric pipette**. Volumetric pipettes are available in sizes ranging from 5.0 mL to 100.0 mL. The volumetric pipettes that you are most likely to use in your school laboratory are the 10.00-mL and 25.00-mL sizes. The number of significant figures used when citing these volumes indicates the precision you can obtain with these pipettes. When you dilute a solution, the volume increases, the concentration of the solute decreases, but the amount of substance, namely the number of moles, stays the same (Figure 6.34).

FIGURE 6.33 A concentrated copper(II) sulfate solution contains a larger amount of solute than a dilute solution for a given volume of solution. When you add solvent to a concentrated solution, the concentration of the solution decreases but the amount of solute remains the same.

FIGURE 6.34 Dilution of a standard solution: a) The concentrated solution is drawn into a pipette. b) The precisely measured volume is transferred to a volumetric flask. c) Water is added up to the graduation mark. d) The flask is capped and then shaken to mix the contents.

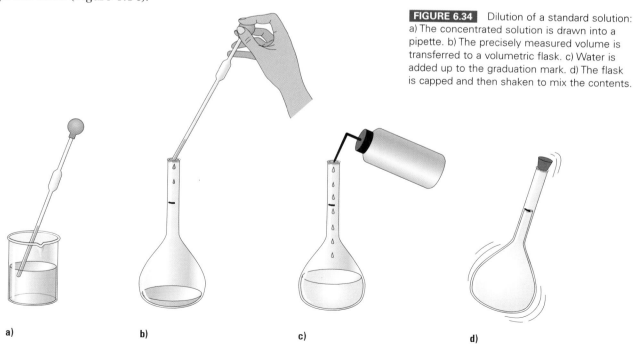

a)   b)   c)   d)

EXAMPLE 10

What volume of a 0.500 mol·L^{-1} sodium hydroxide solution can be prepared from 10.0 mL of a 6.00 mol·L^{-1} solution?

Given
$[NaOH]_{con} = 6.00$ mol·L^{-1}; $V_{con} = 10.0$ mL $= 0.0100$ L
$[NaOH]_{dil} = 0.500$ mol·L^{-1}

Required
$V_{dil} = ?$ L

Analysis
$V_{con}, c_{con} \rightarrow n_{NaOH}$ (using $n = c \times V$)

$n_{NaOH}, c_{dil} \rightarrow V_{dil}$ (using $V = n/c$)

Solution
$n_{NaOH} = 6.00$ mol·L^{-1} NaOH $\times 0.0100$ L $= 6.00 \times 10^{-2}$ mol NaOH

$$V_{dil} = \frac{6.00 \times 10^{-2} \text{ mol NaOH}}{0.500 \text{ mol·L}^{-1} \text{ NaOH}} = 0.120 \text{ L}$$

Statement
The volume of the dilute solution is 0.120 L.

PRACTICE PROBLEMS

1. A saline drip containing a 0.154 mol·L^{-1} sodium chloride solution is to be prepared. Calculate the maximum volume of saline solution that can be prepared if only 7.27 g sodium chloride are available.

2. An oral rinse solution of 5.76 $\times 10^{-2}$ mol·L^{-1} sodium fluoride is to be prepared. Calculate the maximum volume of oral rinse solution that can be prepared if only 7.27 g sodium fluoride are available.

Section 6.4 Review

Understanding Concepts

1. Deduce the two quantities that change and the quantity that remains the same when you dilute a solution of known concentration. Explain your reasoning.

Applying Inquiry/ Communication Skills

2. Give examples where the preparation of a standard solution would be necessary. State the apparatus used to prepare such solutions.

3. An intravenous saline (sodium chloride) drip is labelled as a 0.90% mass-volume solution. Determine the concentration of the saline solution in mol·L^{-1}.

4. Describe the effect that each of the following situations would have on the final concentration of a standard solution.

a) During preparation, some solute is spilled on a laboratory bench.

b) When the distilled water is added, the solution level rises above the graduation mark on the flask.

5. A nurse in a hospital is required to administer a saline drip solution to one of his patients. The solution available is 10% NaCl mass-volume. Calculate how much the solution has to be diluted to create a 0.90% mass-volume solution.

6. Determine the concentration of a hydrochloric acid solution prepared by diluting 25.0 mL of concentrated hydrochloric acid (12 mol·L^{-1}) to a volume of 2.00 L.

7. A concentration of 1.1 mg·L^{-1} fluoride ions is present in drinking water. Outline the steps you would use to prepare a 1.0-L solution of fluoride ions starting with solid sodium fluoride.

6.5 Two Theories Describing Acids and Bases

Key Understandings

When you have completed this section, you will be able to:

- understand the Arrhenius theory of acids and bases including its limitations
- understand the Brønsted-Lowry theory of acids and bases and how it differs from the Arrhenius theory
- describe the qualitative difference between strong and weak acids and bases; explain qualitatively, in terms of degree of dissociation, the difference between strong and weak acids and bases
- write balanced dissociation and ionization chemical equations for reactions involving acids and bases

a)

b)

c)

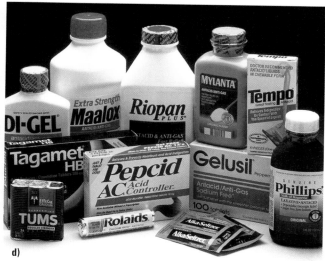

d)

FIGURE 6.35 All the items in these photos either contain acids or bases, or produce acids or bases when they dissolve in water. a) Tomatoes are rich in ascorbic acid (vitamin C). b) Tannic acid is found in tea. c) Human blood at room temperature is slightly basic, and its basicity must be kept within a narrow range to maintain good health. d) Sodium hydrogen carbonate is just one of the many bases found in antacids. These bases react with excess stomach acid to produce water.

Both bees and wasps will sting you if they feel threatened, but there is a big difference between the poisons they inject into you. A wasp's poison is a compound that is highly basic, while a bee's poison is highly acidic. Putting vinegar (acid) on a wasp sting and baking soda (base) on a bee sting will neutralize the poison and ease the pain.

Most of us associate a burning sensation and a sour taste with acids. Some people realize that bases have a slippery feel to them (the slipperiness is caused by the reaction of the bases with the oils on the skin to produce soap). Acids turn blue litmus paper red, while bases turn red litmus paper blue. But how do we define acids and bases in chemistry? This might seem to be a fairly simple question, but it is not. In fact, the development of acid-base theories is an excellent example of how science develops. A theory is proposed to explain known observations. The theory may be simple and may explain the observations from a set of experiments. Then new observations from different experiments are made that may not fit the theory. Can the old theory be adapted or is a new theory needed?

The Arrhenius Theory of Acids and Bases

The simplest definition of acids and bases was given by Arrhenius in 1884. The **Arrhenius theory** of acids and bases states:

An acid is a substance that produces H^+ ions when it is dissolved in water.

$$HCl(aq) \rightarrow H^+(aq) + Cl^-(aq)$$

A base is a substance that produces OH^- ions when it is dissolved in water.

$$NaOH(s) \xrightarrow[\text{in water}]{\text{dissolve}} Na^+(aq) + OH^-(aq)$$

The Arrhenius theory is still useful today as a simple explanation of acids and bases for introductory science. Over the years, scientists noticed two limitations of the Arrhenius theory—one had to do with salts and the other with solvents.

FIGURE 6.36 Svante Arrhenius was awarded the Nobel prize in chemistry in 1903 for his contributions to our understanding of solutions.

The Salt Problem According to the Arrhenius theory, only substances containing H^+ could be classified as acids, and only those containing OH^- could be classified as bases. Furthermore, salts should theoretically be neutral. But this is not always the case. Although many salts are neutral, there are others that dissolve in water to give acidic solutions and some that dissolve to give basic solutions. For example, a solution of sodium carbonate is basic, yet it does not contain hydroxide ions.

Even more surprising is the behaviour of the phosphate ions, dihydrogen phosphate, $H_2PO_4^-$, and hydrogen phosphate, HPO_4^{2-}. If sodium dihydrogen phosphate is dissolved in water, as you would expect, the solution is acidic. Yet a solution of disodium hydrogen phosphate gives a basic solution. How can something that apparently contains H^+ ions give a basic solution? The answer leads to the second limitation of the Arrhenius theory.

The Solvent Problem   According to the Arrhenius theory, an acid should always produce hydrogen ions and a base should always produce hydroxide ions. If hydrogen chloride gas is dissolved in water, as you would expect, the solution acts as an acid. For example, a strip of magnesium metal placed in the solution will react to give a solution of magnesium chloride and hydrogen gas as predicted by the activity series. However, if the hydrogen chloride is dissolved in a non-polar **organic** solvent, the solution will not react with magnesium. Why not? The clue is provided by a conductivity test. The aqueous solution of hydrogen chloride (hydrochloric acid) conducts electricity, while the hydrogen chloride in the organic solvent does not. Therefore, the latter solution cannot contain ions. It is this experiment that indicates that the solvent plays a key role in acid-base properties.

The Brønsted-Lowry Theory of Acids and Bases

In 1923, Johannes Brønsted, a Danish chemist, and Thomas Lowry, an English chemist, independently developed a more general theory of acids and bases. This theory was able to explain the role of the solvent as well as the existence of acidic and basic salt solutions. The **Brønsted-Lowry theory** can be stated as follows:

> **An acid is any molecule or ion that can give up a hydrogen ion. A base is any molecule or ion that can combine with a hydrogen ion.**

Therefore, an acid is a **hydrogen-ion donor**, and a base is a **hydrogen-ion acceptor**. Any molecule or ion that contains hydrogen atoms is a potential acid, and any molecule or ion that has a lone pair of electrons available for bonding with a hydrogen ion is a potential base. In other words, acid-base reactions are **hydrogen-ion exchange reactions** or **proton transfer reactions**. As well, an acid can behave as an acid only in the presence of a base willing and able to accept the hydrogen ion.

For a hydrogen atom to be a potential acid, it must be partially positive in a significantly polar bond. So hydrogen atoms attached to carbon atoms are not acidic. For example, in acetic acid, CH_3COOH, only the hydrogen attached to the oxygen atom is acidic.

CH_3COOH
acetic acid

FIGURE 6.37 Space-filling model of acetic acid

Professor Paul Giguère, a Canadian chemist, at the Université Laval, Quebec, showed that the hydronium ion was present in all acidic solutions.

H_3O^+
hydronium ion

FIGURE 6.39 Space-filling model of the hydronium ion

Brønsted-Lowry Acids When the gas hydrogen chloride is added to water, an acid-base reaction takes place between the molecules of hydrogen chloride and water. The covalent bond in a hydrogen chloride molecule is broken, and the hydrogen ion bonds to the oxygen of a water molecule. Because this process creates ions, it is called **ionization**. This type of chemical equation, in which a molecular compound separates into ions, is called an **ionization equation**.

We can represent this reaction as:

$$HCl(g) + H_2O(l) \xrightarrow[\text{in water}]{\text{dissolve}} H_3O^+(aq) + Cl^-(aq)$$

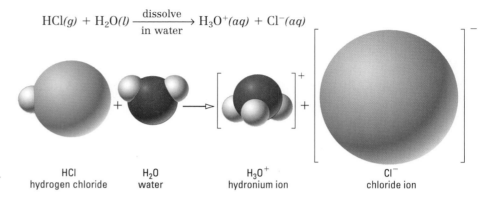

| HCl | H_2O | H_3O^+ | Cl^- |
| hydrogen chloride | water | hydronium ion | chloride ion |

FIGURE 6.38 Space-filling models for the chemical reaction of hydrogen chloride and water

There are two important points about this equation. First, as water is a hydrogen-ion acceptor, it must be acting as a base. Second, the equation requires the product $H_3O^+(aq)$. Brønsted and Lowry proposed the existence of this ion, and they named it the **hydronium ion**. A free H^+ ion cannot exist in aqueous solution since the hydrogen ion is simply a proton. On the other hand, the hydronium ion makes chemical sense because it would have the same number of electrons as ammonia. Draw the hydronium ion and the ammonia molecule, and show this is the case. Because the whole theory depended on the existence of this ion in aqueous solution, it was a great relief when chemists found evidence for its existence.

Brønsted-Lowry Bases The common Brønsted-Lowry bases are soluble metal hydroxides, such as sodium hydroxide or barium hydroxide. They are solid ionic compounds in which sodium ions and hydroxide ions occupy separate locations within the crystal. When they dissolve in water, the process is simply one of the ions becoming attracted and surrounded by water molecules. This process is known as **dissociation**. For example, sodium hydroxide dissociates to give sodium ions and hydroxide ions, and its **dissociation equation** is:

$$Na^+OH^-(s) \xrightarrow[\text{in water}]{\text{dissolve}} Na^+(aq) + OH^-(aq)$$

Soluble metal hydroxides also fit the definition of an Arrhenius base, but the common base ammonia, NH_3, does not. When ammonia gas is dissolved in water, a basic solution is produced. To explain this observation, the Brønsted-Lowry theory is necessary. The lone electron pair on the ammonia molecule can act as a hydrogen-ion acceptor, removing a hydrogen ion from a water molecule. The resulting solution will contain a free hydroxide ion. In this case, water has acted as an acid.

$$NH_3(g) + H_2O(l) \rightarrow NH_4^+(aq) + OH^-(aq)$$

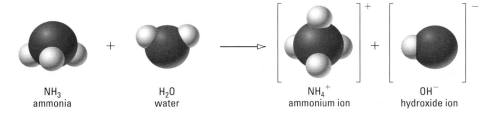

NH₃
ammonia

H₂O
water

NH₄⁺
ammonium ion

OH⁻
hydroxide ion

FIGURE 6.40   Space-filling models for the chemical reaction of ammonia and water

Conjugate Acid-Base Pairs

According to the Brønsted-Lowry theory, every base has a corresponding acid and every acid has a corresponding base. These are called a **conjugate acid** and a **conjugate base** respectively, and they differ in formula by one hydrogen ion. Table 6.7 shows some common conjugate acid-base pairs. Notice that some compounds, such as water, can act as an acid or a base, depending on which compound they are paired with.

The following two equations illustrate the conjugate acid-base pairs. The first shows water acting as a base, and the second shows water acting as an acid:

$$HCl(g) \quad + \quad H_2O(l) \quad \rightarrow \quad H_3O^+(aq) \quad + \quad Cl^-(aq)$$
acid   base   conjugate acid   conjugate base

$$NH_3(g) \quad + \quad H_2O(l) \quad \rightarrow \quad OH^-(aq) \quad + \quad NH_4^+(aq)$$
base   acid   conjugate base   conjugate acid

TABLE 6.7   Some Common Conjugate Acid-Base Pairs

Acid	Base
H_3O^+	H_2O
H_2O	OH^-
HCl	Cl⁻
H_2SO_4	HSO_4^-
HSO_4^-	SO_4^{2-}
H_3PO_4	$H_2PO_4^-$
$H_2PO_4^-$	HPO_4^{2-}
HPO_4^{2-}	PO_4^{3-}
NH_4^+	NH_3

Substances, such as water, that can behave as bases in some circumstances and as acids in other situations are called **amphoteric** substances.

EXAMPLE 11

Liquid hydrogen perchlorate, $HClO_4$, dissolves in water to form a solution of perchloric acid. Identify the Brønsted-Lowry conjugate acid-base pairs, and write a balanced ionization equation.

Given
solution of $HClO_4(l)$

Required
chemical equation for reaction
conjugate acid = ?
conjugate base = ?

Analysis
$HClO_4(l) + H_2O(l) \rightarrow$?

As perchloric acid is an acid, the water must act as a base. The conjugate base of hydrogen perchlorate would be ClO_4^-. The conjugate acid of water is H_3O^+.

Solution
$$HClO_4(l) + H_2O(l) \rightarrow H_3O^+(aq) + ClO_4^-(aq)$$

Statement
The conjugate acid-base pairs are:

$HClO_4$ (acid) and ClO_4^- (conjugate base), and H_2O (base) and H_3O^+ (conjugate acid).

The balanced equation is:

$$HClO_4(l) \quad + \quad H_2O(l) \quad \rightarrow \quad H_3O^+(aq) \quad + \quad ClO_4^-(aq)$$
acid   base   conjugate acid   conjugate base

PRACTICE PROBLEM

Write balanced ionization equations and identify the corresponding Brønsted-Lowry conjugate acid-base pairs for the dissolving of the following substances in water:
a) nitric acid, HNO_3
b) phosphine, PH_3 (a very weak base similar to ammonia)

Applying the Brønsted-Lowry Theory to Salts

Why are some salts acidic and some basic? Consider the example of the basic carbonate ion. According to the Brønsted-Lowry theory, the carbonate ion can react with water to form its conjugate acid, the hydrogen carbonate ion. The water will act as an acid to form the hydroxide ion; that is, the solution will be basic.

$$CO_3^{2-}(aq) \quad + \quad H_2O(l) \quad \rightarrow \quad OH^-(aq) \quad + \quad HCO_3^-(aq)$$
base   acid   conjugate base   conjugate acid

In the case of the ammonium ion, it will react with water to form its conjugate base, ammonia. The water will act as a base to form the hydronium ion. Therefore, the solution will be acidic.

$$NH_4^+(aq) \quad + \quad H_2O(l) \quad \rightarrow \quad H_3O^+(aq) \quad + \quad NH_3(aq)$$
acid   base   conjugate acid   conjugate base

You will explore this topic in further detail in your grade 12 chemistry course.

Strong and Weak Acids

We eat and drink certain acids every day. Citrus fruits, such as oranges, contain citric acid and ascorbic acid (Figure 6.41). Most soft drinks, such as colas, contain phosphoric acid. Many Canadians like to put vinegar, a dilute solution of acetic acid, on French fries. We do not consume some common acids, such as sulfuric acid, the acid used in automotive batteries. Most laboratory acids are corrosive, so why is it possible for us to safely ingest 1 mol·L^{-1} of acetic acid but not 1 mol·L^{-1} of hydrochloric acid?

FIGURE 6.41 Citric acid is the predominant acid in citrus fruits.

A simple experiment provides the answer. You use conductivity tests to distinguish between solutions of ionic substances and covalent substances. In doing so, you will notice that solutions that are electrolytes cause the bulb to glow brightly, while solutions that are non-electrolytes do not. The conclusion is that ionic substances that dissolve in water form ions, and it is the ions that enable the current to flow.

If you were to test the conductivity of a 3 mol·L^{-1} hydrochloric acid solution, you would find that the bulb glows brightly. However, a 3 mol·L^{-1} acetic acid solution causes the bulb to glow only dimly (Figure 6.42). Even though the solutions are of the same concentration, the acetic acid solution must contain fewer ions! How can this be explained? If there is a smaller proportion of ions, then a proportion of the acetic acid must still be in molecular form. Since there are few hydronium and acetate ions to convey the charge through the solution, there will be a much smaller current through the circuit. To indicate that a proportion of reactants still remains in solution, the normal arrow in the chemical equation is replaced by double-headed arrows. Such reactions are known as equilibrium reactions.

$$CH_3COOH(aq) + H_2O(l) \rightleftharpoons H_3O^+(aq) + CH_3COO^-(aq)$$

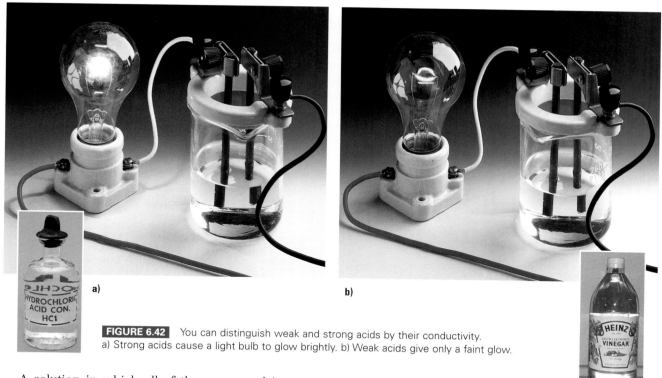

a)   b)

FIGURE 6.42 You can distinguish weak and strong acids by their conductivity. a) Strong acids cause a light bulb to glow brightly. b) Weak acids give only a faint glow.

A solution in which all of the compound is present as ions is called a strong electrolyte. Acids that ionize completely are therefore called **strong acids**. A solution in which a proportion of the compound is in molecular form is said to be a weak electrolyte. Acids that ionize partially are therefore called **weak acids**. If a very small proportion of the acid ionizes, the acid is said to be a very weak acid. Representing an acid as HA, Figure 6.43 shows the differences in ionization between a strong and a weak acid. The strength of an acid is directly related to its degree of ionization.

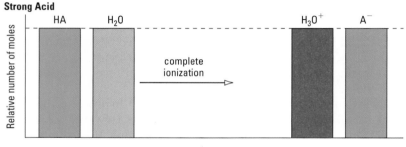

Strong Acid

HA(aq) + H$_2$O(l) ⟶ H$_3$O$^+$(aq) + A$^-$(aq)

FIGURE 6.43 The upper bar graph shows that a strong acid ionizes completely. The lower bar graph shows that, for a weak acid, a significant proportion of the acid remains un-ionized.

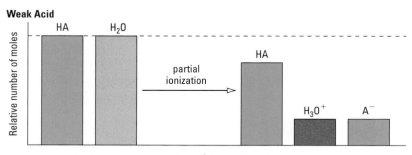

Weak Acid

HA(aq) + H$_2$O(l) ⇌ H$_3$O$^+$(aq) + A$^-$(aq)

TABLE 6.8 Concentrations of Some Common Laboratory Acids*

Acid	Strength	Concentration in mol·L^{-1}
conc. HCl	strong[1]	12
dilute HCl	strong[1]	3
conc. H$_2$SO$_4$	strong[1]	18
dilute H$_2$SO$_4$	strong[1]	3
conc. HNO$_3$	strong[1]	16
dilute HNO$_3$	strong[1]	3
dilute CH$_3$COOH	weak[2]	6
conc. H$_3$PO$_4$	weak[2]	15

* Acids are corrosive and should be handled with care.
[1] almost fully dissociated
[2] partially dissociated

HSO$_4^-$
hydrogen sulfate ion

FIGURE 6.44 In the structure of hydrogen sulfate, the hydrogen atom is polar-covalently bonded to one of the oxygen atoms.

In the chemistry laboratory, four acids that are commonly used are hydrochloric acid, sulfuric acid, nitric acid, and acetic acid (also called ethanoic acid). The first three are all strong acids. Hydrochloric acid is produced in the stomach to assist in the breakdown of some types of food. Concentrated hydrochloric acid has a concentration of 12 mol·L^{-1} and is potentially a very hazardous solution; you should be very careful when using it.

Concentrated sulfuric acid is a dense, oily liquid with a concentration of 18 mol·L^{-1}. *Extreme caution should be used if you are ever required to mix concentrated sulfuric acid with water since the process of dissolving generates a great deal of heat. Remember, always add acid to a larger amount of water so that the heat is dissipated. Never add water to acid.* Dilute sulfuric acid is used in automotive batteries. Upon ionization, each of the 2 hydrogen atoms in H$_2$SO$_4$ could potentially form hydrogen ions when it dissolves in water. In practice, one hydrogen is "lost" much more readily than the other. Therefore, in addition to hydronium ions, a solution of sulfuric acid contains hydrogen sulfate (HSO$_4^-$) (Figure 6.44) and sulfate (SO$_4^{2-}$) ions.

$$H_2SO_4(l) + H_2O(l) \rightarrow H_3O^+(aq) + HSO_4^-(aq)$$

$$HSO_4^-(aq) + H_2O(l) \rightleftharpoons H_3O^+(aq) + SO_4^{2-}(aq)$$

In your laboratory, most of the reagent bottles that contain acids and bases are made of colourless glass. Nitric acid is one substance that is stored in brown glass bottles. It decomposes slightly in light to give brown fumes of nitrogen dioxide, NO$_2$(g). This decomposition can be minimized by storing the nitric acid in a brown bottle out of direct light. All acids produce a burning sensation if they come in contact with the skin, but nitric acid also causes the skin to turn yellow-brown.

Acetic acid is the most common of the weak acids. Pure (100%) acetic acid is sometimes called glacial acetic acid since it is a solid (melting point 17°C) and has an ice-like crystalline appearance. Vinegar with its characteristic odour is a dilute solution of acetic acid in water, often with flavourings added. Because acetic acid is a weak acid, we are able to add a dilute solution of it to foods such as salads and French fries.

Strong and Weak Bases

Solutions of all alkali metal hydroxides are strong bases since the solid compounds dissociate completely into aqueous metal ions and aqueous hydroxide ions. Bases that dissociate completely are therefore called **strong bases**, and bases that dissociate partially are called **weak bases**. The strength of a base is directly related to its degree of dissociation.

WORD ORIGIN

Alkali comes from the Arabic word *al-qili*, "ashes of the saltwort plant." Originally, it applied to the hydroxides and carbonates of potassium that were dissolved out of plant ashes. Now it is used to describe the group 1 metals whose oxides form the strongest bases when they react with water.

Sodium hydroxide (also known as caustic soda) is the base you will use most often in the laboratory. Sodium hydroxide feels soapy to the skin because it reacts with the fats in the skin to form soap. The base also reacts with the proteins in the skin and can completely destroy living tissue. Drain cleansers and oven cleansers contain sodium hydroxide because the hydroxide ion reacts with the fats that block drains and splatter ovens (Figure 6.45). These products should be used with care; in particular, you should wear gloves and ensure that none of the product comes in contact with your skin. Eye protection is also

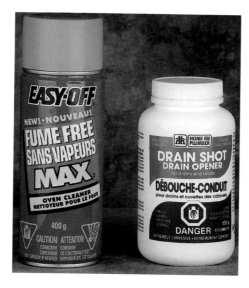

FIGURE 6.45 Many oven and drain cleansers contain sodium hydroxide and should be handled with great care.

essential when using sodium hydroxide since the hydroxide ion will react with the cornea of the eye and form an opaque coating. A concentrated solution of sodium hydroxide will etch glass, so it is advisable to use rubber or plastic stoppers in containers of sodium hydroxide solution, since glass stoppers can become seized in place.

Aqueous ammonia is the only common weak base. Ammonia gas dissolves in water to form a solution of ammonium ions and hydroxide ions.

$$NH_3(g) + H_2O(l) \rightleftharpoons NH_4^+(aq) + OH^-(aq)$$

TABLE 6.9 Concentrations of Some Common Laboratory Bases*

Base	Strength	Concentration in mol·L^{-1}
dilute NaOH	strong[1]	3
conc. NH$_3$	weak[2]	15
dilute NH$_3$	weak[2]	3

* Bases are corrosive and should be handled with care.
[1] almost fully dissociated
[2] partially dissociated

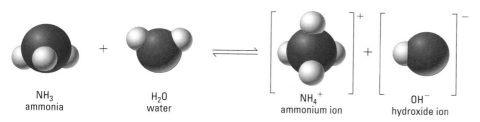

NH$_3$ ammonia   H$_2$O water   NH$_4^+$ ammonium ion   OH$^-$ hydroxide ion

FIGURE 6.46 The reaction of ammonia with water to give ammonium and hydroxide ions

FIGURE 6.47 Solutions of ammonia are used as mild household cleansers.

There is no such pure compound as ammonium hydroxide. If you evaporate a solution containing ammonium ions and hydroxide ions, you obtain just ammonia gas. In fact, ammonium hydroxide solution is sometimes called aqueous ammonia which is used in some mild household cleansers. (Figure 6.47).

What Makes a Substance an Acid or a Base?

Why do some substances produce hydrogen ions and others produce hydroxide ions when dissolved in water? An examination of electronegativities and bond strengths will help you answer this question. For example, compare the two compounds sodium hydroxide (NaOH) and hypochlorous acid (HClO). When the ionic compound sodium hydroxide dissolves, the existing sodium ions and hydroxide ions are dissociated by the polar water molecules into hydrated ions. When covalent hypochlorous acid dissolves, the bond between oxygen and hydrogen is broken (Figure 6.48). In this case, chlorine has a higher electronegativity than hydrogen, pulling the oxygen's valence electrons toward the chlorine and away from the hydrogen. This results in the bond between hydrogen and oxygen becoming weakened, allowing the hydrogen to be released as a hydrogen ion. This ion then becomes a hydronium ion in water, H_3O^+.

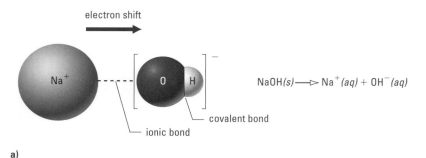

a)

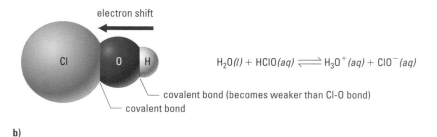

b)

FIGURE 6.48 Electron pairs are pulled toward the element of higher electronegativity. You can use this concept to explain why a) sodium hydroxide produces hydroxide ions, but b) hypochlorous acid produces hydrogen ions.

WEBLINK

Most commercial glass cleansers contain one of two inorganic ingredients. Research the active components in these products. Devise a formulation for your own cleanser. Have your teacher check the formulation, and if your teacher determines that the mixture is safe, prepare it. Devise a test to see how it compares with a commercial cleanser. Begin your research at **www.pearsoned.ca/chemistry11**.

In figure 6.48a: electron shift → ; Na$^+$ ... [O H]$^-$; covalent bond; ionic bond; NaOH*(s)* ⟶ Na$^+$*(aq)* + OH$^-$*(aq)*

In figure 6.48b: electron shift ← ; Cl O H ; covalent bond; covalent bond (becomes weaker than Cl-O bond); $H_2O(l) + HClO(aq) \rightleftharpoons H_3O^+(aq) + ClO^-(aq)$

Understanding Concepts

1. Make a Venn diagram to compare the Arrhenius and Brønsted-Lowry theories of acids and bases.

2. Compare the descriptors "strong/weak" and "concentrated/dilute" as they pertain to acids and bases.

3. Identify the hydrogen-ion donor and hydrogen-ion acceptor in each of the following reactions:

   a) $HNO_3(l) + H_2O(l) \rightarrow$
   $\qquad NO_3^-(aq) + H_3O^+(aq)$

   b) $CH_3CH_2NH_2(l) + H_2O(l) \rightleftharpoons$
   $\qquad CH_3CH_2NH_3^+(aq) + OH^-(aq)$

   c) $CH_3COOH(l) + H_2O(l) \rightleftharpoons$
   $\qquad CH_3COO^-(aq) + H_3O^+(aq)$

4. Identify all the ions and molecules that can act as Brønsted-Lowry bases:

   a) Br^-

   b) Li^+

   c) H_3PO_4

   d) NH_4^+

   e) H_2O

   f) NH_2^-

Applying Inquiry/Communication Skills

5. Suppose you are given a solution of barium hydroxide and another of caffeine. Describe how you would go about determining which of these substances is a strong or weak base. Predict what you think your results might be.

6. Write balanced equations for the reaction of water with the following substances that form acids. Assume that only one hydrogen ion is transferred in each case.

   a) hydrogen bromide

   b) perchloric acid, $HClO_4$

   c) hydrogen cyanide

   d) hydrogen sulfide

   e) formic acid, HCOOH

7. Write equations for the ionization of HNO_3 in water and the reaction of CO_3^{2-} with water. For each equation, identify the hydrogen-ion donor and hydrogen-ion acceptor. Label the conjugate acid-base pairs in each equation.

8. Complete the following acid-base reactions. Identify the conjugate acid-base pairs by writing them below the equations.

   a) $HBr(aq) + H_2O \rightarrow$
   (HBr is a strong acid)

   b) $H_3PO_4(aq) + NH_3(aq) \rightarrow$

   c) $HClO_4(aq) + H_2O \rightarrow$

   d) $CO_3^{2-}(aq) + H_2SO_4(aq) \rightarrow$

   e) $HCN(aq) + H_2O \rightarrow$
   (HCN is a weak acid)

9. Write the Brønsted-Lowry equations for each of the following acids/bases reacting with water.

   a) fluorosulfonic acid, FSO_3H (strong acid)

   b) calcium oxide, CaO (strong base)

   c) sulfurous acid, H_2SO_3 (weak acid)

   d) sodium dihydrogen phosphate, NaH_2PO_4 (weak acid)

   e) sodium hydrogen carbonate, $NaHCO_3$ (weak base)

Making Connections

10. Drain cleansers containing pellets of sodium hydroxide and some small metallic particles are among the most caustic chemicals used domestically. Research other household products that use caustic chemicals, and describe their use and any alternative products that are less caustic. Design an action plan that would inform consumers about the pros and cons of using and disposing of household products that use caustic chemicals and alternative products.

6.6 The Meaning of pH and Its Measurement

Key Understandings

When you have completed this section, you will be able to:
- understand the chemical meaning of pH
- calculate the pH of acids and bases
- know the effect of dilution on the pH of an acid or a base by experimentation

Is your shampoo pH balanced? What do the manufacturers mean? Why is pH so important? It is much more crucial than your hair care. Your blood has to have a pH of about 7.4 or you will die. Acid rain can kill the trees in forests and the fish in lakes. But what is pH? How can you calculate the pH of a solution? Since the concentrations of hydronium ions cover an enormous range, it is more convenient to use a logarithmic scale when measuring them. A change in pH by 1 unit represents a change in hydronium ion concentration by a factor of 10. Such exponential scales are often used in science. For example, the strength of earthquakes (measured on the Richter scale) and the loudness of noises (measured in decibels) are also measured using a logarithmic scale (Figure 6.50).

In 1909, Søren P. Sørensen, a Danish biochemist, introduced the **pH scale**. If a solution has a pH of 7 at 25°C, then it is considered to be neutral. Solutions that have a pH less than 7 are acidic, while those with a pH greater than 7 are basic. The scale has no finite limit, but most solutions have a pH somewhere in the range of 0 to 14.

Sørensen defined pH as follows:

$$pH = -\log_{10}[H_3O^+ (aq)]$$

FIGURE 6.49 Altering soil pH can affect plant growth and even the colour of flowers. Hydrangeas produce blue flowers in acidic soils and pink flowers in basic soils.

Note that pH is a logarithmic relationship and an inverse relationship (because of the negative sign). It is a **logarithm** to base 10, meaning that every increase by 1 pH unit corresponds to a concentration decrease by a factor of 10.

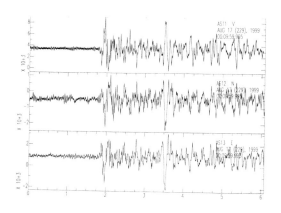

a)

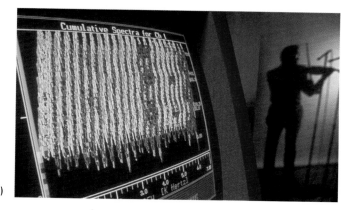

b)

Why does pure water have a pH of 7? Water molecules ionize to a very small extent, as follows:

$$H_2O(l) + H_2O(l) \rightleftharpoons H_3O^+(aq) + OH^-(aq)$$

This process is known as **self-ionization**. At 25°C, the concentration of hydronium ions (and hydroxide ions) in water is experimentally determined to be 1.00×10^{-7} mol·L^{-1}. From Figure 6.52, you can see that the corresponding pH is 7.

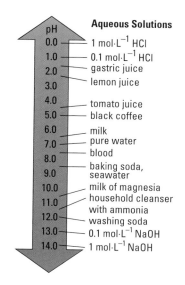

FIGURE 6.50   a) Like the pH scale, scientists use a logarithmic unit to measure the strength of an earthquake —the Richter scale. An earthquake measuring 8 on the Richter scale is 10 times as strong as one of 7. b) The intensity of sound is measured by the logarithmic unit of bels. A sound of 90 dB is 10 times the intensity of a sound of 80 dB.

H$_2$O
water molecule

$+$

H$_2$O
water molecule

H$_3$O$^+$
hydronium ion

$+$

OH$^-$
hydroxide ion

FIGURE 6.51   The reaction of water molecules to give hydronium and hydroxide ions

How do you calculate the pH for an acid? Suppose you have a hydrochloric acid solution of concentration 1.0×10^{-2} mol·L^{-1}, and you want to find its pH. First of all, since hydrochloric acid is a strong acid, the concentration of hydronium ion must be the same as that of the hydrochloric acid (1.0×10^{-2} mol·L^{-1}).

$$HCl(g) + H_2O(l) \xrightarrow[\text{in water}]{\text{dissolve}} H_3O^+(aq) + Cl^-(aq)$$

You then use the formula for pH. Notice that when you take the log of a number, the result is dimensionless. Therefore, using dimensional analysis, the pH formula is actually:

$$pH = -\log_{10}\left(\frac{[H_3O^+]}{1 \text{ mol·L}^{-1}}\right)$$

Substituting in the value gives:

$$pH = -\log_{10}(1.0 \times 10^{-2})$$

The calculator gives an answer of 2, but how many significant figures do you have? In a logarithm to base 10, the numbers in front of the decimal represent the powers of 10 (so 10^{-2} becomes 2). Therefore, these numbers do not count toward the number of significant figures. So, since the concentration had two significant figures, the answer must have two figures after the decimal. The answer is pH = 2.00.

pH	Aqueous Solutions
0.0	1 mol·L^{-1} HCl
1.0	0.1 mol·L^{-1} HCl
2.0	gastric juice
3.0	lemon juice
4.0	tomato juice
5.0	black coffee
6.0	milk
7.0	pure water
8.0	blood
9.0	baking soda, seawater
10.0	milk of magnesia
11.0	household cleanser with ammonia
12.0	washing soda
13.0	0.1 mol·L^{-1} NaOH
14.0	1 mol·L^{-1} NaOH

FIGURE 6.52   The pH of some common household substances

EXAMPLE 12

What is the hydronium ion concentration of a solution with a pH of 2.50?

Given
pH = 2.50

Required
$[H_3O^+] = ?$ mol·L^{-1}

Analysis
pH → $[H_3O^+]$ (using pH = $-\log_{10}[H_3O^+]$ or $[H_3O^+] = 10^{-pH}$)

Solution
$$[H_3O^+] = 10^{-2.50}$$
$$= 3.16 \times 10^{-3} \text{ mol·L}^{-1}$$

Statement
The hydronium ion concentration is 3.16×10^{-3} mol·L^{-1}.

PRACTICE PROBLEM

Calculate the hydronium ion concentration of a solution with a pH of:
a) 5.00
b) 8.43
c) 12.01

How can you find the pH of a basic solution? There is a link between the concentration of hydronium ions and the concentration of hydroxide ions (Table 6.10). As one goes up, the other goes down. The mathematical relationship (the ion-product constant) between them is:

$$[H_3O^+][OH^-] = 1.0 \times 10^{-14} \text{ at } 25°C$$

TABLE 6.10 Relationship between $[H_3O^+]$, pH, $[OH^-]$, and pOH

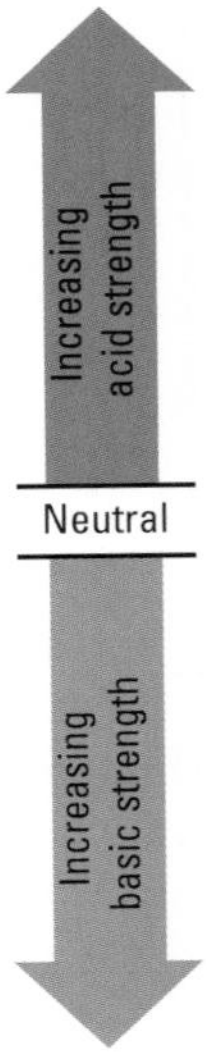

$[H_3O^+]$ in mol·L^{-1}	pH	pOH	$[OH^-]$ in mol·L^{-1}
1	0	14	10^{-14}
10^{-1}	1	13	10^{-13}
10^{-2}	2	12	10^{-12}
10^{-3}	3	11	10^{-11}
10^{-4}	4	10	10^{-10}
10^{-5}	5	9	10^{-9}
10^{-6}	6	8	10^{-8}
10^{-7}	7	7	10^{-7}
10^{-8}	8	6	10^{-6}
10^{-9}	9	5	10^{-5}
10^{-10}	10	4	10^{-4}
10^{-11}	11	3	10^{-3}
10^{-12}	12	2	10^{-2}
10^{-13}	13	1	10^{-1}
10^{-14}	14	0	1

Increasing acid strength

Neutral

Increasing basic strength

Just as the pH unit is used to measure the concentration of hydronium ions, pOH is used to measure the concentration of hydroxide ion, using the relationship:

$$pOH = -\log_{10}[OH^-(aq)]$$

There is an easy way to convert from pOH to pH and vice versa through a simple mathematical relationship. The relationship can be derived using the formula for the ion-product constant by taking the logarithms of all the terms:

$$[H_3O^+][OH^-] = 1.0 \times 10^{-14}$$
$$\log_{10}[H_3O^+] + \log_{10}[OH^-] = -14$$

but $\log_{10}[H_3O^+] = -pH$ and $\log_{10}[OH^-] = -pOH$

Therefore,

$$(-pH) + (-pOH) = -14$$

Multiplying through by -1 gives:

$$pH + pOH = 14$$

EXAMPLE 13

What will be the pH of an aqueous solution containing 0.040 mol·L^{-1} sodium hydroxide (a strong base)?

Given
[NaOH] = 0.040 mol·L^{-1}

Required
pH = ?

Analysis
[NaOH] → [OH$^-$] (using mole ratio, 1 mol NaOH : 1 mol OH$^-$)
[OH$^-$] → pOH (using pOH = $-\log_{10}$[OH$^-$])
pOH → pH (using pH = 14.00 − pOH)

Solution
[OH$^-$] = 0.040 mol·L^{-1}
pOH = $-\log_{10}(0.040)$ = 1.40
pH = 14.00 − 1.40 = 12.60

Statement
The pH of the NaOH solution is 12.60.

PRACTICE PROBLEM

Calculate the pH of a solution containing 0.012 mol·L^{-1} hydroxide ions.

EXAMPLE 14

A solution has a pH of 11.18. What is the concentration of the hydroxide ion in the solution?

Given
pH = 11.18

Required
$[OH^-]$ = ? $mol \cdot L^{-1}$

Analysis
pH → pOH (using pOH = 14 − pH)
pOH → $[OH^-]$ (using $[OH^-] = 10^{-pOH}$)

Solution
pOH = 14 − 11.18 = 2.82
$[OH^-] = 1.514 \times 10^{-3}\ mol \cdot L^{-1}$

Statement
The concentration of the hydroxide ion is $1.514 \times 10^{-3}\ mol \cdot L^{-1}$.

PRACTICE PROBLEM

Calculate the pOH and the concentration of a potassium hydroxide solution that has a pH of 11.14.

pH Measurements

How is pH measured? An approximate value can be obtained using an indicator. An indicator is an organic dye that changes colour depending on the pH of a solution. For example, the natural dye litmus turns red in acids and blue in bases. But litmus will tell you only if the pH is greater than or less than 7. Other indicators change colour over different pH ranges. Three of these are shown in Figure 6.53.

FIGURE 6.53 Each acid-base indicator changes colour over a different pH range. Identify the range over which each of these indicators change colour.

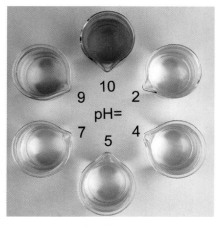
phenolphthalein

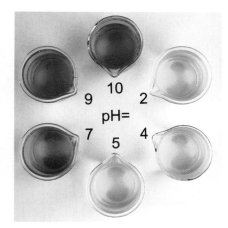
bromthymol blue

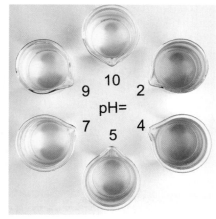
methyl red

You could test a solution with several different indicators until you have narrowed down the pH value, but there is an alternative: use a universal indicator. This is a mixture of several indicators blended together. Using a universal indicator solution or universal indicator paper, you can determine the approximate pH of a solution to about ± 1 pH unit (Figure 6.54). However, if you want to measure pH values precisely, you need a calibrated pH meter or a sensor for a portable or lab computer system (Figure 6.55).

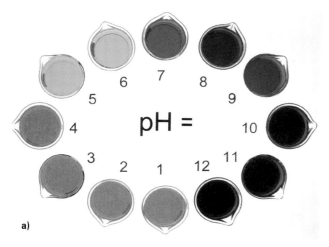

a)

b)

FIGURE 6.54 a) Using a universal indicator and comparing the colour with standards enable you to determine the pH of a solution to approximately ± 1 pH unit. b) Using the colour standards in a), what is the pH of these common household solutions?

FIGURE 6.55 The pH of a river can be measured using a pH probe (inset) and a portable computer.

WEBLINK

For a simulation to show how dilution affects a solution, go to
www.pearsoned.ca/chemistry11.

Discovering Chemistry *Dilution and pH*

What happens to the pH of an acid when it is diluted?

Materials

 1.0 mol·L^{-1} hydrochloric acid
 50-mL beaker
 10-mL pipette and pipette bulb
 100-mL volumetric flask
 pH meter
 spreadsheet program or graphing calculator

1. Pour about 30 mL of the 1.0 mol·L^{-1} hydrochloric acid in the beaker. Measure its pH. Using a pipette, transfer 10.0 mL of the solution to the 100-mL volumetric flask.

2. Fill the flask to the graduation mark, stopper, and shake vigorously.

3. Rinse out the beaker and dry it. Pour into it about 30 mL of the diluted solution. Measure its pH.

4. Pour out the contents of the volumetric flask. Rinse it and the pipette thoroughly with water.

5. Pipette 10.0 mL of the diluted solution into the volumetric flask, and repeat the dilution process. Measure the pH.

6. Repeat the dilutions until you have a total of six pH measurements.

- For each pH measurement you took, calculate the concentration of the corresponding solution. Tabulate your data as follows:

Concentration	pH

- Plot the data by hand or with a graphing program. Discuss how the shape of the plot can be explained.

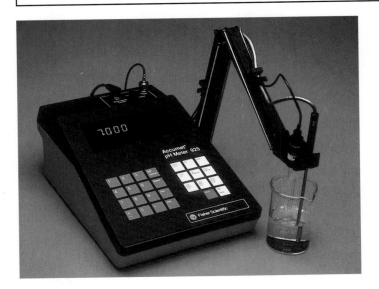

FIGURE 6.56 A pH meter provides a more accurate measurement of pH than an indicator or litmus paper.

Decision-Making Skills

▷ Defining the Issue
▷ Developing Assessment Criteria
▷ Researching the Issue
▷ Analyzing Data and Information
▷ Proposing a Course of Action
▷ Justifying the Course of Action
▷ Communicating Your Proposal

Case Study

Acid Rain and pH

BACKGROUND INFORMATION

Acid rain is a major environmental problem worldwide. Although most people think that acid rain refers to rain or snow that has an acidic pH, it also refers to fog and dry acidic deposits (sulfur and nitrogen salts). Rainwater is naturally acidic due to dissolved carbon dioxide in water (carbonic acid). Human activity has greatly decreased the pH of wet and dry precipitation in certain areas, such as the forests in northern Ontario, over the last 30 years. These activities (fossil fuel-fired electric utilities; industrial, commercial, and residential heating; transportation vehicles; metal ore smelting plants; and industrial chemical processing plants) have produced more than 90% of the various sulfur oxide emissions and 95% of the various nitrogen oxide emissions in eastern North America. According to Environment Canada, 50% of the sulfate deposited in Canada comes from U.S. sources.

Normal precipitation reacts with basic compounds in rocks, soil, air, and water and becomes neutralized. The granite and other igneous rocks in the Canadian Shield have a minimal ability to neutralize acidic precipitation. Therefore, acid rain has caused serious damage to natural habitats, both terrestrial and aquatic. It has been estimated that acid rain causes $1 billion worth of damage in Canada each year. Thousands of lakes have become damaged, and a significant portion of the salmon habitat in the Maritimes has been destroyed. The reason that fish are affected by acid rain has to do with the increased solubility of aluminum ions as the pH drops. The aluminum in lakes is mostly in the form of insoluble aluminum hydroxide. When the pH drops, aluminum hydroxide reacts with hydronium ions to form soluble aluminum ions, which are toxic to fish. For forests, there has been a steady decline in sugar maple groves in parts of Canada. Considerable damage to monuments and buildings has also been observed. Many Canadian and U.S. studies have found a link between acid rain and human respiratory ailments. The problem is that 80% of Canadians live in areas exposed to high levels of acid rain-related pollution.

In Canada, where a significant part of our economy is based on our fisheries, forests, and agriculture, acid rain could translate into fewer jobs.

Analyzing the Issue

1. Create a diagram that illustrates how acid rain is created and how it can have an impact far from its original source.

2. Brainstorm a list of possible economic and environmental consequences related to acid rain. Determine if the extent of these consequences differs for urban areas and rural areas. Explain why or why not.

3. Research the statements related to acid rain that are part of the Ministry of the Environment and the Ministry of Natural Resources' policies. Assess whether or not the initiatives have been effective in addressing the consequences you have identified. Explain why or why not.

4. Choose one of the following roles, and prepare a presentation from that perspective, defending a possible course of action. Your presentation is for a symposium that is being convened between Canadians and Americans to develop future policy statements related to acid rain. Consider how the country of origin may affect the different positions.

Roles:
government official
industrialist
environmental chemist
municipal officer
wildlife expert
marine biologist
forest ranger
average citizen

Section 6.6 Review

Understanding Concepts

1. Describe how the pH scale enables us to assess the basicity or acidity of a solution.

2. Explain whether the pH of a solution can be less than 0 or greater than 14. Justify your answer with an example.

3. Dairy milk, pH $\approx$ 6.5, exposed to air and warm temperatures becomes spoiled and develops a sour taste. Suggest a reason for this and indicate how its pH will change.

Applying Inquiry/ Communication Skills

4. Calculate the pH of each of the following:

   a) an aqueous solution that has a hydronium ion concentration of 3.0×10^{-3} mol·L^{-1}

   b) an aqueous solution that has a hydroxide ion concentration of 6.0×10^{-4} mol·L^{-1}

   c) an aqueous solution containing 0.0020 mol·L^{-1} barium hydroxide

   d) 250.0 mL of an aqueous solution containing 1.26 g nitric acid

   e) 2.0×10^{-3} mol·L^{-1} nitric acid solution

   f) 2.0×10^{-5} mol·L^{-1} sodium hydroxide solution

5. The beakers in Figure 6.57 contain the same solution. In the one on the right, phenolphthalein indicator was added. On the left, bromocresol green was added. Predict the approximate pH of the solution. Identify how you could get a more accurate answer.

6. The solubility of strontium hydroxide is 0.410 g per 100 mL of water. Determine the pH of a saturated solution of strontium hydroxide. State two assumptions.

7. Calculate the pH of a saturated solution of calcium hydroxide (1.50 g·L^{-1} solution). The *Merck Index* lists the pH of limewater at 25°C as 12.4. State if the pH you calculated agrees with the *Merck Index* value. If not, suggest a reason why not.

Making Connections

8. Acid rain is a global problem. Express an informed opinion on whether you think it is fair for one country to complain that another is polluting its atmosphere. Outline factors that need to be addressed, and propose ways in which the complaint can be resolved.

9. You are a member of a town council that has asked a company that is a major emitter of SO_2 in your area to cut its level of acidic pollution. The company has responded that in order to pay for the technology to cut emissions, it will have to lay off 250 employees, many of whom live in your town. Consider all factors that affect this issue, and propose a plan of action that will lead to a solution.

10. Identify the effects of acid rain on plant and animal life. Identify the technologies that are being used to reduce acidic emissions, and give reasons why these technologies are not more extensively used. Consider all factors related to these reasons, and describe possible economic and environmental consequences.

FIGURE 6.57

Investigation 1 (Section 6.1)

Inquiry Skills

Initiating and Planning

▶ Applying Technical Skills

▶ Using Tools, Materials, and Equipment

▶ Conducting and Recording

▶ Analyzing and Interpreting

▶ Concluding and Communicating

How Temperature Affects Solubility and Plotting a Solubility Curve

Problem

To investigate the effect of temperature on the solubility of gases in water and the miscibility of some liquids in water, and determine the solubility of a solid in 100 g of water. To also investigate the dependence of solubility on temperature and plot the solubility curve for the solid solute potassium nitrate.

Materials

- safety goggles
- ethanol, vegetable oil, hexane, potassium nitrate (and sodium chloride, if time permits), distilled water
- 100-mL beaker
- 5-mL pipette
- three 10-cm long (small) test tubes, large (20 cm by 2.5 cm) test tube with a two-hole stopper (one for a thermometer, the other for a firm copper wire with a loop at the bottom end for stirring)
- plastic weighing dish
- thermometer
- test-tube clamp
- tripod stand, ring clamp
- gas burner

> **CAUTION: Wear safety glasses. Hexane is very flammable; do not use near any heat source. Do not inhale hexane vapours.**

Procedure

Part 1: Solubility of Gases in Water

1. Place the beaker on a tripod stand with a ring clamp to hold the beaker in position.

2. Place about 50 mL of distilled water in the beaker, and gently heat the water until it reaches about 60°C.

3. Carefully observe any changes in the water as the temperature is being raised. Record your observations.

> **CAUTION: Do not start Part 2 until all gas burners have been extinguished.**
> **CHEMICAL DISPOSAL: All solutions and remaining solids can be rinsed down the sink with copious amounts of water.**

Part 2: Solubility of Different Liquids in Water

4. In each of three 10-cm long test tubes, add 2 mL of distilled water (equivalent to 2 cm in depth).

5. To the first test tube, add 2 mL of ethanol; to the second one, add 2 mL of vegetable oil; and to the third one, add 2 mL of hexane. Shake each test tube gently.

6. Allow the test tubes to stand, and record your observations in chart form.

> **CAUTION: Do not start Part 3 until all the hexane has been disposed of.**
> **CHEMICAL DISPOSAL: Dispose of hexane and hexane mixtures in a special waste bottle.**

Part 3: Solubility Curve for Potassium Nitrate

7. Accurately measure the mass of about 10 g potassium nitrate on a plastic weighing dish. Then transfer the solid to a large test tube. Attach the test tube to a test-tube clamp on a stand.

8. Using a pipette, add exactly 5.0 mL of distilled water to the test tube.

9. Your teacher will provide you with a two-hole stopper with a thermometer in one hole and a stiff copper wire with a loop in the other. Place the stopper in the test tube, and very gently adjust the thermometer and the copper wire so the bulb is in the solution and the loop of the copper wire is around the thermometer. Caution: You must never push a glass thermometer through the stoppered hole.

10. Using a gas burner, heat the solution gently and evenly while constantly stirring until all the solute has dissolved. Take care not to touch the insides of the test-tube wall with the copper wire.

11. As soon as all the solute has dissolved, remove the burner, cool the solution, and continue to stir it.

12. Note the *temperature* at which the crystals *begin* to form. Gently heat the solution just a few degrees above this temperature until all the crystals dissolve.

13. Remove the burner, cool, and record the temperature to the nearest 0.2°C at which the crystals begin to form again.

14. Now add another 5.0 mL of distilled water to the test tube, heat to dissolve the solute, and determine the *new temperature* at which crystals *begin* to form.

15. Repeat three more times using an additional 5.0 mL of distilled water each time, and record your results.

16. Present your data in tabular form.

17. If time permits, repeat Part 3, this time using sodium chloride. Compare the solubility of potassium nitrate and sodium chloride at the lowest temperature, and at the highest temperature.

Analyzing and Interpreting

Part 1

1. Describe what happens to the kinetic energy of the solute as the temperature of the solvent increases.

2. Explain the effect of an increase in temperature on the solubility of gases in water. Provide evidence in your answer.

Part 2

3. Describe the miscibility of water and ethanol, water and vegetable oil, and water and hexane.

4. Discuss the type of bonding between the solute molecules in water, ethanol, vegetable oil, and hexane.

Part 3

5. Given that the density of water is 1.0 g·mL^{-1}, calculate the mass of water added in each solubility determination.

6. Calculate the solubility as mass of solute (in grams) per 100 g of water.

7. Present your data in tabular form, giving the volume of water added, the mass of water, the temperature in degrees Celsius, and the solubility in grams of solute per 100 g water.

8. Draw the solubility curve for potassium nitrate by plotting the temperature on the x-axis and the solubility on the y-axis.

Concluding and Communicating

Part 1

9. State the conclusions that you can make about the solubility of the dissolved gases in water when heated.

10. Account for the change in solubility of gases in water.

11. Explain why gases such as oxygen dissolve in water.

Part 2

12. Formulate conclusions about the solubility of the various liquids tested. Account for any miscibility or immiscibility.

Part 3

13. Draw conclusions on the basis of the solubility curve for potassium nitrate.

14. Deduce if it is possible to conclude that all solids behave in the same way. Explain your answer.

15. Determine the solubility of potassium nitrate at 25°C, and compare this with the literature value. Calculate the percent difference between the two values.

16. Suggest improvements to the procedure to reduce the percent difference between the two values.

17. Other than temperature, state other factors that can increase the rate of dissolving. Describe how these factors would affect solubility.

Extending

18. Predict the effect of thermal pollution on marine life.

19. Suggest two alternatives to dumping warm water from cooling towers into lakes and rivers that would minimize the impact of thermal pollution.

20. Investigate experimentally how the solubility of sodium sulfate is affected by an increase in temperature. Compare this result with the solubility curve of potassium nitrate, and explain any differences you observe.

Investigation 2 (Section 6.4)

Preparation of a Standard Solution of Sodium Carbonate

Solutions that contain a precisely known mass of a solute in a precisely known volume of solution are called **standard solutions**. If a pure solid (> 99.9% purity) is available, a balance can be used to measure the mass and, therefore, the amount of solute accurately. Such a solid is called a primary standard. A primary standard is a solid that meets the following criteria:

a) It is obtained from the supplier in a very pure form.
b) Heating it in an oven overnight at a temperature between 70°C to 110°C will remove any adsorbed water.
c) It is stable in solution.

Problem

To prepare 100.0 mL of a standard solution of sodium carbonate with a concentration close to 0.5 mol·L^{-1}.

Materials

- a sample of sodium carbonate that has been dried in an oven at 110°C for 2 or more hours, and cooled to room temperature in a desiccator
- distilled water
- stock bottle
- 100-mL volumetric flask or 100-mL graduated cylinder
- beaker
- wash bottle (filled with distilled water)
- centigram balance
- desiccator
- pair of tongs
- shiny paper or plastic weighing dish
- spatula or scoopula

CHEMICAL DISPOSAL: Sodium carbonate can be dissolved in water and flushed down the sink.

Pre-lab Calculation   Showing all calculations, determine the mass of sodium carbonate required to make 100 mL of a 0.5 mol·L^{-1} solution. Your teacher will check your calculated mass before you proceed.

Experimental Design

1. In a 100-mL beaker, measure the exact amount of dry, pure sodium carbonate as calculated from pre-lab calculation.
2. Dissolve the sodium carbonate with 50 mL to 60 mL of distilled water.
3. Using a funnel, transfer the solution to the 100-mL volumetric flask. Wash the beaker several times with small amounts of distilled water.
4. Remove the funnel, and add more distilled water to the volumetric flask using the wash bottle. Be careful not to go beyond the 100-mL mark. (Note that the bottom of the meniscus must be on this 100-mL mark.)

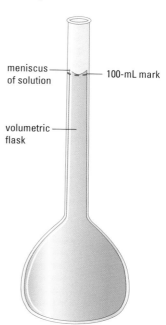

FIGURE 6.58

5. Stopper the volumetric flask and shake it to mix the solution thoroughly.

Inquiry Skills

Initiating and Planning
▶ Applying Technical Skills
▶ Using Tools, Materials, and Equipment
▶ Conducting and Recording
▶ Analyzing and Interpreting
▶ Concluding and Communicating

(continued)

Analyzing and Interpreting

1. Explain why you should use a pair of tongs when weighing the beaker.

2. Give a reason why the same analytical balance should be used for the two mass measurements.

Concluding and Communicating

3. State the properties that sodium carbonate must possess for it to be used as a primary standard. Check the label of the stock bottle. Indicate the purity of the sodium carbonate.

4. Explain why a primary standard must be heated in an oven before using. If this were not done, describe the effect it would have on the concentration of the solution.

Extending

5. Briefly describe the method used to prepare a standard solution of potassium hydrogen phthalate ($KHC_8H_4O_4$), an acid primary standard, whose concentration is close to 0.1 mol·L^{-1}.

6. Determine the mass of sodium tetraborate decahydrate ($Na_2B_4O_7 \cdot 10H_2O$), another acid primary standard, required to produce 500 mL of a 0.25 mol·L^{-1} solution.

7. Explain why sodium hydroxide cannot be used as a primary standard. Suggest a method to determine the concentration of a sodium hydroxide solution accurately.

CHAPTER SUMMARY

Key Terms

amphoteric
aqueous solution
Arrhenius theory
Brønsted-Lowry theory
carbon bed
concentration
conjugate acid
conjugate base
dilution
dissociation
hydration
hydrogen bonding

hydronium ion
immiscible
insoluble
logarithm
mass percent
miscible
molarity
moles per litre
parts per billion
parts per million
percent mass-volume
pH scale

polar
primary sewage treatment
recrystallization
reverse osmosis
saturated solution
secondary sewage treatment
solar distillation
solubility
soluble
solute
solution
solvation

solvent
standard solution
strong acid
strong base
tertiary sewage treatment
volume percent
volumetric flask
volumetric pipette
weak acid
weak base

Key Equations

$$\text{concentration} = \frac{\text{amount of solute (moles)}}{\text{volume of solution (L)}} \text{ or } c = \frac{n}{V}$$

$$\% \text{ solute (by volume)} = \frac{\text{volume of solute}}{\text{volume of solution}} \times 100\%$$

$$\% \text{ solute (by mass)} = \frac{\text{mass of solute}}{\text{(mass of solution)}} \times 100\%$$

$$\% \text{ mass-volume (m/v)} = \frac{\text{mass of solute (g)}}{\text{volume solution (mL)}} \times 100\%$$

$$\text{ppm} = \frac{\text{mass of solute}}{\text{mass of solution}} \times 10^6$$

$$\text{ppb} = \frac{\text{mass of solute}}{\text{mass of solution}} \times 10^9$$

$$\text{pH} = -\log_{10}[H_3O^+(aq)]$$

$$\text{pOH} = -\log_{10}[OH^-(aq)]$$

$$\text{pH} + \text{pOH} = 14$$

Essential Understandings

■ The polarity of the water molecule and its ability to form hydrogen bonds explain why many ionic and polar compounds can dissolve in water.

■ The solubility of a compound in a solvent tends to depend on the chemical properties of both the solute and the solvent, as well as temperature.

■ Knowledge of solubility and chemical reactions gives rise to water treatment technologies.

■ The units used to express the concentration of a solution depend on the type of solute and solvent used and the relative amounts of solute and solvent.

■ Standard solutions are prepared by using analytical chemical techniques.

■ The tendency of a substance to donate or be attracted to a proton is used to define acids and bases by the Brønsted-Lowry theory.

■ For two acids of the same concentration, their hydronium ion concentrations determine the strength or weakness of the acids. Similarly, for two bases of the same concentration, their hydroxide ion concentrations determine the strength or weakness of the bases.

■ pH is a measure of the hydrogen ion concentration; for acids or bases of the same concentration, it is a quantitative measure of the strength or weakness of the acids or bases.

Consolidate Your Understanding

1. Discuss how solutions can be described with respect to composition, concentration, and acidity.

2. Construct a concept map starting with the word "solutions."

3. Explain what the effects on our society would be if we could not rely on our water quality.

4. Explain why accuracy of measurements is important when preparing solutions. Use examples in your explanations.

CHAPTER 6 REVIEW

Understanding Concepts

1. Identify which group of aqueous solutions is acidic.
   a) yogurt, orange juice, carbonated water
   b) window cleaner, rainwater, milk of magnesia
   c) ASA, antacid tablet, lime juice
   d) lemon juice, distilled water, vinegar

2. To make 250 mL of a 0.10 mol·L^{-1} sodium hydroxide solution (molar mass of NaOH = 40.0 g·mol^{-1}), the mass in grams of solid sodium hydroxide you would need is:
   a) 0.10 × 250
   b) 0.10 × 0.250
   c) 0.10 × 0.250 × 40.0
   d) 40.0

3. A characteristic of a weak acid is that it:
   a) is harmless
   b) does not easily ionize
   c) reacts with very few substances
   d) is a dilute acid

4. Identify the conjugate acid-base pairs from the list below:
   I H_2O and OH^-
   II $H_2PO_4^-$ and HPO_4^{2-}
   III H_2SO_3 and H_2SO_4

   a) I and II
   b) I and III
   c) II and III
   d) all three

5. Choose the compound that can act as a Brønsted-Lowry base but not as an Arrhenius base.
   a) NH_3
   b) NaOH
   c) LiOH
   d) $Ca(OH)_2$

6. Explain why water is an excellent solvent for most ionic compounds and polar-covalent molecules but not for non-polar molecules.

7. Describe two factors that affect the solubility of an ionic compound in water.

8. Explain why a non-polar solute does not dissolve in a polar solvent.

9. Explain why an ionic substance does not dissolve in a non-polar solvent.

10. Draw a concept map to illustrate primary, secondary, and tertiary methods of sewage treatment, their relative effectiveness, and the various tertiary methods available to improve water quality.

11. The solubility of each compound listed in Table 6.11 is given as the mass of substance (in grams) that will dissolve in 1 L of water at 25°C. Classify each compound as very soluble, slightly soluble, or insoluble.

TABLE 6.11

Compound	Solubility (g·L^{-1})
sodium chloride	359
calcium carbonate	1.30×10^{-2}
potassium chlorate	52.2
lithium fluoride	1.32
silver iodide	2.61×10^{-5}

12. Describe in words what is meant by the following equation: $CaCl_2(s) \rightarrow Ca^{2+}(aq) + 2\ Cl^-(aq)$

13. Explain why HNO_3 is considered to be an Arrhenius acid.

14. Explain why KOH is considered to be an Arrhenius base.

15. Describe the difference between a weak acid and a dilute solution of a strong acid.

16. A few drops of phenolphthalein indicator were added to one portion of an unknown solution. The solution remained colourless. A few drops of bromthymol blue added to a second portion turned the solution blue. Identify whether the solution was acidic, neutral, or basic. Estimate the approximate pH.

17. Compare the percents of fruit juices in several brands of juice drinks. Note whether the percents are measures by volume percent or mass-volume percent. Write an article that includes your findings, and give an informed opinion as to whether these reported values could be misleading.

Applying Inquiry/Communication Skills

18. Write equations for the ionization/dissociation of the following in water. Identify if the equation describes an ionization or dissociation process.
    a) $MgCl_2$
    b) KCl
    c) $Ca(NO_3)_2$
    d) $Ba(OH)_2$
    e) $Al_2(SO_4)_3$

19. Calculate the mass of solute required to prepare 1.00 L of each of the following solutions:
    a) sodium hydroxide with a concentration of 0.100 mol·L^{-1}
    b) calcium nitrate with a concentration of 0.40 mol·L^{-1}

20. Ethanol (CH_3CH_2OH) is a liquid with a density of 0.790 g·mL^{-1}. Describe how you would prepare 1.00 L of an aqueous solution of ethanol with a concentration of 1.25 mol·L^{-1}.

21. Calculate the concentration of chloride ions when 1.5 g sodium chloride and 1.5 g calcium chloride are dissolved together in water to give 2.5×10^2 mL of solution.

22. 10.0 mL of sodium chloride solution (0.250 mol·L^{-1}) are mixed with 40.0 mL of sodium sulfate solution (0.100 mol·L^{-1}). Calculate the total concentration of sodium ions in the resulting solution.

23. Describe how you would prepare the following:
    a) 5.00×10^2 mL of hydrochloric acid (0.10 mol·L^{-1}) from 12.0 mol·L^{-1} hydrochloric acid
    b) 1.50 L of calcium chloride solution (0.200 mol·L^{-1}) from 1.00 mol·L^{-1} calcium chloride

24. If 10.0 mL of 0.560 mol·L^{-1} aluminum nitrate is diluted to 250.0 mL, calculate:
    a) the concentration of aluminum nitrate in the new solution
    b) the concentration of nitrate ions in the new solution

25. Calculate the concentration of the solution formed if a 25.0-mL sample of nitric acid (10.0 mol·L^{-1}) is placed in a 500.0-mL volumetric flask and the flask is filled up to the mark with distilled water.

26. Sketch graphs to show the effect of increasing temperature on:
    a) the solubility of a solid in a liquid
    b) the solubility of a gas in a liquid

27. For the following six hydrogen-ion concentrations [H$^+$] in mol·L^{-1}: 10^{-2} 10^{-3} 10^{-4} 10^{-5} 10^{-6} 10^{-7}
    a) calculate each of the [H$^+$] values as a factor of 10^{-4}. For example, [H$^+$] $= 10^{-2}$ mol·L^{-1} is the same as 100×10^{-4} mol·L^{-1}.
    b) calculate the pH values corresponding to each [H$^+$] value.
    c) present your results in two rows as [H$^+$] $\times 10^{-4}$ mol·L^{-1} and pH values. Describe your conclusion for the trend of pH values as the [H$^+$] value decreases.
    d) draw a graph of [H$^+$] $\times 10^{-4}$ (mol·L^{-1}) on the y-axis against pH on the x-axis. On the basis of the graph, describe what conclusion you can make about the relationship between [H$^+$] and pH values.

28. An alloy of gold and copper is used for making jewellery. The composition of the alloy is normally expressed in karats, where 24 karats represents 100% gold. Calculate the composition (mass percent) of 14-karat gold.

29. In Canada, people who consume fish that have been caught in polluted waters are particularly susceptible to mercury poisoning. Health and Welfare Canada recommended in 1977 that fish containing more than 500 ppb of mercury should not be sold or consumed. Calculate the mass of mercury that would be present in a trout weighing 1.00 kg that has a mercury concentration of 500 ppb.

30. a) Predict whether the pH of an aqueous solution of each of the following will be above 7, below 7, or equal to 7:
    i) acetic acid
    ii) sugar
    iii) ammonia
    b) Predict the approximate pH of each of the following:
    i) rainwater
    ii) household ammonia
    iii) the acid from a car battery
    c) Calculate the pH of an aqueous solution containing:
    i) 3.7×10^{-5} mol·L^{-1} HNO$_3$
    ii) 1.8×10^{-3} mol·L^{-1} H$_2$SO$_4$
    d) Calculate the pH of each of the following aqueous solutions:
    i) 5.1×10^{-6} mol·L^{-1} CH$_3$COOH
    ii) 2.5×10^{-4} mol·L^{-1} KOH

Making Connections

31. Industrial smokestacks emit a variety of chemicals that contribute to acid rain in areas far away from those industries. Of particular concern are nitrogen oxides and sulfur dioxide. This rain turns into sulphuric acid and nitric acid and, due to weather patterns, can fall in areas far away from its original source. Outline the political, economic, and environmental consequences, and create an action plan to reduce this problem. Be sure to justify any decisions you make.

32. You have recently discovered that the garden nursery in your community has been storing several barrels of banned pesticides on its property. You organize a community action committee to investigate the problem. The task of the committee is to write a report outlining the extent of the pollution; the economic, health, and environmental consequences; and recommendations to solve this issue.

33. Since Canada has more than enough fresh water to satisfy its own needs, it should sell excess water to other countries. Take a position on this statement and research information that will support your position. Write an essay that outlines your position and includes supporting evidence. Include a description of your information sources, and identify any potential biases.

34. A railway company is planning to expand its tracks through your community in order to provide more cost-effective transportation between two industrial cities. Several industries in these cities rely on acid and base substances and find it more economical to transport these in a very concentrated form. Brainstorm a list of stakeholders who would support and dispute the building of this new transportation route. For each stakeholder, make a chart outlining the pros and cons that the stakeholder would raise for this issue. Finally, choose one perspective and write a short essay elaborating on that viewpoint. In your essay, address how your perspective may address concerns of the other stakeholders.

Reactions in Solution

The branch of chemistry that most affects our daily health is analytical chemistry, the study of the chemical composition of substances. Samples of the water we drink, the food we eat, and the pharmaceuticals that we take have all been analyzed to ensure acceptable purity. The growth of analytical chemistry has been largely in response to our needs. For example, a major problem in the dairy industry used to be the watering down of milk by dishonest farmers. A professor of agricultural chemistry was able to devise a test in the late 19th century—the Babcock test—to put an end to these practices. His test could accurately determine the fat percent in milk, and it is still used, essentially unchanged, even today. As governments decree ever more strict requirements as to the levels of impurities in our air, water, and foodstuffs, analytical chemists are challenged to devise ways of measuring the concentrations of elements and compounds to the increasingly greater precision demanded.

FIGURE 7.1 Analytical chemistry has changed a lot in the last 100 years, but the glassware we use is essentially unchanged.

Analytical chemistry, which has always relied on equipment, is one of the best examples of the links between science and technology. In the early history of analytical chemistry, it was the instrument makers, the manufacturers of the early brass balances, who enabled chemists to measure masses to the necessary precision and accuracy. These specialists in metal work and engineering were as highly esteemed as their colleagues who made the chronometers used for navigation. Then came the glass workers, producing the analytical glassware capable of holding solutions of precisely known volume. Other equipment had to be custom-designed for the needs of analytical chemists—even the analytical filter paper. Now chemists often use equipment designed by electronics specialists and constructed by a new generation of engineers. Without their contributions, the analytical chemist would be helpless.

Many of the analyses, even today, are performed by solution reactions, the topic of this chapter. You will discover how to write solution reactions in terms of the ions and how to test for the presence of ions in solution. Then you will learn how to perform calculations involving solution reactions and quantitatively analyze solutions for their ion content.

WEBLINK

Write a brief biography of Stephen Babcock, the inventor of the Babcock test. Describe how the Babcock test is performed on milk samples. Begin your research at
www.pearsoned.ca/ chemistry11.

Discovering Chemistry

Counting Drops

What happens when you add hydrochloric acid to sodium hydroxide?

Materials

    0.1 mol·L^{-1} hydrochloric acid
    dilute solution of sodium hydroxide
    universal indicator or red cabbage juice
    10-mL graduated cylinder
    test tube
    dropper

1. Pour 5 mL of the sodium hydroxide solution in the test tube.

2. Add 3 to 5 drops of the universal indicator or red cabbage juice solution to the test tube.

3. Add the hydrochloric acid drop by drop to the test tube.

4. Swirl the liquid in the test tube after each drop.

5. Record the number of drops added.

■ Describe the colour of the solution in the test tube after you added the indicator, and after you added the hydrochloric acid.

■ Identify the name of the process you are carrying out.

■ Use chemical equations to help you account for any changes in colour.

CHECK**POINT**

Describe how you would prepare 400.0 mL of 0.680 mol·L^{-1} potassium hydroxide.

    Write a balanced equation that represents the dissolving of solid potassium hydroxide in water.

7.1 Net Ionic Equations

Key Understandings

When you have completed this section, you will be able to:
- identify reactions involving aqueous solutions that produce precipitates
- define total ionic equation, spectator ions, and net ionic equation
- use appropriate scientific vocabulary to communicate ideas related to aqueous solutions
- write balanced net ionic equations for reactions that produce precipitates
- understand how hard water forms
- describe the different ways of treating hard water

When substances are analyzed in laboratories, they are often found to contain ionic compounds. How can the component ions be identified? How can you find out how much of a particular ion is present? To do so, you need to understand what is happening when solutions of two ionic compounds are mixed. This is the topic of net ionic equations, in which chemical equations are represented as reactions not between ionic compounds but between their constituent ions. In many cases, this makes it easier to understand what is happening during the reaction.

In the previous chapter, you saw how soluble ionic compounds are present in solution as aqueous ions. For example, potassium sulfate dissolves in water as follows:

$$K_2SO_4(s) \xrightarrow[\text{in water}]{\text{dissolve}} 2\ K^+(aq) + SO_4^{2-}(aq)$$

So when solutions of ionic compounds are mixed, it is the component ions that mix and are capable of participating in a chemical reaction. By examining chemical reactions in terms of the interaction of ions, you can obtain a better understanding of what is happening in the solution.

Net Ionic Equations for Reactions in Solution

In Chapter 3, you read about double displacement reactions in which a precipitate was formed. For example, if a solution of barium chloride is added to a solution of potassium carbonate, a precipitate of barium carbonate is formed. The chemical equation that represents this process is:

$$K_2CO_3(aq) + BaCl_2(aq) \rightarrow 2\ KCl(aq) + BaCO_3(s)$$

The process was depicted as a switching of ion partners:

$$\begin{array}{cc} K^+ & CO_3^{2-} \\ & \diagdown\!\!\!\diagup \\ Ba^{2+} & Cl^- \end{array}$$

But what is the result of this reaction? In this case, it is the formation of a precipitate. You can see this if all the free ions are written in their ionic form:

$$2\ K^+(aq) + CO_3^{2-}(aq) + Ba^{2+}(aq) + 2\ Cl^-(aq) \rightarrow$$
$$2\ K^+(aq) + 2\ Cl^-(aq) + BaCO_3(s)$$

This equation is an example of a **total ionic equation** because every substance that exists as free ions when it is dissolved in water has been written in ionic form.

If you look at the previous equation, you will see that the potassium ions and chloride ions are unchanged by the reaction and are written in exactly the same way on each side of the equation.

$$2\ K^+(aq) + CO_3^{2-}(aq) + Ba^{2+}(aq) + 2\ Cl^-(aq) \rightarrow$$
$$2\ K^+(aq) + 2\ Cl^-(aq) + BaCO_3(s)$$

As these ions do not take part in the reaction, they are called **spectator ions**. The equation can be simplified to involve only those ions that chemically reacted. The simplified equation is known as the **net ionic equation**.

$$CO_3^{2-}(aq) + Ba^{2+}(aq) \rightarrow BaCO_3(s)$$

A net ionic equation shows the essence of a reaction in aqueous solution. In this example, it is the reaction of aqueous carbonate ions with aqueous barium ions to form solid barium carbonate.

In the lab, you cannot obtain a bottle of carbonate ions or of barium ions. There has to be another ion present of the opposite charge. But the net ionic equation does tell you that you can take any soluble carbonate and react it with any soluble barium salt and obtain the same result. You can try this for yourself by writing the chemical, total ionic, and net ionic equations for the reaction of aqueous sodium carbonate with aqueous barium nitrate. The net ionic equation should be exactly the same as that above.

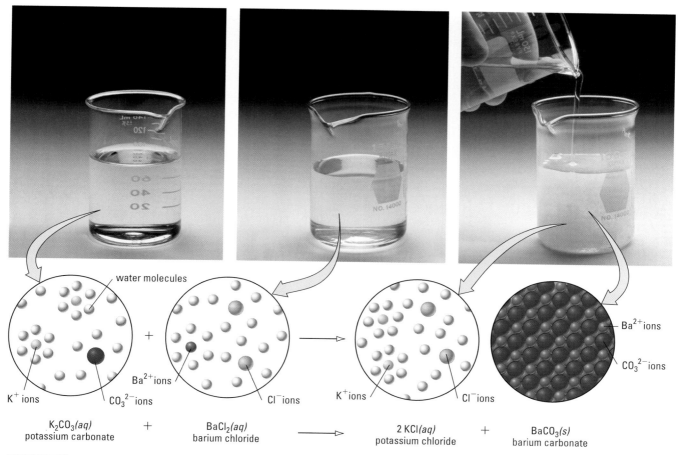

water molecules

K^+ ions CO_3^{2-} ions Ba^{2+} ions Cl^- ions K^+ ions Cl^- ions Ba^{2+} ions CO_3^{2-} ions

$K_2CO_3(aq)$ + $BaCl_2(aq)$ → $2\ KCl(aq)$ + $BaCO_3(s)$
potassium carbonate   barium chloride   potassium chloride   barium carbonate

FIGURE 7.2 Aqueous solutions of potassium carbonate and barium chloride are added to form a white precipitate.

There are several guidelines for writing net ionic equations.

- Solutions of all soluble salts are written as ions. $NaNO_3$, KCl, $CaCl_2$, and $(NH_4)_2SO_4$ are some examples of soluble salts.
- Solutions of all strong acids are written as ions. HCl, HNO_3, H_2SO_4, and $HClO_4$ are the most common examples of strong acids.
- Solutions of all strong bases are written as ions. $NaOH$, KOH, and $Ba(OH)_2$ are the most common examples of strong bases.
- All covalent compounds are left in molecular form with their states written beside them; this includes all gases *(g)*, all liquids (e.g., H_2O) and all soluble covalent compounds (e.g., ethanol, CH_3CH_2OH) *(l)*, and all insoluble compounds *(s)*.

EXAMPLE 1

Write the balanced net ionic equation for the reaction of aqueous sodium carbonate with aqueous calcium nitrate.

$$Na_2CO_3(aq) + Ca(NO_3)_2(aq) \rightarrow 2\ NaNO_3(aq) + CaCO_3(s)$$

Given
$$Na_2CO_3(aq) + Ca(NO_3)_2(aq) \rightarrow 2\ NaNO_3(aq) + CaCO_3(s)$$

Required
net ionic equation

Analysis
chemical equation $\rightarrow$ total ionic equation

total ionic equation $\rightarrow$ net ionic equation

Solution
total ionic equation (the solid calcium carbonate remains in molecular form):

$$2\ Na^+(aq) + CO_3^{2-}(aq) + Ca^{2+}(aq) + 2\ NO_3^-(aq) \rightarrow 2\ Na^+(aq) + 2\ NO_3^-(aq) + CaCO_3(s)$$

net ionic equation:

$$CO_3^{2-}(aq) + Ca^{2+}(aq) \rightarrow CaCO_3(s)$$

Statement
The balanced net ionic equation is:

$$CO_3^{2-}(aq) + Ca^{2+}(aq) \rightarrow CaCO_3(s)$$

PRACTICE PROBLEM

Write the balanced chemical equation, total ionic equation, and net ionic equation for the reaction of sodium iodide solution and aqueous bromine.

EXAMPLE 2

Write the balanced chemical equation, total ionic equation, and net ionic equation for the reaction that occurs when zinc metal is added to copper(II) sulfate solution.

Given
reactants = Zn*(s)*, CuSO$_4$*(aq)*

Required
chemical equation
total ionic equation
net ionic equation

Analysis
chemical equation

type of reaction—A metal reacting with a metal salt is a single displacement reaction.

As zinc is above copper in the activity series, the zinc will displace the copper(II) ions to give zinc sulfate and copper metal.

Then:
chemical equation → total ionic equation
total ionic equation → net ionic equation

Solution
chemical equation:

Zn*(s)* + CuSO$_4$*(aq)* → Cu*(s)* + ZnSO$_4$*(aq)*

total ionic equation (the two metals remain in molecular form):

Zn*(s)* + Cu^{2+}*(aq)* + ~~SO$_4^{2-}$*(aq)*~~ → Cu*(s)* + Zn^{2+}*(aq)* + ~~SO$_4^{2-}$*(aq)*~~

net ionic equation:

Zn*(s)* + Cu^{2+}*(aq)* → Cu*(s)* + Zn^{2+}*(aq)*

Statement
The net ionic equation is:

Zn*(s)* + Cu^{2+}*(aq)* → Cu*(s)* + Zn^{2+}*(aq)*

PRACTICE PROBLEM

Write the balanced chemical equation, total ionic equation, and net ionic equation for the reaction of lead(II) nitrate solution and potassium chloride solution.

EXAMPLE 3

Write the balanced chemical equation, total ionic equation, and net ionic equation for the reaction that occurs when sodium hydroxide solution reacts with hydrochloric acid.

Given
reactants = NaOH*(aq)*, HNO$_3$*(aq)*

Required
chemical equation
total ionic equation
net ionic equation

Analysis

chemical equation

type of reaction—A base reacting with an acid is a double displacement (neutralization) reaction.

An acid reacts with a base to give a salt and water.

Then:

chemical equation → total ionic equation

total ionic equation → net ionic equation

Solution

chemical equation:

$NaOH(aq) + HNO_3(aq) \rightarrow NaNO_3(aq) + H_2O(l)$

total ionic equation:

$\cancel{Na^+(aq)} + OH^-(aq) + H^+(aq) + \cancel{NO_3^-(aq)} \rightarrow \cancel{Na^+(aq)} + \cancel{NO_3^-(aq)} + H_2O(l)$

net ionic equation:

$OH^-(aq) + H^+(aq) \rightarrow H_2O(l)$

Statement

The net ionic equation is:

$OH^-(aq) + H^+(aq) \rightarrow H_2O(l)$

Note that for any neutralization between a strong acid and a strong base, the net ionic equation is the reaction of the hydroxide ion with the hydrogen (hydronium) ion to give molecular water.

WEBLINK

Nearly all the large caverns in Earth's surface have been in limestone formations. Write a report explaining where Canada's major limestone caves are located and how they were formed. Provide evidence that the climate was different from today at the time the caves formed. Begin your research at **www.pearsoned.ca/chemistry11**.

FIGURE 7.3 Limestone cliffs at Tews Falls in the Niagara escarpment near Hamilton. Hard water results from the reaction of the rainwater (very dilute carbonic acid solution) with the calcium carbonate of limestone rocks.

Ions and the Water Supply

If you look inside a well-used teakettle or coffeemaker, you may see a deposit. What is the substance and where has it come from? Tap water is never pure water. It contains ions that have dissolved in the water as the water percolates down from the earth's surface to where it accumulates. One ion in particular, the calcium ion, is very common in many natural waters including those in parts of Ontario. To understand why, you have to realize that rain is not pure water either. Among the many compounds that the raindrop has picked up during its descent is carbon dioxide, making pure rainwater acidic (pH ≈ 5·6). Carbon dioxide dissolves in water to give carbonic acid:

$$CO_2(g) + H_2O(l) \rightarrow H_2CO_3(aq)$$

Many of the surface rocks in southern Ontario consist of limestone, calcium carbonate. Calcium carbonate reacts with the very dilute solution of carbonic acid to give a solution containing calcium ions and hydrogen carbonate ions:

$$CaCO_3(s) + H_2CO_3(aq) \rightleftharpoons Ca^{2+}(aq) + 2\ HCO_3^-(aq)$$

Therefore, drinking water in such areas is rich in these two ions. Water with a high concentration of calcium ions is said to be **hard water**, while that with a low concentration is called **soft water**.

You can tell if you are in a hard water area if you have difficulty making soap foam (lather) when you are washing. Also, a scum forms in sinks and bathtubs. This consists of insoluble calcium (and magnesium and iron) salts in the soap. Detergents, on the other hand, do not create this problem because their metal salts are soluble. While washing with hard water is a nuisance, there are more serious problems associated with hard water. When the water is heated or evaporated, the reaction occurs in the opposite direction:

$$Ca^{2+}(aq) + 2 \ HCO_3^-(aq) \rightarrow CaCO_3(s) + CO_2(aq) + H_2O(l)$$

The aqueous carbon dioxide becomes gaseous carbon dioxide at higher temperatures. As a result, the carbon dioxide gas escapes and more calcium carbonate is formed.

The calcium carbonate will crystallize over the heating elements in electric kettles, industrial hot water boilers, and hot water pipes. This rock-hard layer is called scale. When there are layers of crystals over heating elements, the crystals will act as an insulator, therefore it will take longer to heat the water. Sometimes water pipes become so clogged that the hot water pipes have to be replaced. Experiments have shown that as little as a 0.08-cm scale buildup on a heat exchange surface (hot water heater, boiler, cooling tower, etc.) uses almost 10% more energy than clean metal surfaces. A 0.6-cm buildup will increase energy consumption by an astonishing 40%! This can cost hundreds or even thousands of wasted energy dollars per year for your home or business.

FIGURE 7.4 A deposit of calcium carbonate (scale) on an electric heating element

Removing Ions from Water

There are three ways that ions can be removed from water. The most common way is called **ion exchange**; the other two processes are **chemical precipitation** and **electrodialysis**.

Ion Exchange To remove calcium ions (and other ions such as magnesium and iron(II)), you can use an ion exchanger. In this case, a cation exchanger is usually employed. A cation exchanger usually contains beads of a polymer (a long molecule consisting of repeating units), which has negative ions on its surface (Figure 7.6). To balance the charge, sodium ions are ionically bonded to the surface. As the hard water flows over the beads, the calcium ions replace pairs of sodium ions. The water exiting the ion exchanger will have the calcium ions removed and sodium ions in their place. The water output will be "soft." However, it will have a measurable concentration of sodium ions. Consequently, health experts usually advise people with home ion exchangers to use non-softened water or bottled water for drinking.

FIGURE 7.5 The interior of Carlsbad Caverns, New Mexico. These caves are the most spectacular in North America. The limestone was dissolved away by the dilute carbonic acid. Then later, the stalagmites and stalactites were formed by the evaporation of calcium hydrogen carbonate solution as it dripped from the ceiling to the floor of the cave.

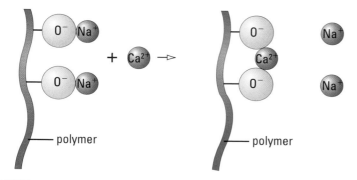

FIGURE 7.6 The workings of an ion exchanger

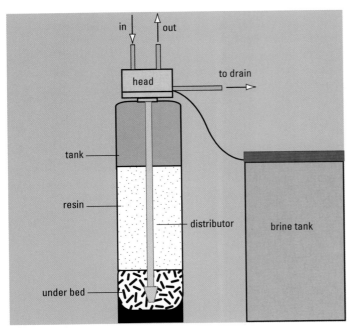

FIGURE 7.7 A typical ion-exchange unit consists of a tank containing pressurized water to hold the resin (polymer beads) in place, a head that controls the flow of water during use, the resin that provides the sites for the bonding of ions, the distributor that transports the treated water out of the exchanger, the brine tank to store the sodium chloride solution used to recharge the exchanger, and the under bed gravel that supports the resin and provides a reservoir for the treated water.

Once the ion-exchange column is saturated with the hard water ions, a concentrated solution of sodium chloride is poured through the exchanger. The high concentration of sodium ions forces the calcium ions off the ion-exchange column and recharges the column with sodium ions so it can be used again.

Chemical Precipitation Certain toxic, heavy metal ions such as cadmium, lead, and mercury can easily be precipitated because their sulfide salts are insoluble in water. If a careful amount of hydrogen sulfide gas is bubbled through a solution containing heavy metal ions, the corresponding sulfides can precipitate out of solution and then be filtered out.

$$M^{2+}(aq) + H_2S(g) \rightarrow MS(s) + 2 H^+(aq)$$

Electrodialysis Electrostatics is at the core of a lot of chemistry, such as the explanations for ionic and covalent bonding. It is also a means for removing most of the ions from a solution. **Electrodialysis** is a technique that depends on the attraction of positive ions toward a negative electrode and on negative ions toward a positive electrode. In an electrodialysis unit, there are three compartments filled with salty or contaminated water, separated by a pair of semipermeable membranes (Figure 7.8). However, unlike the reverse osmosis membrane, these membranes allow the ions to pass through. The electrodes are charged, and the ions in solution will move toward the electrode of opposite charge. The level of ions in the water in the middle compartment will be reduced, while that in the side compartments (the wastewater) will have increased ion levels. The water in the middle compartment will, therefore, become drinkable.

The purpose of the selective membrane is to allow the movement of only the positive ions from the middle part of the cell to the left side, but not allow any negative ions from the left side to enter the middle part. Similarly, a selective membrane allows the negative ions to move to the right part of the cell but does not allow any positive ions from the right side to move to the middle. The net result is the movement of ions away from the middle compartment, producing pure water here, while the ion concentration increases in the two side compartments.

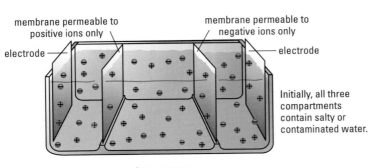

membrane permeable to positive ions only

membrane permeable to negative ions only

electrode

electrode

Initially, all three compartments contain salty or contaminated water.

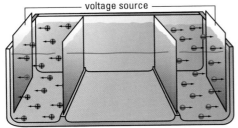

voltage source

After a voltage is applied to the electrodes, the positive and negative ions migrate to the left and right compartments respectively. The centre compartment contains pure water.

FIGURE 7.8 Electrodialysis equipment is used in the desalination and treatment of water, for processing food, and for manufacturing chemical and pharmaceutical products.

Understanding Concepts

1. Describe the differences in writing chemical equations, ionic equations, and net ionic equations. Give an example of each that is not in this section.

2. Define the term "hard water" in your own words, and explain why it reduces the effectiveness of soap.

Applying Inquiry/Communication Skills

3. Write equations to show the process that occurs when the following compounds dissolve in water:
   a) sodium sulfide
   b) ammonium chloride
   c) calcium nitrate
   d) sodium phosphate
   e) ammonium carbonate
   f) aluminum sulfate

4. Write the net ionic equation for each of the following reactions:
   a) When aqueous sodium carbonate solution is added to a solution of calcium chloride, solid calcium carbonate is formed and sodium chloride remains in solution.
   b) When solid magnesium metal is added to a solution of zinc chloride, solid zinc metal is formed, leaving a solution of magnesium chloride.
   c) When sodium iodide solution is mixed with aqueous lead(II) nitrate, a yellow lead(II) iodide precipitate is formed, leaving a solution of sodium nitrate.

5. Write the net ionic equation for each of the following reactions. (Remember that you must write first the balanced chemical equation and then the total ionic equation.)
   a) An aqueous solution of sodium sulfide reacts with hydrochloric acid to produce hydrogen sulfide gas and a solution of sodium chloride.
   b) An aqueous solution of potassium hydroxide reacts with nitric acid to give a solution of potassium nitrate and water.

Making Connections

6. The buildup of scale on heat exchange surfaces as opposed to clean metal surfaces has a direct impact on the amount of energy used. Given rising energy costs and the need to conserve resources, identify household appliances that can be affected by scale buildup, and design an action plan to inform consumers about how to avoid this wasteful cost and use of energy.

7.2 Double Displacement Reactions in Qualitative Analysis

Key Understandings

When you have completed this section, you will be able to:
- define qualitative analysis
- describe the procedure used to identify unknown anions and cations in solution
- use appropriate scientific vocabulary to communicate reactions in qualitative analysis
- represent precipitation reactions by their net ionic equations
- write balanced chemical equations for reactions involving acids and bases
- analyze qualitatively the ions present in a solution

How can you find out which ions are present in a water sample? You can use simple test tube reactions—particularly the double displacement reactions that you learned in Chapter 3. However, instead of writing the chemical equations in molecular form, you will find it much more useful to write them in net ionic form. The technique of identifying which ions are present is known as **qualitative analysis**. The key to this analysis is to perform the tests in a certain order. If the test for a particular group of ions is positive, then you perform specific tests to identify exactly which ion of that group is present. If the test is negative, then you proceed to the next test in the sequence. You continue the tests until all the ions have been identified.

How to Identify Anions in Solution

To identify an anion, you need to find a cation with which it will give a characteristic reaction. To illustrate, suppose you have a solution that you know contains one of the following colourless anions: carbonate, chloride, bromide, or sulfate. Then you can perform the following test sequence:

Procedure 1:	add hydrogen ion (dilute hydrochloric acid) to a sample of the test solution
Observation:	gas produced
Deduction:	carbonate ion

Procedure 2a):	add silver ion (silver nitrate solution) to a sample of the test solution
Observation:	white or cream-coloured precipitate
Deduction:	chloride ion or bromide ion

Procedure 3:	add barium ion (barium chloride solution) to a sample of the test solution
Observation:	white precipitate
Deduction:	sulfate ion

To distinguish between chloride and bromide ions, you can use a single displacement reaction involving the halogen activity series.

Procedure 2b):	add aqueous chlorine (also known as chlorine water, $Cl_2(aq)$)
Observation:	brown colour
Deduction:	bromide ion (no colour change would have indicated chloride ion)

For each positive test, you should always write a corresponding balanced net ionic equation.

How to Identify Cations in Solution

To identify a cation, you need to find an anion with which it will give a characteristic reaction. To illustrate, suppose you have a solution that you know contains one of the following colourless cations: barium, magnesium, silver, or sodium. Then you can perform the following test sequence:

Procedure 1:	add chloride ion (sodium chloride solution) to a sample of the test solution
Observation:	white precipitate
Deduction:	silver ion

Procedure 2:	add sulfate ion (sodium sulfate solution) to a sample of the test solution
Observation:	white precipitate
Deduction:	barium ion

Procedure 3:	add carbonate ion (sodium carbonate solution) to a sample of the test solution
Observation:	white precipitate
Deduction:	magnesium ion

Procedure 4:	to distinguish between sodium and potassium ion, take a concentrated solution of the unknown ion and perform the flame test (dip the end of a wooden stick or piece of wire into the solution, then place the tip into a burner flame and observe any colour produced). This test only works for pure K^+ ions that are not contaminated with Na^+ ions.
Observation:	yellow or lilac colour to flame
Deduction:	sodium ion (yellow) or potassium ion (lilac)

For each positive test, you should always write a corresponding balanced net ionic equation.

Discovering Chemistry — *Mystery Solutions*

In this activity, you are to identify an unknown solution using the anion and cation flowcharts.

Materials

  dropper bottles of the following solutions:
    dilute hydrochloric acid, silver nitrate, barium nitrate, sodium chloride, sodium carbonate, and sodium sulfate
  blue glass
  splints
  spot plate
  wash bottle (to rinse the spot plate into a waste container provided by your teacher)

1. Using the tests given, design flowcharts for the identification of an anion (from a choice of CO_3^{2-}, Cl^-, Br^-, or SO_4^{2-}) and for a cation (from a choice of Ag^+, Ba^{2+}, Mg^{2+}, K^+, or Na^+). Your teacher will provide you with a mystery solution containing one anion and one cation from these choices.

2. Design an efficient way to record your observations. Using your flowcharts, perform the tests necessary to identify the solution. If you are performing Procedure 4, the splint should be wet first. Use a blue glass to check for potassium ions.

■ Write net ionic equations for all reactions you performed.

Section 7.2 Review

Understanding Concepts

1. Define qualitative analysis in your own words, and describe why it is important.

2. When performing a test to identify anions, state why there is no precipitation test for nitrate.

3. Describe a distinguishing test for iodide ions.

4. When performing a test to identify cations, state why there is no precipitation test for sodium or potassium ions. If your solution contained calcium ions, state the first test that would have caused it to precipitate.

5. When hydrochloric acid is added to the solution of an ionic substance, it does not produce a precipitate. However, when ammonium sulfate is added to the same solution, a brown precipitate forms. Identify the 2 ions that may be present in the original substance, and describe a test you could use to distinguish between the 2 ions.

Applying Inquiry/ Communication Skills

6. Write a balanced net ionic equation for the following reactions:
    a) hydrogen ion (from hydrochloric acid) and hydrogen sulfide ion
    b) hydrogen ion and carbonate ion
    c) silver ion and chloride ion
    d) barium ion and sulfate ion
    e) lead(II) ion and sulfide ion
    f) aqueous chlorine and iodide ion
    g) lead(II) ion and chloride ion
    h) calcium ion and hydroxide ion

7. You are given 2 vials of clear, colourless solutions labelled A and B. You know one contains magnesium sulfate and the other sodium carbonate. Outline the steps you would take and the observations you would expect to make as you attempted to identify which vial contained which solution.

8. Design a test to determine the concentration of chloride ions or ammonium ions in tap water. With the teacher's approval of your design, carry out your test.

7.3 Stoichiometry Involving Solutions

Key Understandings

When you have completed this section, you will be able to:

- solve stoichiometry problems involving solutions
- use appropriate scientific vocabulary to communicate ideas related to stoichiometry involving solutions
- write balanced chemical and ionic equations
- apply stoichiometry to describe the process of extracting titanium ore

INFOBIT

The stomach produces hydrochloric acid in order to break down and digest the food you eat. The lining of the stomach is protected against this acid, but the intestines are not. Partially digested food leaving the stomach is mixed with a liquid called bile. Bile is strongly alkaline and neutralizes the stomach acid before it can damage the intestines.

You have already learned how to use stoichiometry to determine the masses involved in a particular chemical reaction. To do this, you converted mass to moles, moles of one substance to moles of another substance, then moles back to mass again. The mass–mole conversions and the appropriate stoichiometric ratio from a balanced chemical equation were the key requirements for the calculations.

You have also learned how the amount of a substance in solution can be determined from the volume and concentration of a solution. The equation that you used was:

$$n_{solute} = c_{solution} \times V_{solution}$$

As many chemical reactions take place in solution, an important skill in chemistry is to be able to perform stoichiometric calculations involving solutions. The next two examples demonstrate how to do this type of calculation. The first involves a single displacement reaction and the second a double displacement reaction that produces a precipitate.

EXAMPLE 4

Silver metal is expensive and should always be recycled. If your lab has 0.500 L of silver nitrate solution (2.00 mol·L^{-1}), what mass of copper should you add to extract all the silver metal by single displacement?

$$Cu(s) + 2\ AgNO_3(aq) \rightarrow Cu(NO_3)_2(aq) + 2\ Ag(s)$$

Given

Cu(s)	+	2 AgNO$_3$(aq)	→	Cu(NO$_3$)$_2$(aq)	+	2 Ag(s)
1 mol		2 mol				

$$c_{AgNO_3} = 2.00\ \text{mol·L}^{-1}$$
$$V_{AgNO_3} = 0.500\ \text{L}$$

Required

$m_{Cu} = ?$ g

Analysis

$V_{AgNO_3}, c_{AgNO_3} \rightarrow n_{AgNO_3}$, (using $n = c \times V$)

$n_{AgNO_3} \rightarrow n_{Cu}$ (using mole ratio, 2 mol AgNO$_3$: 1 mol Cu)

$n_{Cu} \rightarrow m_{Cu}$ (using $M_{Cu} = 63.55$ g·mol^{-1})

Solution

$n_{AgNO_3} = 2.00 \text{ mol·L}^{-1} \text{ AgNO}_3 \times 0.200 \text{ L} = 0.400 \text{ mol AgNO}_3$

$n_{Cu} = 0.400 \text{ mol AgNO}_3 \times \dfrac{1 \text{ mol Cu}}{2 \text{ mol AgNO}_3} = 0.200 \text{ mol Cu}$

$m_{Cu} = 0.200 \text{ mol Cu} \times \dfrac{63.55 \text{ g Cu}}{1 \text{ mol Cu}} = 12.7 \text{ g Cu}$

Statement

The mass of copper metal needed is 12.7 g.

PRACTICE PROBLEM

You find 25.0 g barium metal in the school chemistry storeroom. If you carefully reacted the barium with 1.00 L of water, determine the concentration of the barium hydroxide solution produced. Assume that the resulting solution is 1.00 L.

EXAMPLE 5

When a solution of silver nitrate is added to a solution of calcium chloride, the following reaction takes place:

$2 \text{ AgNO}_3(aq) + \text{CaCl}_2(aq) \rightarrow 2 \text{ AgCl}(s) + \text{Ca(NO}_3)_2(aq)$

Calculate the volume of 0.105 mol·L^{-1} silver nitrate solution that must be added to 25.0 mL of 0.255 mol·L^{-1} calcium chloride solution in order to produce the maximum mass of silver chloride.

Given

| $2 \text{ AgNO}_3(aq)$ | $+$ | $\text{CaCl}_2(aq)$ | $\rightarrow$ | $2 \text{ AgCl}(s)$ | $+$ | $\text{Ca(NO}_3)_2(aq)$ |

2 mol   1 mol

$c_{AgNO_3} = 0.105 \text{ mol·L}^{-1}$ $c_{CaCl_2} = 0.255 \text{ mol·L}^{-1}$

$V_{CaCl_2} = 25.0 \text{ mL}$

$\phantom{V_{CaCl_2}} = 0.025 \text{ L}$

Required

$V_{AgNO_3} = ? \text{ L}$

Analysis

$c_{CaCl_2}, V_{CaCl_2} \rightarrow n_{CaCl_2}$ (using $n = c \times V$)

$n_{CaCl_2} \rightarrow n_{AgNO_3}$ (using mole ratio, 2 mol AgNO$_3$: 1 mol CaCl$_2$)

$n_{AgNO_3}, c_{AgNO_3} \rightarrow V_{AgNO_3} \left(\text{using } n = c \times V \text{ or } V = \dfrac{n}{c} \right)$

Solution

$n_{CaCl_2} = 0.255 \text{ mol·L}^{-1} \text{ CaCl}_2 \times 0.025 \text{ L} = 6.38 \times 10^{-3} \text{ mol CaCl}_2$

$n_{CaCl_2} = 6.38 \times 10^{-3} \text{ mol CaCl}_2 \times \dfrac{2 \text{ mol AgNO}_3}{1 \text{ mol CaCl}_2} = 1.28 \times 10^{-2} \text{ mol AgNO}_3$

$V_{AgNO_3} = \dfrac{1.28 \times 10^{-2} \text{ mol AgNO}_3}{0.105 \text{ mol·L}^{-1} \text{ AgNO}_3} = 0.121 \text{ L}$

Statement

The volume of silver nitrate required is 0.121 L.

PRACTICE PROBLEM

A 2.00-L waste solution bottle is known to contain lead(II) ions. Concentrated sodium chloride solution is added, and a white precipitate forms. The precipitate is filtered off and dried. Its mass is 0.0112 g. Identify the precipitate. Calculate the concentration of lead(II) ions in the waste solution.

Solution Stoichiometry in Industry: Titanium Dioxide

If you were asked to name a metal, you might think of iron, copper, aluminum, or perhaps sodium or potassium. Yet titanium, or more specifically, titanium compounds, are very important to the Canadian economy. In fact, titanium(IV) oxide, usually called titanium dioxide, represents about 10% of the annual sales of the Canadian inorganic chemical industry. This is true not because large quantities of the oxide are produced, but because it commands a high price.

Why is the compound so valuable? About 50% of titanium dioxide is used in the manufacture of white paint (and is mixed with colours to give pastel-coloured paints). Titanium dioxide is by far the best white pigment in paint because the compound has the best covering ability of any white compound. Also, it does not discolour with age, and it has a very low toxicity. Before the use of titanium dioxide, lead hydroxide carbonate, $PbCO_3(OH)_2$, known as "white lead," was used. Lead-based paints are dangerous since infants can chew on toys painted with them and develop lead poisoning. Many of the workers who synthesized white lead suffered painful deaths as a result of lead poisoning.

Why is titanium dioxide produced in Canada? The world's second-largest deposits of titanium ore are found in Quebec. The ore is called ilmenite, $FeTiO_3$, chemical name iron(II) titanate. The first step in its extraction involves using concentrated sulfuric acid to separate the metal ions in the ore. The titanium forms the titanyl ion, $(TiO)^{2+}(aq)$.

FIGURE 7.9 The titanium dioxide plant at Varennes, Quebec

$$FeTiO_3(s) + 2\ H_2SO_4(aq) \rightarrow TiOSO_4(aq) + FeSO_4(aq) + H_2O(l)$$

The titanyl sulfate is separated from the iron(II) sulfate, and water is added. The following reaction occurs:

$$TiOSO_4(aq) + H_2O(l) \rightarrow TiO_2(s) + H_2SO_4(aq)$$

Approximately 10% of all titanium dioxide is converted into titanium, an extremely strong, low-density metal used in the aerospace industry and for the hulls of nuclear submarines. However, because the conversion of titanium dioxide to titanium metal is not carried out in Canada, we must rely on imported titanium metal for our own aerospace industry.

This particular extraction process (the sulfate process) results in considerable amounts of waste material, particularly iron(II) sulfate and dilute sulfuric acid. Another process used (the chloride process) also has significant environmental impact. New processes are needed to produce the compound in a more environmentally benign way.

FIGURE 7.10 Titanium metal is used for the construction of high-performance aircraft such as this Lockheed SR-71 Blackbird, which holds many of the world's speed and altitude records.

Section 7.3 Review

Applying Inquiry/Communication Skills

1. Aluminum reacts with hydrochloric acid according to the equation:

    $$2 \text{ Al}(s) + 6 \text{ HCl}(aq) \rightarrow$$
    $$2 \text{ AlCl}_3(aq) + 3 \text{ H}_2(g)$$

    Calculate the volume of 1.50 mol·L^{-1} hydrochloric acid that is required for 5.40 g aluminum to react completely.

2. Zinc metal reacts with hydrochloric acid according to the equation:

    $$\text{Zn}(s) + 2 \text{ HCl}(aq) \rightarrow$$
    $$\text{H}_2(g) + \text{ZnCl}_2(aq)$$

    A piece of zinc metal requires 75.0 mL of 3.00 mol·L^{-1} hydrochloric acid for a complete reaction. Determine the mass of the zinc metal used.

3. Calculate the volume of 0.110 mol·L^{-1} sodium sulfate required to precipitate the maximum mass of barium sulfate from 60.0 mL of 0.145 mol·L^{-1} barium chloride solution. The balanced equation is:

    $$\text{BaCl}_2(aq) + \text{Na}_2\text{SO}_4(aq) \rightarrow$$
    $$\text{BaSO}_4(s) + 2 \text{ NaCl}(aq)$$

4. Copper reacts with concentrated nitric acid according to the equation following:

    $$3 \text{ Cu}(s) + 8 \text{ HNO}_3(aq) \rightarrow$$
    $$3 \text{ Cu(NO}_3)_2(aq) + 2 \text{ NO}(g) + 4 \text{ H}_2\text{O}(l)$$

    Calculate the volume of nitric acid (16.0 mol·L^{-1}) required for a complete reaction if 25.0 g copper metal are used.

5. Write net ionic equations for each step in the extraction process of titanium ore shown on page 298.

Making Connections

6. About 20 000 t of titanium dioxide are produced each year in Quebec by the sulfate process. Calculate the mass of pure iron(II) titanate that must be mined to obtain this mass of product and the volume of concentrated sulfuric acid (18 mol·L^{-1}) that the plant has to purchase each year. Determine the environmental consequences of extracting titanium using the sulfate process.

7.4 Double Displacement Reactions in Quantitative Analysis

Key Understandings

When you have completed this section, you will be able to:

- define quantitative analysis, volumetric analysis, and acid-base titration
- write balanced net ionic equations
- solve stoichiometry problems involving solutions
- use appropriate scientific vocabulary to communicate ideas related to analytical chemistry
- perform a titration to determine the concentration of an unknown solution
- solve problems to determine the concentration of an unknown solution using volumetric analysis
- solve problems to identify unknown elements using gravimetric analysis

How much of a particular ion is present in a solution? This is the topic of **quantitative analysis**. There are two common types of quantitative analysis: volumetric analysis and gravimetric analysis. Volumetric analysis is a technique that involves precise volume measurements, while gravimetric analysis involves precise mass measurements. Both methods are used to determine the concentration of a particular ion in an unknown solution.

Martin Klaproth and his Contributions to Modern Analytical Chemistry

As quantitative analysis is such a core part of chemistry, it is curious that its history is never mentioned. After all, the development of atomic theory and the development of the periodic table are always described in high school and university chemistry texts. Since the 14th century, the driving force for analytical chemistry has been public need, the most pressing of which has been the purity of water supplies—a need that still exists today. Many major discoveries in chemistry have resulted from the work of analytical chemists. Mendeléev could not have devised the periodic table without the precise atomic masses of his analytical colleagues. In the early part of the 20th century, small differences in the atomic mass of lead samples were observed, and this led to the discovery of isotopes. Again it was analytical chemists that provided the techniques and skills necessary to make such precise and accurate measurements.

Although many chemists contributed to the advances in analytical chemistry, the most renowned was Martin Klaproth. Klaproth was born in Germany in 1743. Until the beginning of the 19th century, methods used in analytical chemistry were very sloppy. Values would be adjusted to fit expectations, precipitates were weighed when wet, and apparatus was often dirty and contaminated by other substances. Klaproth was concerned with sources of errors and ways of eliminating them. He emphasized the need for purity of reagents and devised ways of purifying them. It is Klaproth's

FIGURE 7.11 Martin Klaproth (1743–1817) developed many of the standard laboratory procedures that are performed in chemistry today.

heritage of carefulness, accuracy and precision, and emphasis on purity of reagents that is still at the core of modern quantitative analysis.

In present-day analytical chemistry, many compounds are available from suppliers in different grades: the purer the compound, the higher its cost. When purchasing a reagent, a chemist must decide which level of purity is most appropriate. The three most common categories are *General Purpose Grade* (the least pure, good for qualitative analysis), *AnalaR* (good purity for quantitative analysis), and *Spectroscopic Grade* (very high purity). Look in a chemical catalogue for a common chemical, and write out each grade available, the levels of impurity listed, and the cost for the same mass of reagent of each type.

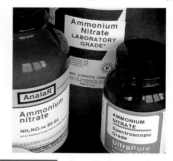

FIGURE 7.12 Chemical reagents can be purchased in different purities. The three most common categories are General Purpose Grade, AnalaR, and Spectroscopic Grade.

Investigation

Refer to page 307, Investigation 1

Volumetric Analysis

Volumetric analysis is a procedure that accurately measures the volumes of solutions in order to determine the concentration of an unknown solution. The experimental procedure is called a **titration**. The most common type of volumetric analysis conducted in high school laboratories is the **acid-base titration**. This involves the neutralization reaction (Section 3.3) between an acid and a base. Using this technique, you are able to determine the volume of acid (or base) of known concentration that will neutralize a given volume of base (or acid) of unknown concentration.

Volumetric analysis is used to determine the concentration of a solution, the molar mass of a substance, and the percent composition of a mixture. Consequently, it is carried out in most industrial laboratories. Typical analyses involve checking that the quality of the product is maintained from one batch to another. For example, Allen's prints on the label of its "Canada Pure

Vinegar" that it is "5% acetic acid by volume." A technician in the quality control lab checks each batch of vinegar for its acetic acid content. If there is less than 5%, more acetic acid is added. If there is more than 5%, water is added to dilute the solution. After the appropriate adjustments are made, the batch of vinegar is bottled. Incorrect measurements could cost a manufacturer a great deal of time, money, and embarrassment. Therefore, it is important that the procedures of volumetric analysis be performed with utmost care. With practice, the skills of volumetric analysis can be mastered and very precise and accurate analyses can be carried out.

To perform a titration, you need three pieces of glassware, and before starting a titration, it is important to understand the purpose of each one (Figure 7.13).

- An **Erlenmeyer flask** (or conical flask) is the reaction vessel used in a titration. The most common Erlenmeyer flask has a 250-mL capacity. Suggest reasons why the Erlenmeyer flask has sloped sides.
- A **pipette** is used for transferring precise and very accurate volumes of solution from a storage container into an Erlenmeyer flask. By placing a squeezed rubber bulb over the wider end, you can draw up the solution until the bottom of the meniscus (the curved water surface) is level with the mark on the stem of the pipette. If you allow the solution to run into the Erlenmeyer flask, leaving the small volume in the tip of the pipette, then the precise volume has been transferred. The more common pipette is 10 mL in size, but its precision is usually to ±0.02 mL. Therefore, in significant figure calculations, you should write the volume used as 10.00 mL. The precision is either marked on the stem or listed in the supply catalogue. Suggest reasons why you should not use your mouth to draw solutions into a pipette.
- A **burette** is a device for dispensing very precise volumes of solutions. When the first solution has been placed in the Erlenmeyer flask using a pipette, the other reagent is added from the burette, adjusting the rate of flow with the stopcock. It is vital to read the burette before you start running in the second reagent since the volume added will be the difference between the final and initial burette readings. The common burette can deliver 50 mL. The smaller divisions are 0.1 mL, and it is possible to estimate a second decimal place if you are making precise measurements. Suggest why the volume readings on a burette have 0.00 mL at the top and are read downward.

FIGURE 7.13 The photo shows five types of glassware used in volumetric analysis. Starting from the left, they are a volumetric flask, an Erlenmeyer flask, a graduated cylinder, a burette with a beaker below, and a pipette in front. Beakers, graduated cylinders, and Erlenmeyer flasks can only measure volume approximately. If precision and accuracy are required, chemists use burettes, pipettes, and volumetric flasks to measure volume.

a)   b)   c)

FIGURE 7.14 The steps for determining the concentration of an acid or base by titration:

a) Using a pipette, a measured volume of the acid is placed into an Erlenmeyer flask.

b) Several drops of the indicator phenolphthalein are added.

c) The solution of base is added from the burette until the indicator changes colour from colourless to pink.

WEBLINK

The conical shaped flask used in a titration is called an Erlenmeyer flask. Write a brief biography on Emil Erlenmeyer, a German chemist, who invented such an important piece of chemical glassware. Discuss why an Erlenmeyer flask is so much better for titrations than a beaker. Begin your research at **www.pearsoned.ca/chemistry11**.

The procedure for performing a volumetric analysis is as follows:

- Fill the burette to near the top graduation with the titrant solution (usually the base). Open the stopcock briefly to fill the stem with titrant and allow any air bubbles to escape.
- Use a pipette to measure out the other solution (usually the acid) into the Erlenmeyer flask.
- Add the required number of drops of indicator (usually 2 or 3).
- Note the burette reading, remembering to read downward.
- Add the titrant slowly to the flask, swirling the flask to ensure mixing. Once the indicator colour change remains for more than a couple of seconds, reduce the rate of adding the titrant to dropwise.
- Stop the addition of the titrant as soon as the colour change remains permanent. Record the new burette reading.

The change in colour marks the end point of the titration, that is, the point at which neutralization is complete. This is determined by the use of a chemical indicator. When the indicator has changed colour, then it is assumed that you have added the precise number of moles from the burette that is needed to react completely with the reagent in the flask. This is a theoretical point known as the equivalence (or stoichiometric) point. The equivalence point is the point at which chemically equivalent quantities of reactant are present. The indicator end point should, in theory, coincide with the equivalence point of the reaction. Knowing the volumes of each reagent and the concentration of one reagent (the standard solution) allows you to calculate the concentration of the other reagent. A sample calculation is shown in Example 6.

EXAMPLE 6

In the food industry, potatoes have their skins removed by soaking them in a bath of sodium hydroxide solution. The skins float free, and the excess base is washed off. The concentration of sodium hydroxide solution must be above a certain value, so samples have to be titrated from time to time to check the concentration of the base. In a titration, 10.00 mL of sodium hydroxide solution was neutralized by 16.36 mL of sulfuric acid ($0.1286 \ mol \cdot L^{-1}$). Determine the concentration of the sodium hydroxide solution. The balanced chemical equation for the reaction is:

$2 \ NaOH(aq) + H_2SO_4(aq) \rightarrow Na_2SO_4(aq) + 2 \ H_2O(l)$

Given

| $2 \ NaOH(aq)$ | $+$ | $H_2SO_4(aq)$ | $\rightarrow$ | $Na_2SO_4(aq)$ | $+$ | $2 \ H_2O(l)$ |

2 mol   1 mol

$V_{NaOH} = 10.00$ mL $V_{H_2SO_4} = 16.36$ mL

       $= 0.01000$ L $= 0.01636$ L

                             $c_{H_2SO_4} = 0.1286 \ mol \cdot L^{-1}$

Required

$c_{NaOH} = ? \ mol \cdot L^{-1}$

INFOBIT

ExLax™, a laxative pill, contains phenolphthalein, which is an acid-base indicator. Crush an ExLax™ pill, and add half of it to a few millilitres of acid and the other half to a few millilitres of base. Identify the colour of phenolphthalein in an acid and in a base.

Analysis

$c_{H_2SO_4}, V_{H_2SO_4} \rightarrow n_{H_2SO_4}$ (using $n = c \times V$)

$n_{H_2SO_4} \rightarrow n_{NaOH}$ (using mole ratio, 2 mol NaOH : 1 mol H_2SO_4)

$n_{NaOH}, V_{NaOH} \rightarrow c_{NaOH}$ $\left(\text{using } c = \dfrac{n}{V}\right)$

Solution

$n_{H_2SO_4} = 0.1286 \text{ mol·L}^{-1} \text{ } H_2SO_4 \times 0.01636 \text{ L} = 2.104 \times 10^{-3} \text{ mol } H_2SO_4$

$n_{NaOH} = 2.104 \times 10^{-3} \text{ mol } H_2SO_4 \times \dfrac{2 \text{ mol NaOH}}{1 \text{ mol } H_2SO_4}$

$= 4.208 \times 10^{-3} \text{ mol NaOH}$

$c_{NaOH} = \dfrac{4.208 \times 10^{-3} \text{ mol NaOH}}{0.01000 \text{ L}} = 0.4208 \text{ mol·L}^{-1} \text{ NaOH}$

Statement

The concentration of the sodium hydroxide solution is 0.4208 mol·L^{-1}.

Gravimetric Analysis

The analytical method that relies on mass measurements is known as **gravimetric analysis**. Gravimetric analysis for a particular ion is usually accomplished by precipitating an insoluble compound containing that ion. The method can also be used to establish the purity of a substance. Gravimetric analysis was the traditional way of determining the composition of an unknown compound or identifying a new element.

The technique used is as follows:

- Determine the precise mass of a sample of the unknown compound (or it may already be in solution).
- Add an excess of a reagent that will give a precipitate with one of the ions.
- Filter off the precipitate.
- Dry the precipitate.
- Determine the precise mass of the precipitate.

The filtration procedure is shown in Figure 7.15, and a sample calculation follows.

FIGURE 7.15 The filtration of a precipitate through a sintered glass crucible: a) The mixture is poured down the glass rod into the crucible. b) The last of the precipitate is scraped into the crucible with a spatula.

PRACTICE PROBLEMS

1. As part of a summer job, you are working in a studio producing metal sculptures. Nitric acid is sometimes used to clean the metal parts. Your task is to determine the concentration of a nitric acid bath to see if it is too dilute to continue using that batch of acid. In a series of titrations with sodium hydroxide solution, you find that an average of 25.24 mL of 0.2000 mol·L^{-1} sodium hydroxide solution is needed to exactly neutralize 5.00 mL samples of the nitric acid. Calculate the concentration of the nitric acid.

2. The label on a bottle of barium hydroxide solution has fallen off. You volunteer to determine its concentration using titration with dilute hydrochloric acid (0.120 mol·L^{-1}). In three separate titrations to neutralize 10.00-mL samples of the base, you use the following volumes of hydrochloric acid: 23.6 mL, 23.7 mL, and 23.5 mL. Determine the concentration of the barium hydroxide solution.

Investigation
Refer to page 310, Investgation 2

INFOBIT

The technique of drying, weighing, and redrying until a constant mass is obtained is known as **weighing to constant mass**. It was another concept devised by Klaproth. He discovered the existence of more chemical elements than any other chemist—and all through gravimetric analysis. Example 7 shows a simplified gravimetric procedure for the identification of one of these elements.

EXAMPLE 7

Your chemical storage room has a large bottle of a chemical with part of the label missing. From the rest of the label, you deduce it must contain an alkali metal sulfate. The question is, which one? The key is to determine its molar mass. You recall that barium sulfate is insoluble, so you undertake a gravimetric analysis to find out the unknown alkali metal. You weigh out 0.872 g of the compound, dissolve it in water, and add barium chloride solution until no more precipitate is formed. You filter off and dry the precipitate. The mass of the precipitate is 1.167 g. If the unknown alkali metal is represented by the symbol X, then the double displacement reaction is:

$$X_2SO_4(aq) + BaCl_2(aq) \rightarrow BaSO_4(s) + 2\ XCl(aq)$$

Given

$$X_2SO_4(aq) \quad + \quad BaCl_2(aq) \quad \rightarrow \quad BaSO_4(s) \quad + \quad 2\ XCl(aq)$$

1 mol   1 mol

$m_{X_2SO_4} = 0.872$ g $m_{Ba_2SO_4} = 1.167$ g

Required
molar mass of X

Analysis
$m_{BaSO_4} \rightarrow n_{BaSO_4}$ (using $M_{BaSO_4} = 233.39$ g·mol^{-1})

$n_{BaSO_4} \rightarrow n_{X_2SO_4}$ (using 1 mol $BaSO_4$: 1 mol X_2SO_4)

$n_{X_2SO_4},\ m_{X_2SO_4} \rightarrow$ molar mass, $M_{X_2SO_4}\ \left(\text{using } M = \dfrac{m}{n}\right)$

Solution
$$n_{BaSO_4} = 1.167 \text{ g } \cancel{BaSO_4} \times \frac{1 \text{ mol } BaSO_4}{233.39 \text{ g } \cancel{BaSO_4}} = 5.000 \times 10^{-3} \text{ mol } BaSO_4$$

$$n_{X_2SO_4} = 5.000 \times 10^{-3} \text{ mol } \cancel{BaSO_4} \times \frac{1 \text{ mol } X_2SO_4}{1 \text{ mol } \cancel{BaSO_4}} = 5.000 \times 10^{-3} \text{ mol } X_2SO_4$$

$$M_{X_2SO_4} = \frac{0.872 \text{ g } X_2SO_4}{5.000 \times 10^{-3} \text{ mol } X_2SO_4} = 174 \text{ g·mol}^{-1}$$

This is the molar mass of the compound X_2SO_4, so you can find the molar mass of X from:

$$174 \text{ g} = 2(M_X) + 1(M_S) + 4(M_O)$$

$$174 \text{ g} = 2(M_X) + 32.06 \text{ g} + 64.00 \text{ g}$$

molar mass of X = 39.0 g

Statement
The molar mass of element X is 39.0 g·mol^{-1}, so the element X must be potassium.

An alkali metal sulfate was analyzed, and its molar mass was 362 g·mol^{-1}. Identify the alkali metal.

EXAMPLE 8

An unknown element forms a yellow ion, XO_4^{2-}. It forms a precipitate with silver ions. If 48.0 mL of a 0.250 mol·L^{-1} solution of silver ions is added to a solution of the unknown ion, 1.856 g of a red-brown precipitate are formed. Determine the identity of metal X.

Given

$$XO_4^{2-}(aq) \quad + \quad 2\,Ag^+(aq) \quad \rightarrow \quad Ag_2XO_4(s)$$

$\qquad\qquad\qquad\qquad$ 2 mol $\qquad\qquad\qquad\qquad$ 1 mol

$\qquad\qquad\qquad\qquad c_{Ag^+} = 0.250$ mol·L^{-1} $\qquad m_{Ag_2XO_4} = 1.856$ g

$\qquad\qquad\qquad\qquad V_{Ag^+} = 48.0$ mL

$\qquad\qquad\qquad\qquad\quad = 0.0480$ L

Required

molar mass of X

Analysis

$c_{Ag^+}, V_{Ag^+} \rightarrow n_{Ag^+}$ (using $n = c \times V$)

$n_{Ag^+} \rightarrow n_{Ag_2XO_4}$ (using 2 mol Ag$^+$: 1 mol Ag$_2$XO$_4$)

$n_{Ag_2XO_4}, m_{Ag_2XO_4} \rightarrow$ molar mass, $M_{Ag_2XO_4}$ $\left(\text{using } M = \dfrac{m}{n}\right)$

Solution

$n_{Ag^+} = 0.250$ mol·L^{-1} Ag$^+ \times 0.0480$ L $= 1.20 \times 10^{-2}$ mol Ag$^+$

$n_{Ag_2XO_4} = 1.20 \times 10^{-2}$ mol Ag$^+ \times \dfrac{1 \text{ mol Ag}_2\text{XO}_4}{2 \text{ mol Ag}^+}$

$\qquad\quad = 6.00 \times 10^{-3}$ mol Ag$_2$XO$_4$

$M_{X_2SO_4} = \dfrac{1.992 \text{ g Ag}_2\text{XO}_4}{6.00 \times 10^{-3} \text{ mol Ag}_2\text{XO}_4} = 332$ g·mol^{-1}

This is the molar mass of the compound Ag$_2$XO$_4$, so you can find the molar mass of X from:

332 g $= 2(M_{Ag}) + 1(M_X) + 4(M_O)$

332 g $= 215.74$ g $+ 1(M_X) + 64.00$ g

$M_X = 52.3$ g

Statement

The molar mass of element X is 52.3 g·mol^{-1}, so element X must be chromium.

WEBLINK

 SIMULATION

For a simulation of an acid-base titration, go to **www.pearsoned.ca/chemistry11**.

PRACTICE PROBLEM

Another element that Klaproth discovered formed the ion XO_4^{3-}. It, too, forms a precipitate with silver ions. If 84.0 mL of a 0.250 mol·L^{-1} solution of silver ions is added to a solution of the unknown ion, 2.930 g of a red-brown precipitate are formed. Determine the identity of element X.

Section 7.4 Review

Understanding Concepts

1. Explain the difference between the end point of a titration and its equivalence point.

2. Summarize in a paragraph why qualitative analysis of aqueous solutions is important.

Applying Inquiry/ Communication Skills

3. In an experiment involving a titration, a student found that 18.72 mL of 0.09975 $mol \cdot L^{-1}$ nitric acid was required to neutralize 25.00 mL of potassium hydroxide solution. Calculate the concentration of the potassium hydroxide solution.

4. A 25.00-mL sample of phosphoric acid was titrated against a solution of 0.1074 $mol \cdot L^{-1}$ sodium hydroxide. It was found that 33.24 mL of the sodium hydroxide solution was required to bring about neutralization. Calculate the concentration of the phosphoric acid.

5. An excess of calcium nitrate solution was added to 50.0 mL of a sodium fluoride solution. The white precipitate of calcium fluoride that was obtained was filtered off and dried. The mass of this calcium fluoride precipitate was 2.93 g. The equation for the reaction is:

    $Ca(NO_3)_2(aq) + 2\ NaF(aq) \rightarrow$
    $\qquad CaF_2(s) + 2\ NaNO_3(aq)$

    Determine the concentration of the sodium fluoride solution.

6. When 0.1155 g of an unknown alkali metal carbonate, M_2CO_3, was dissolved in water and 30.0 mL of 0.500 $mol \cdot L^{-1}$ calcium chloride solution was added to it, a precipitate of calcium carbonate was obtained:

    $M_2CO_3(aq) + CaCl_2(aq) \rightarrow$
    $\qquad CaCO_3(s) + 2\ MCl(aq)$

    After filtering and drying to constant mass, the calcium carbonate precipitate was found to have a mass of 0.0501 g. Determine the molar mass of the alkali metal, M, and its identity.

7. Draw a qualitative analysis flow-chart representing how you would analyze a solution for the presence of Na^+ ions and/or Ag^+ ions.

8. The equation for the neutralization of sulfuric acid with potassium hydroxide is:

    $H_2SO_4(aq) + 2\ KOH(aq) \rightarrow$
    $\qquad K_2SO_4(aq) + 2\ H_2O(l)$

    If 25.00 mL of a potassium hydroxide solution requires 47.25 mL of sulfuric acid (0.5830 $mol \cdot L^{-1}$) to neutralize it, determine the concentration of the potassium hydroxide.

9. A solution of copper(II) sulfate is prepared by placing 5.80 g copper(II) sulfate in a flask and adding enough water to prepare 125 mL of solution. When a 25.0-mL sample of this solution is added to 125 mL of sodium hydroxide (0.125 $mol \cdot L^{-1}$), the following reaction occurs:

    $CuSO_4(aq) + 2\ NaOH(aq) \rightarrow$
    $\qquad Cu(OH)_2(s) + Na_2SO_4(aq)$

    a) Identify the limiting reagent.

    b) Calculate the mass of copper(II) hydroxide produced.

10. The formula of a hydrate of an alkali metal carbonate may be determined by titration with standard hydrochloric acid. If 2.316 g of a hydrate of sodium carbonate ($Na_2CO_3 \cdot xH_2O$) is required to completely neutralize 38.49 mL of hydrochloric acid (0.4198 $mol \cdot L^{-1}$), determine the formula of the hydrate.

Making Connections

11. Research the contributions of Klaproth to modern analytical chemistry. Describe the technologies that developed as a result of his contributions and how they benefit our society.

Inquiry Skills

Initiating and Planning
▶ Applying Technical Skills
▶ Using Tools, Materials, and Equipment
▶ Conducting and Recording
▶ Analyzing and Interpreting
▶ Concluding and Communicating

Investigation 1 (Section 7.4)

Standardization of Approximately 1 mol·L⁻¹ Hydrochloric Acid

Hydrochloric acid is not a primary standard. A stock bottle of hydrochloric acid guarantees only a minimum mass of hydrogen chloride. The actual mass is not known because hydrochloric acid is a solution of hydrogen chloride gas in water. Some molecules of the gas will escape from the solution, lowering its concentration in the solution. That is why the concentration of the stock acid is not known very accurately. Consequently, it is not possible to make up accurate solutions of hydrochloric acid from a stock bottle of the chemical. However, it is possible to make up solutions that are close to a required concentration and then use a primary standard to standardize them. Standardization involves determining the actual concentration of a solution.

Problem

To prepare approximately a 1 mol·L⁻¹ solution of hydrochloric acid and standardize it.

Materials

- stock bottle of hydrochloric acid
- sodium carbonate solution (primary standard)
- methyl orange indicator
- two 150-mL beakers
- 50-mL burette
- three 250-mL Erlenmeyer flasks
- 100-mL graduated cylinder
- 10-mL pipette and pipette bulb
- 500-mL storage bottle
- 500-mL volumetric flask
- wash bottle
- burette clamp
- funnel
- medicine dropper
- meniscus highlighter
- retort stand
- stirring rod
- stopper

CAUTION: Use gloves when handling stock acid containers. Pour stock acids inside a fume hood.

CHEMICAL DISPOSAL: Your teacher will instruct you to either save the solutions or neutralize them before disposal. Disposal down the sink requires copious amounts of water.

Pre-lab Calculation   Determine the volume of stock hydrochloric acid required to prepare 500 mL of 0.1 mol·L⁻¹ hydrochloric acid. Assume the stock acid is 38% by mass hydrogen chloride and has a density of 1190 kg·m⁻³ (or 1190 g·L⁻¹).

Procedure

Part 1: Preparation of Hydrochloric Acid Solution

1. Use the 100-mL graduated cylinder to measure the required volume of stock acid solution. Pour the required volume of stock acid into a 150-mL volumetric flask.

2. Use a funnel to transfer the hydrochloric acid solution into the 500-mL volumetric flask.

3. Add small volumes of water to the volumetric flask, swirling the contents with each addition. Be careful not to go over the calibration mark. A wash bottle or medicine dropper should be used to add the last few drops of water required to raise the bottom of the meniscus until it just touches the calibration mark. (Use a meniscus highlighter.) Stopper the flask, invert it, and swirl the contents. Invert and swirl the contents several times in order to mix them thoroughly.

4. Use a funnel to transfer the contents of the volumetric flask into a storage bottle. Label the bottle as shown below. DO NOT write the value for the concentration on the label. The concentration of the solution is only approximately 1 mol·L⁻¹. After the solution is standardized, you can write that value on the label.

HYDROCHLORIC ACID STANDARD ACID SOLUTION
HCl *(aq)*
Concentration: mol·L⁻¹   Student's Initials
Date:

(continued)

5. Clean all the glassware by rinsing it several times with tap water.

Part 2: Standardization of Hydrochloric Acid Solution

6. Label 2 small beakers, one as waste and the other as sodium carbonate.

7. Obtain from your teacher approximately 50 mL of the sodium carbonate (primary standard) solution in a dry beaker.

8. Use the pipette bulb and a 10-mL pipette to transfer 10.00 mL of the sodium carbonate solution to each of the three Erlenmeyer flasks.

9. Clamp the burette in the burette clamp, and set the funnel in the burette.

> **CAUTION: Handle the burette with care since the tip is delicate and will break very easily.**

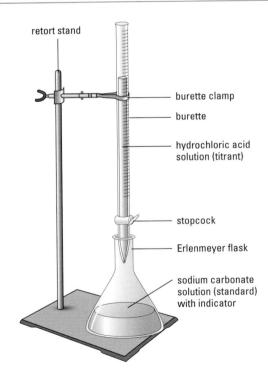

retort stand

burette clamp

burette

hydrochloric acid solution (titrant)

stopcock

Erlenmeyer flask

sodium carbonate solution (standard) with indicator

FIGURE 7.16

10. Rinse the burette with three 5-mL portions of your hydrochloric acid solution. Allow the waste to drain into the beaker marked "Waste."

11. Close the stopcock and fill the burette with your hydrochloric acid solution until it is above the zero graduation on the burette. Remove the funnel. Eliminate any air bubbles in the tip by allowing some of the acid to drain into the waste beaker. If the bottom of the meniscus is still above the zero graduation, open the stopcock and allow the acid to drain into the waste beaker until the bottom of the meniscus just touches the zero mark. If the meniscus is below the zero graduation mark, make no further adjustments in the position of the meniscus.

12. Record the initial burette reading to the nearest 0.02 mL. (Use a meniscus highlighter.) Add 3 or 4 drops of methyl orange indicator to one of the Erlenmeyer flasks containing the 10.00 mL of sodium carbonate solution. Open the stopcock and allow the acid to drain into the Erlenmeyer flask. Swirl the contents of the flask. Shut the stopcock at the first appearance of a red colour. Swirl the contents vigorously to expel any carbon dioxide gas. Use the wash bottle to rinse the sides of the flask with distilled water. Open the stopcock to allow the acid solution to drain drop by drop into the flask. **Swirl the contents of the flask.** Close the stopcock at the first permanent appearance of a red colour.

13. Record the final burette reading to 2 decimal places (use a meniscus highlighter), and determine the volume of acid used.

14. Repeat steps 13 and 14 at least two more times or until the results from three trials are obtained that agree within 0.1 mL.

15. Drain and discard any hydrochloric acid in the burette in a container provided by your teacher. Rinse the burette several times with water. Leave the burette inverted, tip up with the stopcock open, in the place designated by your teacher.

16. Discard the contents of the Erlenmeyer flasks down the drain with plenty of water. Rinse the flasks, beakers, pipette, etc., before returning them.

17. Prepare a data sheet as follows to record your quantitative results:

Trial	Initial Reading (in mL)	Final Reading (in mL)	Volume HCl Used (in mL)
1			
2			
3			

(continued)

Analyzing and Interpreting

1. Determine the average volume of hydrochloric acid used from the best three trials.

2. The reaction between hydrochloric acid and sodium carbonate is a double displacement reaction. Write the balanced chemical equation for the reaction.

3. Determine the amount of sodium carbonate in the 10.00 mL of solution.

4. Determine the amount of hydrogen chloride that was dissolved in the average volume of acid used. Assume that all the sodium carbonate reacts.

5. Determine the concentration of your hydrochloric acid solution. Write the concentration of your acid solution to two decimal places on the label of the bottle.

Concluding and Communicating

6. A commercial solution of muriatic acid (hydrochloric acid) is used for cleaning the surface of concrete before painting it. The label on the bottle says the solution is 3.7% hydrogen chloride. You wish to determine the actual concentration. You fill a burette with the acid, but before you do the titration, you would like to know approximately how much acid you will have to add to the 10.00 mL of 1.00 $mol \cdot L^{-1}$ sodium hydroxide to turn the blue bromthymol blue solution green. You can assume that the density of the dilute acid is essentially that of water.

Extending

7. The acidic waste from a student's experiment needs to be disposed of, but pouring it down the sink would increase the impact of acid rain on the local water supply. Explain how you could determine the amount of limestone needed to neutralize the environmental impact of the experiment. (Assume that the limestone is mainly calcium carbonate.) Write balanced chemical equations for any reactions you intend to use.

8. An average of 27.8 mL of 0.100 $mol \cdot L^{-1}$ sulfuric acid reacts with 25.00 mL of a sodium hydroxide solution used for cutting grease. Determine the concentration of the sodium hydroxide solution.

Investigation 2 (Section 7.4)

Inquiry Skills

▶ Initiating and Planning
▶ Applying Technical Skills
▶ Using Tools, Materials, and Equipment
▶ Conducting and Recording
▶ Analyzing and Interpreting
▶ Concluding and Communicating

Analysis of Vinegar

In this activity, you will determine the acetic acid content of several brands of vinegar. Based on your analysis, you will be able to select the "best" brand and evaluate the manufacturer's claim regarding the percent of acetic acid in the vinegar solution.

Problem

Predict the concentration(s) of acetic acid in the vinegars used for your investigation. Is the manufacturer's claim on the label true or false?

Materials

- a standardized sodium hydroxide solution
- several brands of vinegar
- phenolphthalein indicator
- two 150-mL beakers
- 50-mL burette
- three 250-mL Erlenmeyer flasks
- 10-mL pipette and pipette bulb
- wash bottle
- funnel
- meniscus highlighter

Experimental Design

1. To begin the investigation, record the following information (found on the label of the vinegar bottle) in a table like the one below:

Brand Name	Cost per Litre	Manufacturer's Claim Regarding Percent of Acetic Acid in the Vinegar

2. Develop a scientific investigation to determine the percent of acetic acid in each vinegar sample. Include any design features you intend to use.

3. Select the control variables you would use to determine this percentage.

4. Design a procedure to test each variable.

5. Before you carry out your experiment, have the teacher review your procedure.

6. Explain how you will calculate the percent of acetic acid in each vinegar sample.

7. Provide a summary table with the following headings:

	Vinegar Sample 1	Vinegar Sample 2
Volume of Sample (mL)		
Density of Sample (g·mL^{-1})		
Mass of Sample (g)		
Volume Percent of Acetic Acid in Vinegar		
Percent on Vinegar Label		

Analyzing and Interpreting

1. Present the calculations from your observations.

2. Calculate the concentration of acetic acid in each brand of vinegar used.

   a) Express the concentration in mol·L^{-1}.

   b) Express the concentration in the same units as those used by the manufacturer on the label. (The density of pure acetic acid is 1049 kg·m^{-3} or 1049 g·L^{-1}.)

3. Which brand is the best buy? Show appropriate calculations to support your choice.

4. Prepare a lab report to summarize your findings.

Concluding and Communicating

5. a) Determine the percent difference between your value for the concentration of acetic acid and the value printed on the label.

   b) Would you be justified in suing for false advertising? Explain why or why not.

Extending

6. Outline the steps you would have to do to analyze the mass of sodium hydroxide in oven cleansers.

CHAPTER SUMMARY

Key Terms

acid-base titration
burette
chemical precipitation
electrodialysis
gravimetric analysis

hard water
ion exchange
net ionic equation
pipette
qualitative analysis

quantitative analysis
soft water
spectator ion
titration
total ionic equation

volumetric analysis
weighing to constant mass

Essential Understandings

■ Net ionic equations summarize the chemical reactions between ions in aqueous solutions.

■ Some ions in our water supply can cause scale buildup that reduces the energy efficiency of appliances.

■ The technology used to purify hard water is based on knowledge of chemical reactions and the solubility of ions.

■ Performing double displacement reactions in a particular sequence can help identify unknown cations and anions in an unknown solution.

■ Applying stoichiometry to solutions enables us to calculate the concentration of a particular solution and the volume required for a reaction to go to completion.

■ In analytical chemistry, titrations are used to determine the concentration of unknown solutions.

Consolidate Your Understanding

1. Explain why it is important to have an understanding about the ions that are present in solutions.

2. Construct a concept map starting with the word "water pollution."

3. Describe the techniques involved in gravimetric and volumetric analyses. Identify the conditions for which each method would apply.

4. Explain why chemical solutions must be disposed of safely in a science laboratory. List the steps that every consumer should consider when disposing of household chemical solutions.

Understanding Concepts

1. Identify which equation shows how calcium nitrate dissociates in water.
   a) $Ca(NO_3)_2(s) \rightarrow Ca^+(aq) + 2\ NO_3^-(aq)$
   b) $Ca(NO_3)_2(s) \rightarrow Ca^{2+}(aq) + 2\ NO_3^-(aq)$
   c) $Ca(NO_3)_2(s) \rightarrow Ca^{2+}(aq) + NO_3^-(aq)$
   d) $Ca(NO_3)_2(s) \rightarrow Ca^{3+}(aq) + 2\ NO_3^-(aq)$
   e) $Ca(NO_3)_2(s) \rightarrow Ca^+(aq) + 2\ NO_3^{2-}(aq)$

2. An indicator (HIn) solution can be described by the following equation:

   $$HIn(aq) + OH^-(aq) \rightarrow In^-(aq) + H_2O(l)$$

   $HIn(aq)$ is yellow and $In^-(aq)$ is blue. If a few drops of the yellow indicator solution is added to a solution of potassium hydroxide, identify what colour the resultant solution will have.
   a) yellow   b) blue
   c) green   d) blue-green
   e) yellow-green

3. You want to measure accurately three 20.0-mL samples of a solution. Identify which piece of glassware you would not use to do this.
   a) graduated cylinder
   b) beaker
   c) burette
   d) pipette
   e) volumetric flask

4. Sulfuric acid is used to separate titanium(IV) oxide from its ore. The first step in the sulfate process is:

   $$TiO_2(s) + H_2SO_4(l) \rightarrow TiOSO_4(aq) + H_2O(l)$$

   Identify what type of reaction this is.
   a) double displacement
   b) combination
   c) single displacement
   d) decomposition
   e) dissociation

5. Identify which process is part of measuring the mass of a precipitate.
   a) neutralization
   b) acid-base titration
   c) gravimetric analysis
   d) volumetric analysis
   e) ionic equations

6. Explain the difference between a total ionic equation and a net ionic equation. Illustrate your answer with an example.

7. Identify the spectator ions in the following reaction:
   $Ba^{2+}(aq) + 2\ NO_3^-(aq) + 2\ Na^+(aq) + SO_4^{2-}(aq) \rightarrow$
   $$BaSO_4(s) + 2\ Na^+(aq) + 2\ NO_3^-(aq)$$

8. Describe in your own words what is meant by the following equation:

   $$CaCl_2 \rightarrow Ca^{2+}(aq) + 2\ Cl^-(aq)$$

9. Explain the difference between hard water and soft water. Include in your explanation a description of the advantages and disadvantages of using each type.

10. Explain why it is necessary in areas of hard water to regularly check the hot water pipes and central heating water pipes in older buildings and homes.

11. Identify the following reactions that occur in the production of titanium dioxide:
    a) a reaction between a basic oxide and an acid
    b) a reaction in which a precipitate is formed

12. Compare and contrast a volumetric analysis and a gravimetric analysis.

13. Identify two factors that are essential in order for a gravimetric analysis to be successful.

Applying Inquiry/ Communication Skills

14. Use a flowchart to illustrate the process you would follow to perform a qualitative analysis on the following aqueous solutions:
    a) Mg^{2+} and/or Ba^{2+}
    b) Ag^+ and/or Li^+
    c) Cu^{2+} and/or Ba^{2+}
    d) Cu^{2+} and/or K^+

15. A 25.0-mL sample of sodium hydroxide solution of unknown concentration is titrated with a solution of $1.0\ mol \cdot L^{-1}$ HCl. The graph (Figure 7.17) shows the amount of water in millimoles that would be formed by the reaction.
    a) Write a chemical and net ionic equation for the reaction.
    b) Use the graph to estimate the concentration of the unknown sodium hydroxide solution.

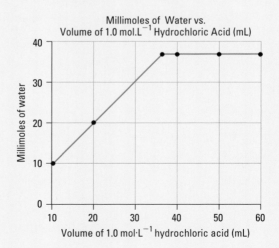

16. A saturated solution of calcium hydroxide is called lime-water. The solubility of calcium hydroxide (commonly called slaked lime) is 0.185 g per 100 mL of cold water.
    a) Write a chemical equation to describe the dissolving of calcium hydroxide in water.
    b) Determine the OH^- concentration in limewater. Identify any assumption you have to make.

17. Write the equation to show the process that occurs when each of the following compounds dissolves and dissociates in water:
    a) solid zinc sulfate
    b) solid iron(III) nitrate
    c) solid ammonium phosphate
    d) solid strontium hydroxide
    e) solid mercury(I) nitrate

18. An antacid ingredient is $NaAl(OH)_2CO_3$, which reacts with excess hydrochloric acid in the stomach according to the equation:

    $NaAl(OH)_2CO_3(s) + 4\ HCl(aq) \rightarrow$
    $$NaCl(aq) + AlCl_3(aq) + 3\ H_2O(l) + CO_2(g)$$

    Calculate the mass of $NaAl(OH)_2CO_3$ that is required to react with 0.150 L of hydrochloric acid ($0.100\ mol \cdot L^{-1}$).

19. 2.00 g calcium hydroxide is to be reacted with hydrochloric acid ($0.100\ mol \cdot L^{-1}$) according to the following equation:

    $$Ca(OH)_2(s) + 2\ HCl(aq) \rightarrow CaCl_2(aq) + 2\ H_2O(l)$$

    Calculate the volume of acid that would be required for a complete reaction.

20. When 25.00 mL of a sodium hydroxide solution of unknown concentration was titrated with a standard hydrochloric acid solution ($0.098\ 30\ mol \cdot L^{-1}$), 14.73 mL of the acid was required in order to neutralize the base exactly. Calculate the concentration of the sodium hydroxide solution.

21. A 25.0-g sample of impure silver was treated with excess nitric acid to produce a solution of silver nitrate. When an excess of sodium iodide solution was added to the silver nitrate, 25.0 g silver iodide was precipitated. Determine the purity of the original sample of silver.

22. If 12.0 g barium nitrate is dissolved in water and added to a solution of 10.0 g potassium sulfate, a double displacement reaction occurs:

    $$Ba(NO_3)_2(aq) + K_2SO_4(aq) \rightarrow BaSO_4(s) + 2\ KNO_3(aq)$$

    a) Identify which reagent is in excess.
    b) Calculate the mass of barium sulfate that is produced.

23. A 2.083-g sample of a mixture containing sodium carbonate and sodium bromide was placed in a 250.0-mL volumetric flask and enough water added to fill to the mark. A 25.00-mL portion of this solution required 17.56 mL of hydrochloric acid ($0.1396\ mol \cdot L^{-1}$) for complete neutralization. Calculate the percent of sodium carbonate in the mixture.

24. You have a sample of an unknown soluble alkali metal sulfate. Your task is to identify the unknown sulfate. Design an experiment indicating the procedure you would use, the measurements you would make, and the equipment and materials you would require to carry out this task.

25. Imagine you are writing a report on quality control data that you have gathered for a company producing antacids. Describe the process you would use to gather data to see if a particular batch of tablets met the company's standards. Don't forget to include the equipment you would use and how you would know when the reaction was complete.

Making Connections

26. Volumetric and gravimetric analyses form an important part of a field of chemistry called analytical chemistry. Use career reference material, university or college calendars, or reference material from a library or the Internet to find out what an analytical chemist does and what training is required. Prepare an electronic presentation that will inform people on the important contributions of analytical chemists to issues related to health, environment, industry, and consumerism.

27. You are the marketing director of a company that has produced a new device that converts hard water to soft water through an ion-exchange process. You have been asked to appear on a consumer show to address concerns people have expressed related to your product. In order to prepare for this, you need to consider a list of questions that you may be asked by panel members representing consumers, the health community, environmentalists, and the host of the show. Write these questions and your responses that will defend your product by outlining the advantages of using soft water.

28. Using both primary and secondary sources of information, research the costs to an industry, business, or school that uses boilers for a heating system. Gather statistical information related to the energy costs and the maintenance costs to run the system. Determine the energy and maintenance costs of alternative heating systems. Make sure you include the costs of converting from one system to another. Analyze your information, and make a chart showing the operating costs for the next 5 years, 10 years, and 20 years. Include in your chart a consideration of the environmental costs of energy use during these time periods. Write a report informing the company or school about the results of your research and analysis.

29. You are the director of a consumer advocacy group that has received complaints about advertised claims related to a new brand of soap. Describe a process you would use to determine whether the complaints are valid. Outline how you would use the information on the product label. Create a flowchart illustrating your decision-making process to address the complaints.

Ask a Chemist

One of the best ways to find out about a career is to talk to someone in it. While everyone's experiences will be different, you will gain valuable information about what's involved, whether this career might be for you, and how to prepare for it. Not too long ago, if you wanted information from someone working in a career of interest to you, you'd most likely communicate by phone or letter. The Internet has changed all that.

There are two features available to you on the Internet which will help you investigate careers. The first is the "search engine," a tool that lets you request a list of Web sites containing specific information. The second feature is email. People in a variety of careers, especially within science, post their email addresses and welcome students' questions. Be sure to check your school and family's guidelines about contacting people via email before you do so.

Who to Interview

1. Choose a field you are interested in and search the Internet to find and contact a person who works in that field.

   Search engines are wonderful, but can give too many results. Make your search as focussed as possible. For example, if you enjoyed learning about water quality, search for "careers in environmental chemistry." The words in quotation marks are typed into the search engine's field. Why the word "careers"? Because

this will take you to Web sites committed to supplying career information and you are more likely to find someone to contact. Here are some hints.

- Web sites of associations, universities, and large businesses often supply email addresses for people willing to be interviewed.
- If the Web site looks promising, but only lists a "webmaster," send an email to that person stating you wish to find and interview someone working in the career that interests you.
- Your first email should contain: where you found this person's email address, why you are interested in this career (briefly), and a polite request to ask a few questions. Do not include personal information.

Looking Outward

Keep track of people who could be helpful as mentors or contacts later in your careers with a good contact list.

2. For all professional or academic contacts you make, record: when you contacted them, how or where you met, why you contacted them, and anything else you'd like to remember. This list will become very important to you as it grows.

FIGURE 1 Sona Arslan is a quality control analyst for a major pharmaceutical company. Her work includes using various technologies, including high performance liquid chromatography (HPLC), to be sure products comply with the manufacturer's specifications before being released to consumers.

A Sample Email Interview

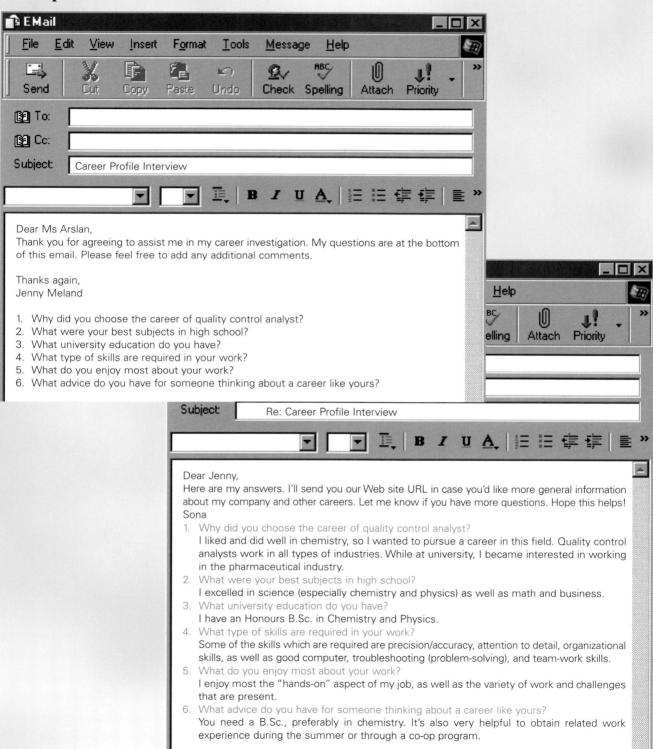

EMail

File   Edit   View   Insert   Format   Tools   Message   Help

Send   Cut   Copy   Paste   Undo   Check   Spelling   Attach   Priority

To:

Cc:

Subject: Career Profile Interview

Dear Ms Arslan,
Thank you for agreeing to assist me in my career investigation. My questions are at the bottom of this email. Please feel free to add any additional comments.

Thanks again,
Jenny Meland

1. Why did you choose the career of quality control analyst?
2. What were your best subjects in high school?
3. What university education do you have?
4. What type of skills are required in your work?
5. What do you enjoy most about your work?
6. What advice do you have for someone thinking about a career like yours?

Help

Spelling   Attach   Priority

Subject: Re: Career Profile Interview

Dear Jenny,
Here are my answers. I'll send you our Web site URL in case you'd like more general information about my company and other careers. Let me know if you have more questions. Hope this helps!
Sona

1. Why did you choose the career of quality control analyst?
    I liked and did well in chemistry, so I wanted to pursue a career in this field. Quality control analysts work in all types of industries. While at university, I became interested in working in the pharmaceutical industry.
2. What were your best subjects in high school?
    I excelled in science (especially chemistry and physics) as well as math and business.
3. What university education do you have?
    I have an Honours B.Sc. in Chemistry and Physics.
4. What type of skills are required in your work?
    Some of the skills which are required are precision/accuracy, attention to detail, organizational skills, as well as good computer, troubleshooting (problem-solving), and team-work skills.
5. What do you enjoy most about your work?
    I enjoy most the "hands-on" aspect of my job, as well as the variety of work and challenges that are present.
6. What advice do you have for someone thinking about a career like yours?
    You need a B.Sc., preferably in chemistry. It's also very helpful to obtain related work experience during the summer or through a co-op program.

What Am I Drinking?

Background Information

The incident in Walkerton in May 2000 has made many Canadians raise concerns about the quality of their municipal water supplies. More and more people are using bottled water for drinking and cooking. They feel this offers them a safer alternative. Bottled water is labelled as either "spring water" or "mineral water." This water could be water from various sources that may have been treated to make it safe for human consumption and then placed in sealed containers and sold.

In Canada, bottled water is considered to be a food and is regulated under Division 12 of the *Food and Drugs Act* and *Regulations* of Health Canada. Bottled water that is labelled as mineral water or spring water has to come from an underground source, and cannot come from a public water supply. Mineral water is similar to spring water except that it has a larger amount of dissolved salts. Neither mineral nor spring waters can have their compositions modified through the use of chemicals. However, carbon dioxide and ozone can be added during the bottling process to preserve the freshness of the water.

Bottled water that is not labelled as mineral or spring water is water that is taken from any source and then treated to make it safe for human consumption. Treatments include filtration, carbonation, ozonation, and ultraviolet irradiation to remove harmful bacteria. These water products must show on their labels how they have been treated (e.g., carbonation, demineralization, distilled).

Consumers are always advised to read labels carefully before deciding which products to purchase. In doing so, they are able to make more informed choices about the products they purchase.

SCENARIO

The members of the student newspaper want to start a consumer report feature in the next issue. This feature will compare and analyze products that are commonly used by students. The editor of the paper has asked you to investigate different bottled water products that students commonly drink and to write the first consumer article for the newspaper.

Your investigative report should include:

- a comparative analysis of the substances dissolved in different brands of bottled water
- a summary of the effects that these substances could have on health
- an analysis of bottled water compared with tap water
- regulations by Health Canada regarding water quality standards for both municipal and bottled water
- recommendations on how to make an informed consumer choice

Write a summary of your report in the form of an informative newspaper article.

Part A: Researching the Issue

1. Examine the labels from a variety of popular bottled water products. Gather as much information as you can from each label.

2. Contact the local municipal office and obtain the data analysis of tap water from your school.

3. Use electronic and print resources to gather information from Health Canada about regulations that govern the manufacture of bottled water. Include any recommendations and health concerns related to using bottled water.

4. Minerals we ingest become part of the body (e.g., bones, tissues, body fluids). Research the significance of the dissolved substances in relation to their effect (if any) on our bodies.

Part B: Testing Water Products

5. Test each sample for pH using a pH meter.

6. Test each sample for chloride ions by adding 5 drops of $0.01 \ mol \cdot L^{-1}$ silver nitrate solution. Observe each water sample carefully for any changes.

Part C: Comparative Analysis

7. Compare the qualitative observations of the chloride test with the quantities given on the labels and with the information obtained from the municipality on the tap water.

8. Create a spreadsheet that summarizes the following information for each bottled water product and for tap water:
   - cost per litre
   - comparison of dissolved substances
   - comparison of any water treatments
   - pH
   - presence of chloride ions
   - possible health considerations (e.g., use of sulfides and salts)

Part D: Summarizing Your Results

9. Write a set of recommendations for consumers to use when considering which water to drink.

Part E: Communicating Your Information

10. Write a newspaper article for your school paper that summarizes the results of your investigation.

UNIT 3 REVIEW

Understanding Concepts

1. Identify which substances are solutions.
   I   brass
   II dental amalgam
   III air
   IV tea
   a) IV only
   b) III and IV only
   c) I and II only
   d) I, II, and III only
   e) I, II, III, and IV

2. Identify which unit does NOT express concentration.
   a) $mol \cdot L^{-1}$
   b) $g \cdot mol^{-1}$
   c) ppm
   d) grams per 100 mL
   e) mass or volume %

3. A conductivity apparatus and some blue litmus is placed in an unknown solution. The light glows brightly and the blue litmus turns pink. Determine which solution could be the unknown:
   I   hydrochloric acid, $HCl(aq)$
   II acetic acid, $CH_3COOH(aq)$
   III sodium hydroxide, $NaOH(aq)$
   IV aqueous ammonia, $NH_3(aq)$

   a) I only
   b) III only
   c) I and II only
   d) III and IV only
   e) I, II, III, and IV

4. The solubility of $Al(OH)_3$ is 1.28×10^{-5} $mol \cdot L^{-1}$. Identify which expression represents the amount of hydroxide ion per litre from the dissociation of the aluminum hydroxide.

   a) $\dfrac{1.28 \times 10^{-5}}{3}$ mol

   b) $\dfrac{1.28 \times 10^{-5}}{2}$ mol

   c) 1.28×10^{-5} mol
   d) $2 \times 1.28 \times 10^{-5}$ mol
   e) $3 \times 1.28 \times 10^{-5}$ mol

5. A mole of sugar is dissolved in 100 mL of water. The solution is placed in a 1-L beaker. Water is slowly added to the beaker until the 1-L mark is reached. Identify which one of the following represents what is happening to the amount of solute, the amount of solvent, and the concentration of the solution as the water is added.
   a) amount of solute stays same, amount of solvent increases, concentration of solution stays same
   b) amount of solute increases, amount of solvent stays same, concentration of solution decreases

   c) amount of solute decreases, amount of solvent increases, concentration of solution decreases
   d) amount of solute stays same, amount of solvent increases, concentration of solution decreases
   e) amount of solute stays the same, amount of solvent increases, concentration of solution increases

6. Identify the products of an acid-base neutralization.
   a) a salt and water
   b) an acid and a salt
   c) a base and a salt
   d) an acid and a base
   e) a base and water

7. A dog suffering liver failure was given a 5% (mass-volume) glucose ($C_6H_{12}O_6$) intravenous drip solution to keep her fluids up. Identify which one of the following represents the concentration of glucose in $mol \cdot L^{-1}$.

   a) $\dfrac{100}{5} \times \dfrac{180}{1} \times \dfrac{1}{1000}$

   b) $\dfrac{5}{100} \times \dfrac{180}{1} \times \dfrac{1000}{1}$

   c) $\dfrac{5}{100} \times \dfrac{1}{180} \times \dfrac{1}{1000}$

   d) $\dfrac{100}{5} \times \dfrac{1}{180} \times \dfrac{1000}{1}$

   e) $\dfrac{5}{100} \times \dfrac{1}{180} \times \dfrac{1000}{1}$

8. You require 2.0 L of 0.010 $mol \cdot L^{-1}$ Na_2CO_3 solution. Determine which one of the following represents the mass of sodium carbonate required to make the solution.
   a) 0.53 g
   b) 1.1 g
   c) 2.1 g
   d) 4.2 g
   e) 8.5 g

9. Identify the ions formed when magnesium bromide dissolves in water.
   a) Mg^{2+}, $2 Br^-$
   b) Mg^{2+}, Br^{2-}
   c) $2 Mg^+$, Br^{2-}
   d) Mg^+, Br^-
   e) $2 Mg^+$, $2 Br^-$

10. Copper sulfate and potassium hydroxide solutions react to form a precipitate. Identify which one of the following correctly shows the ions involved in this reaction.
    a) $Cu^{2+}(aq) + 2 OH^-(aq) \rightarrow Cu(OH)_2(s)$
    b) $SO_4^{2-}(aq) + 2 K^+(aq) \rightarrow K_2SO_4(s)$
    c) $Cu^{2+}(aq) + SO_4^{2-}(aq) \rightarrow CuSO_4(s)$
    d) $K^+(aq) + OH^-(aq) \rightarrow KOH(s)$
    e) $Cu^{2+}(aq) + K^+(aq) \rightarrow OH^-(aq) + SO_4^{2-}(aq)$

11. Describe what is meant by a 5% silver nitrate solution.

12. State three things you could do to increase the solubility of a salt in water.

13. a) Write a definition for a strong base and give an example.
    b) Write a definition for a weak base and give an example.

14. Describe the difference between mass percent and volume percent.

15. Identify the essential feature of the water molecule that makes it such a good solvent for ionic compounds.

16. Describe the process of neutralization and classify what type of reaction it is.

17. Arrange the following substances in order of increasing acidity:

    lemon juice, pH 2.1
    cow's milk, pH 6.5
    egg white, pH 7.8
    shampoo, pH 6.7

18. Explain why the density of ice is less than that of liquid water.

19. Identify the factors that affect the rate of solution and for each one, describe its effect.

20. Name two factors that affect the solubility of a gas in a liquid, and state the effect of each on solubility.

21. A yogurt container is labelled as 4.5% M.F. (milk fat). Explain what this means.

22. a) Write a definition of a strong acid and give an example.
    b) Write a definition of a weak acid and give an example.

23. List the properties that all bases have in common.

24. A tanker truck carrying hydrochloric acid overturns on the highway creating a major acid spill. Describe how this spill should be treated.

25. Complete the following chart:

Acid or Base	$[H_3O^+]$ mol·L^{-1}	$[OH^-]$ mol·L^{-1}	pH
	1×10^{-3}		
		6.5×10^{-5}	
			3.4

26. You are presented with 5 different solutions in 5 different-sized containers. The containers are 0.5 L, 1.0 L, 1.5 L, 2.0 L, and 3.0 L and are labelled M, N, O, P, and Q. The solutions consist of the following:
    • 0.5 mol·L^{-1} sodium hydroxide
    • 0.5 mol·L^{-1} acetic acid
    • 0.5 mol·L^{-1} nitric acid
    • 0.5 mol·L^{-1} aqueous ammonia
    • pure water

    Container Q is the largest, and M is the smallest. The contents of O when full have a mass of 1500 g. P and Q contain substances that react with metals. Solution P

has a lower pH than solution Q. The contents of M feel slippery and, in a conductivity tester, cause a light bulb to glow brightly. P contains 63 g of solute in the given volume of solution when the container is full. The solution in the 1.0-L container turns red litmus paper blue. Based on these descriptions, identify the solution and size of the container for M to Q.

27. A solution of copper sulfate in water is divided into two equal portions, A and B. A is left alone. B has distilled water added. Identify whether each of the following statements is true or false and explain why.
    a) A contains more copper sulfate than B
    b) A contains less copper sulfate than B
    c) A and B contain the same amount of copper sulfate.

28. Identify the two factors that help explain why polar solutes dissolve in polar solvents. Provide an example of each factor.

29. Explain what is meant by a conjugate acid-base pair. Provide an example.

30. Classify each of the following as an Arrhenius acid or an Arrhenius base:
    a) $Ca(OH)_2$
    b) CH_3CH_2COOH
    c) HBr
    d) NaOH

31. For each of the following aqueous solutions, decide whether the pH will be above 7, below 7, or equal to 7.
    a) acetic acid
    b) sugar
    c) ammonia

32. a) Give the conjugate base for each of the following: NH_4^+, HPO_4^{2-}, HCO_3^-
    b) Give the conjugate acid for each of the following: PO_4^{3-}, $H_2PO_4^-$, HCO_3^-

Applying Inquiry/ Communication Skills

33. A student wished to determine the percent of acetic acid in commercial vinegar products. Brand X was selected. Three 20.0 mL volumes were titrated with a 2.20 mol·L^{-1} sodium hydroxide solution until the indicator phenolphthalein turned pink. The density of acetic acid is 1049.2 kg·m^{-3}. The data gathered in the experiment is recorded below. Calculate the volume percent of acetic acid in vinegar.

Initial burette reading	$V_i = 0.00$ mL
Volume reading first trial titration	$V_1 = 8.82$ mL
Volume reading second titration	$V_2 = 16.84$ mL
Volume reading third titration	$V_3 = 24.80$ mL
Concentration of the NaOH	$c_{NaOH} = 2.20$ mol·L^{-1}
Volume of vinegar	$V_{vin} = 20.0$ mL

34. Calculate the mass of potassium hydroxide that is required to prepare 6.00×10^2 mL of a solution with a concentration of 0.225 mol·L^{-1}.

35. Calculate the pH of an aqueous solution containing the following:
    a) 2.5×10^{-5} mol·L^{-1} HCl
    b) 1.0×10^{-3} mol·L^{-1} NaOH
    c) 4.2×10^{-6} mol·L^{-1} HNO$_3$
    d) 5.5×10^{-5} mol·L^{-1} Ba(OH)$_2$

36. Calculate the concentration of a hydrochloric acid solution that is prepared by diluting 25.0 mL of concentrated hydrochloric acid (12 mol·L^{-1}) to a volume of 2.00 L.

37. Design an experiment to measure the pH of rainfall in your area.

38. A laboratory technician requires 1.00 L of dilute aqueous ammonia with a concentration of 0.150 mol·L^{-1}. The only ammonia solution in stock has a concentration of 15.0 mol·L^{-1}. List the instructions the technician would have to follow in order to prepare the required dilute solution.

39. Zinc metal reacts with hydrochloric acid according to this equation:

    Zn(s) + 2 HCl(aq) → H$_2(g)$ + ZnCl$_2(aq)$

    A piece of zinc metal is found to require 75.0 mL of 3.00 mol·L^{-1} hydrochloric acid for complete reaction. Calculate the mass of the piece of zinc metal used.

40. Calculate the hydronium ion concentration of the following:
    a) 100.0 mL of an aqueous solution containing 0.60 g sodium hydroxide
    b) a urine sample with a pH of 6.30
    c) orange juice with a pH of 3.20

41. You are given a concentrated solution of hydrochloric acid that has a concentration of 9.47 mol·L^{-1}. Describe how you would prepare 1.00 L of hydrochloric acid solution with a concentration of 0.100 mol·L^{-1}.

42. Calculate the volume of 0.110 mol·L^{-1} sodium sulfate required to precipitate the maximum mass of barium sulfate from 60.0 mL of 0.145 mol·L^{-1} barium chloride solution. The balanced equation is:
    BaCl$_2(aq)$ + Na$_2$SO$_4(aq)$ → BaSO$_4(s)$ + 2 NaCl(aq)

43. In an experiment involving a titration, a student found that 18.72 mL of 0.099 75 mol·L^{-1} nitric acid was required to neutralize 25.00 mL of potassium hydroxide solution. Calculate the concentration of the potassium hydroxide solution.

44. An excess of calcium nitrate solution was added to 50.0 mL of a sodium fluoride solution. The white precipitate of calcium fluoride that was obtained was filtered off and dried. The mass of this calcium fluoride precipitate was 2.93 g. Calculate the concentration of the sodium fluoride solution. The equation for the reaction is:
    Ca(NO$_3$)$_2(aq)$ + 2 NaF(aq) → CaF$_2(s)$ + 2 NaNO$_3(aq)$

45. Complete the following equations:
    a) H$_2$SO$_4$ + NaHCO$_3$ →
    b) HNO$_3$ + CaCO$_3$ →
    c) HC$_2$H$_3$O$_2$ + Mg →

46. Write the balanced equation for the neutralization reaction between phosphoric acid and calcium hydroxide.

47. You are given a concentrated solution of acetic acid that has a concentration of 17.0 mol·L^{-1}. Describe how you would prepare 5.00 L of acetic acid solution with a concentration of 0.858 mol·L^{-1} for commercial use as vinegar.

48. A glucose drip has a concentration of 0.28 mol·L^{-1}. Determine the concentration of glucose (C$_6$H$_{12}$O$_6$) as a mass-volume percent of solution.

49. Design an experiment to determine the pH of different household cleaning products. Make a table that lists the active ingredients of each product, and then predict whether the product is acidic or basic.

50. Describe how you would prepare 250 mL of a standard solution of sodium oxalate (Na$_2$C$_2$O$_4$). The concentration should be approximately 0.5 mol·L^{-1}.

51. Write a net ionic equation to show why powdered limestone has been added to lakes northeast of Sudbury.

52. Calculate the volume of 0.280 mol·L^{-1} NaOH that would be required to neutralize 28.73 mL of 0.150 mol·L^{-1} HCl.

53. Calculate the concentration in moles per litre of each of the following aqueous solutions:
    a) 1.06 g potassium carbonate dissolved in 100.0 mL of solution
    b) 111.0 g magnesium chloride dissolved in 20.0 L of solution
    c) 3.40×10^2 g silver nitrate dissolved in 5.00 L of solution.

54. Calculate the mass of copper sulfate pentahydrate that is required to prepare 2.25 L of aqueous copper sulfate solution with a concentration of 0.400 mol·L^{-1}.

55. Aluminum reacts with hydrochloric acid according to the equation:
    2 Al(s) + 6 HCl(aq) → 2 AlCl$_3(aq)$ + 3 H$_2(g)$
    Calculate the volume of 1.00 mol·L^{-1} hydrochoric acid that is required for 10.8 g aluminum to react completely.

56. A 25.00-mL sample of phosphoric acid was titrated against a solution of 0.1074 mol·L^{-1} sodium hydroxide. To bring about neutralization, 33.24 mL of the sodium hydroxide solution was required. Calculate the concentration of the phosphoric acid.

57. When 0.1145 g of an unknown alkali metal carbonate, M$_2$CO$_3$, was dissolved in water and 30.00 mL of 0.5000 mol·L^{-1} calcium chloride solution was added to it, a precipitate of calcium carbonate was obtained.
    M$_2$CO$_3(aq)$ + CaCl$_2(aq)$ → CaCO$_3(s)$ + 2 MCl(aq)
    After filtering and drying to constant mass, the calcium carbonate precipitate had a mass of 0.0108 g. Calculate the molar mass of the alkali metal, X, and determine its identity.

58. Compare the cleansing efficiency of hard and soft water with the cleansing efficiency of detergents.

59. Just prior to when the endpoint in titration is reached, it is good experimental technique to wash down the sides of the flask with distilled water. Explain why this should be done.

60. Hydrogen peroxide is used as an antiseptic and to lighten the colour of hair. If a dilute solution of hydrogen peroxide contains 3.00 g hydrogen peroxide in 100 mL of solution, calculate the volume percent of hydrogen peroxide in the solution. The density of hydrogen peroxide is 1.40 g·mL^{-1}.

61. a) Convert a 0.003% solution into ppm.
b) Convert the concentration of 300 ppm into mg·L^{-1}.
c) Convert 0.085 g·L^{-1} to mg·L^{-1} and then to ppm.

62. In an experiment, an empty evaporating dish had a mass of 28 g. When filled with a saturated solution at 25°C, it had a mass of 45 g. After complete evaporation, the dish with the residue had a mass of 35 g. Calculate the solubility of the salt at 25°C.

63. a) Describe how you would prepare a 5% solution of potassium nitrate.
b) Describe how you would prepare 250 g of a 1% potassium chloride solution.

64. Suppose you are given a solution of sulfuric acid and a solution of sodium hydroxide, but that the concentration of each is unknown. By titration, you find that 25.0 mL of the sulfuric acid is neutralized by 34.2 mL of the sodium hydroxide solution. The product of this reaction is a solution of sodium sulfate. When you evaporate all the water from this solution, the mass of sodium sulfate obtained, after drying to constant mass, is 0.489 g. Determine the concentration of both the sulfuric acid solution and the sodium hydroxide solution.

Making Connections

65. A manufacturer, charged with polluting a lake by discharging acidic solutions, performed a titration of the plant effluent using the indicator methyl red. The manufacturer claimed the discharges were within the limits set by the government and produced titration data to support the claim. The Ministry of the Environment used a pH meter to produce the graph on the right (Figure 1), collected the fine, and forced the manufacturer to clean up its corporate act. Explain how the Ministry of the Environment was able to win the case when the titration data supported the manufacturer's claim.

66. In Canada, detergent manufacturers are not required to list ingredients on the box. State whether you agree or disagree with this practice. Choose one of the points of view in the following list, and write an essay that considers all factors related to your perspective.

Points of view:
detergent manufacturer
consumer
government official
environmentalist
public utilities official involved in waste management

67. Water may be polluted by bacteriological contamination, industrial wastes, thermal pollution, agricultural run-off, and household detergents. Describe the actions that can be taken by sewage treatment plants and public utilities commissions to ensure that the quality of water used in the community is safe and free of contaminants. Identify the alternatives and choices that a community can examine to ensure they have safe drinking water that is affordable and accessible.

68. Your local community is debating whether or not to add fluoride to the water supply. At the next town council meeting, you have been given 10 min to state your position and provide convincing arguments to support it. To prepare for this presentation, write a persuasive argument that outlines your point of view.

69. Many chemical sprays are used to protect fruit, vegetable, and grain crops from fungi and insects. Use primary and secondary sources of information to research the positive and negative effects of using these chemicals. Complete a PMI chart on the use of these sprays and write a summary paragraph stating your opinion on this issue. Be sure to provide supporting evidence for your opinion.

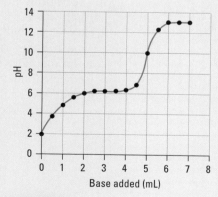

FIGURE 1

4

Gases and Atmospheric Chemistry

OVERALL EXPECTATIONS

By the end of this unit, you will be able to:

■ demonstrate an understanding of the laws that govern the behaviour of gases

■ investigate through experimentation the relationships among the pressure, volume, and temperature of a gas, and solve problems involving quantity of substance in moles, molar mass and volumes, and the gas laws

■ describe how knowledge of gases has helped to advance technology, and how such technological advances have led to a better understanding of environmental phenomena and issues

For hundreds of millions of years, the atmosphere of our planet has been essentially in balance. Vegetation, such as green plants, have been absorbing atmospheric carbon dioxide. Through biochemical reactions, much of our oxygen has been released back into the atmosphere as oxygen gas, while the carbon has been incorporated into the complex molecules in plant structures. When dead, some of the plants decayed to produce carbon dioxide while a portion became buried to form layers of coal. Volcanic eruptions returned much carbon dioxide into the atmosphere, thereby maintaining roughly the same level.

Then came humans. At first, our influence on the atmosphere was small—just some tiny amount of additional carbon dioxide from fires and a trace of sulfur dioxide from simple metal-smelting. When the industrial revolution began, large volumes of these two gases were produced. Two revolutions followed in the 20th century, the transport and chemical revolutions. Our dependence on combustion-powered transportation has meant the pumping of even larger quantities of carbon dioxide into the atmosphere. The chemical revolution resulted in new synthetic products, such as fluids for our air conditioners. Many of these new compounds ended up in the atmosphere.

Until the late 20th century, most people regarded the atmosphere as a giant waste disposal site. A new branch of science—atmospheric chemistry—has enabled us to realize how and why our atmosphere is changing. As with other subjects, you have to study the basics before you can understand the more sophisticated topics. So in this first chapter on gases, you will study the fundamental properties of gases and then, in the subsequent chapter, look at the elementary chemistry of the atmosphere.

Antarctica's Ice Very Sensitive to Global Warming

Temperature changes of a few degrees are making the ice shelves in Antarctica much more susceptible to cracking than was previously thought. Scientists have found that a temperature increase of just a few degrees is enough to trigger the cracking process. If the rate of cracking were to double, the sea level could increase by 1.0 mm to 1.2 mm per year.

U.S. Accused of Weakening Kyoto Targets

Climate talks held in November 2000 in The Hague broke down as European Union delegates accused the United States, Canada, and Russia of avoiding cutting greenhouse gas emissions. The U.S. climate negotiators insisted that their managed forests should count as "credits" in lieu of cutting emissions. The U.S. proposal would in effect allow a 2% increase in emissions instead of the 7% decrease set out by Kyoto—all without planting a single tree!

Zeppelins Make a Comeback

A modern zeppelin was launched over Friedrichshafen, Germany, almost 60 years after the tragic Hindenburg disaster. The new zeppelin consists of a multilayer laminate envelope, a simple triangular framework, and a helium-air mixture at a pressure 4% higher than the external atmospheric pressure. Five of these zeppelins are scheduled to be built; four will be used for advertising and one for scientific measurement.

ACHIEVEMENT TASK PREVIEW

At the end of this unit, you will demonstrate your learning by completing the task "A Fundamental Constant." As a chemist asked by IUPAC, you will research the best value of the ideal gas constant to date, determine its value by performing three experiments, account for any discrepancies between your value and the literature value, and write a report and an abstract on this exercise. See page 430.

Volcanoes have played a vital role in maintaining Earth's atmospheric balance.

In the Carboniferous era, the forests looked quite different from those today, being dominated by such primitive plants as these cycads (now rare).

CHAPTER 8

Properties of Gases

All around you, there are solids, such as concrete, glass, stone, and metal, and liquids, such as water, gasoline, and cooking oil. It is unlikely that you ever think of your dependence on the third state of matter—gases. Yet we live in a gas: air, a mixture of gases that are essential to life. One property of a gas becomes apparent when we fly—the gas pressure decreases as the altitude increases. If you have blocked ear passages—for example, as the result of a cold—intense pain can develop because of the pressure difference. In fact, taking a flight can illustrate several aspects of gas behaviour. If you partially inflate a small balloon before takeoff, you will see that at cruising altitude, the balloon will be larger. If you request a carbonated drink at this altitude, you might observe that the drink produces more bubbles than at ground level. A cup of tea served on a plane might taste weaker than what you are used to because water boils at a lower temperature than at ground level.

FIGURE 8.1 Hot air balloons. What property of a gas enables hot air balloons to work? What is happening in the gas at the molecular level?

The variations in volume, pressure, and temperature are common to all gases. However, gases exhibit a wide variety of chemical behaviours. Some are chemically inert, such as helium and neon; some are very reactive, such as fluorine; some are acidic, like hydrogen chloride; and one is basic, ammonia. Almost every common gas is important in our lives in some way, whether it is beneficial, such as the vital oxygen gas, or harmful, such as the deadly carbon monoxide.

The properties of gases affect you directly. Why do you pant after vigorous exercise? Panting removes excess carbon dioxide from your bloodstream and provides a fresh supply of oxygen. During a hospital operation, you are totally dependent on gas mixtures—the gaseous anesthetic to render you unconscious and the oxygen to keep you alive. But to understand gases and how they affect our lives, you must first study the properties of gases and the laws that relate to their behaviour.

Discovering Chemistry

Properties of Gases

How do gases differ from liquids and solids?

Materials

    corn kernels
    test tube with clamp
    gas burner

Place the corn kernels in the test tube and start heating gently, then more strongly.

- Describe what you see happening. Suggest what caused this.
- Deduce what this tells you about one property of gases.

CHECK**POINT**

Suppose you took a very flexible, sealed container of air from sea level to the top of a mountain. Draw a diagram of the container at sea level and again at the top of the mountain. Include drawings of the air molecules in each case. Write an explanation to accompany each diagram.

8.1 Properties of Gases

Key Understandings

When you have completed this section, you will be able to:

- identify the properties of gases and how they differ from the properties of solids and liquids
- understand the safety concerns associated with using compressed gases
- describe the relationship among atmospheric pressure, relative pressure, and absolute pressure, and the devices used to measure them
- express gas pressures in different units
- explain the difference between STP (standard temperature and pressure) conditions and SATP (standard ambient temperature and pressure) conditions
- use appropriate scientific vocabulary to communicate ideas related to the properties of gases

Unlike solids and liquids, which have definite volumes, gases expand to fill any space made available to them. Because gases do not have clear boundaries, the volume of a gas is defined by the volume of the vessel in which it is contained. As most gases are colourless and many are odourless, detecting them can sometimes be quite difficult.

For the same mass of a substance, a gas occupies a far larger volume than either a liquid or a solid. For example, if half a cup of water evaporates, the resulting water vapour at atmospheric pressure and 100°C will occupy a volume roughly equal to that of a 200-L oil drum. Because the volume is so much greater than that of the same mass of liquid or solid, the density of a gas is much less than that of the other two states. This is fortunate. Imagine what life would be like for you if air had the density of liquid water!

Provided that they do not react with one another to form a solid or liquid, any two or more gases can be mixed together to form a solution. This differs from the behaviour you observe when you try to mix either solids or liquids. For example, certain pairs of liquids, such as oil and water, cannot be mixed together to form a solution. If these two liquids are mixed together, two distinct layers are formed, with the oil floating on top of the water. Similarly, when a solution is formed from a solid and a liquid, there is a limit to the amount of solid that will dissolve in a given volume of liquid. If you try to exceed this amount, some of the solid will not dissolve. This is quite different from the way gases behave. Gases can be mixed together in *any* proportion to form a homogeneous solution. The reason for this is that the intermolecular spaces in gases are much greater than for liquids and solids, so different gases can be mixed together provided they don't react with each other.

As the temperature and pressure increase or decrease, the change in volume of a solid or liquid are so small as to be negligible. In contrast, the volume of a gas changes dramatically with a change in pressure or temperature. The volume, pressure, and temperature of a specific mass of gas are interrelated.

What Are the Common Gases?

Although gases have many common physical properties, they differ widely chemically. There are three common classes of gases: gaseous elements, gaseous oxides, and gaseous hydrides. All of the gaseous elements (Table 8.1) are non-metals. One of the elements, oxygen, has been observed to exist in

INFOBIT

Between 1894 and 1898, chemists discovered the gaseous elements helium, neon, argon, krypton, xenon, and radon. The observed inability of these gases to form compounds with other elements prompted chemists to refer to them as "noble" gases. The term "noble" was chosen because it implied that the elements were members of an aristocracy that was too proud to associate with other chemical elements.

two forms (called allotropes): O_2 (dioxygen, commonly called oxygen) and O_3 (trioxygen, commonly called ozone). Nitrogen, oxygen, and ozone will be central to our discussion of the atmosphere in the next chapter. Fluorine is such a chemically reactive element that it is sometimes called the "Tyrannosaurus Rex" of the elements, while the noble gases tend to be unreactive.

TABLE 8.1 Properties of Gaseous Elements

Name of Gas	Space-filling Model	Properties
hydrogen, H_2		colourless, odourless, least dense gas, flammable
nitrogen, N_2		colourless, odourless, very unreactive
oxygen, O_2		colourless, odourless, supports combustion
ozone, O_3		colourless, "metallic" smell, poisonous
fluorine, F_2		pale yellow, choking smell, poisonous, extremely reactive
chlorine, Cl_2		pale green, choking smell, poisonous, very reactive
helium, He		colourless, odourless, second-least dense gas, unreactive
neon, Ne		colourless, odourless, unreactive
argon, Ar		colourless, odourless, unreactive
krypton, Kr		colourless, odourless, unreactive
xenon, Xe		colourless, odourless, dense gas
radon, Rn		colourless, odourless, very dense gas, radioactive

FIGURE 8.2 Although people commonly refer to glowing signs of all colours as neon signs, neon is the gas that produces the bright red glow. The other noble gases are used to produce colours such as blue and green.

Among the gaseous oxides (Table 8.2), the two most common oxides of nitrogen make an interesting contrast. Nitrogen dioxide is a poisonous air pollutant, while dinitrogen oxide (or nitrous oxide), commonly called laughing gas, is sometimes used as an anesthetic. Dinitrogen oxide is the only gas apart from oxygen that supports combustion. The extra energy produced when substances burn in this gas is the reason it is used in some drag-racing engines. In the next chapter, you will see that both nitrogen dioxide and carbon dioxide play important roles in the atmosphere.

TABLE 8.2 Properties of Some Common Gaseous Oxides

Name of Gas	Space-filling Model	Properties
carbon monoxide, CO		colourless, odourless, flammable, very poisonous
carbon dioxide, CO_2		colourless, odourless
dinitrogen oxide, N_2O		colourless, sweet-smelling, supports combustion
nitrogen dioxide, NO_2		brown, choking smell, very acidic gas
sulfur dioxide, SO_2		colourless, choking smell, acidic gas

The gaseous hydrides (Table 8.3) range from the acidic hydrogen chloride (which dissolves in water to form hydrochloric acid) to the basic ammonia. Few people realize that hydrogen sulfide is as poisonous as hydrogen cyanide. These two gases, as well as carbon monoxide, are such dangerous poisons because they bond to the hemoglobin in your blood more effectively than oxygen. So only low concentrations are required to "lock up" the hemoglobin in your body, causing death through asphyxiation. Most of the natural gas found in Alberta contains high levels of hydrogen sulfide (and so it is commonly called sour gas). Leaks from pipelines carrying sour gas can, therefore, be extremely dangerous. Of the three gases that bond strongly to hemoglobin, carbon monoxide presents the most common danger. Leaks from the flues of wood-burning stoves or gas- or oil-burning appliances can cause dangerous levels of carbon monoxide to accumulate. For this reason, any dwelling with a combustion-based heating system should have a carbon monoxide detector installed.

FIGURE 8.3 Every house with a wood-burning stove or gas- or oil-burning appliance should have a carbon monoxide detector to warn of any high concentrations of this deadly gas.

TABLE 8.3 Properties of Some Common Gaseous Hydrides

Name of Gas	Space-filling Model	Properties
methane, CH_4		colourless, odourless, flammable
ammonia, NH_3		colourless, ammonia smell, basic gas
hydrogen chloride, HCl		colourless, choking smell, very acidic gas
hydrogen sulfide, H_2S		colourless, rotten-egg smell, extremely poisonous
hydrogen cyanide, HCN		colourless, faint odour of almonds, extremely poisonous

Compressed Gases: Safety First!

You will find compressed gases in many aspects of your life. They are used in medical applications, welding, refrigeration and air conditioning systems, and heating and cooking fuels, and to inflate party balloons, to name just a few of their uses. There are three major groups of compressed gases: liquefied, non-liquefied, and dissolved gases (Figure 8.4).

Liquefied Gases   These are gases that liquefy under pressure at room temperature. A cylinder is almost filled with liquid and as gas is removed, liquid evaporates to replace it. When a cylinder is almost filled with liquid, some of the liquid evaporates and creates pressure in the cylinder. When the valve is opened to let some of the gas out (e.g., when barbecuing), the pressure in the cylinder drops. This causes some liquid to evaporate to replace the lost gas. Examples of liquefied gases are ammonia (used mostly as a fertilizer), carbon dioxide (for carbonated drinks), chlorine (for water chlorination), dinitrogen oxide (for medical anesthesia), and propane, $CH_3CH_2CH_3$ (for cooking in barbecues and camper trailers).

Non-liquefied Gases   Some gases, no matter how much they are compressed, will not liquefy at room temperature. These are called the permanent gases. Common examples are helium (for party balloons), hydrogen, nitrogen, and oxygen (for medical and welding uses particularly).

Dissolved Gases   The welding gas acetylene (C_2H_2—chemical name ethyne) is chemically unstable. To store it safely in cylinders, the cylinders are filled with a porous solid that is soaked in acetone (CH_3COCH_3). Acetylene is very soluble in acetone, so when the gas is pumped into the cylinder, it dissolves into the liquid in the pores of the filler. Acetylene in acetone is quite stable.

All cylinders of compressed gases are hazardous simply because of the very high pressures inside the cylinders. If a cylinder is knocked over and the valve breaks off, then the pressure is often enough for the cylinder to accelerate like a rocket and injure or even kill anyone in its path. For this reason, cylinders should always be fastened to a wall or bench. If it is necessary to move a cylinder, then it should be fastened onto a cart. When a valve is not attached to the cylinder, a cap should always be placed on the cylinder.

FIGURE 8.4 There is an enormous variety of compressed gases. Check with a local compressed gas supplier. Find out the different types of compressed gases sold and purchasers of these gases.

If a cylinder leaks, there are two types of hazards. If the gas is toxic, such as chlorine or ammonia, then the odour usually alerts you to leakages, and you should leave the room immediately and call for help before you have major damage to your lungs. It is important to keep flames away from flammable gases, such as hydrogen or propane, to prevent a leak from causing an explosion. Oxygen gas will not burn, but any oxygen leak causes any flammable material to burn more intensely. Finally, even inert gases, such as nitrogen and helium, present a hazard. If they leak in a poorly ventilated room, they will reduce the concentration of oxygen in the air, and unconsciousness and even death may result.

The Measurement of Gas Pressure

Gases exert a pressure. You can illustrate this with a simple, spectacular demonstration. You take an empty soft-drink can and place some water in it. Then, using tongs, you heat the can until a steady stream of steam issues from the opening (Figure 8.5). Lift the can from the heat, invert the can, and place it in a large beaker of cold water. The can crumples. How can this be explained? Normally, the can will have air inside and outside the can, producing an equal pressure. The vaporizing water pushes the air out of the can. When the can is plunged into the cold water, the gaseous water will condense back to a liquid. This will create a partial vacuum inside the can, so there will be less pressure inside the can than outside. The pressure of the outside air will then collapse the can.

As pressure is such a characteristic physical property of a gas, ways to measure it are needed. The device for measuring the **absolute pressure** of a gas is called a **barometer**, while a simple device for measuring **relative pressure** is the **manometer**. Absolute pressure is the actual pressure exerted by the gas, whereas relative pressure is the pressure exerted by the gas relative to the **atmospheric pressure**. You can write this relationship mathematically like this:

$$P_{\text{absolute}} = P_{\text{relative}} + P_{\text{atmospheric}}$$

The Barometer

Early in the 17th century, Evangelista Torricelli, an Italian mathematician and physicist, designed the first barometer, an instrument used for measuring atmospheric pressure. In its simplest form, a barometer consists of a long glass tube that is sealed at one end and filled with liquid. The tube is then inverted with the open end immersed in a dish containing the same liquid as in the tube (Figure 8.6).

Some of the liquid flows from the tube into the dish, creating a vacuum at the sealed end of the tube. However, some of the liquid remains in the tube. The force exerted by the atmosphere on the surface of the liquid in the dish supports a column of liquid in the sealed tube. The height,

FIGURE 8.5 A soft-drink can containing some water is heated until a steady stream of steam is emitted. Plunging the inverted can into water causes the can to collapse.

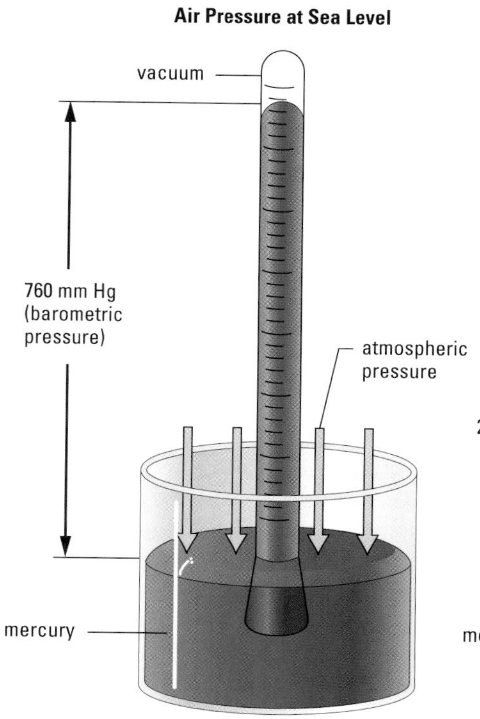

Air Pressure at Sea Level

vacuum

760 mm Hg
(barometric
pressure)

atmospheric
pressure

mercury

FIGURE 8.6 A visual representation of a mercury barometer. The column height at sea level will be between 750 mm Hg and 775 mm Hg, depending on the weather system.

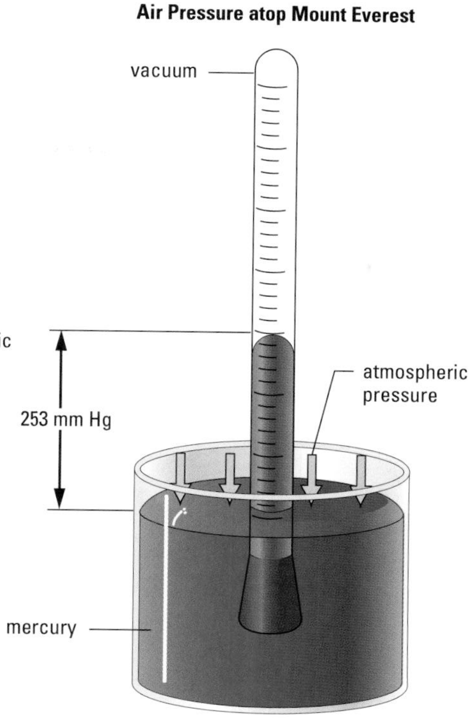

Air Pressure atop Mount Everest

vacuum

253 mm Hg

atmospheric
pressure

mercury

FIGURE 8.7 The air pressure on top of Mount Everest at an altitude of 9000 m is only about 253 mm Hg.

FIGURE 8.8 Although laboratories still use mercury-filled barometers, the aneroid barometers for home-use function differently. Find out how they work.

h, of the column of liquid is a measure of the pressure being exerted by the atmosphere. The height of this column of liquid depends on the density of the liquid used. If water is used, the atmosphere will support a column about 10 m high; however, if mercury is used, the height of the column will be about 760 mm. The mercury column is about 13 times shorter because mercury is 13 times denser than water.

The pressure exerted by the atmosphere fluctuates throughout the day. This causes the weather to change as air flows from areas of high pressure to areas of low pressure. Atmospheric pressure also changes with altitude; as the altitude increases, the atmospheric pressure decreases (Figure 8.7). On very high mountains, such as those in the Himalayas, climbers often experience difficulty in breathing. The low atmospheric pressure at these very high altitudes means that the density of the air is very low and there is insufficient oxygen to meet the body's normal oxygen requirements (Figure 8.9).

FIGURE 8.9 a) Additional oxygen is necessary for all climbers except those who live at very high altitudes (the Sherpas) or those who are acclimatized and superfit. b) High altitude pilots also require additional oxygen supplies.

The Manometer

Scientists often have to measure the pressure exerted by a gas in a closed container. If the gas pressure is not extremely high, they can use a simple instrument that compares the pressure of the gas in the container with the atmospheric pressure. This device, called a manometer, is similar to the barometer in its construction and also in the way it measures gas pressure. One end of a glass U-tube is connected to a container of gas, and the other end is open to the atmosphere. The U-tube contains a known volume of liquid, usually mercury. Medical practitioners traditionally used a version of a manometer to measure blood pressure. This device is called a sphygmomanometer.

Figure 8.10 shows a flask containing a gas connected to a simple manometer. The mercury level is lower on the flask side than on the open side. This indicates that the pressure of the mercury on the flask side must be greater than that on the side open to the atmosphere. If you call the gas pressure inside the container P_{gas}, atmospheric pressure P_{atm}, and the difference in the height of the mercury column Δh, then you can say:

$$P_{gas} = P_{atm} + \Delta h$$

If the level of the mercury in the left arm of the U-tube is higher than the level of the mercury in the right arm, then the pressure of the gas in the container is less than atmospheric pressure. In this case:

$$P_{gas} = P_{atm} - \Delta h$$

mercury

FIGURE 8.10 A manometer connected to a flask containing a gas

EXAMPLE 1

When a container of gas is connected to a manometer of the type shown in Figure 8.10, the mercury in the open-ended arm rises by 41 mm. If the atmospheric pressure is 754 mm Hg, what is the gas pressure in the container?

Given
$P_{atm} = 754$ mm Hg

$\Delta h = 2 \times 41$ mm Hg $= 82$ mm Hg (because a rise on one side by 41 mm must be accompanied by a fall of 41 mm on the other side)

Required
pressure of gas, $P_{gas} = ?$ mm Hg

Analysis
Since the level of mercury rose in the open-ended arm of the manometer, this means that the pressure of the gas is greater than that of the atmosphere. Therefore:

$$P_{gas} = P_{atm} + \Delta h$$

Solution

P_{gas} = 754 mm Hg + 82 mm Hg = 836 mm Hg

Statement

The gas pressure in the container is 836 mm Hg.

PRACTICE PROBLEM

When the gas container shown in Figure 8.10 is connected to a vacuum pump and partially evacuated, the level of the mercury in the arm attached to the container rises until it is 645 mm above the level of the mercury in the open-ended arm. Calculate the pressure of the gas in the partially evacuated flask. Assume that the atmospheric pressure remains at 754 mm Hg.

Units of Pressure

Millimetres of Mercury   In his early experiments with the mercury barometer, Torricelli measured gas pressures in **millimetres of mercury** (mm Hg). These units were used for many years and are still sometimes used today.

Torrs   Because "millimetres of mercury" is rather cumbersome to write, these units are often called **torrs** (after Torricelli).

Pascals   The SI unit of pressure is the **pascal** (symbol Pa), named after Blaise Pascal, a French philosopher, mathematician, and physicist. The pascal is a very small unit. In fact, a $20-bill lying flat on a table exerts a pressure of about 1 Pa! For most purposes, the kilopascal is a more practical unit, although for very high pressures, the megapascal (MPa) is more appropriate.

TABLE 8.4 Approximate Pressures in Terms of Kilopascals

Human blood pressure	10–20 kPa
Atmospheric pressure at sea level	88–108 kPa
Automobile tire pressure reading	200–240 kPa

Bars   Meteorologists sometimes express pressure in **bars**. One bar is equal to 100 kPa. The smaller unit, the millibar, is often used for the day-to-day measurement of atmospheric pressure. Although a metric unit, the bar is not part of SI.

Atmospheres   Another non-SI unit, the **atmosphere** (atm), is still used, particularly when measuring very high pressures. One atmosphere is defined as being equal to 760 mm Hg and 101.3 kPa.

Pounds per Square Inch   In some English-speaking countries, **pounds per square inch** (lb·in^{-2} or psi) are still used frequently as a unit of pressure. Some automobile tire pressure gauges (especially older ones) show pressures in these units, but newer gauges give readings in kilopascals. Many gases are supplied to laboratories and industry in pressurized cylinders, and the gauges that are attached to these cylinders are normally calibrated in pounds per square inch. In this system, atmospheric pressure at sea level is approximately 14.7 lb·in^{-2}.

When you measure a tire or cylinder pressure, you should be aware that the measurement is relative to atmospheric pressure. Therefore, to find the absolute pressure, you have to add the value of atmospheric pressure. The conversion factors are summarized in Table 8.5.

WEBLINK

The unit of pressure is named after Blaise Pascal. Research his life and work, focussing on his contributions to the study of gases. Write an account suitable for an obituary in a newspaper. Begin your research at **www.pearsoned.ca/chemistry11**.

TABLE 8.5 Conversion Factors between Pressure Units

1 standard atmosphere	= 101.3 kPa
	= 760 mm Hg
	= 14.7 lb·in^{-2}

EXAMPLE 2

The pressure on the top of Mount Everest is about 253 mm Hg. What is the pressure in units of kilopascals?

Given
$P_{mm} = 253$ mm Hg

Required
pressure of atmosphere, $P_{kPa} = ?$ kPa

Analysis
760 mm Hg = 101.3 kPa

Solution
$$P_{kPa} = 253 \text{ mm Hg} \times \frac{101.3 \text{ kPa}}{760 \text{ mm Hg}} = 33.7 \text{ kPa}$$

Statement
The pressure on the top of Mount Everest is about 33.7 kPa.

PRACTICE PROBLEM

If the pressure on the top of Mount Everest is about 253 mm Hg, determine the pressure in units of:
a) atmospheres
b) pounds per square inch

Standard Ambient Temperature and Pressure (SATP)

From the earliest days of gas measurements, scientists needed some type of standard conditions so that measurements in different units could be compared. The original values chosen were a pressure of 760 mm Hg (one standard atmosphere) and a temperature of 0°C (273 K), and this was known as **standard temperature and pressure (STP)**.

However, chemistry, like any discipline, is constantly evolving. As chemists learn more, new terminology is needed, new units have to be invented, and current definitions have to be modified. This is part of the task of the International Union of Pure and Applied Chemistry (IUPAC).

In the 1970s, IUPAC decided new standard conditions should be defined. The need for a real standard temperature was particularly important because chemists working with gases were using 0°C as a standard while chemists studying heat changes had always defined 25°C as standard. As a result, there was always confusion as to whether a measurement at "standard temperature" was recorded at 0°C or 25°C. At the same time, with the introduction of SI, it made little sense to use 101.325 kPa as a standard pressure at 25°C. So IUPAC defined a new standard of pressure as exactly 100 kPa and a standard temperature as 25°C (298 K). To distinguish the new standard from the old one, IUPAC called the new one **standard ambient temperature and pressure (SATP)**.

Change is slow to trickle through any discipline, and chemistry is no exception. The first data tables using SATP appeared in 1982, yet even today the old

STP is still mentioned in many books. To provide a bridge between the old and new, this text uses both STP and SATP.

To keep chemists up to date with the changes, IUPAC publishes seven books defining the latest rules for naming substances, defining symbols and units, and so on. The "red book," mentioned in Chapter 2, defines the rules for naming inorganic compounds. The "green book" defines the quantities, units, and symbols (including SATP) that should be used in chemistry (Figure 8.11).

Section 8.1 Review

Understanding Concepts

1. Compare the common properties of gases to the properties of liquids and solids.

2. Describe what would happen to the mercury level in a barometer if you took it down a deep mine. Explain why.

3. Compare the function and use of a barometer and a manometer.

4. Make a chart summarizing the names of different units for measuring pressure. Provide an example of where you would commonly see the unit used.

5. Compare the conditions referred to as STP and SATP.

Applying Inquiry/ Communication Skills

6. A manometer is connected to a gas container. The mercury level on the container side drops until the difference in manometer mercury levels is 25 mm Hg. The atmospheric pressure is 755 mm Hg. Calculate the pressure in the gas container.

7. If the pressure on a gas cylinder gauge reads 105 lb·in^{-2}, calculate the absolute pressure in the cylinder in SI units.

8. A mercury-filled manometer was connected to a container of gas. The level of mercury on the side connected to the container was 7.4 cm higher than that on the side open to the atmosphere. The atmospheric pressure was measured at 756 mm Hg. Calculate the pressure of the gas in the container in kilopascals.

Making Connections

9. Make a poster describing safe work practices that are needed to protect people working with and near containers of compressed gases.

10. You have been assigned the job of purchaser in a manufacturing company whose products require the use of oxygen gas. One supplier sells oxygen gas by the kilogram and the other by the cubic metre. Decide which supplier would be more advantageous for your company to use and explain why.

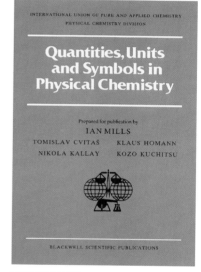

FIGURE 8.11 The "green book" defines the units and symbols for chemists.

8.2 Three Ideal Gas Relationships

Key Understandings

When you have completed this section, you will be able to:

- perform an experiment to quantitatively determine the relationship between the pressure and volume of an ideal gas
- explain Boyle's law and solve problems using it
- express temperature in different units
- understand Charles's law and solve problems using it
- perform an experiment to quantitatively determine the relationship between the pressure and temperature of an ideal gas
- describe Gay-Lussac's law and solve problems using it
- use appropriate scientific vocabulary to communicate ideas related to gas relationships

Investigation

Refer to page 375, Investigation 1

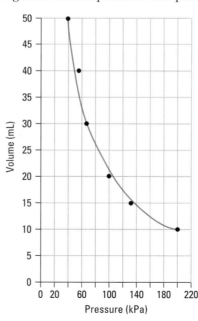

FIGURE 8.12 A simple apparatus for demonstrating the relationship between pressure and volume in an ideal gas

If you have a large syringe that is sealed at one end and press down on the plunger (Figure 8.12), you will find that as the volume, V, decreases, the pressure, P, increases. If you record pairs of values of volume and corresponding pressure, the plotted data will resemble the curve in Figure 8.13. However, scientists like straight lines. A straight-line plot indicates a simple linear mathematical relationship. It also makes it easy to check if any points are in error since they will not be on the line.

The Relationship between Pressure and Volume: Boyle's Law

By trying a variety of functions, you would discover a plot of the volume against the reciprocal of the pressure gives a straight line (Figure 8.14).

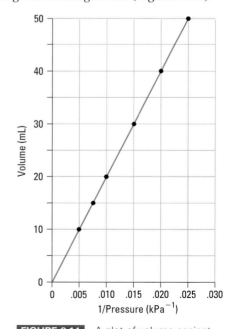

FIGURE 8.13 A plot of volume against pressure for a gas at constant temperature

FIGURE 8.14 A plot of volume against 1/pressure for a gas at constant temperature

The general form for the equation of a straight line that passes through the origin of a graph is $y = mx$, where m, the slope of the line, is a constant. If $1/P$ (1/pressure) is substituted for x, V (volume) for y, and m replaced with k, the following proportionality is obtained:

$$V \propto \frac{1}{P} \text{ where the temperature } (T) \text{ and the amount of gas } (n) \text{ are constant}$$

Writing the proportionality as an equation, you would get:

$$V = k\left(\frac{1}{P}\right)$$

Robert Boyle, a British physicist and chemist, was the first to establish this mathematical relationship, therefore it is known as **Boyle's law**. Boyle's law can be stated as follows:

At a constant temperature, the volume of a fixed mass of gas is inversely proportional to its pressure.

The last equation can be rearranged by multiplying both sides by P:

$$PV = k\left(\frac{P}{P}\right) \text{ or } PV = k$$

A more useful "working" formula can be derived as follows. Suppose you have a gas of volume V_1 at a pressure P_1. Then $P_1V_1 = k$. Now suppose the same mass of gas is subjected to new conditions so that there is a new pressure, P_2, which results in a new volume, V_2. Then $P_2V_2 = k$. Since things that are equal to the same thing are equal to each other, we can write:

$$P_1V_1 = P_2V_2$$

It is usually this form of Boyle's law that is more useful in solving problems.

FIGURE 8.15 Robert Boyle (1627–1691) was a pioneer in the study of gases.

FIGURE 8.16 Gases are mostly empty space at normal pressures. To carry a reasonable quantity of gaseous fuel, a natural gas–powered vehicle could either tow a gasoline-tanker–sized trailer of gas at a pressure of 1 atm or (according to Boyle's law) have a small fuel tank containing gas at high pressure. Since the tank is under high pressures, a very thick steel-walled tank must be used to prevent a tank rupture and a possible explosion.

EXAMPLE 3

In Vancouver, a balloon with a volume of 5.0 L is filled with air at 101 kPa pressure. The balloon is then taken to Banff, where the atmospheric pressure is only 91 kPa (Banff is 1386 m above sea level). Will the balloon's volume be larger or smaller at Banff? If the temperature is the same in both places, what will the new volume of the balloon be?

Given
$P_1 = 101$ kPa, $V_1 = 5.0$ L
$P_2 = 91$ kPa

Required
final volume, $V_2 = ?$ L

Analysis
Since the balloon is going from an area of high pressure to one of low pressure, the volume of the balloon will increase. Using Boyle's law:

$$P_1V_1 = P_2V_2 \text{ or } V_2 = \frac{P_1V_1}{P_2}$$

Solution
$$V_2 = \frac{(101 \text{ kPa})(5.0 \text{ L})}{(91 \text{ kPa})} = 5.5 \text{ L}$$

Statement
The volume of the balloon in Banff would become 5.5 L.

PRACTICE PROBLEMS

1. A certain mass of gas in a 2.00-L container has a pressure of 164 kPa. Calculate the new pressure of the gas if the volume of the container is reduced to 1.00 L.

2. A balloon is filled with a gas at a pressure of 102 kPa, and its volume is determined to be 1.37 L. Calculate the volume of the balloon if the pressure increases to 110 kPa after more gas is added.

Discovering Chemistry   *Marshmallows and Boyle's Law*

What is the effect of pressure on a marshmallow?

Materials
   large marshmallow
   filter flask
   filter pump or hand vacuum pump
   rubber stopper

1. Place a large marshmallow in a thick-walled filter flask.

2. Place a rubber stopper in the neck of the flask, and connect the flask to a filter pump (water aspirator) or to a hand vacuum pump.

3. Turn on the water supply or pump the hand pump, and observe the marshmallow.

4. Disconnect the pump, and examine the marshmallow.

■ Describe what you saw happening when you were reducing the pressure around the marshmallow. Suggest why it happened.

■ Explain what you noticed about the marshmallow at the end. Suggest an explanation.

■ Suggest how your observations relate to Boyle's law.

■ Predict what would have happened if you had subjected the marshmallow to a high pressure.

The Relationship between Volume and Temperature: Charles's Law

Although Boyle's name is attached to the law relating pressure and volume of a gas, a large proportion of the work on gases was performed by scientists in France. This was because French scientists were pioneers in hot air ballooning, the most famous being the Montgolfier brothers. Using hot air balloons, the French scientists studied how the pressure and temperature of the atmosphere varied with altitude (Figure 8.17). In those times, ballooning was extremely hazardous. The fabric of the balloon was lacquered silk, and the occupants stood in a wicker basket. In the centre of the basket stood a brazier containing burning charcoal to heat the air in an envelope. Sparks from the fire would often ignite the very flammable envelope, causing the basket to plummet to Earth, killing the occupants. The first successful ascent by people in a hot air balloon was made by two French volunteers in November 1783. They rose to a height of 915 m, and the flight lasted about 25 min.

FIGURE 8.17 This colourful engraving shows Charles's and Robert's first ascent in a hydrogen balloon in Paris on December 1, 1783.

Jacques Charles, a French physicist, had realized earlier that the lightness of hydrogen would make it more efficient than air in lifting a balloon. So in August 1783, he made the first passengerless hydrogen balloon, which floated off into the distance, landing in a farmer's field. Believing it to be a flying monster, farm workers attacked and destroyed it with spades and pickaxes. Later, in December 1783, Charles and Nicolas Robert made the first flight in a hydrogen balloon (Figure 8.17). The flight lasted for over 2 h and covered 43 km.

Charles found that when a gas is heated, it expands. He found that for each one degree Celsius rise in temperature, the gas expanded by 1/273 of its volume at 0°C. Conversely, when a gas is cooled, it contracts by the same proportion, namely 1/273 of its volume for each degree decrease in temperature. This idea can be demonstrated by taking a fully inflated balloon and observing what happens when it is cooled, for example, by pouring liquid nitrogen at −196°C over it (Figure 8.18).

FIGURE 8.18 If you take an inflated balloon (top) and pour cold liquid nitrogen over it, the balloon collapses. Temperature and volume of a gas must therefore be related.

A Modern Zeppelin for Our Century

Decision-Making Skills

Defining the Issue

Developing Assessment Criteria

▶ Researching the Issue

▶ Analyzing Data and Information

▶ Proposing a Course of Action

▶ Justifying the Course of Action

▶ Communicating Your Proposal

BACKGROUND INFORMATION

Zeppelins are rigid airships of a type originally manufactured by the German company Luftschiffbau Zeppelin.

The first landing of a zeppelin took place in Echterdingen, Germany on August 5, 1908. It was an achievement for Count Ferdinand von Zeppelin and his company, Luftschiffbau Zeppelin, and it seemed to promise the dawn of a new age of transport for all those who watched it float in the air. Although von Zeppelin built more than 100 airworthy zeppelins, their fate was soon to change. The disaster of the Hindenburg in 1937, the advent of World War II, and the increased popularity of travelling by large-capacity propeller planes made the former excitement of airships seem a relic of a bygone era. However, on September 18, 1997 a new zeppelin experienced its maiden voyage in Friedrichshafen, Germany— an event no less historic than that in 1908.

This modern zeppelin, called LZ N07, was the marriage of the elegance and grace of historic airships with modern state-of-the-art aeronautic and electronic technology. The engineers and researchers from Luftschiffbau Zeppelin who built it, studied the extensive archives that the company has on zeppelins. They realized, however, that airship research and development had virtually ended in 1940 and there had been no theoretical or scientific studies on airship design since. So the design team had to develop their own theories and generate their own data.

The design of the LZ N07 includes a helium-air system with a slight overpressure within the envelope, about 4% higher than the external atmospheric pressure; three engines for exceptional manoeuverability; a gearing system and carbon-fibre housings for all engine/propeller units to reduce noise; and a simple triangular framework consisting of an aluminum alloy and a carbon-fibre composite material. The zeppelin's cockpit features state-of-the-art electronics to control its movement, and the gondola can accommodate 12 passengers. In addition, the zeppelin only requires three ground crew to land and take off.

Analyzing the Issue

1. Research the similarities and differences between the LZ N07 and the original zeppelins. Summarize your research in a Venn diagram.

2. Two company executives at Luftschiffbau Zeppelin realized that zeppelins could be used in advertising, sightseeing, and for environmental protection. Describe how these objectives could be achieved by a modern airship.

3. To date, Luftschiffbau Zeppelin has five orders to build zeppelins: four for advertising and tourism, and one for scientific measurement. Design a storyboard that can be used to film a television commercial that is intended to convince tourists to try the zeppelin. Consider what tourists will want to know about the zeppelin as you plan your presentation.

4. Identify the advantages and disadvantages if airships are used for tourism. Consider environmental, economic, social, and scientific impacts. Write a paragraph identifying which impacts, if any, you feel Luftschiffbau Zeppelin and other companies should address. Provide supporting evidence for your opinion.

To illustrate Charles's law, you can perform another simple experiment. A thin glass tube is sealed at one end, and a plug of oil is inserted at the top of the tube. The tube is then attached to a scale and inserted in a water bath (Figure 8.19). The temperature of the water bath is varied, and, at each temperature, the height of the air in the column is measured.

The quantity of air trapped in the tube remains constant since the oil prevents the air from escaping. The top of the tube is open, and, therefore, the pressure on the trapped air is also constant. From the area of the cross-section of the tube and the length of the air column, you can calculate the volume of the gas at each temperature. A plot of the data obtained will show the relationship between temperature and volume.

Typical results from such an experiment are shown in Table 8.6 and Figure 8.20. (Since the cross-section of the tube is a constant, you could have simply plotted length of air column rather than volume of air.)

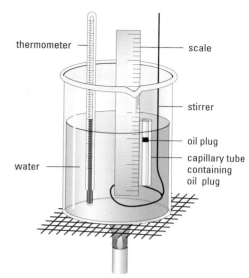

thermometer
scale
stirrer
oil plug
capillary tube containing oil plug
water

TABLE 8.6 The Relationship between the Temperature and the Volume of a Gas at Constant Pressure

Temperature (°C)	0	15	30	50	75	100
Volume (mm³)	32	34	36	38	41	44

FIGURE 8.19 An apparatus for investigating the effect of temperature on the volume of a gas

If you extrapolate the straight line shown in Figure 8.20 back to the temperature axis, you will find that the point of intersection is about $-275°C$. More precise measurements would give you a value of $-273.15°C$.

A temperature scale using $-273.15°C$ as the zero point was developed by Lord Kelvin in 1848 and is called, not surprisingly, the **Kelvin temperature scale**. Degrees used on the Kelvin scale are called kelvins and are the same size as those used on the Celsius scale. (Note that the symbol for kelvins is K, not °K.)

As a Celsius degree is the same size as a kelvin, the conversion factor is 1:1. For example, to convert 25°C to kelvins:

$$\text{Kelvin temperature} = \left(25°C \times \frac{1\ K}{1°C}\right) + 273\ K = 298\ K$$

To simplify, it is quite acceptable to write this as:

$$(25 + 273)K = 298\ K$$

If you plot a graph of volume against Kelvin temperature, a straight line passing through the origin is produced (Figure 8.21). The proportionality for this line can be written as:

$V \propto T$ where the pressure (P) and the amount of gas (n) are constant

Writing this proportionality as an equation, you would get:

$$V = kT \text{ or } \frac{V}{T} = k$$

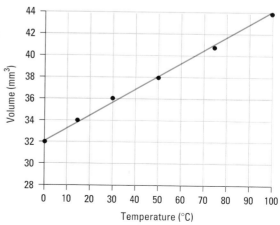

FIGURE 8.20 A plot of volume against temperature for a sample of gas at constant pressure

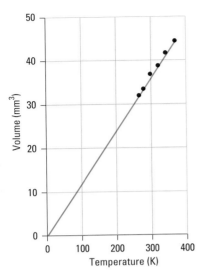

FIGURE 8.21 A plot of volume against Kelvin temperature for a sample of gas at constant pressure

The relationship between the volume and temperature of a gas is known as **Charles's law** and can be expressed as follows:

At constant pressure, the volume of a fixed mass of any gas is directly proportional to its Kelvin temperature.

A more useful form of the formula can be obtained as follows. If a gas occupying volume V_1 at a temperature of T_1 is cooled or heated to a new temperature of T_2, at which point it occupies volume V_2 (at constant pressure), then:

$$\frac{V_1}{T_1} = \frac{V_2}{T_2}$$

EXAMPLE 4

A balloon is filled with helium gas to a volume of 1.20 L and at a temperature of 15°C. If the pressure remains constant and the temperature rises to 30°C, what will the new volume of the balloon be?

Given
$V_1 = 1.20$ L, $T_1 = 273 + 15 = 288$ K,

$T_2 = 273 + 30 = 303$ K

Required
volume, $V_2 = ?$ L

Analysis
Using Charles's law:
$$\frac{V_1}{T_1} = \frac{V_2}{T_2} \text{ or } V_2 = \frac{V_1 \times T_2}{T_1}$$

Solution
$$V_2 = \frac{(1.20 \text{ L})(303 \text{ K})}{288 \text{ K}} = 1.26 \text{ L}$$

Statement
The volume of the balloon will be 1.26 L.

PRACTICE PROBLEMS

1. A balloon is filled with helium gas to a volume of 1.20 L and a temperature of 15°C. If the pressure remains constant and you take the balloon outside where the temperature is −15°C, calculate the new volume of the balloon.

2. A balloon contains 5.00 L of air at 25°C. Deduce at what temperature the balloon will shrink to half that volume. Assume that the pressure is held constant.

Investigation
Refer to page 376, Investigation 2

The Relationship between Pressure and Temperature: Gay-Lussac's Law

If a gas is contained in a vessel that cannot expand significantly, such as a steel cylinder or an automobile tire, as the temperature is increased, the pressure will increase (Figure 8.22). You will find that tire manufacturers always provide the recommended cold tire pressure. Reading tire pressures when tires are hot will not give you a reliable value to compare with the recommended value. Check the pressure on a tire when it is cold, and then recheck after running the vehicle on a highway. How large is the pressure difference between cold and hot?

The mathematical relationship between pressure and temperature was discovered by Joseph Gay-Lussac, a French scientist. He was another "balloonatic,"

setting an altitude record of 6000 m, which was held for over 50 years. He determined the relationship to be:

$P \propto T$ where the volume (V) and the amount of gas (n) are constant

or $P = kT$ or $\dfrac{P}{T} = k$

Gay-Lussac's law expresses this relationship as follows:

At constant volume, the pressure of a fixed mass of any gas is directly proportional to its Kelvin temperature.

Again, a more useful mathematical form of the relationship is:

$$\frac{P_1}{T_1} = \frac{P_2}{T_2}$$

WEBLINK

For a simulation to show how the ideal gas relationships work, go to **www.pearsoned.ca/chemistry11**.

EXAMPLE 5

At a temperature of 10°C, a container is filled with gas at a pressure of 225 kPa. What will the pressure be if the container is placed in the hot sun to reach a temperature of 42°C?

Given
$P_1 = 225$ kPa, $T_1 = 273 + 10 = 283$ K,
$T_2 = 273 + 42 = 315$ K

Required
final pressure, $P_2 = ?$ kPa

1. A steel cylinder with a volume of 450 mL contains a gas at a pressure of 520 kPa at 25°C. If the cylinder is heated to 410°C, determine what the new pressure will be.

2. A glass vessel that can only withstand a maximum internal pressure of 225 kPa is filled with gas at 21°C and 100.0 kPa and then heated. Calculate at what temperature the vessel will burst.

Analysis
Using Gay-Lussac's law:

$$\frac{P_1}{T_1} = \frac{P_2}{T_2} \text{ or } P_2 = \frac{P_1 \times T_2}{T_1}$$

Solution

$$P_2 = \frac{(225 \text{ kPa})(315 \text{ K})}{283 \text{ K}} = 250 \text{ kPa}$$

Statement
The pressure in the container will increase to 250 kPa.

Section 8.2 Review

Understanding Concepts

1. Draw a graphical representation of each of the three gas laws. Don't forget to label the axes on your graphs.

2. Describe how you would reduce the pressure of a volume of gas to one-quarter of its original value assuming that the gas is at constant temperature.

3. Describe the effects on gas pressure when there are changes in the amount of gas and in the volume of the container.

4. Weather balloons are partially inflated before they are released, but as they ascend, the balloons expand. Write a short paragraph explaining why.

Applying Inquiry/ Communication Skills

5. In an experiment, the volume of a container of gas is reduced to one-third of its original volume. Predict the relative change in pressure.

6. The melting point of sodium chloride is 804°C. Convert its melting point to kelvins.

7. If you double the Kelvin temperature of a volume of gas, predict the effect on the volume of the gas if the pressure is constant.

8. Temperatures in a burning building can reach 1.50×10^{3}°C. Calculate the pressure inside an airtight building at this temperature, assuming that the initial temperature and pressure are 20°C and 102 kPa respectively.

9. The gauge pressure of an inflated tire is 240 kPa at a temperature of 5°C. After the car is driven at high speed, the tire warms to 35°C. Calculate the gauge pressure of the warm tire if the external (atmospheric) pressure is 102 kPa.

Making Connections

10. A company manufactures a successful room disinfectant in 150-mL aerosol containers. The manufacturer wants to introduce a new variation for the product that offers twice the amount of gas in the same size container. List the issues that need to be considered, and give your reasons why. Include a calculation showing how the pressure of the new product compares with that of the gas in the original container.

8.3 Gases and the Kinetic-Molecular Theory

Key Understandings

When you have completed this section, you will be able to:

- use the kinetic-molecular theory to explain the motion of atoms, molecules, and ions in solids, liquids, and gases
- explain the gas laws in terms of the kinetic-molecular theory
- describe the difference between an ideal gas and a real gas
- compare quantitatively the kinetic energy of different gases
- describe the relationship between the effusion and diffusion of different gases
- use appropriate scientific vocabulary to communicate ideas related to gases

The gas laws are called laws because they state facts, to the best of our knowledge, about the world we live in. For example, the doubling of the pressure on a gas will cause its volume to be halved at constant temperature. However, a law does not offer any explanation. To provide an explanation, a theory is needed—in this case, the kinetic-molecular theory.

According to the kinetic-molecular theory, substances consist of moving particles. In the solid state, these particles are locked in a crystal lattice. The molecules or ions vibrate but do not move with respect to one another. As the temperature is increased, the vibrations become greater, until the particles have enough energy to partially overcome the attractive forces between them. The particles then move or slide over one another. This is what scientists picture happening when a substance melts. If the temperature is increased even more, the particles gain enough kinetic energy to completely overcome the interparticle attractions and escape. This represents the process of boiling, and the free-moving particles are in the gaseous state. For a substance to exist as a gas at normal temperatures, the intermolecular attractions must be very weak. Consequently, only small covalent molecules will be gases (or liquids) at SATP. Ionic compounds, on the other hand, have very strong attractions between the constituent ions. They do not melt or boil until temperatures in the hundreds or thousands of degrees Celsius are reached.

Using the kinetic-molecular theory, a container full of gas is pictured as an enormous number of tiny particles (atoms or molecules) moving around randomly and independently. In developing this theory, a number of assumptions are made about these particles. These are summarized below:

1. The volume of the particles is negligible compared to the volume of the container. In other words, a sample of gas is mainly empty space.
2. The particles move in rapid, straight-line motion between collisions with one another and with the walls of the container.
3. There is no loss of energy when two particles collide.
4. In the gas phase, there are no attractive forces between particles. (This is in contrast with the liquid and solid phases.)
5. At any given temperature, the average kinetic energy of the particles in all gases is the same.

A gas for which all these statements are valid is known as an **ideal gas**. The importance of these assumptions is discussed next.

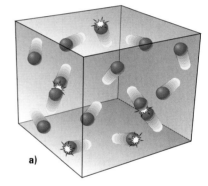

a)

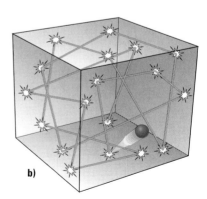

b)

FIGURE 8.23 a) According to the kinetic-molecular theory, gases are mostly empty space and have particles that move rapidly. b) The particles move in straight-line motion in between collisions with each other and with the walls of the container.

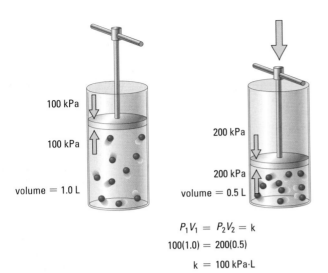

100 kPa
100 kPa
volume = 1.0 L

200 kPa
200 kPa
volume = 0.5 L

$$P_1 V_1 = P_2 V_2 = k$$
$$100(1.0) = 200(0.5)$$
$$k = 100 \ kPa \cdot L$$

FIGURE 8.24 When the volume of a gas container is decreased, the gas particles collide with the container walls more frequently and an increase in pressure is observed (Boyle's law).

Explaining the Gas Laws Using the Kinetic-Molecular Theory

A test of a theory is that it explains observations. For example, Boyle's law can be understood in terms of the kinetic-molecular theory. Suppose you have a small sample of gas consisting of several million particles moving around in a confined space. According to the kinetic-molecular theory (assumption #2), there will be collisions occurring between the particles and also between the particles and the surface of the container. When the particles collide with the walls of the container, pressure is created within the container. The greater the number of collisions per second on a given surface area, the greater the pressure. As the volume of the gas container is decreased, the particles will have shorter distances to travel before they hit the container walls again. This means that the number of collisions with the container walls per unit of time will increase, resulting in an increase in measured pressure (Figure 8.24).

Conversely, if the volume of the container is increased, the particles will have much farther to travel in between collisions with the container walls. Consequently, in the same period of time, the number of particles colliding with a given area of the wall at any instant will be lower than before, and a decrease in pressure will be observed.

Gay-Lussac's law and Charles's law can be similarly explained. To account for these laws, you need to realize that temperature is simply a measurement of the motion of the particles. The heating of a gas means that the velocity of the particles is being increased. In a fixed volume of gas, as the temperature is increased, the particles move faster and hit the walls of the container more often—what you would measure as an increase in pressure (Gay-Lussac's law) (Figures 8.25 and 8.26).

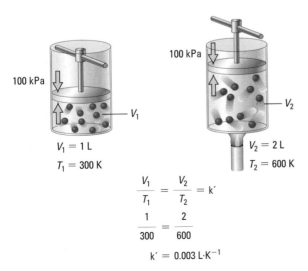

100 kPa

100 kPa

V_1

$V_1 = 1 \ L$
$T_1 = 300 \ K$

V_2

$V_2 = 2 \ L$
$T_2 = 600 \ K$

$$\frac{V_1}{T_1} = \frac{V_2}{T_2} = k'$$
$$\frac{1}{300} = \frac{2}{600}$$
$$k' = 0.003 \ L \cdot K^{-1}$$

FIGURE 8.25 When the temperature of a gas container is increased, the average kinetic energy of the gas particles increases. As a result, the volume must be increased if the rate of collisions with the cylinder walls (the pressure) is to remain constant (Charles's law).

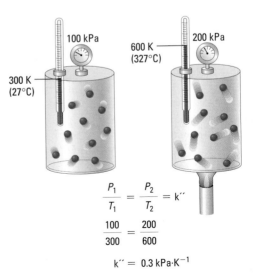

100 kPa
300 K
(27°C)

200 kPa
600 K
(327°C)

$$\frac{P_1}{T_1} = \frac{P_2}{T_2} = k''$$
$$\frac{100}{300} = \frac{200}{600}$$
$$k'' = 0.3 \ kPa \cdot K^{-1}$$

FIGURE 8.26 When the temperature of a gas container is increased, the average kinetic energy of the gas particles increases. As a result, the pressure increases at constant volume (Gay-Lussac's law).

Finally, the pressure inside a container can be increased even if the volume and temperature are kept constant. This is accomplished by increasing the number of particles of the gas. This is what happens when you pump up tires. A pump is simply a means of transferring particles from the outside to the inside of a tire (Figure 8.27). Mathematically, you can say:

$P \propto n$ where the volume (V) and the temperature (T) are constant

The Behaviour of Real Gases

An ideal gas is one that satisfies all the assumptions of the kinetic-molecular theory, especially the assumptions that the particles of a gas do not experience attractive forces and that the total volume of the actual particles is negligible compared to the volume of the gas itself. For such a gas, Boyle's and Charles's laws apply at all temperatures and pressures, and the gas is therefore called an ideal gas. However, experiments have shown that all gases deviate from Boyle's law at high pressures and from Charles's law at low temperatures. Therefore, they are not ideal gases but **real gases**. Real gases experience forces of attraction at high pressures, and the volumes of the molecules themselves become a significant proportion of the total volume at low temperatures. This is why gases like ammonia and chlorine can be liquefied fairly easily. Real gases behave like an ideal gas when their temperature is increased and their pressure is reduced (Figure 8.28).

a) Low tire pressure

b) High tire pressure

FIGURE 8.27 a) A tire with low pressure has few particles inside it. b) Using a pump, you increase the number of particles inside the tire and therefore increase the pressure.

FIGURE 8.28 Most commercial gases are transported as liquids. The fact that a gas can be liquefied shows it is not an ideal gas.

In addition to the three common states of matter, there is an in-between state, a gas-liquid hybrid called a supercritical fluid. Under very high pressures, the density of a gas becomes indistinguishable from its liquid state. This gas-liquid has some very useful properties as a solvent. The most commonly used supercritical fluid is carbon dioxide. Above pressures of 7.4 MPa and a temperature of 30°C, carbon dioxide exists as a supercritical fluid. Its major use is to extract caffeine from coffee beans to produce decaffeinated coffee. Supercritical carbon dioxide is an excellent solvent for caffeine. The fluid is filtered from the decaffeinated beans and evaporated, leaving caffeine, which can then be used in anti-drowsiness pills and in some analgesic formulations. Supercritical fluids are now being used as solvents in dry cleaners to replace the ozone-destroying chlorofluorocarbons.

WEBLINK

SIMULATION

For a simulation to show how the
kinetic-molecular theory works, go to
www.pearsoned.ca/chemistry11.

The Kinetic Energy of Gas Molecules

The first four assumptions of the kinetic-molecular theory have been discussed, but the fifth assumption is also very important, particularly in terms of the atmosphere of our planet. According to assumption #5, at any given temperature, the average kinetic energy of the particles in all gases is the same. Kinetic energy (KE) is the energy possessed by a moving object, and it depends on both its mass (m) and the square of its velocity (v).

$$KE = \frac{1}{2}mv^2$$

Hydrogen gas (H_2) and oxygen gas (O_2) can be used as examples. Assumption #5 states that, at the same temperature, the hydrogen molecules and the oxygen molecules will have the same average kinetic energy.

$$\frac{1}{2}m_{H_2}\,v^2_{H_2} = \frac{1}{2}m_{O_2}v^2_{O_2}$$

The expression can be rearranged and solved to give:

$$\frac{v_{H_2}}{v_{O_3}} = \sqrt{\frac{m_{O_2}}{m_{H_2}}} = \sqrt{\frac{32.0}{2.0}} = \sqrt{16.0} = 4.00$$

Because the mass of a hydrogen molecule is one-sixteenth that of an oxygen molecule, the average velocity of a hydrogen molecule must be four times greater than that of an oxygen molecule in order for both molecules to have the same average kinetic energy. In general, at any given temperature, the higher the molar mass of a gas, the lower the average velocity of its molecules (Table 8.7).

TABLE 8.7 Average Velocity of Selected Gas Molecules at 25°C

Gas	Molecular Mass (relative)	Average Velocity (m·s⁻¹)	Average Velocity (km·h⁻¹)
H_2	2.02	1770	6370
He	4.00	1250	4500
N_2	28.02	473	1700
O_2	32.00	442	1590
CO_2	44.01	377	1360

Although the average velocities of all gas molecules are high, those of hydrogen and helium are exceptionally high. The very high average velocities of hydrogen and helium account for the fact that Earth's atmosphere contains very little of these two gases. The molecules of these two gases escaped from Earth's gravitational field thousands of millions of years ago.

Graham's Law of Diffusion and Effusion

The inverse relationship between molecular velocity and molecular mass was experimentally observed by Thomas Graham, a Scottish scientist, in the 19th century. He showed that gases with large molar masses diffuse (spread)

more slowly than those with smaller molar masses (Figure 8.29). This relationship of **diffusion** can be written as:

$$\text{rate of diffusion} \propto \frac{1}{\sqrt{M}}$$

You may have noticed that helium balloons deflate faster than air-filled balloons. This phenomenon is called **effusion**, the passage of molecules through tiny holes (orifices) such as those you find in the walls of a balloon.

An Application of Gas Effusion—Isotope Separation

By means of slight differences in molecular masses, it is possible to separate isotopes of elements. For example, uranium is found as uranium-235 (abundance 0.720%) and uranium-238 (abundance 99.275%). The former isotope is useful for nuclear power (and weapons). In one method of separating isotopes, uranium metal is converted to uranium hexafluoride, a gas above 56°C. When the gas is passed through microscopic holes in a membrane, the molecules of uranium-235 hexafluoride will travel through the holes 1.0043 times faster than those of uranium-238 hexafluoride. In other words, the gas passing through the membrane will contain 0.720% × 1.0043 = 0.723% of the uranium-235 compound. That does not sound like much of an improvement, but suppose the process is done about 2000 times. Then the gas coming out at the end will be almost 99% uranium-235 hexafluoride, giving a nearly complete isotope separation.

FIGURE 8.29 When you smell a skunk, the "smelly" molecules have diffused through the air to reach your nose. The rate of diffusion is inversely proportional to the square root of the molar mass of the compounds.

Understanding Concepts

1. Describe the difference between a law and a theory.

2. Compare the properties of an ideal gas and a real gas.

3. Use the kinetic-molecular theory to compare the compressibility of gases to solids and to liquids. Illustrate your answer with labelled diagrams.

4. Use the kinetic-molecular theory to explain how an odour moves across a room.

5. Describe what happens to the kinetic energy of gas particles when they collide and when the temperature increases.

Applying Inquiry/ Communication Skills

6. Predict which gas molecules at the same temperature will have the higher average velocity, nitrogen or neon. Do not use a calculation method.

7. Radioactive radon gas is a problem in houses built over rocks containing radioactive ores. It seeps through cracks in basement walls, and because of its high molecular mass, it takes a long while to disperse (unless you have an air exchanger). Assuming the same temperature and pressure, calculate the relative speed the radon atoms will be travelling compared with the nitrogen molecules of the air.

8. Use the kinetic energy relationship to show that uranium-235 hexafluoride molecules are travelling, on average, 1.0043 times the velocity of those of uranium-238 hexafluoride.

8.4 The Combined and Ideal Gas Laws

Key Understandings

When you have completed this section, you will be able to:

- solve problems using the combined gas law and the ideal gas law
- understand how to determine the molar volume of a gas
- use the gas laws to explain natural phenomena, such as volcanoes and geysers
- describe technological products associated with gases
- determine the density and molar mass of a gas using the ideal gas law
- use appropriate scientific vocabulary to communicate ideas related to the combined and ideal gas laws

In each of the three gas laws discussed, one of the variables (pressure, volume, or temperature) was held constant. In practice, all three variables can be changed at the same time. For example, when a weather balloon is released, the temperature, volume, and pressure of the gas inside the balloon all change as the balloon ascends into the atmosphere.

The Combined Gas Law

You can calculate the new value of any one of the three variables (P, V, and T), provided that the new values of the other two are known, by using the following relationship:

$$\frac{P_1V_1}{T_1} = \frac{P_2V_2}{T_2} \text{ where the amount of gas } (n) \text{ is constant}$$

This relationship is known as the **combined gas law** because it is a combination of the equations pertaining to Boyle's, Charles's, and Gay-Lussac's laws. Any units of pressure or volume may be used in this equation, but the temperature must be expressed in kelvins.

EXAMPLE 6

A weather balloon with a volume of 55.0 L is filled with hydrogen gas at a pressure of 98.5 kPa and a temperature of 13°C. When the balloon is released, it rises to the stratosphere, where the temperature is −48°C and the pressure is 19.7 kPa. What is the volume of the balloon under these conditions?

Given
$P_1 = 98.5$ kPa, $V_1 = 55.0$ L, $T_1 = 273 + 13 = 286$ K
$P_2 = 19.7$ kPa, $T_2 = -48°C = 225$ K

Required
final volume, $V_2 = ?$ L

Analysis
Using the combined gas law:
$$\frac{P_1V_1}{T_1} = \frac{P_2V_2}{T_2} \text{ or } V_2 = \left(\frac{P_1V_1}{T_1}\right)\left(\frac{T_2}{P_2}\right)$$

Solution
$$V_2 = \left(\frac{(98.5\text{ kPa})(55.0\text{ L})}{286\text{ K}}\right)\left(\frac{225\text{ K}}{19.7\text{ kPa}}\right) = 216\text{ L}$$

Statement
The volume of the balloon is 216 L at 19.7 kPa and −48°C.

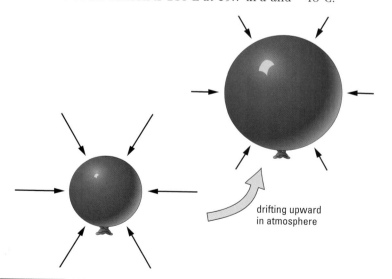

drifting upward in atmosphere

FIGURE 8.31   When the balloon ascends, its volume increases as the external pressure decreases.

PRACTICE PROBLEMS

1. An aerosol can with a volume of 325 mL contains propellant gas at 445 kPa and 12°C. Calculate the volume that the gas would occupy if it were allowed to escape at 101 kPa and 21°C.

2. A weather balloon contains 15.0 L of helium at a pressure of 97.6 kPa and a temperature of 11°C. If this gas was stored in a 1.00 L cylinder at 19°C, determine the pressure that must have been in the cylinder.

When using the combined gas law (or any of the gas laws) to solve a problem, you should always check your answer to see if it seems reasonable. For example, in Example 6, the pressure dropped to about one-fifth of its original value. This would cause the volume to increase about five times. The Kelvin temperature decreased by about 20%, which would lead to a small decrease in volume. The new volume should, therefore, be about four times its old value, about 220 L. Consequently, a calculated value of 216 L is quite reasonable.

Gas Laws and Volcanoes

The combined gas law, which can be applied to explain many natural phenomena, is important in such areas of study as volcanology. Some volcanoes, such as those in Hawaii, quietly produce enormous volumes of molten lava, while others emit gases, often explosively. It is the gas-producing volcanoes that provide us with the most dramatic examples of the gas laws in action. Gases (particularly water in the form of steam) trapped within Earth are at high temperatures and extremely high pressures. Travelling through cracks in the rocks, they reach near Earth's surface. The pressure builds against the thin rock layer at the surface until it finally gives way, causing the gas to expand rapidly, often in a dramatic explosion. The explosion is so violent that cubic kilometres of surrounding rock are fragmented into dust and spewed into the upper atmosphere.

About 2000 years ago, the gas explosion of Mount Vesuvius in Italy destroyed the cities of Pompei and Herculanium. These cities, buried in ash, have been excavated in recent times, enabling visitors to see two preserved Roman cities. The most spectacular explosion in recent times was that of Mount St. Helens in Oregon in 1980 (Figure 8.32). However, this was a small eruption compared to two that occurred in the Far East in the 19th century. The explosion of Krakatoa on one of the Indonesian islands in 1883 was heard 3500 km away in Australia. The dust cloud was so intense that it plunged the region into darkness for 3 days, while the associated 37 m-high tidal wave killed 36 000 people living on surrounding islands. Even more powerful was Tambora, also in Indonesia, in 1815, with the volume of rock converted to atmospheric dust being so great that global temperatures were reduced drastically. In fact, the cooling was so great that 1816 was known as the "year without a summer." The explosion of the island of Thera in the eastern Mediterranean about 3500 years ago was about five times greater than Tambora. The destruction of Thera is commonly believed to account for the myth of the lost continent of Atlantis. Even dramatic explosions like these follow the combined gas law.

FIGURE 8.32 Mount St. Helens erupting. This photograph shows an extreme example of the combined gas law. The gases, which are at a high temperature and very high pressure inside Earth, expand with explosive force when they are exposed to atmospheric pressure at Earth's surface. Where are most of the active volcanoes found on our planet?

Determining the Molar Volume of an Ideal Gas

Gases are much less dense than liquids or solids, but how much less dense? A convenient measurement to use is the volume occupied by a mole of gas under a set of fixed conditions of temperature and pressure, such as SATP or STP. It is simple to calculate the **molar volume** of a gas using its density. For example, the measured densities of the gases helium and neon at SATP (25°C and 100 kPa) are 0.192 g·L^{-1} and 0.815 g·L^{-1} respectively. These values can be used as conversion factors to convert molar mass to molar volume, V_m.

$$V_m, \text{ molar volume of He} = 4.00 \text{ g·mol}^{-1} \times \frac{1 \text{ L}}{0.192 \text{ g}} = 24.8 \text{ L·mol}^{-1}$$

$$V_m, \text{ molar volume of Ne} = 20.2 \text{ g·mol}^{-1} \times \frac{1 \text{ L}}{0.815 \text{ g}} = 24.8 \text{ L·mol}^{-1}$$

You can see that the volume occupied at SATP by one mole of both of these gases is 24.8 L. This is true not only for helium and neon, but for all the noble gases. In fact, the volume of one mole of any gas at SATP is usually quite close to 24.8 L. As a fair approximation, you can say that, at SATP, one mole of any gas occupies a volume of 24.8 L.

Using the old STP (0°C and 101 kPa), you will find that, at STP, one mole of any gas occupies a volume of 22.4 L.

Therefore, 24.8 L·mol^{-1} is known as the molar volume at SATP, while 22.4 L·mol^{-1} is known as the molar volume at STP. Just as molar mass may be considered to be a conversion factor relating moles of substance to mass, molar volume relates moles of gas to volume measured at SATP or STP. The only additional information that is used is the formula for density, which is made specific for molar quantities:

$$\text{density} = \frac{\text{mass}}{\text{volume}} = \frac{\text{molar mass, } M}{\text{molar volume, } V_m},$$

where the molar volume is defined as $V_m = \dfrac{V}{n}$.

EXAMPLE 7

Calculate the density of hydrogen gas at STP.

Given
gas is hydrogen, H_2
conditions are STP

Required
density of hydrogen, $d_{H_2} = ? \text{ g·L}^{-1}$

Analysis
V_m at STP $= 22.4 \text{ L·mol}^{-1}$

$M_{H_2} = 2.02 \text{ g·mol}^{-1}$

$d = \dfrac{M}{V_m}$

Solution

$$d_{H_2} = \frac{2.02 \text{ g·mol}^{-1}}{22.4 \text{ L·mol}^{-1}} = 9.02 \times 10^{-2} \text{ g·L}^{-1}$$

Statement

The density of hydrogen gas at STP is 9.02×10^{-2} g·L^{-1}.

The Ideal Gas Law

So far, you have seen how changes in pressure, volume, and temperature affect gases. However, the most useful aspect for chemists is how pressure, volume, and temperature information can be used to determine the amount of gas in a container.

The amount of a gas could be determined by measuring the mass of the gas in the container, pumping it out, measuring the mass of the evacuated container, and converting the mass difference to moles. But gases are of such low density that the difference in masses would be tiny and the errors potentially very large. However, it is very straightforward to measure the pressure, volume, and temperature of a gas—and to a high degree of precision. The relationship that links moles, pressure, volume, and temperature for a gas is known as the **ideal gas law**.

You can derive the formula starting from the combined gas law:

$$\frac{P_1 V_1}{T_1} = \frac{P_2 V_2}{T_2}$$

Suppose that P_2, V_2, and T_2 apply to n moles of gas at SATP. Then:

$P_2 = 100$ kPa, $T_2 = 298$ K, and $V_2 = n \times 24.8$ L·mol^{-1}

Substituting into the combined gas law, you would get:

$$\frac{P_1 V_1}{T_1} = \frac{(100 \text{ kPa})(n \times 24.8 \text{ L·mol}^{-1})}{298 \text{ K}}$$

Dividing both sides by n, deleting subscripts, and evaluating the numerical part gives:

$$\frac{PV}{nT} = 8.31 \text{ kPa·L·mol}^{-1}\text{·K}^{-1}$$

Therefore, for all ideal gases, the product of pressure (in kPa) and volume (in L) divided by the product of moles and temperature (in K) will give 8.31 kPa·L·mol^{-1}·K^{-1}. This constant is known as the **ideal gas constant** and is given the symbol R.

Substituting the symbol R into the formula and multiplying both sides by nT gives the usual form of the ideal gas law:

$$PV = nRT$$

Although R is a constant, it does have other values that correspond to different units. For example, if the pressure is given in atmospheres instead of kilopascals, the constant is 0.0821 atm·L·mol^{-1}·K^{-1}.

EXAMPLE 8

A 2.50-L container is filled with sulfur dioxide gas at a pressure of 120 kPa and a temperature of 26°C. Calculate the mass of sulfur dioxide gas in the container. The ideal gas constant is 8.31 kPa·L·mol^{-1}·K^{-1}.

Given
P = 120 kPa, V = 2.50 L, T = 26°C = 299 K, R = 8.31 kPa·L·mol^{-1}·K^{-1}

Required
mass of sulfur dioxide, m_{SO_2} = ? g

Analysis
$P, V, R, T \rightarrow n_{SO_2}$ (using $PV = nRT$)

$n_{SO_2} \rightarrow m_{SO_2}$ (using M_{SO_2} = 64.1 g·mol^{-1})

Solution

$$n_{SO_2} = \frac{PV}{RT} = \frac{(120 \text{ kPa})(2.50 \text{ L})}{(8.31 \text{ kPa·L·mol}^{-1}\text{·K}^{-1})(299 \text{ K})} = 0.121 \text{ mol}$$

$$m_{SO_2} = 0.121 \text{ mol} \times \frac{64.1 \text{ g}}{1 \text{ mol}} = 7.76 \text{ g}$$

Statement
The mass of sulfur dioxide gas is 7.76 g.

PRACTICE PROBLEM

A gas cylinder with a capacity of 105 L contains helium at a pressure of 6.70 MPa and a temperature of 27°C. Calculate the mass of helium gas in the cylinder.

EXAMPLE 9

Find the volume of 1.00 g of water in the gas phase at its boiling point (100°C) at 101 kPa. The ideal gas constant is 8.31 kPa·L·mol^{-1}·K^{-1}.

Given
m_{H_2O} = 1.00 g, T = 100°C = 373 K, P = 101 kPa, R = 8.31 kPa·L·mol^{-1}·K^{-1}

Required
volume of gaseous water, V_{H_2O} = ? L

Analysis
$m_{H_2O} \rightarrow n_{H_2O}$ (using M_{H_2O} = 18.02 g·mol^{-1})

$P, T, R, n_{H_2O} \rightarrow V_{H_2O}$ (using $PV = nRT$)

Solution

$$n_{H_2O} = 1.00 \text{ g} \times \frac{1 \text{ mol H}_2\text{O}}{18.02 \text{ g}} = 5.55 \times 10^{-2} \text{ mol H}_2\text{O}$$

$$V_{H_2O} = \frac{nRT}{P} = \frac{(5.55 \times 10^{-2} \text{ mol})(8.31 \text{ kPa·L·mol}^{-1}\text{·K}^{-1})(373 \text{ K})}{101 \text{ kPa}} = 1.70 \text{ L}$$

Statement
The volume of 1.00 g of water (gas) at 100°C and 101 kPa is 1.70 L.

PRACTICE PROBLEM

Determine the pressure that 20.0 g of solid carbon dioxide gas will exert if it vaporizes in an evacuated 2.00-L container at 18°C.

FIGURE 8.33 Balloons filled with a gas less dense than air will rise, while those with a density similar to, or denser than, air will not.

This last example has real practical significance. As water has a density of 1.00 g·mL^{-1}, the volume occupied by 1.00 g of liquid water is:

$$V_{H_2O} = 1.00 \text{ g} \times \frac{1 \text{ mL}}{1.00 \text{ g}} = 1.00 \text{ mL}$$

Consequently, vaporizing water at constant pressure and 100°C increases its volume by 1700 times, showing that a substance as a gas occupies a far larger volume than in its liquid or solid phases. However, if the vaporized water (or other liquid) is in a sealed container, instead of expanding, the pressure will build up to extremely high values, causing the container to rupture explosively and disperse glass or metal fragments at high speeds. Many severe injuries and even deaths have been attributed to the accidental heating of sealed containers.

It was such an explosion in 1984 that caused the world's worst industrial accident in Bhopal, India. According to most accident investigators, on the night of December 2, some water was accidentally pumped into a tank of methylisocyanate, CH_3NCO (abbreviated to MIC). MIC is an extremely toxic compound used in the manufacture of an insecticide; it boils at 40°C and reacts violently with water. The heat from the reaction was sufficient to vaporize a significant proportion of the MIC. Under the extreme pressure, the tank exploded, shattering the surrounding shell of concrete. The vapour poured out of a 30-m tower. Unfortunately, the night was very still, and the dense MIC vapour drifted down to ground level where it spread. Over 20 t were released. Any concentration of MIC in excess of 100 ppm is lethal and over 30 ppm will cause debilitating injury. Despite the toxicity of the materials, the plant was situated in a city. As a result, according to the most reliable estimates, about 3800 people died and 350 000 suffered severe damage to their health.

WEBLINK

The Bhopal industrial accident was the worst chemical-related disaster in the world. Study a detailed report on the incident. As the safety officer for the company, write a report on what could have been done to prevent the accident from happening, and what precautions should be taken in the future. Begin your research at **www.pearsoned.ca/chemistry11**.

EXAMPLE 10

In the middle layer of the stratosphere (where ozone is concentrated), the ozone concentration is about 5.0×10^{15} molecules·L^{-1} at a temperature of about −42°C. What is the pressure in Pa of the ozone under these conditions? The ideal gas constant is 8.31 kPa·L·mol^{-1}·K^{-1}.

Given
number of molecules = 5.0×10^{15}, $T = -42°C = 231$ K, $V = 1.0$ L,
$R = 8.31$ kPa·L·mol^{-1}·K^{-1}

Required
pressure, P_{O_3} = ? Pa

Analysis
molecules of $O_3 \rightarrow n_{O_3}$
(using Avogadro's number, 6.02×10^{23} molecules·mol^{-1})

V, T, R, $n_{O_3} \rightarrow P_{O_3}$ (using $PV = nRT$)

Solution
$n_{O_3} = 5.0 \times 10^{15}$ molecules $\times \dfrac{1 \text{ mol } O_3}{6.02 \times 10^{23} \text{ molecules}} = 8.3 \times 10^{-9}$ mol O_3

$$P_{O_3} = \frac{nRT}{V} = \frac{(8.3 \times 10^{-9}\ \text{mol})(8.31\ \text{kPa}\cdot\text{L}\cdot\text{mol}^{-1}\cdot\text{K}^{-1})(231\ \text{K})}{1.0\ \text{L}}$$

$$= 1.6 \times 10^{-5}\ \text{kPa}$$

$$= 1.6 \times 10^{-2}\ \text{Pa}$$

Statement
The pressure of ozone gas in the stratosphere is about 1.6×10^{-2} Pa.

PRACTICE PROBLEM

Calculate the number of air molecules in 1.0 L of air at SATP.

Gas Laws and Geysers

The large expansion that occurs when water turns from a liquid into a gas is the driving force in geysers. These natural phenomena occur in regions where the underlying rock is abnormally hot, such as a region of present or past volcanic activity (Figure 8.34). The process starts with rainwater seeping down through porous rock layers until the rock temperature is greatly in excess of the boiling point of water. The superheated water rises back to the surface through cracks and fissures, collecting into larger tubes that act as

the "plumbing" for the geyser (Figure 8.35). Near the surface, the pressure is reduced enough for the water to vaporize rapidly, pushing water near the surface ahead of it out of the tubes. Many geysers produce spurts of water at regular intervals as a result of constrictions in the tubes. If there is insufficient water, jets of steam are produced; these are known as fumeroles.

FIGURE 8.34 Geysers are jets of hot water pushed out from deep within Earth by steam pressure.

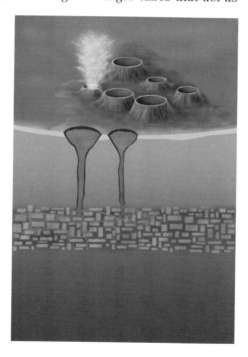

FIGURE 8.35 A geyser functions through an underground network of water-filled tubes and fissures.

How Do Hot Air Balloons Work?

In our discussion of molar volume, you learned how to calculate the density of a gas at STP or SATP. Using the ideal gas law, you can calculate the density of any gas at any temperature and pressure.

Air has an average molar mass of 28.8 g·mol^{-1}. Calculate the density of air at a temperature of 18°C and a pressure of 102 kPa.

Given
M_{air} = 28.8 g·mol^{-1}, P = 102 kPa, T = 273 + 18 = 291 K, n = 1.00 mol

Required
density of air, d_{air} = ? g·L^{-1}

Analysis
$$PV = nRT$$

$$V_m = \frac{V}{n} = \frac{RT}{P}$$

$$d_{air} = \frac{M_{air}}{V_m}$$

Solution

$$V_m = \frac{(8.31 \text{ kPa·L·mol}^{-1}\text{·K}^{-1})(291 \text{ K})}{102 \text{ kPa}}$$

$$= 23.7 \text{ L·mol}^{-1}$$

$$d_{air} = \frac{28.8 \text{ g·mol}^{-1}}{23.7 \text{ L·mol}^{-1}}$$

$$= 1.22 \text{ g·L}^{-1}$$

Statement
The density of air at 18°C and 102 kPa is 1.22 g·L^{-1}.

Chlorine gas was used as a poison gas in World War I in part because of its high density, making it "flow" along the ground, poisoning any living creature in its path (until it was dispersed by diffusion). Calculate the density of chlorine gas at 12°C and 101 kPa pressure.

FIGURE 8.36 The flame from the propane burner of a hot air balloon heats the air within the canopy, reducing its density compared to that of the external cold air.

Suppose you do the same density calculation for air at 100°C instead of 18°C. Then the density of air becomes 0.948 g·L^{-1} instead of 1.22 g·L^{-1}. The hot air inside a hot air balloon has a significantly lower density than the surrounding air, and this difference determines the lifting capacity of the balloon. As the air inside the balloon cools, the density difference will decrease and the lifting ability will decrease, causing the balloon to descend to the ground unless a gas burner is used to reheat the trapped air (Figure 8.36).

Airships Live Again

Sometimes an old technology can regain popularity. A good example of this is the airship. With the development of new fabrics, lower-density structural materials, and small powerful engines, there has been a renewed interest in this means of staying airborne. The ability to stay in the air for extensive periods of time and to hover silently has many applications. For years, the U.S. Coastguard used radar-equipped airships to hover over the Caribbean to spot drug smugglers in small aircraft. An airship has been used to study the upper canopies of the rain forest, where it can gently lower an observation platform onto the tops of trees without disturbing the forest canopy occupants as would a helicopter (Figure 8.37). Heavy equipment, such as oil and mineral exploration equipment, can be lifted by airships into environmentally sensitive areas without the need for building roads. As well, logging can be accomplished in rugged terrain by airlifting the logs out with less environmental damage.

FIGURE 8.37 This modern airship is carrying a "treetop raft" in French Guyana. The airship is part of an expedition that will study the insects, plants, and animals in the rain forest.

Determining the Molar Mass of an Ideal Gas

The ideal gas law is of particular use in determining the molar mass of an unknown gas. The most common experimental procedure involves pumping the air out of a glass bulb of known volume, measuring the mass of the evacuated bulb, and then filling it with the gas of unknown molar mass at a known temperature and pressure. The mass of the bulb and its contents is then measured, and by subtracting the mass of the evacuated bulb, you can then determine the mass of the unknown gas. The required molar mass can then be calculated as shown in Example 12.

EXAMPLE 12

At 100°C, a glass bulb with a volume of 248 mL contains 1.24 g of a compound, X, in the gas phase. If the pressure of the gas is 101 kPa, what is the molar mass of compound X?

Given
$m_X = 1.24$ g, $P = 101$ kPa, $V = 248$ mL $= 0.248$ L, $T = 273 + 100 = 373$ K

Required
molar mass of compound X, $M_X = ?$ g·mol^{-1}

Analysis
$P, V, T \rightarrow n_X$ (using $PV = nRT$)

$m_X, n_X \rightarrow M_X \left(\text{using } M = \dfrac{m}{n} \right)$

PRACTICE PROBLEM

A chemist isolated an unreactive gas. At 30.0°C and 98.0 kPa, it was found that 2.00 L of the gas had a mass of 6.52 g. Calculate the molar mass of the gas. Deduce the identity of the gas.

Solution

$$n_X = \frac{PV}{RT} = \frac{(101 \text{ kPa})(0.248 \text{ L})}{(8.31 \text{ kPa·L·mol}^{-1}\text{·K}^{-1})(373 \text{ K})} = 8.08 \times 10^{-3} \text{ mol}$$

$$M_X = \frac{1.24 \text{ g}}{8.08 \times 10^{-3} \text{ mol}} = 153 \text{ g·mol}^{-1}$$

Statement

The molar mass of compound X is 153 g·mol^{-1}.

Determining the Molecular Formula of a Gas

You learned how the empirical formula of a compound can be determined from its percent composition. You also saw that the molar mass of the compound is required in order to find its molecular formula once the empirical formula is known. In this section, you have just seen how the molar mass of a compound can be determined experimentally. The following example shows how the ideal gas law, in combination with percent composition data, can be used to determine the molecular formula of an unknown compound.

EXAMPLE 13

One of the components of gasoline is benzene, a compound that consists of 92.24% carbon and 7.76% hydrogen. When a sample of 15.62 g of benzene was placed in a sealed container with a volume of 3.78 L and heated to 110°C, the benzene vaporized and the resulting pressure inside the container was 168 kPa. Determine the molecular formula of benzene.

Given
C = 92.24%, H = 7.76%

$m_{C_6H_6} = 15.62$ g, $P = 168$ kPa, $V_{C_6H_6} = 3.78$ L, $T = 273 + 110 = 383$ K

Required
molecular formula of benzene

Analysis
The problem is in three parts:

1. Use the percent composition to find the empirical formula of benzene.

2. Use P, V, and T in an ideal gas law calculation to find the moles of benzene.

3. Knowing the mass and moles of benzene, find the molar mass and molecular formula.

Solution

Part 1
In 100.0 g of compound, $m_C = 92.24$ g; $m_H = 7.76$ g

$$n_C = 92.24 \text{ g C} \times \frac{1 \text{ mol C}}{12.01 \text{ g C}} = 7.680 \text{ mol C}$$

Part 2

$$n_H = 7.76 \text{ g H} \times \frac{1 \text{ mol H}}{1.01 \text{ g H}} = 7.68 \text{ mol H}$$

Ratio of $n_C : n_H = \dfrac{7.680 \text{ mol C}}{7.68 \text{ mol}} : \dfrac{7.68 \text{ mol H}}{7.68 \text{ mol}} = 1 \text{ C} : 1 \text{ H}$

The empirical formula is CH.

Part 3

$$n_{benzene} = \frac{PV}{RT} = \frac{(168 \text{ kPa})(3.78 \text{ L})}{(8.31 \text{ kPa·L·mol}^{-1}\text{·K}^{-1})(383 \text{ K})} = 0.200 \text{ mol}$$

Part 4

$$M_{benzene} = \frac{15.62 \text{ g}}{0.200 \text{ mol}} = 78.10 \text{ g·mol}^{-1}$$

Empirical-formula mass of benzene is:

12.01 g + 1.01 g = 13.02 g

and its molar mass is 78.10 g·mol^{-1}. So,

$$\frac{\text{molar mass}}{\text{empirical formula mass}} = \frac{78.10 \text{ g}}{13.02 \text{ g}} = 6.00$$

molecular formula = 6 × empirical formula

Therefore, the molecular formula is C_6H_6.

Statement

The molecular formula of benzene is C_6H_6.

PRACTICE PROBLEM

A certain liquid compound contains 85.6% carbon and 14.4% hydrogen.
a) Calculate the empirical formula of the compound.
b) When 0.781 g of this liquid was evaporated in a 226-mL container, the vapour produced exerted a pressure of 101 kPa at 121°C. Determine the molar mass of the compound.
c) Use the results of your calculations in parts a) and b) to determine the molecular formula of the compound.

Section 8.4 Review

Understanding Concepts

1. Explain why aerosol containers have a warning label that says, "Do not incinerate."

2. Describe in your own words what causes geysers to erupt.

Applying Inquiry/Communication Skills

3. If a sample of gas is heated to double its Kelvin temperature and its volume is halved, predict the effect on the pressure.

4. A balloon is filled with 2.2 L of gas at a pressure of 108 kPa and a temperature of 21°C. It is then taken down to the bottom of the ocean where the pressure is 11.8 MPa and the temperature is 6°C. Calculate the new volume of the balloon.

5. The density of a certain noble gas at STP is 5.86 g·L^{-1}. Determine the molar mass of the gas, and identify it.

6. The ill-fated airship Hindenburg contained 18.0 t of hydrogen gas. Calculate the volume occupied by this mass of hydrogen at a temperature of 27°C and a pressure of 105 kPa.

7. A Goodyear blimp holds 5.74×10^6 L of helium at 17°C and a pressure of 101 kPa. Calculate the mass of helium in the blimp.

Making Connections

8. Recently scientists have tried to harness volcanic steam (geothermal energy) to produce usable heat and power. Using electronic and print resources, research the results of their efforts. Make a list of criteria to assess whether this is a practical source of power for the future.

8.5 Vapour Pressure and Dalton's Law

Key Understandings

When you have completed this section, you will be able to:

■ explain Dalton's law of partial pressures
■ solve quantitative problems involving Dalton's law of partial pressures
■ describe how knowledge of gases is applied to other areas
■ use appropriate scientific vocabulary to communicate ideas related to gases

FIGURE 8.38 In a sealed terrarium, the air is saturated with water vapour, resulting in a lush growth of plants.

FIGURE 8.39 When the relative humidity temporarily exceeds 100% and the air temperature is above 0°C, a fog forms. Fog is small suspended particles of liquid water.

The air that you breathe contains water in its gaseous state. You can deduce this from the observation that wet surfaces dry up. On a smaller scale, the level of water in a glass of water left for a day will drop measurably. The concentration of water in the air is commonly referred to as humidity. If the humidity is low, your skin becomes dry and flaky; if it is high, you feel "sticky."

John Dalton, an English science teacher, performed many experiments that involved measuring the water content of air. In the course of his experiments, Dalton found that if water is placed in a sealed container, some of the liquid evaporates to form water vapour, that is, water in the gas phase (Figure 8.38). He also observed that the water vapour exerted a pressure on the walls of the container. This pressure is known as the **vapour pressure** of water.

At any given temperature and pressure, only a certain proportion of a liquid will evaporate. The air above the liquid is said to be saturated when it can no longer hold any more vapour of that liquid. Consequently, at any given temperature, there is a maximum value for the vapour pressure of a liquid. This maximum value is called the **saturated vapour pressure** at that temperature.

In the atmosphere, the vapour pressure is usually equal to the saturated value only during the middle of a rainstorm. Normally, the vapour pressure is less than the saturated value. It is for this reason that the term relative humidity is used. **Relative humidity** is defined as the ratio of the actual vapour pressure to the saturated vapour pressure at that temperature expressed as a percent (Figure 8.39).

Freeze-drying Foods

Have you ever noticed that ice cubes in the freezer shrink with time? This is because water as a solid exerts a vapour pressure (less than 1 kPa). That is, a very small proportion of the water molecules in the solid state have enough energy to escape into the gas phase, a phenomenon called **sublimation**. Most of these molecules will resolidify on the colder walls of the freezer, thereby reducing the vapour pressure. To re-establish the vapour pressure, more molecules will escape from the surface of the ice cubes. What do you think would happen if you left the ice cubes in the freezer for a very long time?

This same process is used in freeze-drying foods. Freeze-dried foods are particularly convenient for hikers and astronauts, and in emergencies (Figure 8.40). When all the water has been extracted from foods, they are much lower in mass. In addition, without water, bacteria cannot grow on the food. To freeze-dry a food item, it is first cooled below 0°C. Then the container is connected to a vacuum pump. The pump will remove the water molecules as they vaporize to establish the vapour pressure. Ultimately, all the water molecules are removed, leaving the freeze-dried solid behind.

FIGURE 8.40 Freeze-dried foods are a boon for hikers and for emergencies. The freeze-drying process relies on the vapour pressure of water.

The Boiling Point of a Liquid

Every liquid evaporates until either the air above that liquid is saturated, as in a closed container, or all the liquid has vapourized, as in an open container. In other words, every liquid exerts a vapour pressure, and this vapour pressure increases with increasing temperature. For water, the variation of the saturated vapour pressure with temperature is shown in Figure 8.41.

When the vapour pressure equals the external pressure, the liquid begins to boil. The temperature at which this occurs is called the boiling point of the liquid. The **boiling point** of a liquid is correctly defined as the temperature at which its vapour pressure equals the external pressure. As atmospheric pressure varies from one location to another, you can say that the *normal* boiling point of a liquid is the temperature at which its vapour pressure is 101.325 kPa. It is a widely accepted myth that water boils at exactly 100°C at this pressure. In fact, very precise measurements of the boiling point of water have shown that, at 101.325 kPa pressure, water actually boils at 99.975°C (Table 8.8). Fortunately, it is rare that such precision is required, and, for practical purposes, you can say that water boils at 100°C at a pressure of 101 kPa.

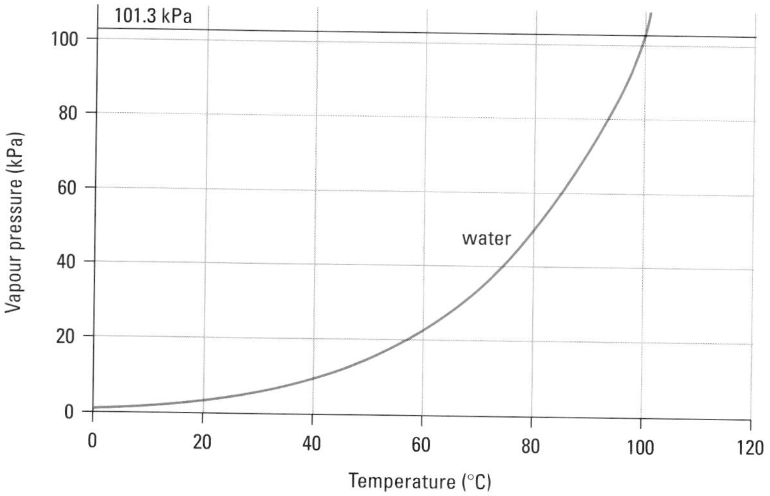

FIGURE 8.41 The variation of the vapour pressure of water with temperature

TABLE 8.8 Variation of the Boiling Point of Water with Pressure

Boiling Point (°C)	Vapour Pressure (kPa)
99.610	100.000
99.975	101.325
100.000	101.414

At sea level, then, water boils at a temperature close to (but rarely exactly) 100°C (Figure 8.42). However, at high altitudes where the air pressure is significantly less, water boils at a much lower temperature (Figure 8.43). For example, at an altitude of 5000 m, where the air pressure is only about 53 kPa, water will boil at a temperature of 83°C. Consequently, in cities at high altitudes, such as Mexico City or Denver, Colorado, hot coffee or soup made using near-boiling water can never be as hot as in other cities closer to sea level.

Sea Level

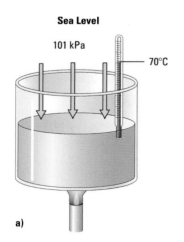

a)

Sea Level

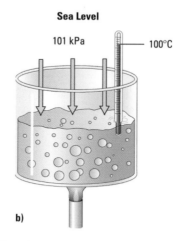

b)

Atop Mount Everest

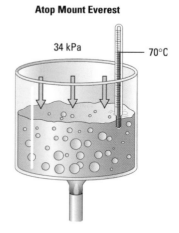

FIGURE 8.42 a) At sea level, at a temperature of 70°C, water will not boil since its vapour pressure is only 30 kPa, much less than the external pressure. b) At sea level, water will boil when its vapour pressure matches that of the external pressure, typically at 100°C, assuming the atmospheric pressure is about 101 kPa.

FIGURE 8.43 Water will boil at a temperature of 70°C on top of Mount Everest where the external pressure is the same as the water vapour pressure at that temperature (34 kPa).

Comparing the Vapour Pressures of Different Substances

Every substance has its own corresponding unique vapour pressure curve. Figure 8.44 shows the vapour pressures and boiling points of some common liquids. Notice that the higher the vapour pressure at room temperature, the lower the boiling point. These substances with a high vapour pressure at room temperature are said to be **volatile**.

Some organic liquids, such as acetone (the main ingredient in most types of nail polish remover), have a high vapour pressure at room temperature. Such compounds will evaporate rapidly if left in open containers (Figure 8.45). These liquids should always be stored in sealed containers to slow the evaporation process.

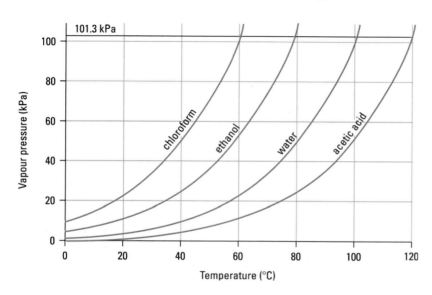

FIGURE 8.44 The variation of vapour pressure with temperature for some common liquids

The Theory of Vapour Pressure

The increase in the vapour pressure of a substance with increasing temperature can be explained using the kinetic-molecular theory. Up to now, our discussions have focussed on the average kinetic energy of the molecules of a substance. By stating "average," we imply that some molecules have more energy and others have less than the average. Some of the high-energy molecules will have enough energy to overcome the attractive forces in the solid or liquid phase. These molecules will escape from the surface, enter the gas phase, and provide the vapour pressure.

When the temperature of a substance reaches its melting point, only a very small portion of the molecules will have sufficient kinetic energy to escape to the gas phase. As a result, at the melting point, the vapour pressure is very low. As the temperature increases, the average kinetic energy of the molecules increases, and so will the proportion of molecules with high enough energies to escape the liquid surface. Therefore, the vapour pressure increases.

Why do different liquids have different boiling points? Substances are held in the liquid state by the attraction between particles (molecules). If this attraction is strong, only a small number of molecules will have enough energy to overcome it and escape into the gas phase. If the attraction is weak, more particles will escape. Therefore, at any given temperature, liquids with strong attractive forces between molecules have a lower vapour pressure than liquids with weak attractive forces between molecules.

Vapour Pressure in the Electric Light Bulb: Some Hot Chemistry

Why does a light bulb burn out? You have probably noticed how the top of the bulb is usually blackened when the bulb fails. This is a clue as to what has happened. The key part of the bulb is the filament, the very fine-coiled wire suspended across the centre of the bulb. This filament is made of tungsten, the metal with the highest melting point (3422°C). All warm bodies emit electromagnetic radiation. You, at 37°C, emit radiation in the infrared part of the spectrum. To emit radiation in the middle of the visible region, the wire in a light bulb must be at a temperature of about 2500°C (iron melts at 1537°C), so tungsten is the best choice. But at 2500°C, even tungsten has a measurable vapour pressure, so atom after atom sublimes off the surface of the hot wire and condenses on the cool glass envelope, until finally the wire becomes too thin and breaks.

The evaporation of the tungsten can be slowed down by having a gas in the envelope (Figure 8.46). This causes some of the tungsten atoms to collide with the gas molecules, lose their energy, and condense back on the filament surface. Nitrogen or argon are usually used, but premium bulbs contain krypton. The atoms of this gas have a much higher atomic mass and are more effective in preventing the vaporization of tungsten.

a)

b)

FIGURE 8.45   a) All liquids (and solids) exert a vapour pressure. Here you can see the red-brown vapour rising from red-black liquid bromine. b) Over time, the vapour diffuses away into the atmosphere. If you left the cylinder for a few days, what would remain?

FIGURE 8.46   A tungsten filament light bulb—vapour pressure in action

Decision-Making Skills

Defining the Issue
Developing Assessment Criteria
▷ Researching the Issue
▷ Analyzing Data and Information
▷ Proposing a Course of Action
▷ Justifying the Course of Action
▷ Communicating Your Proposal

Case Study

Personal Protective Equipment and Dimethylmercury

BACKGROUND INFORMATION

In August 1996, Dr. Karen Wetterhahn, a chemistry professor at Dartmouth College, spilled a few drops of dimethylmercury, $(CH_3)_2Hg$, on one of her latex gloves while transferring some of the compound into a narrow glass tube. Dimethylmercury is a highly toxic, volatile liquid and is lethal at a dose of approximately 400 mg of mercury (the equivalent of a few drops). No one realized at the time that this single exposure to dimethylmercury would result in Wetterhahn's death in June 1997. This tragedy raised many questions as to how her death occurred, what could be done about personal protection against a substance as lethal as dimethylmercury, and whether dimethylmercury should continue to be manufactured and used.

During the investigation of this accident, it was found that the Material Safety Data Sheets (MSDSs) from the manufacturer and supplier of dimethylmercury provided erroneous information on the appropriate gloves to be worn when handling this dangerous compound. Studies by Dartmouth College found that dimethylmercury could penetrate latex

or PVC (polyvinylchloride) gloves within less than 15 seconds. It was later found that a specialized glove (Silver Shield®) was the only one to offer adequate protection against dimethylmercury.

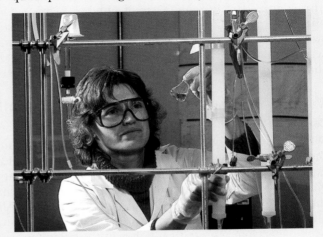

FIGURE 8.47 Karen Wetterhahn was an internationally recognized bio-inorganic chemist whose research focussed on the biologic toxicity of heavy metals.

Analyzing the Issue

1. Use electronic and print resources to research the uses of dimethylmercury. Describe the toxicity of dimethylmercury and form an opinion as to whether its uses outweigh its risks.

2. Dimethylmercury is a form of organic mercury and is more dangerous than mercury itself. Wetterhahn handled dimethylmercury in a ventilated fume hood. Before she performed the transfer of the compound, a colleague chilled the dimethylmercury vial in ice water. Explain the significance of performing this procedure when handling this compound.

3. Mercury and some mercury compounds are used in several industries. Discuss the origin of the phrase "mad as a hatter" in *Alice in Wonderland*. Describe the events that occurred in Minamata Bay, Japan, during the 1950s, in Lake St. Clair during the 1970s, and in Iraq in 1972 that increased our awareness of the toxicity of mercury compounds.

4. Develop an action plan that could be implemented by chemical manufacturers and personal protective equipment suppliers that would provide accurate MSDS information.

5. Share your action plan with the rest of the class.

Gas Mixtures: Dalton's Law of Partial Pressures

In medical operations, patients are given gas mixtures containing oxygen (so they can continue breathing) and an anesthetic gas (to render them unconscious). It is very crucial that the mixture contains just the right molar proportion of the two gases. How can you make up the correct gas mixtures? Fortunately, there is a direct relationship between the molar composition and the pressure of each constituent gas (called **partial pressure**).

The crucial step came from work by John Dalton. His gas studies led to the formulation of the **law of partial pressures** (Figure 8.48). This law states that:

The total pressure of a mixture of gases is equal to the sum of the partial pressures of the component gases.

For example, if you take an empty flask and fill it with helium gas to a pressure of 45 kPa, then add nitrogen gas until the total pressure is 102 kPa, Dalton's law tells you that the pressure due to the added nitrogen gas is given by:

$$P_{total} = P_{He} + P_{N_2}$$
$$P_{N_2} = P_{total} - P_{He}$$
$$= 102 \text{ kPa} - 45 \text{ kPa}$$
$$= 57 \text{ kPa}$$

The law of partial pressures is most useful when it is combined with the ideal gas law. This enables chemists to relate the pressures in gas mixtures to their molar composition. Consider a mixture of gases A and B that has a pressure P_{total} in a volume V and at a temperature T, containing n_{total} moles of gas. Using the ideal gas law, you can write:

$$P_{total}V = n_{total}RT$$

If one of the components, A, of this mixture consists of n_A moles of gas exerting a partial pressure P_A, the ideal gas law can be applied to this single component:

$$P_A V = n_A RT$$

Dividing one expression into the other gives the following equation:

$$\frac{P_A V}{P_{total}V} = \frac{n_A RT}{n_{total}RT}$$

Simplifying gives the following equation:

$$\frac{P_A}{P_{total}} = \frac{n_A}{n_{total}}$$

which can be rearranged to an expression for the partial pressure of A:

$$P_A = P_{total} \times \frac{n_A}{n_{total}}$$

The fraction n_A/n_{total} (that is, the number of moles of gas A divided by the total number of moles of gas) is called the **mole fraction** of A, symbol X_A.

Science Is about the Unanticipated: John Dalton (1766–1844)

There is a lot of pressure for scientists to do "useful" research. But research is rarely predictable. Sometimes what is thought to be important turns out to be a dead end, while some trivial topic can become a core piece of knowledge. The work of John Dalton illustrates this dilemma. His first and lifelong interest was meteorology. For 57 years, he made detailed and copious notes of the weather, looking for patterns in rainfall and temperature. Using this information, he hoped to predict the weather for months and years ahead, thereby making his contribution to society. Although this was a fruitless task, he did discover the law of partial pressures.

What eventually brought fame and recognition to Dalton were his musings on the nature of matter, *The Atomic Theory of Matter*, something that at the time was regarded as unimportant. In fact, when he published his ideas, they were strongly criticized. Yet it was the atomic theory that laid the groundwork for 19th century chemistry and gave him eternal fame. Unfortunately, Dalton never explained how he came up with the concept.

The conflict between pure and applied science is much greater in

FIGURE 8.50 John Dalton, founder of modern atomic theory

our modern times. Most scientific research needs large amounts of funding for staff salaries and equipment purchases. Government and industry are reluctant to pour money

into projects that will provide only new knowledge. They usually want the research to lead to new products that can be marketed or that solve particular problems. Military funding, a major source of science dollars in the United States, is particularly focussed on defined goals. Yet without pure research, it is impossible to wander off into the realms of the unknown, which may open new avenues of research that we cannot now see. Would scientists like Dalton be allowed to work on atomic theory today or would they be told to stick to their main objective?

FIGURE 8.51 Laser eye surgery. Lasers were invented as a result of studying energy levels in atoms. At the time, no one imagined their potential use for many things, from supermarket checkout counters to medical procedures. It is often these pure science discoveries that provide the greatest leaps in applied science and technology.

A similar expression can be derived for the partial pressure of component B of the gas mixture, that is:

$$P_B = P_{total} \times \frac{n_B}{n_{total}}$$

This relationship between mole fraction and partial pressure is applied in Example 14.

Discovering Chemistry — Detecting the Vapour Pressure of Acetone

How can you qualitatively detect the vapour pressure of a substance?

Materials
- acetone
- small test tube
- rubber stopper

CAUTION: Make sure there are no flames in the room!

1. Holding the test tube between two fingers at the neck, add about 10 drops of acetone and stopper the tube tightly. Shake thoroughly, making sure you continue to hold the tube just at the neck.
2. Gently remove the stopper. Dispose of the acetone into an organic waste container.

- Describe what you heard when the stopper was removed. Explain your observation.
- For this experiment, suggest why it was important not to wrap your hand around the tube.
- Give a reason why you used acetone rather than water for this activity.

EXAMPLE 14

A mixture of 6.0 g of argon gas and 8.0 g of oxygen gas has a total pressure of 66 kPa. Calculate the partial pressure exerted by each gas.

Given

$m_{Ar} = 6.0 \text{ g}, m_{O_2} = 8.0 \text{ g}, P_{total} = 66 \text{ kPa}$

Required

pressures of argon and oxygen,

$P_{Ar}, P_{O_2} = ? \text{ kPa}$

Analysis

$m_{Ar} \rightarrow n_{Ar}$ (using $M_{Ar} = 39.95 \text{ g·mol}^{-1}$)

$m_{O_2} \rightarrow n_{O_2}$ (using $M_{O_2} = 32.00 \text{ g·mol}^{-1}$)

$$P_{Ar} = P_{total} \times \left(\frac{n_{Ar}}{n_{Ar} + n_{O_2}}\right)$$

$$P_{O_2} = P_{total} \times \left(\frac{n_{O_2}}{n_{Ar} + n_{O_2}}\right)$$

Solution

$$n_{Ar} = 6.0 \text{ } \cancel{\text{g Ar}} \times \frac{1 \text{ mol Ar}}{39.95 \text{ } \cancel{\text{g Ar}}} = 0.15 \text{ mol Ar}$$

$$n_{O_2} = 8.0 \text{ } \cancel{\text{g } O_2} \times \frac{1 \text{ mol } O_2}{32.00 \text{ } \cancel{\text{g } O_2}} = 0.25 \text{ mol } O_2$$

▶

WEBLINK

SIMULATION

For a simulation to show how evaporation works, go to **www.pearsoned.ca/chemistry11**.

1. A flask contains 0.50 mol of nitrogen gas and 2.50 mol of carbon dioxide gas. The total pressure in the flask is 150 kPa. Determine the partial pressure of each gas.

2. 5.0 g of hydrogen gas and 50.0 g of neon gas are placed in a container to give a total pressure of 100 kPa. Calculate the partial pressure of each gas.

$$P_{Ar} = 66 \text{ kPa} \times \left(\frac{0.15 \text{ mol}}{0.15 \text{ mol} + 0.25 \text{ mol}} \right) = 25 \text{ kPa}$$

$$P_{O_2} = 66 \text{ kPa} \times \left(\frac{0.25 \text{ mol}}{0.15 \text{ mol} + 0.25 \text{ mol}} \right) = 41 \text{ kPa}$$

(Note that, as a check, the sum of the partial pressures must equal the total pressure, and 25 + 41 does add up to 66.)

Statement
The partial pressure of argon gas is 25 kPa, and that of oxygen is 41 kPa.

Gases in Solutions

The discussion of vapour pressure focussed on the gas and liquid states of the same substance. Equally important is life's dependence on gases dissolved in other liquids. The most crucial example is the solubility of oxygen in water. Like you, fish require oxygen. However, they obtain the oxygen from that dissolved in the water, using their gills. It is generally accepted that life developed in marine environments. Without the presence of dissolved gases in water, many organisms would not have evolved, and the kind of life that would exist on Earth would likely have been very different.

To what extent do gases dissolve in water? Table 8.9 shows the solubility of some common gases in water. The first thing to notice is that most gases are not very soluble in water—much less so than many solids such as sugar or salt. Nearly all gases have solubilities similar to that of oxygen or nitrogen, that is, about 10^{-2} g·L^{-1}. Carbon dioxide is one of the few gases with a higher solubility. This can be explained in part by its chemical reaction with the water:

$$CO_2(g) + H_2O(l) \rightarrow H_2CO_3(aq)$$

This equation can also be written with double-headed arrows to indicate that it is reversible. That is, as the temperature of the solution increases, more carbon dioxide will form and there will be less carbonic acid.

$$CO_2(g) + H_2O(l) \rightleftharpoons H_2CO_3(aq)$$

TABLE 8.9 Solubility of Common Gases in Water

Gas	Solubility (g·L^{-1}) at 20°C
O_2	0.04
N_2	0.02
CO_2	1.7

Gas Solubility and Anesthesia

Why does inhaling a gaseous anesthetic render you unconscious? The way in which anesthetics, and vapours such as glue solvents and gasoline, function has intrigued chemists and biochemists for over a hundred years. It is unthinkable to consider a medical operation without an anesthetic today, yet for most of recorded history, all surgical procedures, including amputation, were performed without any painkillers. Soldiers were given a bullet to bite on, hence the origin of the phrase "to bite the bullet," meaning to face a hard task rather than avoiding it.

The first inhalation anesthetic was used in 1846, and from then until the middle of the 20th century, good anesthetics were discovered by trial and error. Scientists now understand much of the mechanism of inhalation anesthesia, and gas solubility is a key part of the mechanism (Figure 8.52). A good anesthetic must have the following properties:

- It must be non-toxic, with minimal side effects, and any breakdown products in the body must have a low toxicity.
- It must be nonflammable.
- It must have a high vapour pressure to ensure that a high concentration can enter the lungs (i.e., it must be a gas or a liquid with a boiling point only slightly above room temperature).
- It must have a reasonably high blood (water) solubility to enable it to be transported from the lungs to the brain (but not so high that the anesthetic will stay in the blood long after the operation has ended).
- It must have a high solubility in the fatty tissues (lipids) of the brain so that it will concentrate in the cells of the central nervous system and cause unconsciousness.

Some current anesthetic gases are dinitrogen oxide (nitrous oxide), N_2O; halothane, $CF_3CHClBr$; and isoflurane, $CF_3CHClOCHF_2$. You might think that by now chemists would have discovered the perfect anesthetic gas, but this is not the case. Some of the current gases have pungent odours, while others have side effects in some patients. Consequently, the synthesis of new and better anesthetic gases is still a very active field of research in chemistry.

WEBLINK

Anesthetics have become vital to hospital surgery. Research the history of anesthesia and explain why most of the early anesthetics are no longer used. Begin your research at **www.pearsoned.ca/chemistry11**.

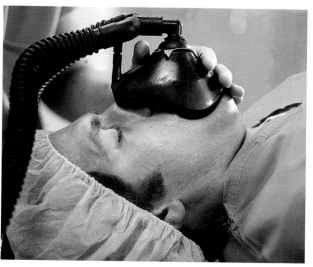

FIGURE 8.52 Inhalation anesthesia depends on the vapour pressure and the solubility of the gaseous anesthetic.

The Effect of Temperature on Gas Solubility

If you take a glass of cold water and let it warm up to room temperature, small bubbles of air will form on the inside of the glass. Warming water close to boiling produces even more bubbles. The reason for this is that the solubility of a gas decreases with temperature (Figure 8.53). As the water warms, less air can stay dissolved in the water. Many of the air-containing bubbles will form on the surface of the glass and remain there. What is the composition of the bubbles likely to be?

The converse, that gases dissolve better at lower temperatures, has a major effect on fishing resources. The largest fish stocks tend to be in colder waters, where the concentration of dissolved oxygen is greater, rather than in warmer waters. It is for this reason that the cold waters of the Labrador current, off the east coast of Canada, were—until overfishing—such a rich fishing area. The species of fish found in certain areas are also dependent on dissolved oxygen concentrations. For example, salmon and trout (two fish with high metabolisms) need oxygen-rich cold water, while slow-swimming catfish can tolerate oxygen-deficient warm water.

FIGURE 8.53 The solubility of gases in water decreases as the temperature increases. Why is this a concern at the cooling water outlets of power plants?

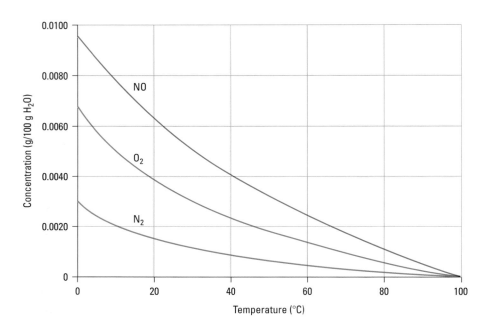

The Effect of Pressure on Gas Solubility

If you open a sealed container of a carbonated beverage, it will froth and foam (Figure 8.54). The reason for this is the decrease in gas solubility with decreasing pressure. The relationship between gas solubility and gas pressure was discovered by William Henry, a British chemist. This relationship, called **Henry's law**, is a very simple one. The mole fraction, X, of a gas in water is proportional to the applied pressure, P, or:

$P = KX$ where K is the Henry's law constant for that gas

Consequently, when the pressure in a can or bottle of a carbonated beverage is released, less gas can dissolve in water, so the gas foams out.

Gases and Divers

Henry's law is of great importance to divers. As divers descend, the pressure increases. A higher proportion of the air that they breathe dissolves in their bloodstream. You can use Henry's law to determine how much of this air ends up in their blood. Let us suppose that the mole fraction of a gas in water at atmospheric pressure (100 kPa) is X_0, and that at a depth of 40 m is X_{40}. The pressure at this depth is about 600 kPa.

Therefore, 100 kPa = KX_0 and 600 kPa = KX_{40}

Dividing one equation by the other gives:

$$\frac{600 \text{ kPa}}{100 \text{ kPa}} = \frac{KX_{40}}{KX_0}$$

$$\frac{X_{40}}{X_0} = 6.00$$

Gases are, therefore, six times more soluble in water (or blood plasma) at a depth of 40 m than they are at atmospheric pressure. It is not the descent that provides the challenge but the ascent. As the pressure is reduced, the

FIGURE 8.54 When the cap of a pop bottle is removed, the pressure in the bottle decreases, causing some of the dissolved carbon dioxide to foam out.

gases will be released from solution in the bloodstream, forming tiny bubbles. Oxygen is not a problem because it reacts chemically with hemoglobin molecules to give oxygenated red blood corpuscles. Nor is carbon dioxide since it can combine with water to form carbonic acid, which can readily be carried to the lungs and exhaled. Nitrogen is the problem. In fact, there are two distinct problems with nitrogen.

The first problem is nitrogen narcosis. Under pressure, the solubility of nitrogen gas in the fatty brain tissue increases, causing an effect similar to glue solvent sniffing. Nitrogen narcosis, or "rapture of the deep" as it is commonly called, causes divers to hallucinate or to forget time and run out of air.

The second effect appears when divers begin to ascend toward the surface. As the pressure is reduced, the solubility of nitrogen in the blood decreases. The nitrogen released into the gas phase forms bubbles in the bloodstream. These bubbles can cause severe pain (the bends) and even death. Therefore, divers have to ascend slowly, giving time for the nitrogen to be exhaled. In an emergency, a decompression—or more accurately, a recompression—chamber is used that recompresses the diver, redissolving the nitrogen gas. The pressure is then reduced at a slower rate.

FIGURE 8.55 Deep diving requires helium-oxygen mixtures.

For deep diving, the solution has been to use an oxygen-helium gas mixture rather than air (Figure 8.55). There are two advantages to using helium instead of nitrogen. First, helium has a much lower solubility in water than nitrogen, and second, the Henry's law constant is 1.6 times that of nitrogen. So helium's solubility does not increase as fast as that of nitrogen (in fact, only $1/1.6 = 0.6$ times the rate of nitrogen). As a result, helium is much less prone to bubble formation in the bloodstream with reducing pressure.

Scuba divers also depend on Boyle's law. As they dive, the external pressure increases dramatically. If they were free diving, their lungs would be compressed from a lung capacity of about 4 L to 6 L in a fit adult to about the volume of an apple. The gas supplied to a scuba diver's lungs must, therefore, be at the same pressure as the water pressure to keep the lungs inflated. To accomplish this, every scuba apparatus has a gas regulator, which ensures that the gas pressure from the cylinders is exactly the same value as that of the surrounding water. This means that divers can breath normally. However, as they return to the surface, it is important for them to keep exhaling so that their internal lung pressure will reduce to match the decreasing water pressure as they rise.

Section 8.5 Review

Understanding Concepts

1. Explain the meaning of Dalton's law of partial pressures in your own words.

2. Describe how to calculate the partial pressure of a gas in a mixture.

3. Describe how vapour pressure is related to humidity and sublimation.

4. A group on a mountaineering expedition has gone climbing up a mountain until they reach the peak at a height of 3000 m. At this point, they set up camp and decide to make a pot of tea. Using a propane torch, they boil the water, only to discover that the water is not really hot. Explain how this could happen.

Applying Inquiry/ Communication Skills

5. Clean, dry air is a mixture of nitrogen, oxygen, and argon with small quantities of other gases. If the partial pressure of nitrogen is 79 kPa and that of argon is 1 kPa, calculate the partial pressure of oxygen in the atmosphere. Assume that the atmospheric pressure is 100 kPa.

6. A flask contains a mixture of hydrogen and carbon dioxide and has a total pressure of 94 kPa. If the partial pressure of hydrogen is 22 kPa, calculate the mole fraction of hydrogen in the mixture.

7. A common gas mixture used in lasers contains 12.5% by mass of neon, with the remainder being helium. If the total pressure of the gas mixture in the laser is 105 kPa, calculate the partial pressure of each of the component gases.

8. A particular compound has a vapour pressure of 7.0 kPa at 25°C compared to 2.3 kPa for water at the same temperature. Determine the boiling point of the compound.

9. Figure 8.56 below shows how the vapour pressure of ethanol varies with temperature.

Vapour pressure of ethanol vs. temperature

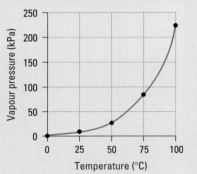

FIGURE 8.56

Determine at what temperature ethanol will boil under conditions of standard pressure.

Making Connections

10. In some ways, it is more dangerous to exercise in conditions of high humidity than low humidity. Research the validity of this statement, and prepare a brief information paragraph for a fitness newsletter specifying the reasons that support this statement.

11. Most scientific research needs large amounts of funding, yet agencies that can provide the funding usually want some gains in the form of new products that can be marketed or that solve particular problems. Brainstorm a list of issues related to this statement, and write a PMI essay summarizing your ideas.

Investigation 1 (Section 8.2)

Inquiry Skills

Initiating and Planning
▶ Applying Technical Skills
▶ Using Tools, Materials, and Equipment
▶ Conducting and Recording
▶ Analyzing and Interpreting
▶ Concluding and Communicating

Pressure-Volume Relationship of a Gas

In this activity, a confined amount of air is compressed to study the effect of an increase in pressure on volume. The pressure of the trapped air is gradually increased, while the change in volume is observed. The pressure-volume data is then plotted on a graph to identify a simple mathematical relationship.

Problem

To investigate the pressure-volume relationship for a gas.

Materials

- pressure gauge or pressure sensor with interface
- 20-mL syringe
- very short length of connecting tubing
- spreadsheet program or graphing calculator

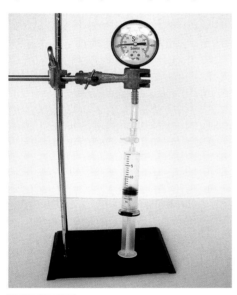

FIGURE 8.57

Procedure (done in pairs)

1. Take the 20-mL syringe and pull the piston back to the 20-mL mark. Connect the syringe to the gauge or pressure sensor with the tubing. Ensure that the tubing is tight-fitting. The gauge pressure should read close to zero. Record the reading of volume and gauge pressure.

2. One partner should then push the piston a short distance while the other partner records the new volume and pressure readings.

3. Repeat step #2 until at least six data points have been recorded. If using a pressure gauge, do not exceed the maximum recommended pressure of 250 mm Hg or 33 kPa.

Analyzing and Interpreting

1. Calculate the absolute pressure readings for the measurements you made.

2. Using a graphing calculator or a spreadsheet program, plot volume against pressure and then volume against the reciprocal of pressure.

3. Determine what the line graph shows about the relationship between:
    a) pressure versus volume
    b) pressure versus 1/volume

Concluding and Communicating

4. Describe the shapes of each of your graphs.

5. State in words the relationship between pressure and volume. Under what conditions is this relationship true?

6. State, as a mathematical equation, the relationship between pressure and volume using your result from 3 b). What is the name of this law?

7. Extrapolate to find the origin of the line in your second graph.

8. Identify the major sources of error in this experiment.

9. Explain the inverse relationship between volume and pressure using the kinetic-molecular theory.

Extending

10. If you had used a different gas, for example, carbon dioxide, predict if the graph would be the same or different. Explain your reasoning.

11. Explain why weather balloons are under-inflated when they are released.

Investigation 2 (Section 8.2)

Pressure-Temperature Relationship of a Gas

Inquiry Skills

▶ Initiating and Planning
▶ Applying Technical Skills
▶ Using Tools, Materials, and Equipment
▶ Conducting and Recording
▶ Analyzing and Interpreting
▶ Concluding and Communicating

Problem

To determine the relationship between the temperature and pressure of a gas.

Materials

- ice
- water
- beaker, slightly larger than the flask
- filter flask
- hot plate
- pressure gauge or pressure sensor with interface
- one-hole stopper with fitted thermometer or temperature sensor
- connecting tubing
- spreadsheet program or graphing calculator

Experimental Design

1. Develop a scientific investigation that explores how temperature and pressure of a gas are related.
2. Select the independent variable that you will manipulate in your investigation.
3. Decide how you will measure and record the results of your experiment.
4. Before you carry out your plan, have the teacher review your experiment.

FIGURE 8.58

Analyzing and Interpreting

1. Describe how the volume of gas affected your results. Explain how you could minimize your sources of error.
2. Present your observations using a data table and a graph.
3. Prepare a lab report to summarize your findings.

Concluding and Communicating

4. State in words the relationship between pressure and temperature. Under what conditions is this relationship true?
5. State, as a mathematical equation, the relationship between pressure and temperature using your results. What is the name of this law?
6. Discuss if the volume of a gas can eventually get to zero. Explain your answer.
7. Describe how different your results would be if you had used another gas. Explain your reasoning.
8. If the temperature of a gas is decreased to 0°C or even lower, determine if the relationship between pressure and temperature would be linear.

Extending

9. Explain the significance of the intercept on the temperature axis.
10. On hair spray cans, the caution reads "Do not place in hot water, near radiators, or a heat source." Explain why there is this warning.

CHAPTER SUMMARY

Key Terms

absolute pressure
atmospheric pressure
bar
barometer
boiling point
Boyle's law
Charles's law
combined gas law
diffusion
effusion

Gay-Lussac's law
Henry's law
ideal gas
ideal gas constant
ideal gas law
Kelvin temperature scale
law of partial pressures
manometer
millimetres of mercury

molar volume
mole fraction
partial pressure
pascal
pounds per square inch
real gas
relative humidity
relative pressure
saturated vapour pressure

standard ambient
    temperature and
    pressure (SATP)
standard temperature and
    pressure (STP)
sublimation
torr
vapour pressure
volatile

Key Equations

$P_{absolute} = P_{relative} + P_{atmospheric}$

$P_{gas} = P_{atm} + \Delta h$ if $P_{gas} > P_{atm}$

$P_{gas} = P_{atm} - \Delta h$ if $P_{gas} < P_{atm}$

$P_1 V_1 = P_2 V_2$ (Boyle's law)

$\dfrac{V_1}{T_1} = \dfrac{V_2}{T_2}$ (Charles's law)

$\dfrac{P_1}{T_1} = \dfrac{P_2}{T_2}$ (Gay-Lussac's law)

$\dfrac{P_1 V_1}{T_1} = \dfrac{P_2 V_2}{T_2}$ (combined gas law)

$PV = nRT$ (ideal gas law)

$d = \dfrac{M}{V_m}$ where M is the molar mass and $V_m = \dfrac{V}{n}$ is the molar volume

$P_{total} = P_A + P_B$ (Dalton's law of partial pressures)

$P_A = P_{total} \times \dfrac{n_A}{n_{total}}$

$\chi_A = \dfrac{n_A}{n_{total}}$

$P = K\chi$ (Henry's law) where K is Henry's law constant for that gas

Essential Understandings

■ The properties of gases can be explained using the kinetic-molecular theory.

■ The gas laws relate variables that can be measured, and these laws help us predict the behaviour of a gas under different conditions.

■ The gas laws are based on a number of assumptions that are valid for gases at low to moderate pressures and moderate temperatures.

■ Volcanoes and other natural phenomena can be explained using the gas laws.

■ Liquids and solids have vapour pressures, and this property must be considered when handling and storing toxic and hazardous chemicals.

Consolidate Your Understanding

1. Describe how the kinetic-molecular theory explains the properties of gases.

2. Construct a concept map that starts with the phrase "gas laws."

3. Scientific laws describe natural events but do not explain them. Discuss this definition of scientific laws in relation to the gas laws.

4. Describe the safety precautions that are taken when transporting gases. Explain why.

Understanding Concepts

1. A gas is placed in a container, and the mercury in a manometer rises by 30 mm Hg on the open side. If the external pressure is 750 mm Hg, the pressure of the gas is:
    a) 780 mm Hg
    b) 720 mm Hg
    c) 810 mm Hg
    d) 690 mm Hg

2. The pressure of a tire is checked, and the gauge reading is 245 kPa. This means the absolute pressure in the tire is:
    a) 346 kPa
    b) 245 kPa
    c) 144 kPa
    d) not able to be determined precisely

3. The temperature of a fixed mass of gas is doubled while its volume is halved. The gas pressure will:
    a) quadruple
    b) double
    c) stay the same
    d) decrease by a factor of 4

4. Which statement is *not* true about an ideal gas in a container?
    a) At a particular temperature, the molecules will all have the same velocities.
    b) The molecular volumes are negligible compared to the volume of the container.
    c) There are no attractive forces between molecules.
    d) The gas pressure is a measure of the molecular impact with the container walls.

5. If the total pressure of a mixture of two gases A and B is 66 kPa and the mole fraction of gas A is 0.33, then the pressure due to gas B is about:
    a) 66 kPa
    b) 33 kPa
    c) 44 kPa
    d) none of the above

6. Make a poster illustrating the gas laws. Your poster should describe each gas law, give its equation, and describe an example of how the law applies to real life.

7. Use the kinetic-molecular theory to explain Dalton's law of partial pressures.

8. Describe the effect of temperature on the pressure of a gas in a container.

9. Use the kinetic-molecular theory to explain that:
    a) gases exert pressure
    b) the pressure remains constant as long as there is no change in temperature

10. Describe what happens to the volume of a balloon when it is taken out on a cold winter day. Explain why.

11. Explain why tire blowouts on bicycles occur on the hottest day of summer. Describe ways that this situation could be remedied.

12. The SI unit of pressure is the pascal.
    a) Discuss why most pressures are measured in kPa and not Pa.
    b) Many gauges still use pounds per square inch. Calculate the pressure in kilopascals corresponding to a car tire pressure of 32 $lb \cdot in^{-2}$.
    c) If the tire were taken into outer space, predict what the approximate pressure reading would be.

13. Explain why IUPAC recommended a change in standard conditions from STP to SATP.

14. Describe how real gases differ from an ideal gas, and explain why it is beneficial to us that gases do not exhibit ideal behaviour.

15. Sketch a graph that illustrates how the vapour pressure of water changes with increasing temperature.

16. In this chapter, volcanoes are discussed. There are a few potential supervolcano sites on Earth. The last time one erupted was 74 000 years ago, and it changed the climate of the planet. Using electronic and print resources, research information on supervolcanoes and where they are found. In your research, include information about other planets in our solar system that have volcanoes. Speculate how the behaviour of volcanic gases would affect these planets.

17. Vegetables may be cooked in a pressure cooker in a much shorter period of time than in an ordinary saucepan. Explain how you would account for this.

Applying Inquiry/ Communication Skills

18. Figure 8.59 shows a graph of volume against temperature for three gases. Data points were only obtained down to −100°C.

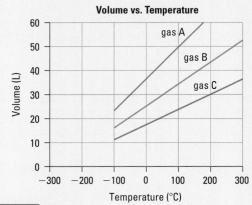

FIGURE 8.59

a) Extrapolate the lines to determine the temperature where they converge. Explain the significance of this point.

b) Discuss what this value for the volume at $-273.15°C$ implies.

c) Justify if your answer to b) is realistic for a real gas.

d) Describe what would have actually happened if you had continued to take measurements of the gas volumes below $-100°C$.

e) Explain what this tells you about the difference between a real and an ideal gas.

19. Sealed in a container are 1 mol of nitrogen gas, 2 mol of neon gas, and 4 mol of argon gas. Calculate the partial pressure of the nitrogen gas if the total pressure is 1400 torr.

20. A gaseous mixture consists of 11.0 g of CO_2 and 48 g of O_2. The volume of the container is 22.4 L, and the temperature is 273°C. Calculate the mole fraction of each gas and the partial pressure of each gas.

21. A diving mixture used at a depth corresponding to a pressure of about 10 times atmospheric pressure is 98% helium and 2% oxygen. Our normal air contains 20% oxygen. Explain how divers survive with only 2% oxygen. (Hint: Calculate the partial pressure of oxygen under a pressure of 1.0 MPa, and compare it with that under normal conditions).

22. Calculate the mass of argon that would be required to fill an electric light bulb having a capacity of 200 mL when the pressure is 1 atm and the temperature is 20°C.

23. A cylinder of oxygen in a laboratory at 27°C has a pressure of 4 atm. The cylinder can withstand an internal pressure of 20 atm. Calculate the temperature at which the cylinder would explode if the building caught fire.

24. A toxic gas is produced as a waste product by an oil refinery at town A. The government has recently prohibited the company from releasing the gas untreated into the air. Detoxifying equipment is extremely expensive. A company in town B comes to the rescue, announcing that it can use the gas in the manufacture of another product. The gas is to be transported in trucks at 15.0 MPa pressure. The tank walls can withstand 16.5 MPa pressure. The first truck loads up in town A at $-8°C$ and drives toward town B at a balmy 20°C. Determine whether the truck is likely to reach its destination without exploding. Justify your answer.

25. A gasoline engine relies on a spark to initiate the reaction between the fuel and the oxygen in the air. A diesel engine, on the other hand, simply uses the increase in pressure and temperature during compression to cause an explosion of the diesel fuel and the oxygen in the air. The volume in a cylinder of a particular diesel engine is 1.00 L at maximum expansion and 0.0714 L under maximum compression. If the air/fuel mixture is admitted into the cylinder at 24°C and 101 kPa, calculate the pressure in the cylinder when the gas is at maximum compression and at a temperature of 480°C.

Making Connections

26. With rising energy costs, researchers are looking for alternative fuels for vehicles. Identify and evaluate the benefits, and risks of using compressed gases such as methane, propane, and hydrogen as fuel for vehicles.

27. In the town of Burgeo, Newfoundland, a major leak has developed in the pressurized ammonia tank that was part of an old unused fish plant refrigeration unit. You are a member of a company that is going to assist the town with this problem. Prepare an informative report for the town council outlining the situation and a plan of action to solve the problem. In your report:

a) Include a description of the characteristic properties of ammonia.

b) Address the concern of citizens that a cloud of poisonous ammonia will roll across the whole small island, killing them all. Calculate the density of ammonia gas at 18°C and 102 kPa, and compare it with that of air (1.22 g·L^{-1}) under the same conditions. Determine whether the citizens should be worried and what could happen under various weather conditions (e.g., windy day).

c) Outline the role of emergency services such as the fire department.

d) Provide a plan of action to dispose of the gas.

28. Use electronic and print resources to research the problems associated with climbing mountains where the partial pressure of oxygen is very low. Prepare an information brochure informing potential mountain climbers of the hazards and safety precautions they need to take.

29. Use electronic and print resources to research information about modern airships, including where they are used and the costs associated with building and maintaining them. Give an informed opinion on whether airships serve a useful purpose, and provide examples to justify your opinion.

30. When tunnels are constructed under rivers, they are pressurized during construction to prevent water from entering the tunnel. To celebrate the completion of excavation of a particular tunnel, a party was held beneath the river. Unfortunately, the champagne proved to be flat. When the dignitaries exited the pressurized area, they suffered severe and agonizing stomach cramps. Explain the events. Describe what you would have done to prevent this from happening.

CHAPTER 9

Gases and Chemical Reactions

What do a cake mixture and a land mine have in common? They both rely on chemical reactions to produce gases. The carbon dioxide produced during the baking process gives a cake the fluffy texture that we like. In fact, the soft pizza crust, the doughnut, and many more cooked foodstuffs rely on gas-producing reactions for their pleasant texture. Far from the pleasure of

FIGURE 9.1   Baking muffins. The chemical reactions that occur during the baking of muffins produce carbon dioxide gas, which gives the fluffy texture in the final product.

FIGURE 9.2
Modern aircraft are propelled by turbofan engines which develop thrust by burning a mixture of jet fuel and air.

baked goods, a land mine also functions by means of a chemical reaction generating a large amount of gas. The pressure inside the mine will become so high that its casing will shatter. It is the rapid expansion of the gas—the shock wave—plus the metal fragments of the mine that make these devices so deadly.

Gas-producing chemical reactions are vital to our society, particularly in transport. When you look up at a high-altitude aircraft, you can see the condensed water vapour trail, the water vapour being part of the gas mixture that the jet engines of the aircraft are adding to the upper atmosphere. On a cold day, you are more aware of the products being pumped out into the atmosphere by the gasoline-powered and diesel-engine vehicles that most of us drive. Many industries have smokestacks. What are these for? They pump out the waste gases from chemical reactions at a high enough altitude that they mix and dilute high above the surface air that we breathe, contributing to atmospheric pollution without offending our noses.

Our atmosphere is an enormous chemical reaction vessel with hundreds, perhaps thousands, of chemical reactions that have been occurring for most of geological history. Now our society is pumping molecules into this mixture that have never before been found in the atmosphere. What is happening to these compounds? How are they affecting the normal chemical reactions? What new reactions are occurring in our atmosphere? This is part of the study of atmospheric chemistry—a subject that you will learn about later in this chapter. First, you will study the principles of gas-producing chemical reactions.

Discovering Chemistry

Properties of the Atmospheric Gas Carbon Dioxide

One component of the atmosphere is carbon dioxide. What are some of its properties?

Materials

      approximately 5 mL of dilute hydrochloric acid
      some marble chips (calcium carbonate)
      glass stirring rod
      25-mL graduated cylinder
      birthday candle

1. Tape the candle, wick end upward, to the bottom of the stirring rod.

2. Place the marble chips in the cylinder, and slowly add the hydrochloric acid.

3. When the bubbling has ceased, light the wick and lower the candle into the cylinder.

■ Write a balanced chemical equation for the reaction.

■ Identify the properties of carbon dioxide that you observed. You should be able to comment on three physical properties and one chemical property.

> ## CHECK**POINT**
>
> Draw and label a diagram that represents the major regions of the atmosphere. Describe the main characteristics of each region. Identify in which region most of Earth's weather occurs and explain why.

9.1   Reactions Producing Gases: Rockets and Air Bags

Key Understandings

When you have completed this section, you will be able to:

- use gas properties to explain how a rocket works
- describe air bags and other products that we use that are associated with gases
- use appropriate scientific vocabulary to communicate ideas related to reactions producing gases

Gas-producing reactions are involved in many aspects of our lives. A common example is the biochemical reactions in the baking of leavened bread, which results in the formation of carbon dioxide gas. It is the trapped gas bubbles that give bread its open texture (Figure 9.3). There are many applications of gas-producing reactions, but here we will discuss two applications: rockets and air bags.

FIGURE 9.3   The chemical reactions involved in the making of leavened bread produce trapped bubbles of carbon dioxide gas, which give the bread a fluffy texture.

A History of Rockets

Although you might think that rockets are a recent invention, in fact, they were developed as weapons of war in China in the early 13th century. It is regrettable but true that war stimulates the most rapid advances in many types of technology. During World War II, a massive scientific and engineering effort was put into the design and development of large rockets. As a result, German military technology produced the V-2, a missile of awesome destructive power. At the end of the war, the German rocket scientists were captured by the allies. Some of them were transported to the United States, while others were taken to the former Soviet Union. It is those scientists who initially led the development of modern military and civilian rockets. As you will discover later in this chapter, atmospheric scientists rely on rockets to launch the many satellites that are used to monitor the chemistry of the different layers of the atmosphere. So what was born as a tool of destruction is now essential to monitor the health of our planet.

How a Rocket Works

A rocket functions according to **Newton's third law of motion**. It states:

For every action, there is an equal and opposite reaction.

For example, a rocket moves forward by expelling gases from the nozzle at the back of the vehicle. But what are the criteria for a rocket fuel? There are, in fact, three requirements:

- The fuel components must react rapidly. This means that the chemical reaction must be extremely fast (i.e., a controlled explosion).
- The product molecules must have low molecular masses.
- The reaction must release a lot of heat (it must be exothermic).

The second and third criteria relate to the kinetic-molecular theory of gases. Let us consider the second criterion using a demonstration. If you take two balloons, fill one with hydrogen gas, and fill the other with carbon dioxide gas, you will find that the balloon filled with hydrogen deflates faster than the balloon filled with carbon dioxide. The balloon has lots of microscopic holes through the rubber, and the gas molecules escape through them. But why is there a difference? First of all, a hydrogen molecule is physically much smaller than a carbon dioxide molecule. Secondly, different gases at the same temperature and pressure have the same kinetic energy, that is:

$$\frac{1}{2}m_{H_2}\,v^2_{H_2} = \frac{1}{2}m_{CO_2}\,v^2_{CO_2}$$

We can rearrange the expression to get:

$$\frac{v_{H_2}}{v_{CO_2}} = \sqrt{\frac{m_{CO_2}}{m_{H_2}}}$$

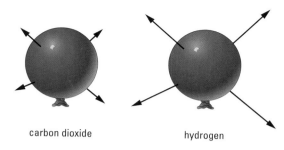

carbon dioxide   hydrogen

FIGURE 9.4 The smaller mass of a hydrogen molecule allows it to escape faster through the holes of a balloon than the larger carbon dioxide molecule.

As carbon dioxide has 44/2 = 22 times the molecular mass of hydrogen, the hydrogen molecules must have $\sqrt{22}$ = 4.7 times the average velocity of carbon dioxide molecules. Therefore, the hydrogen molecules can escape nearly five times faster through the holes (Figure 9.4). It is the molecular velocities that determine the effectiveness of a propellant.

According to the kinetic-molecular theory, as the temperature of a gas is increased, the average kinetic energy increases. So the last criterion for a rocket fuel, the increased temperature, would also lead to an increase in molecular velocities.

FIGURE 9.5 The space shuttle uses both liquid and solid propellant systems.

Common Propellants Used in Rockets

For a combustion reaction, a fuel and an oxidant are needed. In an automobile engine, gasoline (or diesel) is the fuel and oxygen in the air provides the oxidant. For travel into space, the vehicle must carry both components since there is no air to provide the other reactant. The chemistry of the space shuttle propulsion is most interesting because there are two different types of reactions used (Figure 9.5).

For its main thrust, the space shuttle uses liquid hydrogen and liquid oxygen. These react together in a violent exothermic reaction to form water vapour (with a low molecular mass of 18).

$$2\ H_2(g) + O_2(g) \rightarrow 2\ H_2O(l)$$

This reaction is comparatively harmless. However, as the space shuttle climbs through the outer parts of the atmosphere, it is increasing the water vapour concentration at those altitudes by about 0.1%. This increase is not significant at the current rate of shuttle launches.

In addition to the liquid fuel reaction, the space shuttle also employs solid fuel boosters to accelerate it off the launch pad. These enormous tubes contain a mixture of aluminum powder and ammonium perchlorate (in this case,

WEBLINK

Although hydrogen and oxygen are the fuels used for the main engines on the space shuttle, other fuel mixtures are used for other rockets. Research these other fuels, and write a report on them. Be sure to mention any specific safety problems associated with handling them. Begin your research at **www.pearsoned.ca/chemistry11**.

aluminum is the fuel and ammonium perchlorate is the oxidant). Each shuttle launch uses about 850 t of these reagents.

$$6 \text{ NH}_4\text{ClO}_4(s) + 8 \text{ Al}(s) \rightarrow 4 \text{ Al}_2\text{O}_3(s) + 3 \text{ N}_2(g) + 3 \text{ Cl}_2(g) + 12 \text{ H}_2\text{O}(g)$$

Again, you see that the highly exothermic reaction produces gases of low molecular mass (N_2, H_2O), together with chlorine gas and solid aluminum oxide. The aluminum oxide (and water droplets) provides the intense white trail that the shuttle leaves in the sky. As will be discussed in a later section, the addition of more chlorine gas to the atmosphere is not environmentally wise.

Why does the space shuttle use both solid and liquid fuel systems? The solid boosters are essentially giant fireworks. They can be stored until needed, but once ignited, all of the boosters' contents will burn. Nothing can stop them. They are useful in providing an initial acceleration of the spacecraft. By contrast, the liquid fuel system provides controllable thrust. By regulating the flow of fuel to the combustion chamber, the acceleration and direction of the vehicle can be adjusted. The disadvantage of the liquid propellant system is that the two liquids must be kept below about $-250°C$ to prevent them from evaporating. Consequently, liquid fuel loading must be done just prior to launch time. Both solid and liquid fuels have advantages and disadvantages.

Air Bags and Explosives

What do air bags and rockets have in common? Both require extremely fast chemical reactions to produce a controlled explosion. An air bag must inflate very rapidly in the event of an accident (usually in about 0.04 s), and, like a rocket, it uses a fast gas-producing reaction, in this case the decomposition of sodium azide, the azide ion being N_3^-.

$$2 \text{ NaN}_3(s) \rightarrow 2 \text{ Na}(l) + 3 \text{ N}_2(g)$$

The air bag is connected to a steel or aluminum canister (about 6 cm long and about 2 cm in diameter). The reaction is triggered by an electric current initiated by the impact sensor (Figure 9.6). Because the azide ion itself is very toxic, more so than cyanide, it is environmentally important to trigger air bags in a vehicle before it is sent to the wrecking yard. In this way, the azide will be decomposed and will not be washed into water supplies.

FIGURE 9.6 Air bags use an explosive decomposition reaction for gas production.

A second reason for choosing this explosive reaction is that nitrogen gas has a low molar mass. In this case, the high molecular velocities will enable the nitrogen to inflate the bag as rapidly as possible. Incidentally, the liquid sodium produced is reacted with potassium nitrate and silicon dioxide to produce harmless silicates.

All explosives use the same principle of turning a small volume of liquid or solid into a very large volume of gas in a short time period. Also, they must be self-contained, not relying on some other component, such as oxygen in the air, for their reaction. For example, the explosive component of dynamite is nitroglycerin, $C_3H_5(NO_3)_3$. It decomposes explosively as follows:

$$4 \text{ C}_3\text{H}_5(\text{NO}_3)_3(l) \rightarrow 12 \text{ CO}_2(g) + 10 \text{ H}_2\text{O}(g) + 6 \text{ N}_2(g) + \text{O}_2(g)$$

It is the shock wave produced by the massive gas expansion that causes the destructive power of an explosive. Again, though, you should keep in mind that dynamite has positive uses. It was the power of dynamite that enabled the excavation of the Panama Canal, tunnels through the Rockies, and the development of modern mining techniques.

Nitroglycerin, Nitrogen Monoxide, and Nerves

It was over 100 years ago that nitroglycerin was found to have a use in the treatment of pain from heart disease and heart attacks, though no one had any idea how it worked. The discovery in 1987 proved to be a total surprise to biochemists. The nitroglycerin was found to decompose in the bloodstream near the heart to form nitrogen monoxide (nitric oxide). The nitrogen monoxide acted on the smooth muscle of the heart's blood vessels to cause dilation of the arteries. This put less strain on the heart and allowed more oxygenated blood to reach the heart itself, thereby relieving the symptoms.

Up to that time, nitrogen monoxide was considered to be just a poisonous polluting gas in the atmosphere. The discovery of the molecule in our bodies caused a total reassessment of this view and has opened up an exciting new field of biochemistry (Figure 9.7). Nitrogen monoxide is key to a vast range of processes in the body as a biological signalling molecule. This tiny molecule is a signal-conveyor in the nervous system, and it is involved in the body's fight against infections. The biochemical importance of this molecule was recognized by the awarding of the 1998 Nobel prize for physiology and medicine to Robert Furchgott, Louis Ignarro, and Ferid Murad, three Americans, for their pioneering work on the biochemical role of nitrogen monoxide.

The nitrogen monoxide molecule also controls penile erection and uterine contraction. The drug sildenafil citrate was originally developed to treat chest pain, utilizing the release of nitrogen monoxide in a manner similar to nitroglycerin. Although the test subjects reported that the drug was not very effective in this role, the male subjects did report one unexpected side effect: the drug was very effective at producing nitrogen monoxide elsewhere in the body! As a result, the drug now trademarked as Viagra™ was discovered.

FIGURE 9.7 The prestigious journal *Science* called nitrogen monoxide its 1992 Molecule of the Year to indicate the profound biochemical importance of this simple compound.

Section 9.1 Review

Understanding Concepts

1. Outline the advantages and disadvantages of:
   a) solid fuel propellants
   b) liquid fuel propellants

2. Use electronic and print resources to research the historical development of rockets. Create a timeline that depicts the major technological events related to space travel that have led to the development of the International Space Station. Identify which technological milestones required knowledge about chemistry.

3. Write a short paragraph explaining why liquid oxygen is used in rocketry rather than less expensive liquid air.

4. Draw a diagram using the kinetic-molecular theory to illustrate how a rocket works.

5. Chemicals that react to produce gases are useful as rocket fuels because the tremendous volume expansion produces enough pressure to push the rocket forward. Find out which chemicals have been used as propellants, and write the related chemical reactions.

9.2 Calculations Involving Reactions That Require or Produce Gases

Key Understandings

When you have completed this section, you will be able to:

- state Gay-Lussac's law of combining volumes
- understand Avogadro's hypothesis
- describe how Avogadro's work has improved our understanding of the reactions of gases
- solve quantitative problems involving different gas laws
- perform stoichiometric calculations based on reactions that require or produce gases
- determine the molar volume of a gas empirically
- use appropriate scientific vocabulary to communicate ideas related to gases

As discussed in the previous chapter, early scientists were fascinated by gases. One aspect of their fascination was the way in which gases combined. Gay-Lussac (discoverer of the relationship between pressure and temperature) found that when water was formed, 2 volumes of hydrogen at the same temperature and pressure were used for every 1 volume of oxygen gas. The study of other gas-phase reactions showed that gases always combined in simple whole number ratios. For example, 25 mL (1 volume) of hydrogen combines with 25 mL (1 volume) of chlorine to give 50 mL (2 volumes) of hydrogen chloride, provided all the volumes are measured at the same temperature and pressure. This observation became known as **Gay-Lussac's law of combining volumes**, which states:

In any chemical reaction involving gases (at the same temperature and pressure), the volumes of the gases are always in small whole-number ratios.

Avogadro's Hypothesis and the Law of Combining Volumes

A law is a statement of fact. You observe that gases combine in simple ratios, and this is a fact. But what is the explanation? It is **Avogadro's hypothesis** that provides the answer. Avogadro hypothesized that:

Equal volumes of gases at the same temperature and pressure contain equal numbers of molecules (and moles of molecules).

Consider the reaction of hydrogen and chlorine:

1 volume of hydrogen + 1 volume of chlorine →
2 volumes hydrogen chloride

If 1 volume contains n mol of gas, you can write:

n mol hydrogen + n mol chlorine → $2n$ mol hydrogen chloride

Dividing through by n gives:

1 mol hydrogen + 1 mol chlorine → 2 mol hydrogen chloride

Investigation

Refer to page 422, Investigation 1

Therefore, the law of combining volumes is simply a statement about the stoichiometry of the reaction.

This sequence can be taken one step farther using the fact that hydrogen chloride is known to have the formula HCl:

1 mol hydrogen + 1 mol chlorine → 2 HCl(g)

The only way to balance the equation is to assume that hydrogen and chlorine are both diatomic molecules, H_2 and Cl_2 (which, of course, they are).

$$1 \ H_2(g) + 1 \ Cl_2(g) \rightarrow 2 \ HCl(g)$$

FIGURE 9.8   One of the most spectacular and tragic gas-phase reactions was the Hindenburg disaster. A spark is believed to have ignited a leak in the gas envelope, but it was the highly flammable coating on the envelope that is now considered to have caused the fire to spread so rapidly. What is the chemical equation for the reaction of hydrogen with the air?

EXAMPLE 1

Sulfur burns in fluorine to form gaseous sulfur hexafluoride.

$$S(s) + 3 \ F_2(g) \rightarrow SF_6(g)$$

What volume of fluorine is needed to produce 125 mL of sulfur hexafluoride at the same temperature and pressure?

Given

$V_{SF_6} = 125$ mL

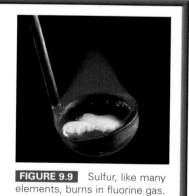

FIGURE 9.9   Sulfur, like many elements, burns in fluorine gas.

Analysis

$V_{SF_6} \rightarrow V_{F_2}$
(using mole ratio, 3 mol F_2 : 1 mol SF_6)

Solution

$$V_{F_2} = 125 \text{ mL} \times \frac{3 \text{ mol } F_2}{1 \text{ mol } SF_6} = 375 \text{ mL } F_2$$

(at the same temperature and pressure)

Statement
A volume of 375 mL of fluorine gas is required to produce 125 mL of sulfur hexafluoride gas.

PRACTICE PROBLEM

Carbon can react with oxygen to give carbon monoxide:

$2 \text{ C}(s) + O_2(g) \rightarrow 2 \text{ CO}(g)$

Calculate the volume of oxygen gas (at the same temperature and pressure) needed to produce 500 mL of carbon monoxide.

EXAMPLE 2

A certain oxide of nitrogen is produced by the high temperature reaction of nitrogen and oxygen. If the reaction of 20 mL of nitrogen with 40 mL of oxygen produces 40 mL of a nitrogen oxide, NO_X (at the same temperature and pressure), what is the formula of the oxide?

Given
V_{N_2} = 20 mL, V_{O_2} = 40 mL, V_{NO_X} = 40 mL

Required
formula of NO_X

Analysis
At the same temperature and pressure, the volumes of gases are proportional to the numbers of molecules.

Solution
Rewriting as a word equation:

20 mL N_2 + 40 mL O_2 → 40 mL (nitrogen oxide)

Dividing by 20 mL:

N_2 + 2 O_2 → 2 (nitrogen oxide)

Thus 2 molecules of the nitrogen oxide must contain 2 nitrogen atoms and 4 oxygen atoms.

So each molecule must contain 1 nitrogen atom and 2 oxygen atoms, and the formula is NO_2.

Statement
The formula of the oxide is NO_2.

PRACTICE PROBLEM

Fluorine reacts with chlorine to form a chlorine fluoride. If 75 mL of fluorine react with 15 mL of chlorine to give 30 mL of the chlorine fluoride (all gases being at the same temperature and pressure), determine the formula of the chlorine fluoride.

Amedeo Avogadro: No, He Didn't Invent the Number!

When you read the name Avogadro, you probably think of Avogadro's number, but the idea of the mole came long after his death. His claim to fame was his hypothesis that equal volumes of gases, at the same temperature and pressure, contain equal numbers of particles (molecules).

Amedeo Avogadro was born in Turin, Italy, in 1776. He originally trained to become a specialist in religious law, but he developed an interest in electricity, a subject that was being studied by Alessandro Volta, an Italian physicist. Avogadro started his own research on electricity.

FIGURE 9.10 Amedeo Avogadro (1776–1856)

About this time, Gay-Lussac found that gases combined in simple whole number ratios. For example, 2 volumes of water (as a gas) could be obtained from 2 volumes of hydrogen and 1 volume of oxygen.

2 vols. hydrogen + 1 vol. oxygen → 2 vols. water

FIGURE 9.11 If oxygen gas had only one atom, then the water molecule would end up with half an atom. This result would not make sense because you can't have a part of any atom as stated in the law of conservation of matter.

Dalton believed water's formula was HO and stubbornly refused to consider other possibilities. So this problem remained unsolvable until Avogadro suggested that the gases were actually diatomic molecules—a radical idea in those days. But with this idea, the 2 volumes of water could be obtained without having to "split" any atoms:

$$2 \ H_2(g) + O_2(g) \rightarrow 2 \ H_2O(g)$$

FIGURE 9.12 If both hydrogen and oxygen gases are diatomic molecules, then the water molecule will end up with 2 hydrogen atoms and 1 oxygen atom. This result would make sense because none of the atoms would be split and the law of conservation of matter would still hold.

You might think such an idea would be quickly accepted, but this was not the case. It was not until 1860, when Stanislao Cannizzaro, an Italian chemist, presented Avogadro's hypothesis to an international conference, that his idea became widely accepted.

So why was Avogadro ignored? This occurred partially because he was pitting his views against those of well-established figures, such as Dalton. But another reason was that Avogadro, a modest and obscure physicist in Italy, was far removed from the world's centres of scientific discovery in Britain and France. In addition, he published his proposal in obscure Italian and French journals, and few scientists read them. This is a problem even to the present day. If you make some important discovery, it is crucial to have your report published in a widely read scientific journal (usually American or British). Many governments encourage (or force) researchers to publish in their own national journals as a matter of national pride, but this can come at a price to the researchers: few scientists in other

FIGURE 9.13 Two of the world's leading scientific journals are *Science* (American) and *Nature* (British). For more specialized articles, the publications *Journal of the American Chemical Society* (American) and *Chemical Communications* (British) are among the most highly regarded.

countries might ever learn about their discovery.

So how did the number get named after Avogadro? Cannizzaro showed that Avogadro's hypothesis was the key to measuring precise values of relative molecular and atomic masses (as you will see in Example 3). It was for this reason, then, that the number of particles in a mole was named after Avogadro. The term "Avogadro's number" was first used by Jean Perrin, a French physicist, in 1909. Its value is determined experimentally, and today's best value is $6.02214199 \times 10^{23}$.

EXAMPLE 3

A sample of an unreactive gas, X, had a mass of 2.301 g. The same container was filled with nitrogen gas at the same temperature and pressure. The mass of nitrogen gas was 0.490 g. Calculate the molar mass of the unknown gas.

Given
$m_{N_2} = 0.490$ g; $m_X = 2.301$ g

Required
molar mass of X, $M_X = ?$ g·mol^{-1}

Analysis
$m_{N_2} \to n_{N_2}$ (using $M_{N_2} = 28.01$ g·mol^{-1})

$n_{N_2} \to n_X$ (using Avogadro's hypothesis)

$m_X, n_X \to M_X \left(\text{using } M = \dfrac{m}{n} \right)$

Solution
$n_{N_2} = 0.490 \text{ g N}_2 \times \dfrac{1 \text{ mol N}_2}{28.01 \text{ g N}_2} = 1.75 \times 10^{-2} \text{ mol N}_2$

$n_X = 1.75 \times 10^{-2} \text{ mol N}_2 \times \dfrac{1 \text{ mol X}}{1 \text{ mol N}_2} = 1.75 \times 10^{-2} \text{ mol X}$

$M_X = \dfrac{2.301 \text{ g}}{1.75 \times 10^{-2} \text{ mol}} = 131.5 \text{ g·mol}^{-1}$

Statement
The molar mass of gas X is 131.5 g·mol^{-1}. (If it is a monatomic gas, then its identity is xenon.)

PRACTICE PROBLEM

2.82 g of a triatomic gas, X_3, occupies the same volume at the same temperature and pressure as 1.18 g of neon gas. Deduce the identity of the triatomic gas.

Using SATP or STP for Reaction Calculations

The law of combining volumes enables chemists to compare volumes of gases in chemical reactions. However, in most chemical reactions, one or more of the reactants or products are solids. How can the quantities of materials be compared in two different phases? Provided the gas is produced at SATP (25°C and 100 kPa) or at STP (0°C and 101.3 kPa), you can use the stoichiometric method introduced in Chapter 5.

In the stoichiometric method, for a reaction A → B, you performed the following steps:

- mass of A ⟶ moles of A (using molar mass of A)
- moles of A ⟶ moles of B (using the mole ratio)
- moles of B ⟶ mass of B (using molar mass of B)

Now you can use the SATP relationship (24.8 L·mol^{-1}) or the STP relationship (22.4 L·mol^{-1}) to relate a gas volume to a molar quantity.

EXAMPLE 4

Sulfur burns in oxygen to form sulfur dioxide:

$S(s) + O_2(g) \rightarrow SO_2(g)$

What volume of gas will be produced at SATP when 14.0 g of sulfur are burned in excess oxygen?

Given

$S(s)$	$+$	$O_2(g)$	$\rightarrow$	$SO_2(g)$
1 mol				1 mol
$m_S = 14.0$ g				$T_{SO_2} = 273 + 25 = 298$ K
				$P_{SO_2} = 100$ kPa

Required

volume of sulfur dioxide, $V_{SO_2} = ?$ mL

Analysis

$m_S \rightarrow n_{SO_2}$ (using $M_S = 32.06$ g·mol^{-1})

$n_S \rightarrow n_{SO_2}$ (using mole ratio, 1 mol S : 1 mol SO$_2$)

$n_{SO_2} \rightarrow V_{SO_2}$ (using SATP conditions, 24.8 L·mol^{-1})

Solution

$n_S = 14.0 \text{ g S} \times \dfrac{1 \text{ mol S}}{32.06 \text{ g S}} = 0.437$ mol S

$n_{SO_2} = 0.437 \text{ mol S} \times \dfrac{1 \text{ mol SO}_2}{1 \text{ mol S}} = 0.437$ mol SO$_2$

$V_{SO_2} = 0.437 \text{ mol} \times \dfrac{24.8 \text{ L}}{1 \text{ mol}} = 10.8$ L

Statement

A volume of 10.8 L of sulfur dioxide gas is produced at SATP when 14.0 g of sulfur is burned.

PRACTICE PROBLEM

Silicon burns in fluorine gas to produce silicon tetrafluoride.

$Si(s) + 2 \text{ F}_2(g) \rightarrow SiF_4(g)$

Calculate the minimum volume of fluorine gas needed to completely react with 5.0 g of silicon powder at STP.

Using the Ideal Gas Law for Reaction Calculations

It is very rare that gases are produced at either SATP or STP. (Unless the heating fails in your school, it is exceedingly unlikely that you will be preparing gases at a temperature of 0°!) A much more useful approach is to combine the stoichiometric calculation with the ideal gas law, $PV = nRT$. Example 5 demonstrates this type of calculation.

EXAMPLE 5

Oxygen gas is produced by the process of photosynthesis:

$$6\ H_2O(l) + 6\ CO_2(aq) \rightarrow C_6H_{12}O_6(aq) + 6\ O_2(g)$$

If a plant absorbs 0.12 g of carbon dioxide, what volume of oxygen gas (in mL) is produced at 15°C and 102 kPa pressure?

FIGURE 9.14 Photosynthesis is one of the most important chemical reactions on our planet.

Given

$$6\ H_2O(l) \quad + \quad 6\ CO_2(aq) \quad \rightarrow \quad C_6H_{12}O_6(aq) \quad + \quad 6\ O_2(g)$$

$\qquad\qquad\qquad$ 6 mol $\qquad\qquad\qquad\qquad\qquad\qquad$ 6 mol

$\qquad\qquad\qquad m_{CO_2} = 0.12$ g $\qquad\qquad\qquad\qquad T_{O_2} = 273 + 15 = 288$ K

$\qquad\qquad\qquad\qquad\qquad\qquad\qquad\qquad\qquad\qquad\qquad P_{O_2} = 102$ kPa

Required

volume of oxygen, $V_{O_2} = ?$ mL

Analysis

$m_{CO_2} \rightarrow n_{CO_2}$ (using $M_{CO_2} = 44.01$ g·mol⁻¹)

$n_{CO_2} \rightarrow n_{O_2}$ (using mole ratio, 6 mol CO_2 : 6 mol O_2)

$n_{O_2} \rightarrow V_{O_2} \left(\text{using ideal gas law, } V = \dfrac{nRT}{P}\right)$

Solution

$$n_{CO_2} = 0.12\ \text{g } CO_2 \times \frac{1\ \text{mol } CO_2}{44.01\ \text{g } CO_2} = 2.7 \times 10^{-3}\ \text{mol } CO_2$$

$$n_{O_2} = 2.7 \times 10^{-3}\ \text{mol } CO_2 \times \frac{6\ \text{mol } O_2}{6\ \text{mol } CO_2} = 2.7 \times 10^{-3}\ \text{mol } O_2$$

$$V_{O_2} = \frac{(2.7 \times 10^{-3}\ \text{mol})(8.31\ \text{kPa·L·mol}^{-1}\text{·K}^{-1})(288\ \text{K})}{102\ \text{kPa}}$$

$$= 6.3 \times 10^{-2}\ \text{L}$$

$$= 63\ \text{mL}$$

Statement

A volume of 6.4 mL of oxygen gas is produced at 15°C and 102 kPa when 0.12 g of carbon dioxide is consumed.

Hydrogen gas can be produced in the laboratory by the reaction of zinc metal with an excess of dilute hydrochloric acid:

$$Zn(s) + 2\ HCl(aq) \rightarrow ZnCl_2(aq) + H_2(g)$$

Calculate the mass of zinc metal needed to produce 250 mL of hydrogen gas at 21°C and 100 kPa pressure.

Section 9.2 Review

Understanding Concepts

1. State Avogadro's hypothesis in your own words, and explain how it provides the explanation for the law of combining volumes.

2. Illustrate how Gay-Lussac's volume data led to the conclusion that a molecule of nitrogen(I) oxide contains 2 atoms of nitrogen and 1 atom of oxygen.

3. Define molar volume in your own words, and give its numerical value at STP and SATP.

Applying Inquiry/ Communication Skills

4. A sample of a gaseous halogen, X_2, has a mass of 0.820 g. An equal volume of neon gas at the same temperature and pressure has a mass of 0.231 g. Calculate the molar mass of the halogen, and deduce its identity.

5. Nitrogen gas and oxygen gas can be made to combine at a high temperature to form dinitrogen oxide:
$$2 \ N_2(g) + O_2(g) \rightarrow 2 \ N_2O(g)$$
Calculate the volume of:
a) nitrogen
b) oxygen that would be required to form 1.25 L of dinitrogen oxide.

Assume that all gas volumes are measured at the same temperature and pressure.

6. Propane burns in oxygen according to the following equation:
$$CH_3CH_2CH_3(g) + 5 \ O_2(g) \rightarrow \\ 3 \ CO_2(g) + 4 \ H_2O(g)$$
Assume all gases are at the same temperature and pressure.
a) Calculate the volume of oxygen that would be required to burn 225 L of propane.
b) Calculate the volumes of carbon dioxide and water that would be produced when 225 L of propane burn in this manner.

7. Sodium metal reacts with water to form hydrogen gas and sodium hydroxide:
$$2 \ Na(s) + 2 \ H_2O(l) \rightarrow \\ 2 \ NaOH(aq) + H_2(g)$$
In an experiment, 0.815 L of hydrogen gas is collected at STP.
a) Calculate the mass of sodium that was added to an excess of water to produce this volume of gas.
b) If the resulting solution is evaporated until dry, calculate the remaining mass of sodium hydroxide.

8. Rusting is a major problem in our steel-based technology (steel cars, ships, etc.). The process can be simply described as the reaction of iron with oxygen to form iron(III) oxide:
$$4 \ Fe(s) + 3 \ O_2(g) \rightarrow 2 \ Fe_2O_3(s)$$
Calculate the volume of oxygen that will be absorbed at SATP by the rusting of 1.00 t of iron.

9. Ammonium sulfate reacts with warm sodium hydroxide solution as follows:
$$(NH_4)_2SO_4(aq) + 2 \ NaOH(aq) \rightarrow \\ Na_2SO_4(aq) + 2 \ H_2O(l) + 2 \ NH_3(g)$$
A mass of 1.20 g of ammonium sulfate is dissolved in an excess of sodium hydroxide solution. Determine the volume of ammonia produced at 21°C and a pressure of 102 kPa.

Making Connections

10. Review the Then and Now feature in this section to recall why Avogadro's ideas were rejected for 50 years. Write a short essay on the issues related to scientific research and their implications.

11. Chemists should devise a method of raising the *Titanic* by the use of chemical reactions that generate gaseous products. Write a report either agreeing or disagreeing with the above statement. Defend your position from ethical, social, and environmental perspectives.

9.3 Calculations Involving Dalton's Law of Partial Pressures

Key Understandings

When you have completed this section, you will be able to:

- use Dalton's law of partial pressures to solve problems involving chemical reactions
- perform stoichiometric calculations involving partial pressure problems
- use appropriate scientific vocabulary to communicate ideas related to partial pressures

You learned that gases are produced in many chemical reactions. For example, you studied the decomposition reaction,

$$2 \text{ H}_2\text{O}_2(aq) \xrightarrow{\text{MnO}_2} 2 \text{ H}_2\text{O}(l) + \text{O}_2(g)$$

the single displacement reaction,

$$\text{Zn}(s) + 2 \text{ HCl}(aq) \rightarrow \text{ZnCl}_2(aq) + \text{H}_2(g)$$

and the double displacement reaction,

$$\text{CaCO}_3(s) + 2 \text{ HCl}(aq) \rightarrow \text{CaCl}_2(aq) + \text{H}_2\text{O}(l) + \text{CO}_2(g)$$

In the laboratory preparation of gases such as oxygen and hydrogen, the gas is usually collected by the displacement of water (Figure 9.15). When all the water is displaced, the pressure of the gas in the jar is equal to the atmospheric pressure. The jar is now full of the gas that you are preparing ... or is it? As discussed in the last chapter, some of the water molecules in the gas jar will have sufficient energy to change into the vapour phase. Therefore, your jar really contains a mixture of two gases: the gas you are collecting and water vapour.

Suppose you are collecting hydrogen gas over water at 25°C, and the measured laboratory pressure is 101.8 kPa. The pressure of hydrogen in the jar will be less than this since the water vapour will exert a pressure of 2.3 kPa at this temperature (this value is obtained from vapour pressure tables). You can calculate the pressure of hydrogen in the jar to be 101.8 kPa − 2.3 kPa = 99.5 kPa.

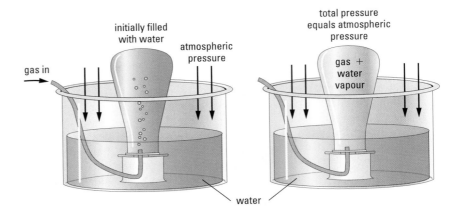

FIGURE 9.15 Collecting a gas by the displacement of water. The gas-filled jar also contains water vapour.

EXAMPLE 6

A student collecting 245 mL of oxygen gas by the method illustrated in Figure 9.15 records the atmospheric pressure as 99.2 kPa and the temperature in the laboratory as 24°C. Given that the vapour pressure of water is 3.0 kPa at 24°C, what mass of oxygen has been collected?

Given
$V_{O_2} = 245$ mL $= 0.245$ L, $P_{atm} = 99.2$ kPa, $P_{H_2O} = 3.0$ kPa,
$T = 273 + 24 = 297$ K

Required
mass oxygen, $m_{O_2} = ?$ g

Analysis
$P_{atm} \rightarrow P_{O_2}$ (using $P_{O_2} = P_{atm} - P_{H_2O}$)

$P_{O_2} \rightarrow n_{O_2}$ $\left(\text{using } n_{O_2} = \dfrac{P_{O_2}V}{RT}\right)$

$n_{O_2} \rightarrow m_{O_2}$ (using $M_{O_2} = 32.00$ g·mol^{-1})

Solution
$P_{O_2} = 99.2$ kPa $- 3.0$ kPa $= 96.2$ kPa

$$n_{O_2} = \frac{(96.2 \text{ kPa})(0.245 \text{ L})}{(8.31 \text{ kPa·L·mol}^{-1}\text{·K}^{-1})(297 \text{ K})} = 9.55 \times 10^{-3} \text{ mol}$$

$$m_{O_2} = 9.55 \times 10^{-3} \text{ mol O}_2 \times \frac{32.00 \text{ g}}{1 \text{ mol O}_2} = 0.306 \text{ g}$$

Statement
The mass of oxygen gas collected is 0.306 g.

PRACTICE PROBLEM

In an experiment, a student collects 375 mL of dinitrogen oxide gas at 19°C and 100.2 kPa. Calculate the mass of dinitrogen oxide gas that has been collected. (The vapour pressure of water at 19°C is 2.2 kPa.)

The partial pressure problem can be combined with gas stoichiometry as is shown in the next example.

EXAMPLE 7

Oxygen gas can be produced by heating potassium chlorate in the presence of a catalyst, such as manganese(IV) oxide:

$$2 \text{ KClO}_3(s) \xrightarrow[\text{MnO}_2]{\Delta} 2 \text{ KCl}(s) + 3 \text{ O}_2(g)$$

At the completion of the reaction, 45.0 mL of oxygen gas are collected at an atmospheric pressure of 101.0 kPa and a laboratory temperature of 22°C. If the vapour pressure of water at 22°C is 2.6 kPa, what mass of potassium chlorate was used?

FIGURE 9.16 For most commercial aircraft, the oxygen supply for the emergency oxygen masks is produced when needed from the decomposition of potassium chlorate contained in cylinders. This is a much more compact and low-weight method of oxygen storage than thick-walled high-pressure cylinders of the gas itself.

Oxygen gas can be produced by adding manganese(IV) oxide to a solution of hydrogen peroxide.

$$2\ H_2O_2(aq) \xrightarrow{\text{MnO}_2} 2\ H_2O(l) + O_2(g)$$

Calculate the mass of hydrogen peroxide needed to produce 100.0 mL of oxygen gas collected over water at 22°C. The atmospheric pressure is 101.8 kPa, and the vapour pressure of water at this temperature is 2.6 kPa.

Given

$$2\ KClO_3(s) \xrightarrow[\text{MnO}_2]{\Delta} 2\ KCl(s) + 3\ O_2(g)$$

2 mol   3 mol

$P_{O_2} = 101.0 \text{ kPa} - 2.6 \text{ kPa} = 98.4 \text{ kPa}$

$V_{O_2} = 45 \text{ mL} = 4.5 \times 10^{-2} \text{ L}$

$T_{O_2} = 273 + 22 = 295 \text{ K}$

Required

mass of potassium chlorate, $m_{KClO_3} = ?$ g

Analysis

$V_{O_2} \to n_{O_2}$ $\left(\text{using ideal gas law, } n = \dfrac{PV}{RT}\right)$

$n_{O_2} \to n_{KClO_3}$ (using mole ratio, 2 mol $KClO_3$: 3 mol O_2)

$n_{KClO_3} \to m_{KClO_3}$ (using $M_{KClO_3} = 122.55$ g·mol^{-1})

Solution

$$n_{O_2} = \frac{(98.4 \text{ kPa})(4.5 \times 10^{-2} \text{ L})}{(8.31 \text{ kPa·L·mol}^{-1}\text{·K}^{-1})(295 \text{ K})} = 1.81 \times 10^{-3} \text{ mol } O_2$$

$$n_{KClO_3} = 1.81 \times 10^{-3} \text{ mol } O_2 \times \frac{2 \text{ mol } KClO_3}{3 \text{ mol } O_2} = 1.20 \times 10^{-3} \text{ mol } KClO_3$$

$$m_{KClO_3} = 1.20 \times 10^{-3} \text{ mol } KClO_3 \times \frac{122.55 \text{ g } KClO_3}{1 \text{ mol } KClO_3} = 0.148 \text{ g } KClO_3$$

Statement

A mass of 0.148 g of potassium chlorate is required to produce 45 mL of oxygen gas under these conditions.

Discovering Chemistry

How Much Fizz Does an Alka-Seltzer™ Tablet Produce?

An Alka-Seltzer™ tablet contains sodium hydrogen carbonate, citric acid, and an analgesic (painkiller). When water is added, the hydrogen ions from the citric acid react with the hydrogen carbonate ion as follows:

$$H^+(aq) + NaHCO_3(aq) \to H_2O(l) + CO_2(g) + Na^+(aq)$$

If you measure the volume of carbon dioxide formed, you can find the percentage of sodium hydrogen carbonate in a tablet.

Materials

    unbroken Alka-Seltzer™ tablet
    1-L beaker
    100-mL graduated cylinder
    centigram balance
    thermometer

1. Fill a 100-mL graduated cylinder with water, cover the mouth with the palm of your hand, and then invert it into a 1-L beaker containing about 700 mL of water.

2. Open an Alka-Seltzer™ packet, and determine the mass of an unbroken tablet.

3. Lift the graduated cylinder until the rim is just under the surface.

4. Quickly place the tablet under the mouth of the graduated cylinder, keeping your fingers across the mouth to prevent the tablet from escaping.

5. When no more gas is formed, lift the cylinder until the water levels inside and out are the same (if this is possible). Then read the volume of gas produced. (If the volume is greater than 100 mL, estimate the total volume.) Record the water temperature and laboratory pressure.

■ Using a table of vapour pressures for water, calculate the pressure due to the carbon dioxide gas.

■ From the volume, pressure, and temperature of carbon dioxide, calculate the amount of carbon dioxide produced. Using the amount of carbon dioxide and the balanced chemical equation, calculate the amount of sodium hydrogen carbonate in the tablet.

■ From the mass of sodium hydrogen carbonate and the total mass of the tablet, calculate the percent of sodium hydrogen carbonate in the tablet.

■ Calculate the class average, and discuss the major sources of error.

■ Suggest how the experiment could be improved. Discuss the advantages of such a tablet over an analgesic tablet or caplet. Describe the disadvantages. Suggest why citric acid is used rather than any other acid.

Section 9.3 Review

Applying Inquiry/ Communication Skills

1. You are a member of a space flight to planet X. On landing, you find that the atmosphere (by volume) is 25% water vapour, 50% carbon dioxide, 4% oxygen, and 21% nitrogen. The normal atmospheric pressure on the planet is 800 kPa. Describe the contribution each gas makes to the air pressure on planet X.

2. Calculate the volume of nitrogen, measured at 20°C and 92 kPa, that is required to react with calcium carbide (CaC_2) to produce carbon and 100.0 g of calcium cyanamide ($CaCN_2$).

3. When iron(III) sulfate is heated slowly, it decomposes according to the following equation:

$$Fe_2(SO_4)_3(s) \rightarrow Fe_2O_3(s) + 3\ SO_3(g)$$

Calculate the maximum volume of sulfur trioxide, measured at 25°C and 102 kPa, that can be expected from the decomposition of 6.00 g of iron(III) sulfate.

4. Zinc metal reacts with hydrochloric acid to give zinc chloride and hydrogen gas:

$$Zn(s) + 2\ HCl(aq) \rightarrow ZnCl_2(aq) + H_2(g)$$

If the hydrogen gas is collected by the displacement of water, calculate the volume of "wet hydrogen" that will be collected at 19°C and 102.3 kPa from the reaction of 0.218 g of zinc with an excess of hydrochloric acid.

5. In an experiment, 28.6 mL of hydrogen gas was collected over water at a pressure of 762 mm Hg and a temperature of 15°C. Assuming the vapour pressure of

water at 15°C is 13 mm Hg, calculate the mass of hydrogen obtained.

6. Manganese(IV) oxide reacts with an excess of concentrated hydrochloric acid to give manganese(II) chloride solution, chlorine gas, and water:

$MnO_2(s) + 4\ HCl(aq) \rightarrow$
$\quad MnCl_2(aq) + 2\ H_2O(l) + 2\ Cl_2(g)$

In an experiment, 34.0 mL of chlorine gas are collected over water at a temperature of 20°C and a pressure of 101.5 kPa. Assuming the vapour pressure of water at 20°C is 2.3 kPa, calculate the mass of manganese(IV) oxide used.

7. A student collects 41.4 mL of oxygen gas having a pressure of 98.3 kPa at 26.0°C by the displacement of water. The water levels inside and outside the collection tube are equal. Calculate the amount of oxygen (moles) present in the sample. Calculate how many molecules are present.

8. Nitrogen is collected by the displacement of water at 26.0°C. When the water levels inside and outside the cylinder are equal, the total pressure is 99.3 kPa. Calculate the partial pressure of the nitrogen.

9. 30.0 g of CO_2, 42.0 g of N_2, and 48.0 g of SO_2 are mixed in a container, and they exert a total pressure of 140 kPa. Calculate the partial pressure of each gas.

10. 248 mL of a gas are collected by the downward displacement of water. The temperature of the gas and the water is 29°C, and the barometric pressure is 104 kPa.

a) Calculate the partial pressure of the gas.
b) Calculate the volume of this gas at STP.
c) Calculate how many moles of the gas are collected.

9.4 Reactions Involving Gases and Solutions

Key Understandings

When you have completed this section, you will be able to:

- solve stoichiometric problems involving chemical reactions with gases and solutions
- determine the value of the ideal gas constant by performing an experiment
- use appropriate scientific vocabulary to communicate ideas related to reactions involving gases

INFOBIT

To extract various gases from air for industrial uses, the air is first cooled and liquefied. As the liquid air warms up, the gas with the lowest boiling point vaporizes first. This gas is then cooled and collected as a liquid. This process of a gas being vaporized, cooled and collected is continued until all the different gases have been separated. The process is called fractional distillation, and is also used to separate various petroleum products from crude oil.

In Chapter 5, you saw how to calculate masses involved in chemical reactions. In Chapter 7, you learned how to calculate volumes of solution involved in chemical reactions. In this chapter, you studied the calculation of volumes of gases involved in chemical reactions. This section is designed to show you how to perform a stoichiometric calculation using any combination of information involving solids, liquids, or gases. Figure 9.17 shows a flowchart that summarizes the possible permutations of information about the given species A and the required species B.

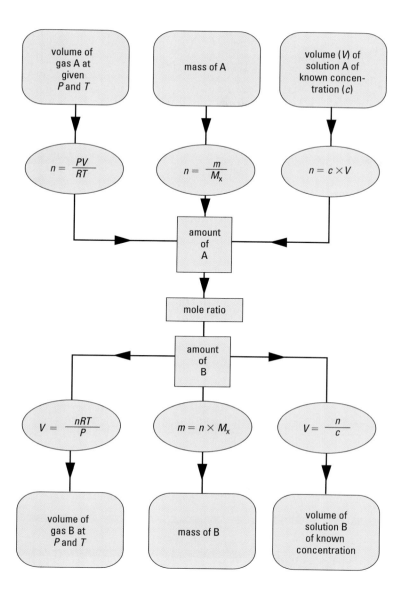

FIGURE 9.17 A summary of the mole method approach to solving problems

Here are some examples that involve the three different problem-solving routes.

EXAMPLE 8

In the presence of manganese(IV) oxide, hydrogen peroxide decomposes to form oxygen gas and water.

$$2\ H_2O_2(aq) \xrightarrow{\ MnO_2\ } 2\ H_2O(l) + O_2(g)$$

What volume of oxygen gas will be produced at 21°C and 103 kPa from 125 mL of 6.00 mol·L^{-1} hydrogen peroxide solution?

Given

$$2\ H_2O_2(aq) \xrightarrow{\text{MnO}_2} 2\ H_2O(l)\ +\ O_2(g)$$

2 mol   1 mol

$V_{H_2O_2} = 125\ mL = 0.125\ L$ $P_{O_2} = 103\ kPa$

$c_{H_2O_2} = 6.00\ mol \cdot L^{-1}$ $T_{O_2} = 273 + 21 = 294\ K$

Required

volume of oxygen gas, $V_{O_2} = ?\ L$

Analysis

Using Figure 9.17 to solve this problem, you need to take the top right fork and then proceed down to the bottom left fork.

$$V_{H_2O_2} \rightarrow n_{H_2O_2}\ \left(\text{using } c = \frac{n}{V}\right)$$

$n_{H_2O_2} \rightarrow n_{O_2}$ (using mole ratio, 2 mol H_2O_2 : 1 mol O_2)

$n_{O_2} \rightarrow V_{O_2}$ (using $PV = nRT$)

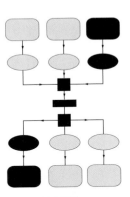

FIGURE 9.18

Solution

$n_{H_2O_2} = 6.00\ mol \cdot L^{-1} \times 0.125\ L = 0.750\ mol\ H_2O_2$

$n_{O_2} = 0.750\ mol\ H_2O_2 \times \dfrac{1\ mol\ O_2}{2\ mol\ H_2O_2} = 0.375\ mol\ O_2$

$V_{O_2} = \dfrac{(0.375\ mol)(8.31\ kPa \cdot L \cdot mol^{-1} \cdot K^{-1})(294\ K)}{103\ kPa} = 8.89\ L$

Statement

A volume of 8.89 L of oxygen gas will be produced at 21°C and 103 kPa from 125 mL of 6.00 mol·L⁻¹ hydrogen peroxide solution.

PRACTICE PROBLEM

Nitric acid reacts with hydrogen sulfide gas according to the equation:

2 HNO₃(aq) + 3 H₂S(g) →
    3 S(s) + 2 NO(g) + 4 H₂O(l)

Calculate the volume of nitrous monoxide that would be produced at 15°C and 120 kPa from 145 mL of 6.00 mol·L⁻¹ nitric acid.

EXAMPLE 9

Lithium metal reacts with hydrochloric acid to produce lithium chloride and hydrogen gas. If 1.3 g of lithium metal are used, what is the minimum volume of 3.0 mol·L⁻¹ hydrochloric acid that is needed for a complete reaction?

Given

$$2\ Li(s)\ +\ 2\ HCl(aq)\ \rightarrow\ 2\ LiCl(aq) + H_2(g)$$

2 mol   2 mol

$m_{Li} = 1.3\ g$ $c_{HCl} = 3.0\ mol \cdot L^{-1}$

Required

volume of hydrochloric acid, $V_{HCl} = ?\ L$

Analysis
Using Figure 9.17 to solve this problem, you need to take the top centre fork and then proceed down to the bottom right fork.

$m_{Li} \rightarrow n_{Li}$ (using $M_{Li} = 6.94$ g·mol^{-1})

$n_{Li} \rightarrow n_{HCl}$ (using mole ratio, 2 mol Li : 2 mol HCl)

$n_{HCl} \rightarrow V_{HCl}$ $\left(\text{using } c = \dfrac{n}{V}\right)$

Solution

$n_{Li} = 1.3 \text{ g Li} \times \dfrac{1 \text{ mol Li}}{63.55 \text{ g Li}} = 0.187 \text{ mol Li}$

$n_{HCl} = 0.187 \text{ mol Li} \times \dfrac{2 \text{ mol HCl}}{2 \text{ mol Li}}$

$= 0.187 \text{ mol HCl}$

$V_{HCl} = \dfrac{0.187 \text{ mol}}{6.24 \text{ mol·L}^{-1}} = 3.0 \times 10^{-2} \text{ L}$

$= 62.4 \text{ mL}$

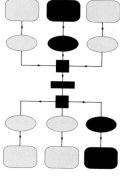

FIGURE 9.19

Statement
A minimum volume of 62.4 mL of 3.0 mol·L^{-1} hydrochloric acid is needed to react with 1.3 g of lithium metal.

PRACTICE PROBLEM

Nickel reacts with sulfuric acid to produce nickel(II) sulfate and hydrogen gas. If 4.2 g of nickel is used, calculate the minimum volume of 6.0 mol·L^{-1} sulfuric acid that is needed for a complete reaction.

EXAMPLE 10

In Example 9, you calculated the minimum volume of nitric acid needed to react with 25.0 g of copper metal in this reaction:

$3 \text{ Cu}(s) + 8 \text{ HNO}_3(aq) \rightarrow 3 \text{ Cu(NO}_3)_2(aq) + 2 \text{ NO}(g) + 4 \text{ H}_2\text{O}(l)$

What volume of dry nitrogen monoxide gas would be produced from 25.0 g of copper metal at a temperature of 22°C and a pressure of 102 kPa?

Given
$3 \text{ Cu}(s) + 8 \text{ HNO}_3(aq) \rightarrow 3 \text{ Cu(NO}_3)_2(aq) + 4 \text{ H}_2\text{O}(l) + 2 \text{ NO}(g)$

3 mol   2 mol

$m_{Cu} = 25.0$ g $P_{NO} = 102$ kPa

                                 $T_{NO} = 273 + 22 = 295$ K

Required
volume of nitrogen oxide gas, $V_{NO} = ?$ L

Analysis
Using Figure 9.17 to solve this problem, you need to take the top centre fork and then proceed down to the bottom left fork.

$m_{Cu} \rightarrow n_{Cu}$ (using $M_{Cu} = 63.55$ g·mol^{-1})

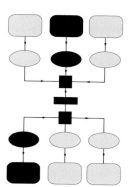

FIGURE 9.20

$n_{Cu} \rightarrow n_{NO}$ (using mole ratio, 3 mol Cu : 2 mol NO)

$n_{NO} \rightarrow V_{NO}$ (using $PV = nRT$)

Solution

$n_{Cu} = 25.0 \text{ g Cu} \times \dfrac{1 \text{ mol Cu}}{63.55 \text{ g Cu}} = 0.393 \text{ mol Cu}$

$n_{HNO_3} = 0.393 \text{ mol Cu} \times \dfrac{2 \text{ mol NO}}{3 \text{ mol Cu}} = 0.262 \text{ mol NO}$

$V_{NO} = \dfrac{(0.262 \text{ mol})(8.31 \text{ kPa·L·mol}^{-1}\text{·K}^{-1})(295 \text{ K})}{102 \text{ kPa}} = 6.30 \text{ L}$

Statement

A volume of 6.30 L of dry nitrogen monoxide will be produced at 22°C and 102 kPa from 25.0 g of copper metal.

PRACTICE PROBLEM

Calcium carbonate decomposes into calcium oxide and carbon dioxide. Determine the volume of carbon dioxide that will be produced at 15°C and 80 kPa from 16.4 g of calcium carbonate.

Investigation

Refer to page 424, Investigation 2

The mole method can be used to solve problems related to reactions in which solutions and/or gases are involved. In such cases, you use the relationship for concentration and/or the ideal gas law. The common step in these calculations is to use the mole ratio.

Section 9.4 Review

Applying Inquiry/Communication Skills

1. Zinc metal reacts with nitric acid to produce hydrogen gas and a solution of zinc nitrate.

   a) Write a balanced equation for the reaction.

   b) Calculate the mass of zinc that must be reacted in order to produce 0.250 L of hydrogen gas at 25°C and 101.3 kPa.

2. The reaction between hydrochloric acid and sodium carbonate produces carbon dioxide gas, a solution of sodium chloride, and water according to the following equation:

   $2 \text{ HCl}(aq) + \text{Na}_2\text{CO}_3(aq) \rightarrow$
   $\qquad 2 \text{ NaCl}(aq) + \text{CO}_2(g) + \text{H}_2\text{O}(l)$

   Calculate the mass of sodium carbonate that must be used to produce 7.86 L of carbon dioxide gas at 19°C and 98.7 kPa.

3. White phosphorus, $\text{P}_4(s)$, is obtained by reacting calcium phosphate, silicon dioxide, and carbon at high temperatures. The reaction can be represented as follows:

   $2 \text{ Ca}_3(\text{PO}_4)_2(s) + 6 \text{ SiO}_2(s) + 5 \text{ C}(s) \rightarrow$
   $\qquad \text{P}_4(s) + 6 \text{ CaSiO}_3(s) + 5 \text{ CO}_2(g)$

   Suppose 1.00 kg of white phosphorus is formed.

   a) Calculate the volume of carbon dioxide that is produced at a temperature of 400°C and a pressure of 105 kPa.

   b) Calculate the mass of silicon dioxide (sand) and carbon (coke) that were required to form 1.00 kg of white phosphorus.

4. If a carbonated beverage is under a pressure of 500 kPa, calculate the proportion of the gas that will be released when the pressure is reduced to 100 kPa.

5. Sodium hydrogen carbonate reacts with sulfuric acid to produce carbon dioxide according to the equation:

   $2 \text{ NaHCO}_3(aq) + \text{H}_2\text{SO}_4(aq) \rightarrow$
   $\qquad \text{Na}_2\text{SO}_4(aq) + 2 \text{ H}_2\text{O}(l) + 2 \text{ CO}_2(g)$

   Calculate the volume of dry carbon dioxide (measured at SATP) that can be produced from the complete reaction of 0.250 L of 1.37 mol·L^{-1} sodium hydrogen carbonate.

6. The reaction of ammonium chloride solution with sodium hydroxide solution produces ammonia gas according to the equation:

$$NH_4Cl(aq) + NaOH(aq) \rightarrow$$
$$NaCl(aq) + H_2O(l) + NH_3(g)$$

a) Calculate the volume of a 2.50 mol·L^{-1} ammonium chloride solution that will be required to produce 2.00 L of dry ammonia collected at 25°C and 101 kPa.

b) Calculate the volume of 6.00 mol·L^{-1} sodium hydroxide that will be required to completely react with the volume of 2.50 mol·L^{-1} ammonium chloride determined in a).

7. Aluminum metal reacts with hydrochloric acid according to the following equation:

$$2 \text{ Al}(s) + 6 \text{ HCl}(aq) \rightarrow$$
$$2 \text{ AlCl}_3(aq) + 3 \text{ H}_2(g)$$

a) Calculate the minimum volume of hydrochloric acid $(6.00 \text{ mol·L}^{-1})$ required for the complete reaction of 1.08 g of aluminum.

b) Calculate the volume of hydrogen gas, measured at 20°C and 100.9 kPa, that should be produced from the reaction of 1.89 g of aluminum with excess hydrochloric acid.

c) If the resulting solution from b) is evaporated until dry, calculate the mass of $AlCl_3 \cdot 6H_2O$ crystals that will be produced.

8. Carbon dioxide is bubbled into 100.0 mL of a sodium hydroxide solution until it has been completely converted to sodium carbonate. When the solution is evaporated until dry, 2.50 g of sodium carbonate are formed.

a) Calculate the initial concentration of the sodium hydroxide solution.

b) Deduce the volume of carbon dioxide gas that had been absorbed at 19°C and 99.7 kPa.

9. If a chemical process uses 1.0×10^3 mol of CO_2 per hour at 20°C and 90 kPa, calculate the volume of CO_2 that will be taken in by the plant per hour on a hot summer day at 29°C and 104 kPa.

9.5 An Introduction to the Atmosphere

Key Understandings

When you have completed this section, you will be able to:
- identify the different components of the atmosphere
- apply knowledge of gases to the study of atmospheric chemistry
- describe the purpose of the Montreal Protocol and its long-term goals
- name the greenhouse gases, and explain how they affect the atmosphere
- explain the purpose of the Kyoto Protocol, and identify some of its shortcomings
- develop alternative courses of action, and assume personal responsibility for our planet
- use appropriate scientific vocabulary to communicate ideas related to atmospheric chemistry

Although there are many important gas reactions, the most important are those that occur in the incredibly thin gaseous layer that surrounds Earth. One of the most important things to note is the uniqueness of our atmosphere compared with that of the other major planets (Table 9.1). The outer planets have atmospheres containing hydrogen and helium, while the inner planets apart from Earth have atmospheres of carbon dioxide and nitrogen (Figure 9.21). Only Earth has predominantly nitrogen and oxygen in the atmosphere.

TABLE 9.1 The Most Common Gas Components of the Planets with Atmospheres

Planet	Hydrogen, H_2	Helium, He	Carbon Dioxide, CO_2	Nitrogen, N_2	Oxygen, O_2
Venus			96%	3%	
Earth			trace	78%	21%
Mars			95%	3%	
Jupiter	90%	10%			
Saturn	96%	4%			
Uranus	85%	15%			
Neptune	85%	15%			

FIGURE 9.21 The atmosphere of Jupiter, like that of all the outer planets, consists almost entirely of hydrogen and helium.

What Is in Our Atmosphere?

The two major gases in our atmosphere are nitrogen and oxygen, but there are many more, some in very tiny proportions. Some of these trace gases are important in controlling the atmosphere. For example, both water vapour and carbon dioxide contribute to the greenhouse effect. Table 9.2 lists all the gases present in the atmosphere above a proportion of one part per million (ppm).

TABLE 9.2 The Percentages of All Atmospheric Gases Present at Greater Than 1 ppm

Gas	Percentage in a Dry Air Sample
nitrogen, N_2	78.083
oxygen, O_2	20.945
argon, Ar	0.933
water, H_2O	variable
carbon dioxide, CO_2	0.0364
neon, Ne	0.0018
helium, He	0.0005
methane, CH_4	0.0002
krypton, Kr	0.0001

Oxygen gas, O_2, is the reactive gas necessary for respiration. Carbon-containing compounds burn in it, so without it, our stocks of oil, coal, and wood would be useless. It is the process of photosynthesis that keeps recycling carbon dioxide into oxygen. In fact, if photosynthesis were suddenly to cease, it would take only 20 years for all the oxygen in the atmosphere to be converted to carbon dioxide. The presence of oxygen in a planet's atmosphere is an immediate indicator of biological processes. As space telescopes become ever more sophisticated, we will be able to identify Earth-like planets around other stars and search for the characteristic radiation from oxygen molecules. That would provide immediate confirmation of life elsewhere in the universe without having to visit neighbouring stars, which would take thousands of years.

WEBLINK

Our moon possesses hardly any atmosphere, but some of the moons of the outer planets have significant gas pressures. One of the moons with a very substantial atmosphere is Titan. Research the composition of Titan's atmosphere. Begin your research at **www.pearsoned.ca/chemistry11**.

It is tempting to dismiss the major component of the atmosphere, unreactive nitrogen gas, N_2, as unimportant. But this is far from the truth. If our atmosphere were predominantly oxygen, forest fires would be far more intense, raging uncontrollably across our planet. Nitrogen dilutes the oxygen, thereby reducing the severity of fires. Nitrogen gas is also absorbed by certain bacteria that convert it into nitrogen compounds in the soil, which are necessary for plant growth (Figure 9.22).

Few people realize that the next atmospheric component in order of concentration is argon, a member of the noble gas family. The argon has been formed over time from the radioactive decay of one isotope of potassium, potassium-40. About 0.1% of all potassium on Earth is of this isotope. Fortunately, the isotope has a half-life of about a billion years. This means that its level of radioactivity is very low, so you don't have to worry about the radioactive dosage from potassium-rich foods. However, over the lifetime of Earth, the decay has been enough to contribute enough argon to now comprise 1% of our atmosphere.

To the nearest percent, those three gases make up 100% of dry air. But our planet is not dry. In the tropics, there is about 4% water vapour in the atmosphere, a figure that drops to less than 1% in the Arctic and desert regions.

Where Did Our Atmosphere Come From?

Geochemists generally agree that our present atmosphere is probably Earth's third. Almost nothing is known about the composition of the atmosphere when Earth first formed. Possibly it contained a mixture of helium, hydrogen, methane, ammonia, and nitrogen. As volcanic activity released gases from within Earth, the concentration of carbon dioxide increased to levels far greater than those of today. This was fortunate, for the sun at that time was between 25% and 30% fainter than present times, so a large "greenhouse effect" was necessary to keep our planet warm.

As the acidic, carbonic acid–rich rains lashed the land, the rocks were weathered. As a result, the silicate minerals were partially converted to carbonates, such as calcium carbonate, "locking up" over 99.99% of the carbon dioxide of that early atmosphere. In addition, bacteria evolved to use photosynthesis as their energy source, converting most of the remaining carbon dioxide into oxygen. By about 700 million years ago, the partial pressure of oxygen in the atmosphere had reached about 7 kPa—enough to enable jellyfish-like creatures to survive.

The continual increase in oxygen concentrations in the seas enabled ever more complex marine organisms to develop. However, organisms could not survive on the land, which was still bathed in intense ultraviolet light from the sun. It was not until about 550 million years ago, when the oxygen level reached about 10 kPa, that an ozone layer started to form in the stratosphere, making the land surface habitable. By about 400 million years ago, the composition of the atmosphere began to resemble our present-day environment (Figure 9.23).

The Stratosphere and the Ozone Layer

The **stratosphere** is a layer of atmosphere located some 10 km above us and has a depth of 40 km. In this region, the chemistry is very different from that on the surface of Earth. As a result of the very low air pressure, many atoms

FIGURE 9.22 Plants need nitrogen in the form of nitrates for growth. Special nodules in the roots of legumes (peas, beans, clover) have bacteria that convert atmospheric nitrogen into nitrates.

WORD**ORIGIN**

Stratosphere (strat'-o-sfear) comes from the Latin word *stratus* (layer) and the Greek word *spheraira* (sphere).

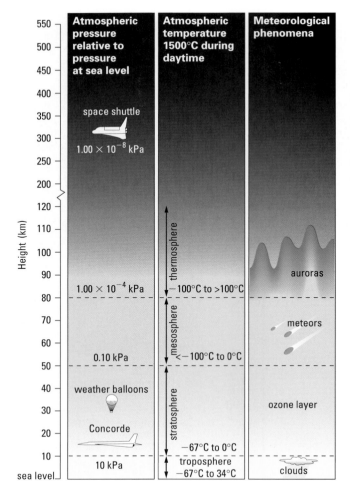

| Atmospheric pressure relative to pressure at sea level | Atmospheric temperature 1500°C during daytime | Meteorological phenomena |

FIGURE 9.23 There are four main regions within the atmosphere of our planet: the troposphere (from sea level to 10 km), the stratosphere (10 km to 50 km), the mesosphere (50 km to 80 km), and the thermosphere (80 km to 120 km).

and molecules exist in the stratosphere that would be rapidly destroyed at sea level by collisions with oxygen or other substances. These species include ozone, which, by blocking most of the sun's ultraviolet rays, enables life to survive on the surface of this planet.

The Ozone Cycle

How does ozone protect you? The initial step of the **ozone cycle** is the fragmentation of oxygen molecules by intense ultraviolet light:

$$O_2(g) \xrightarrow{\text{uv light}} 2\ O(g)$$

The oxygen atoms then combine with oxygen molecules to form ozone molecules:

$$O(g) + O_2(g) \rightarrow O_3(g)$$

Once the ozone is produced, it absorbs a wide range of ultraviolet light, itself being decomposed into oxygen atoms and molecules:

$$O_3(g) \xrightarrow{\text{uv light}} O_2(g) + O(g)$$

This reaction prevents most of the sun's ultraviolet light from reaching Earth's surface. The oxygen molecules and atoms can then recombine to form ozone, and the cycle starts again:

$$O(g) + O_2(g) \rightarrow O_3(g)$$

These last two steps can happen repeatedly, absorbing photon (energy particle that makes up light) after photon of ultraviolet light before the presence of some other atom or molecule breaks the cycle.

The Chlorofluorocarbon Problem

In 1946, **chlorofluorocarbons (CFCs)** first came on the market. This family of molecules containing carbon, chlorine, and fluorine promised to usher in a new era of benign chemistry. Being completely non-toxic, the molecules could be used to replace an enormous range of flammable and toxic compounds (Figure 9.25).

CFCs became a major product of the chemical industry. It was not until the 1970s that two chemists, Mario Molina and F. Sherwood Rowland, showed that the CFC molecules were so stable that they spread unchanged through the troposphere and up into the stratosphere, where ultraviolet light fragmented them, releasing chlorine atoms. These chlorine atoms, called **radicals**, are very reactive because each atom has an unpaired electron. They can, then, attack the ozone molecules and oxygen atoms, removing them from the cycle. The steps are as follows:

$$Cl(g) + O_3(g) \rightarrow ClO(g) + O_2(g)$$
$$ClO(g) + O(g) \rightarrow Cl(g) + O_2(g)$$

TABLE 9.3 The Most Important Chlorofluorocarbons

Trade Name	Formula	Uses
CFC-11	$CFCl_3$	aerosols, foams, air conditioning
CFC-12	CF_2Cl_2	aerosols, foams, air conditioning
CFC-113	$C_2F_3Cl_3$	cleaning electronic components
halon-1211	CF_2ClBr	fire extinguishing
halon-1301	CF_3Br	fire extinguishing
halon-2402	$C_2F_4Br_2$	fire extinguishing
halothan	C_2HF_3ClBr	inhalation anesthetic

Having removed one ozone molecule and oxygen atom from the ultraviolet-light absorbing cycle, the chlorine atom is reformed, enabling it to attack another ozone molecule and another. It is the ability of one chlorine atom to destroy hundreds or thousands of ozone molecules in chain reactions that makes it such a problem.

Saving the Ozone Layer: The Montreal Protocol

Now that scientists are aware of the hazards, CFCs are being phased out—but only slowly. To replace CFCs in many of their uses, chemists have synthesized **hydrochlorofluorocarbons—HCFCs**. These are molecules that contain hydrogen in addition to chlorine, fluorine, and carbon. The presence of hydrogen in the molecule enables the hydroxyl radical, OH, to break down most of the molecules while they are still in the troposphere. An international agreement in Montreal in 1987—the **Montreal Protocol**—specified the rate at which replacement of CFCs should occur. Unfortunately, HCFCs are much more complex and expensive to synthesize, and old air conditioners cannot use the new compounds. As a result, poorer countries are being allowed to phase out their use of CFCs more slowly than richer, industrialized countries. This concept does appear reasonable—except that part of the production of poorer countries is being smuggled into rich countries to enable air conditioner users to replenish their old units without buying new HCFC-containing ones. In fact, smuggling has grown to the point where CFCs are the second biggest illegal import through Miami after illicit drugs.

HCFCs are only a temporary measure until chemists can devise new chemical compounds that are totally environmentally benign and can be used in place of CFCs. For example, Canada plans to ban the production and importation of HCFCs by the year 2020 (Figure 9.26).

Canada has exceeded the Montreal requirements, primarily through industrial initiatives. DuPont Canada, formerly the largest manufacturer of CFCs in Canada, phased out production in 1993. Instead, it produces HCFC-123, which has only 2% of the ozone-depleting capacity of the CFCs. The major Canadian auto manufacturers have largely

FIGURE 9.24 First launch of Bristol Aerospace's Black Brant 12 suborbital rocket in 1988. Rockets are used as part of Canada's upper atmospheric research.

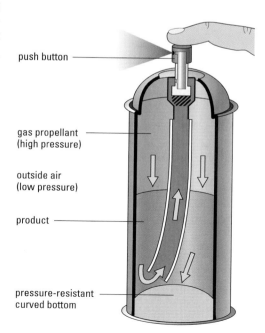

push button

gas propellant (high pressure)

outside air (low pressure)

product

pressure-resistant curved bottom

FIGURE 9.25 CFCs were often used as propellants for aerosol cans. Find out what gases are being used as replacements. Do you always need to use aerosol cans, or could you use the pump-action dispensers instead?

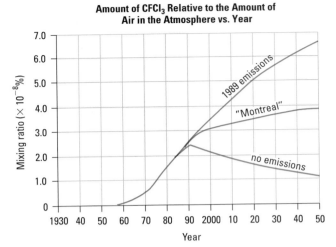

Amount of CFCl₃ Relative to the Amount of Air in the Atmosphere vs. Year

FIGURE 9.26 Without the Montreal Protocol, the use of CFCs would have continued to climb, causing an even more severe depletion of the ozone layer.

shifted to the use of chlorine-free hydrofluorocarbons (HFCs) in automobile air conditioning systems. In 1987, Northern Telecom (now Nortel) was the largest single Canadian user of ozone-depleting solvents, globally consuming about 1000 t of CFCs per year to clean printed circuit boards. Its $1 million research program between 1988 and 1991 found non-CFC replacements that actually saved the company $4 million in solvent purchases and disposal. 3M Canada developed a new family of chemicals, hydrofluoro-ethers (HFEs), for use as propellants in inhalers for the over 1 million asthma sufferers in Canada. These HFE propellants are environmentally benign, unlike the CFCs in the older inhalers. Some drug manufacturers use HFE propellants, while others have developed propellant-free inhaler systems. Finally, just as you have blue boxes for recycling household materials, there is now a Blue Bottle® that companies can use to recycle CFCs from older CFC-using equipment such as refrigeration units.

The Antarctic Ozone Hole

About 30 years ago, atmospheric scientists were stunned to discover a massive depletion of ozone in the lower stratosphere above the Antarctic continent. This "**Antarctic ozone hole**" consists of a decrease in ultraviolet-filtering ozone concentration by about 50% from September to November—spring in the southern hemisphere. Although you might think that the hole is unimportant because no one permanently lives in Antarctica, it is very important. Around the Antarctic continent, the seas are rich in photosynthetic organisms. This means that those cold waters supply a significant portion of the oxygen in our atmosphere. In addition, the organisms are food for a large variety of fish and marine mammals. If a higher concentration of ultraviolet rays reaches the surface waters, it is predicted that many of the organisms will not survive, which will affect fishing as well as our oxygen supply.

Scientists are now aware that chlorine, predominantly from the breakdown of CFCs, is at the root of the dramatic drop in ozone concentration. It has been the task of atmospheric chemists to deduce the process by which the elevated levels of chlorine actually cause the destruction of the ozone. The saga is believed to begin with the buildup of chlorine molecules during the dark winter over the Antarctic and, to a lesser extent, over the Arctic. During the winter, the air masses over the poles do not mix with the surrounding air. As a result, very low temperatures (e.g., −80°C) exist over Antarctica and a reservoir of chlorine forms. At these low temperatures, tiny ice crystals form, which act as surfaces on which the ozone destruction will occur. This is why ozone depletion occurs near the poles and not in warmer regions. The sequence of chemical reactions commences within this cold, isolated air.

With the arrival of spring, the sun's rays cause the chlorine molecules to fragment into chlorine atoms:

$$Cl_2(g) \xrightarrow{\text{light}} 2\ Cl(g)$$

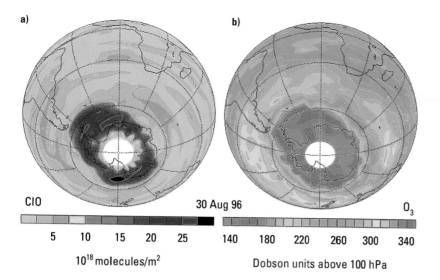

a)

b)

CIO   30 Aug 96 O_3

5 10 15 20 25   140 180 220 260 300 340

10^{18} molecules/m²   Dobson units above 100 hPa

FIGURE 9.27 a) As the ozone hole has grown, b) so has the concentration of chlorine monoxide. It is believed that the rise in concentration of chlorine monoxide has led to the decrease in ozone. The units for measuring total ozone are dobson units (DU), named after G. Dobson, a British physicist. One DU is equal to 2.69×10^{16} molecules·cm⁻². At STP, 1 DU of ozone would form a layer 0.01 mm thick.

The chlorine atoms react with ozone to give chlorine monoxide radicals and oxygen gas:

$$Cl(g) + O_3(g) \rightarrow ClO(g) + O_2(g)$$

If the reaction terminated here, the damage to the ozone layer would be minimal. However, the chlorine monoxide takes part in a reaction cycle that regenerates the chlorine atoms (Figure 9.27). The chlorine atoms convert ozone into oxygen gas. The next step in this process is the combination of 2 chlorine monoxide radicals to form the Cl_2O_2 molecule:

$$ClO(g) + ClO(g) \rightarrow Cl_2O_2(g)$$

Sunlight again becomes involved, this time to break apart the Cl_2O_2 molecule:

$$Cl_2O_2(g) \xrightarrow{\text{light}} 2\ Cl(g) + O_2(g)$$

Then the chlorine atoms are again available to react with ozone molecules. Over time, the chlorine atoms will combine with other elements in the stratosphere and be removed from the cycle. However, while CFCs are still being emitted, the ozone hole will continue to be of concern.

The Troposphere: Our Home

The lower 10 km to 15 km of the atmosphere comprise the **troposphere**, the layer of the atmosphere in which we live. The troposphere serves three main purposes:

- The gas pressure stops the seas (and our blood) from boiling.
- The oxygen cycle enables us to utilize respiration as an internal energy source.
- Some of the trace gases keep the planet warm enough to be habitable.

It is this last role that will be the focus here.

The Energy Source for Atmospheric Reactions: The Sun

Before you look in detail at the atmosphere, you must first look at the energy source that drives most of the chemical and biochemical reactions on our planet (Figure 9.29).

WEBLINK

For a simulation to show how CFCs affect the atmosphere, go to **www.pearsoned.ca/chemistry11**.

WORD**ORIGIN**

Troposphere (trop'-o-sfear) comes from the Greek words *tropos* (turn) and *spheraira* (sphere).

FIGURE 9.28
Scientists now monitor the ozone layer from space. a) The QuikTOMS spacecraft, which will be launched in June 2001, will continue the daily mapping of the global distribution of Earth's ozone. b) Inside the QuikTOMS is a monochromator called the TOMS-5 (Total Ozone Mapping Spectrometer), an instrument used to scan different wavelengths of electromagnetic radiation. As ozone absorbs specific wavelengths in the ultraviolet region, the satellite compares the intensity of ultraviolet light from the sun with that reflected from Earth.

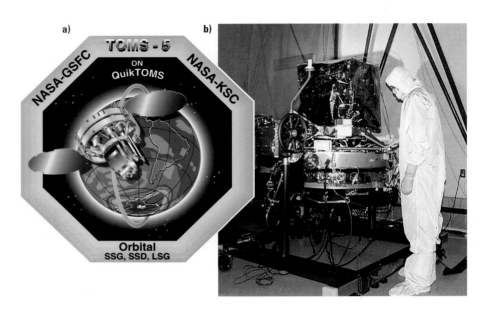

FIGURE 9.29   The surface of the sun. The electromagnetic energy emitted from the sun enables life to exist on the surface of our planet.

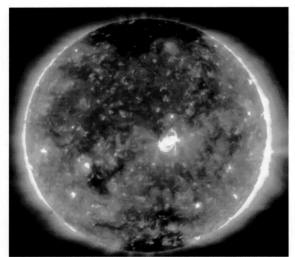

The sun emits energy throughout the electromagnetic spectrum (Figure 9.30). However, most of the energy reaching Earth comes from the outer part of the sun, the photosphere. The maximum region of energy emitted by a radiating body depends on the temperature of that body. Fortunately for us, our particular star has a photosphere temperature of about 6000 K, and the maximum emission from a body at this temperature is in the visible region, with much smaller amounts in the ultraviolet region.

Why Is the Sky Blue?

Everyone is familiar with the fact that the daytime sky is blue, yet do you ever wonder why? If you stood on the moon, the sky would be black, so the presence of an atmosphere on our planet must be the cause of the sky's colour (Figure 9.31). So why is the sky bright, and, in particular, why does it have a blue colour? John Strutt, the third Lord Rayleigh (a British scientist), in 1871 deduced the answer to these questions. He showed that electromagnetic radiation (such as light) is scattered by any particle that is much smaller than the wavelength of the light. Molecules and atoms typically have diameters much smaller than the wavelength of visible light. As a result, the light from the sun is scattered in the atmosphere, giving us the daylight sky.

To understand the blue colour, you need Rayleigh's formula, which shows that the degree of scattering is proportional to the fourth power of the wavelength:

degree of scattering $\propto \lambda^4$ where λ is the wavelength of light
(usually measured in nanometres, nm)

The wavelength of blue light is about 650 nm, while that of red light is about 450 nm. Therefore, blue light will be scattered more than red light by a factor of:

$$\left(\frac{650 \text{ nm}}{450 \text{ nm}}\right)^4 = 4.4$$

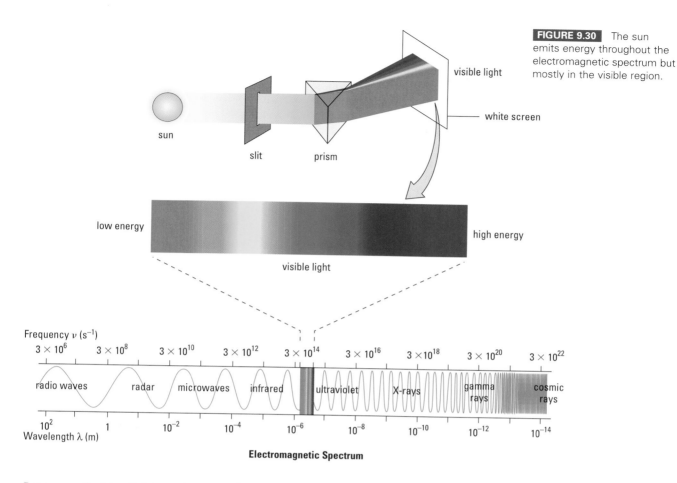

FIGURE 9.30 The sun emits energy throughout the electromagnetic spectrum but mostly in the visible region.

visible light

white screen

sun

slit   prism

low energy   high energy

visible light

Frequency ν (s^{-1})

3×10^6 3×10^8 3×10^{10} 3×10^{12} 3×10^{14} 3×10^{16} 3×10^{18} 3×10^{20} 3×10^{22}

radio waves   radar   microwaves   infrared   ultraviolet   X-rays   gamma rays   cosmic rays

10^2 1 10^{-2} 10^{-4} 10^{-6} 10^{-8} 10^{-10} 10^{-12} 10^{-14}
Wavelength λ (m)

Electromagnetic Spectrum

Consequently, blue light coming to us from the sun is scattered over four times more than red light. As a result, the sky looks blue. (In fact, the sky should look violet, but our eyes are more sensitive to blue wavelengths.) With more of the blue light scattered than red light, the sun's colour looks more orange than it really is.

The "Greenhouse Effect"

Just on the basis of the heat energy received from the sun, Earth's surface should have an average temperature of about $-18°C$. Instead, it is $15°C$. The difference is explained in terms of **radiation trapping**—what is usually, but not accurately, called the **greenhouse effect**.

As already mentioned, much of the sun's energy reaching the surface of Earth is in the visible region of the spectrum. This is fortunate because it enables us to see during daylight. Much of this energy is absorbed by Earth's surface where some is re-emitted as infrared (thermal) radiation. The emission is in the infrared region because Earth's surface has a temperature of only about 300 K. If there were no atmosphere, this thermal radiation would be lost into space and the planet would cool. Clouds reflect some of the radiation back to the surface of Earth, but trace gases in the atmosphere do most of the absorbing.

FIGURE 9.31 The moon's sky is black because it has no gaseous molecules to scatter the light from the sun.

WEBLINK

For a simulation to show how greenhouse gases affect the atmosphere, go to **www.pearsoned.ca/chemistry11**.

Only certain molecules absorb infrared radiation. These are molecules with 3 or more atoms and diatomic molecules consisting of 2 different elements (e.g., carbon monoxide and nitrogen monoxide). The infrared energy is converted into vibrational energy, which you can detect as heat. Thus the three major constituents of the atmosphere, nitrogen (N_2), oxygen (O_2), and argon (Ar), cannot absorb in this region of the spectrum. The compound that contributes the most to radiation trapping is water—that is, water vapour. However, changes in concentrations of the other greenhouse gases, particularly carbon dioxide and methane, cause the most concern. Regardless of whether or not our recent hot years were caused by greenhouse gas emissions, it is an established fact that, over the long term, increases in greenhouse gas concentrations will lead to significant global warming.

Carbon Dioxide Levels in the Atmosphere

Carbon dioxide is a dense, colourless gas. It is formed whenever carbon-containing compounds (e.g., gasoline, oil, coal, wood) burn in the oxygen of the air. For example, 1 mole of octane (a component of gasoline) will burn to give 8 moles of carbon dioxide:

$$C_8H_{18}(l) + {}^{25}/_2\ O_2(g) \rightarrow 8\ CO_2(g) + 9\ H_2O(l)$$

The atmospheric levels of carbon dioxide have always depended on a balance of factors.

Gain
- Volcanoes are the major source of carbon dioxide.
- Organic material reacts with oxygen (e.g., rotting vegetation and forest fires) to produce carbon dioxide.

Loss
- Photosynthesis leads to a loss of carbon dioxide by its conversion to more complex carbon compounds, many of which have been buried to provide the world's deposits of coal, oil, and natural gas.
- Rock weathering, producing calcium carbonate, also leads to a loss of carbon dioxide.

Increased rates of photosynthesis have led to a decrease in carbon dioxide levels and, therefore, to a lesser greenhouse effect. This is fortunate since the sun has become brighter over the same period. The balance has given our planet a fairly stable temperature range. Over shorter time scales, fluctuations in carbon dioxide levels have often resulted from changes in the amount of volcanic activity, volcanoes being a major source of the gas. In fact, we rely on the contribution from volcanoes to replenish the carbon dioxide that has been converted to fossil fuels.

Between 1000 A.D. and 1800 A.D., carbon dioxide levels ranged between 260 and 285 ppm. However, with the onset of the Industrial Revolution, levels have increased and continue to increase by 1.5 ppm per year to the present level of about 370 ppm (Figure 9.33). Most of this increase has resulted from burning fossil fuels (coal, oil, and natural gas) and, more recently, from the burning of tropical forests to produce more farmland.

Will Polar Bears Become Extinct?

Decision-Making Skills

▶ Defining the Issue
  Developing Assessment Criteria
▶ Researching the Issue
▶ Analyzing Data and Information
▶ Proposing a Course of Action
▶ Justifying the Course of Action
▶ Communicating Your Proposal

BACKGROUND INFORMATION

In Canada, the polar bear is an animal closely associated with the great white North. For over 30 years, the Canadian Wildlife Service has been gathering data on the polar bears in Churchill, Manitoba—an achievement envied by other polar bear countries. Scientists have been using this information to determine how long-term changes in climatic or ecological conditions are affecting the bears.

The temperatures in western Hudson Bay have been increasing steadily by 0.3°C to 0.4°C every decade since 1950. This means that the ice is breaking up 2 to 4 weeks earlier than 20 years ago, forcing the polar bears to come ashore hungrier and leaner. With no ice to hunt from, the bears don't eat until the ice freezes up again in late November. The ice is also forming later than it used to. The result is that in 1999, less than two-thirds of the cubs survived. Female polar bears are unable to store enough fat to sustain themselves and their newborn cubs during the winter.

Scientists have observed that for every week that the ice breaks up earlier, the bears are coming ashore 10 kg lighter. As the bears get hungrier, they end up crossing paths with humans more often, sometimes with tragic results. Using climatic models, scientists predict that western and south-ern Hudson Bay will become 3°C to 5°C warmer within 50 years. Because the polar bears of this region are at the southern most extremity of their range, they serve as a warning signal for what could happen to many other species if current trends in global warming continue. Some scientists predict that the polar bear will become extinct in 50 to 100 years. For a town like Churchill, where polar bear tourism accounts for 60% of the economy, this could mean disaster.

FIGURE 9.32 When the ice breaks up early, polar bears become trapped on land and are unable to hunt.

Analyzing the Issue

1. Define the issue in the case study, and list short-term and long-term consequences related to the issue.

2. In 1991, Mount Pinatubo, a volcano in the Philippines erupted. The gases that were released into the atmosphere cooled the planet. Use electronic and print resources to research the effect that this cooling had on the polar bear habitat in Hudson Bay and the polar bear population size in that area.

3. Some polar bears from eastern Canada have been known to travel as far as Greenland and some islands off Norway. Predict what the effect of global warming would be on polar bear migration patterns.

4. You are a community member in the town of Churchill and concerns have been raised about the increased sightings of polar bears in town. Prepare a position paper that you will present at a town council meeting from one of the following points of view:

mayor
meteorologist
local hotel owner
local tourist operator
atmospheric chemist
local parent
animal behaviour specialist
local restaurant owner

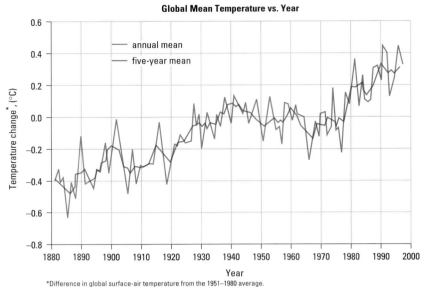

FIGURE 9.33 The global mean temperature has been increasing since 1880, as has the atmospheric concentration of carbon dioxide.

Global Mean Temperature vs. Year

*Difference in global surface-air temperature from the 1951–1980 average.
Source: National Aeronautics and Space Administration's Goddard Institute for Space Studies, *C&E News*, Nov. 17, 1997.

Methane Levels in the Atmosphere

Although most attention is focussed on carbon dioxide, it is important to be aware of other smaller contributors to the greenhouse effect. There is a good reason for this. Each chemical compound containing more than 2 atoms absorbs infrared radiation at wavelengths unique to that compound. So every added gas will block a different wavelength window in the atmosphere.

Over 200 years ago, Earth's atmosphere contained about 0.7 ppm methane. Most of this came from bacterial action on decaying vegetation in wetlands, such as bogs, while a lesser amount came from termites. Modern farming and other activities have upset this balance, increasing the figure to about 1.8 ppm. Now a major source of methane is ruminant animals, particularly gastric and intestinal gases from cattle. In the complex digestive system of ruminants, the fermentation process produces enormous amounts of methane. A second source is anaerobic bacteria in the water-covered soil of rice paddy fields (Figure 9.34).

There are very large deposits of methane beneath the sea floor trapped within ice crystals. These are known as methane hydrates. There is a concern among some scientists that global warming might lead to a melting of these deposits, which, when released, would lead to an acceleration of atmospheric warming because methane is such a potent greenhouse gas.

Nitrogen Oxides in the Atmosphere

Though not major contributors to the greenhouse effect, two of the oxides of nitrogen, colourless nitrogen monoxide, NO (commonly called nitric oxide), and brown nitrogen dioxide, NO_2, are the most crucial compounds in the troposphere because they control the chemical reactions that occur. The reason is that brown nitrogen dioxide is one of the very few molecules in the troposphere to absorb visible light energy and start reaction cycles. In this first step, highly reactive oxygen atoms are formed:

$$NO_2(g) \xrightarrow{\text{visible light}} NO(g) + O(g)$$

Most of the oxygen atoms almost immediately react with oxygen molecules to form ozone:

$$O(g) + O_2(g) \rightarrow O_3(g)$$

While you need ozone as a protective layer in the stratosphere, at sea level, high levels of ozone are a major pollutant (Figure 9.35).

Nitrogen oxides are produced from natural sources, but it is the large amounts generated from industry and transportation that cause much of our current air pollution (Figure 9.36). The corrosive combination of nitrogen oxides, ozone, and other more complex molecules, such as peroxyacetylnitrate (commonly called PAN), $CH_3C(O)OONO_2$, is found in the photochemical smog of urban areas.

Nature's Atmospheric Detergents

Have you ever thought of how smells and pollution finally disappear? Why don't you still smell dinosaur burps? After all, there were millions of dinosaurs roaming the planet for hundreds of millions of years. There has to be some means by which pollutants (both natural and human-made) are decomposed. Atmospheric chemists have found that there are two molecular "detergents," which are constantly destroying pollutant molecules. These are both present in the atmosphere in very tiny concentrations—less than one part per trillion (10^{12}), but they are vital. One is the hydroxyl radical, OH, that is present during the daytime. At night, the nitrate radical, NO_3, roams the troposphere. Ironically, they are both formed from ozone, a molecule that is needed in very small amounts

FIGURE 9.34 Ruminant animals, such as cattle, and paddy fields are the major sources creating an increase in atmospheric methane concentration.

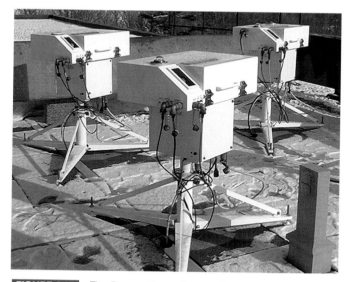

FIGURE 9.35 The Brewer Ozone Spectrophotometer was invented by three Environment Canada scientists—Tom McElroy, James Kerr, and David Wardle—and is named after former University of Toronto professor Alan Brewer, who suggested the original idea for constructing such an instrument. It has been used to monitor ground-level concentrations of ozone since the 1950s. This photo shows the Brewer instruments atop the Meteorological Service of Canada building in Toronto, which set the calibration reference for all the Brewer instruments around the world.

FIGURE 9.36 The brown colour of photochemical smog is due to the nitrogen dioxide.

WEBLINK

Photochemical smog is a major problem for large urban areas such as Toronto. Research what is being done to reduce the pollutant levels. What are the health effects of photochemical smog? Could more be done to minimize this problem? Write a report on your findings. Begin your research at **www.pearsoned.ca/chemistry11**.

to generate the detergent molecules that replace those consumed in the destruction of pollutants.

Sulfur Dioxide in the Atmosphere

The final molecule that we will discuss in the context of the troposphere is sulfur dioxide. This compound is the major contributor to acid rain (Figure 9.37). Rain is always slightly acidic as a result of the carbon dioxide dissolved in it:

$$H_2O(l) + CO_2(g) \rightarrow H^+(aq) + HCO_3^-(aq)$$

However, the ultimate product from the reaction of sulfur dioxide with water is sulfuric acid, a much more potent acid:

$$2\ SO_2(g) + O_2(g) \rightarrow 2\ SO_3(g)$$
$$SO_3(g) + H_2O(l) \rightarrow H_2SO_4(aq)$$

FIGURE 9.37 The Taj Mahal in India. This magnificent building, a world heritage site, is being eroded away by the sulfurous and sulfuric acid from nearby coal-burning industrial plants.

Sulfur dioxide is a colourless gas with a strong, sharp odour. Volcanoes produce significant quantities of this gas, but humans now produce much more from the combustion of oil and coal. Both of these fuels contain sulfur compounds that burn to form sulfur dioxide. Unfortunately, there is a link between the price of a fuel and its sulfur content. A sulfur-rich fuel is much cheaper than a low-sulfur fuel. As a result, poor countries and budget-conscious organizations, such as schools, usually choose to buy high-sulfur fuels.

The Future of Our Atmosphere

It is easy to become despondent when you read about the problems of atmospheric pollution, but progress has been made. The British smog of the 1950s that killed thousands no longer exists. CFCs are being phased out, though too slowly for many environmentalists. More and more companies are investing in new, more efficient plants or are adding pollution controls to older plants. Rapid transit systems are being installed in major cities around the world, from Los Angeles to Bangkok (Figure 9.38). Vehicle emissions have dropped significantly (though the recent increase in popularity of SUVs and other large vehicles is undoing some of the progress). More and more freight traffic (particularly in the United States) is being handled by rail rather than the less energy-efficient trucking systems.

Statistics Canada has shown that, on a nationwide average since 1975, the level of sulfur dioxide in the air has diminished by 62%, while that of nitrogen dioxide has decreased by 42%. A particular success has been the phasing out of leaded gasoline, resulting in a 97% decrease in lead between 1974 and the present. Unfortunately, such improvements are rarely in the news, and the average person rarely realizes the advances that have been made. At the same time, there is a long, long way to go before the atmosphere is as clean as we can make it.

FIGURE 9.38 One of the best ways of reducing urban atmospheric pollution is widespread use of public rapid transit. Many cities are enlarging existing systems or introducing new ones.

The Kyoto Protocol on Climate Change

Just as the Montreal Protocol defined limits on CFCs, so, in 1998, an agreement was signed in Kyoto, Japan, on the control of emissions of greenhouse gases. Under the **Kyoto Protocol**, Canada and 160 other countries agreed to reductions in the production of the following greenhouse gases: carbon dioxide, methane, dinitrogen oxide (nitrous oxide), **hydrofluorocarbons (HFCs)**, **perfluorocarbons (PFCs)**, and sulfur hexafluoride. The chlorofluorocarbons (CFCs) and the hydrochlorofluorocarbons (HCFCs) also contribute to the greenhouse effect. However, many have comparatively short tropospheric lifetimes, and the former are controlled by the Montreal Protocol. The HFCs and PFCs, such as C_2F_6, with their incredibly long tropospheric lifetimes are of most concern. Very little sulfur hexafluoride is used—mostly for the electrical insulation in transformers—but it is an extremely potent greenhouse gas, being 23 900 times more potent than carbon dioxide. As a result, the current atmospheric level of 130 000 t of sulfur hexafluoride is equivalent to about 3 billion tonnes of carbon dioxide. Table 9.4 lists the concentrations of the trace and some of the ultra-trace compounds found in the troposphere. The designation "KP" indicates that the compounds are controlled by the Kyoto Protocol and "MP" by the Montreal Protocol.

TABLE 9.4 The Trace and Some of the Ultra-trace Compounds in the Troposphere

Gas	Pre-industrial Concentration (%)	Current Concentration (%)	Lifetime (in years)
CO_2 (KP)	2.9×10^{-2}	3.6×10^{-2}	120
CH_4 (KP)	8.5×10^{-5}	1.8×10^{-4}	12
N_2O (KP)	2.9×10^{-5}	3.1×10^{-5}	120
O_3	2.5×10^{-6}	2.5×10^{-6}	hours
$CFCl_3$ (MP)	none	2.6×10^{-8}	50
CF_2Cl_2 (MP)	none	5.3×10^{-8}	102
CHF_2Cl (MP)	none	1.2×10^{-8}	12
C_2F_6 (KP)	none	4.0×10^{-10}	10 000
SF_6 (KP)	none	3.5×10^{-10}	3 200

The aim of the Kyoto Protocol was to reduce by the years 2008–2012 worldwide emissions of these gases by 5% of those measured in 1990. Canada's target was set at cutting the emissions of these greenhouse gases to 6% below those of the year 1990, while most European countries agreed to aim for an 8% reduction and the United States to a 7% reduction (Figure 9.39).

There are several ways in which reductions can be accomplished, the most obvious route being to cut down on emissions (Figure 9.40). For example, between 1990 and 1995, Canada's pulp and paper industry reduced net carbon dioxide emissions by 20%, largely through increasing the use of wood waste for heating rather than fuel oil. An alternative route is through emission-reduction credits. These work in several ways, including the following:

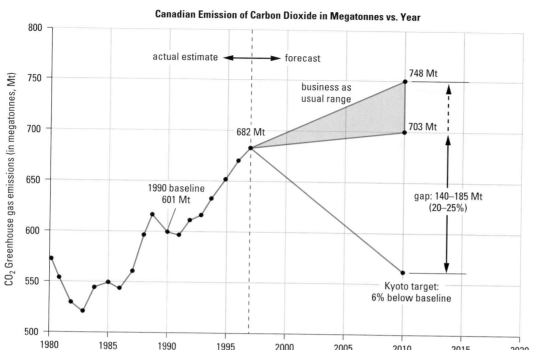

Canadian Emission of Carbon Dioxide in Megatonnes vs. Year

actual estimate ↔ forecast

business as usual range

748 Mt

682 Mt

703 Mt

1990 baseline 601 Mt

gap: 140–185 Mt (20–25%)

Kyoto target: 6% below baseline

FIGURE 9.39 Canada has committed to cutting greenhouse gas emissions by 2010 to a figure 6% less than 1990 emissions. This represents a decrease of about 25% compared to what would be expected from normal economic growth.

- If an industrialized country helps a developing country reduce its emissions, then that industrialized country can count part of the benefits toward its own reduction goal.
- Emission-reduction credits are tradable like stocks. Therefore, any country that reduces its emissions below its own target can "sell" the extra reduction to a country that did not meet its objectives.
- Removing greenhouse gases from the atmosphere by increasing the planting of forests can be counted as credit.

Although the emission-reduction credit system has many positive aspects, it does provide a way for richer countries to avoid having to meet their goals.

FIGURE 9.40 In part from the stimulus of the Kyoto Protocol, TransAlta Corp., producer of 6% of Canada's greenhouse gas emissions, is investing millions of dollars in wind power development as part of its long-term strategy to reduce emissions.

Implementing the Kyoto Protocol

Decision-Making Skills

▶ Defining the Issue
   Developing Assessment Criteria
▶ Researching the Issue
▶ Analyzing Data and Information
▶ Proposing a Course of Action
▶ Justifying the Course of Action
▶ Communicating Your Proposal

BACKGROUND INFORMATION

The Climate Summit talks held at the end of November 2000 in The Hague broke down when the European Union delegates rejected the U.S. proposal. Using a loophole in the original Kyoto Protocol, the United States wanted to use its managed forests to count for carbon credits in place of cutting greenhouse gas emissions. The Europeans saw this as a way that the United States, Canada, Russia, Australia, and New Zealand could increase their greenhouse gas emissions without planting a single tree.

In Kyoto, it was agreed that carbon credits should be claimed for activities, such as tree planting, only if they took place after 1990. However, most of the trees in U.S.–managed forests were planted before 1990. The U.S. proposal would threaten the Kyoto targets and force the European Union to carry an increased burden in cutting its emissions. The United States wanted to claim another carbon credit for the implementation of low-till farming practices.

The purpose of the summit was to create a rule book to govern the Kyoto Protocol, but many other issues remained unresolved: how countries would be punished for not meeting their Kyoto targets, whether to allow countries with bad economies excess permits to pollute, and whether to allow industrialized countries to claim carbon credits for activities in developing countries. The scientific advisers of the protocol say that meeting the Kyoto targets would buy us no more than 10 years. More radical measures (such as cutting emissions by 60% and producing energy without burning fossil fuels) will be necessary to stop global warming.

Analyzing the Issue

1. Explain in your own words the controversial issue that led to the break down of the Climate Summit talks in The Hague in November 2000.

2. Describe how the American position related to carbon credits could affect the implementation of the original Kyoto Protocol. Predict how the American decision could affect Canada's perspective.

3. You are a Canadian youth delegate at the Climate Summit in The Hague, and have been asked to appear on a panel discussion that is being organized by a news broadcaster. Use electronic and print resources as well as the information in this chapter to research information on global warming. Create a mind map illustrating the consequences of global warming.

4. Prepare a summary of your position on the issue of carbon credits and why resolving this issue is important for your generation.

Individual Action

The easy path for many of us is to assume that we are powerless. It takes effort to change the world, but along with that effort, you can gain knowledge and interpersonal skills and, in the process, feel that you have accomplished something. Apart from simple tasks like recycling waste and avoiding the use of personal vehicles (walk, cycle, or use public transit instead), you can lobby industries and governments. What are your local industries doing to reduce emissions? What challenges do they still face? Pollution can't be made to disappear overnight. Can local and regional public transit be enhanced? How can more people be persuaded to use public transit? What else can be done?

FIGURE 9.41 The Honda Insight is the first gasoline-electric hybrid car available in Canada. If people were to use such vehicles, urban atmospheric emissions would decline drastically. A production model of the Insight has set a record in fuel economy— 107 miles per imperial gallon for a round-Britain tour. What is that fuel consumption in $L \cdot 100 \ km^{-1}$?

Section 9.5 Review

Understanding Concepts

1. Identify the major gases that contribute to the greenhouse effect, and give an example of their source(s).

2. Draw a diagram illustrating how the greenhouse effect interferes with Earth's normal balanced process of releasing heat into space.

3. Describe the reasons that CFCs were widely adopted for use in air conditioners, aerosol cans, and other products.

4. Name the main layers of the atmosphere, and arrange them in the correct order beginning with the layer closest to Earth's surface. Describe an important characteristic of each layer.

5. Explain the reason for concern about the rising concentrations of trace gases such as methane in the atmosphere.

Applying Inquiry/ Communication Skills

6. Using chemical equations, explain how N_2O can interfere with the ozone cycle.

7. Nitrogen and oxygen can be made to combine in the stratosphere to form nitrogen monoxide, NO. Using chemical equations, explain what this molecule can do to the ozone cycle.

Making Connections

8. It is often difficult to make industries that are polluting the atmosphere comply with clean air standards. From the informed perspective of a company executive, write a statement justifying non-compliance; write an opposing statement from the informed perspective of a local environmental committee. List the factors that need to be considered in making an informed decision by a pollution control board on whether to fine the company or extend its compliance regulation.

9. Canada has played an active role in participating in environmental conferences that have focussed on setting protocols to reduce the amount of harmful substances released into the atmosphere. Research recent environmental reports outlining Canada's commitment to and progress toward clean air. Summarize the results of your findings as viewed from each of the following perspectives: a taxpayer, an environmentalist, an industrialist, and a politician.

Investigation 1 (Section 9.2)

Inquiry Skills

Initiating and Planning

Applying Technical Skills

▶ Using Tools, Materials, and Equipment

▶ Conducting and Recording

▶ Analyzing and Interpreting

▶ Concluding and Communicating

The Molar Volume of a Gas

According to Avogadro's hypothesis, equal volumes of gases at the same temperature and pressure contain the same number of molecules. The molar volume is generally measured at STP (standard temperature and pressure).

Problem

To obtain an experimental value for the molar volume of a gas.

Materials

- potassium chlorate/manganese(IV) oxide mixture
- gas collecting bottle (approx. 500 mL)
- glass or Plexiglas™ plate
- glass elbow
- 100-mL graduated cylinder
- 15-cm test tube with a one-hole stopper
- centigram balance
- pneumatic trough with rack
- retort stand with clamp
- rubber tubing with a three-way tap in the middle
- thermometer
- gas burner

> **CAUTION: Potassium chlorate is an explosive material. Use only 3 parts potassium chlorate to 1 part manganese(IV) oxide.**

Procedure

1. Add about 2 g to 3 g of the potassium chlorate/manganese(IV) oxide mixture to a *clean*, *dry* 15-cm pyrex test tube, and determine the mass to ±0.01 g.

2. Clamp the tube to the retort stand as shown in Figure 9.42, and attach a one-hole rubber stopper fitted with a glass elbow and a delivery tube. Connect the three-way tap midway between the beaker and the tube. Make sure the valve on the tap is set so the gas can flow from the tube into the gas bottle.

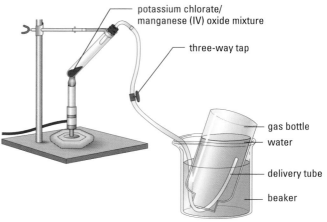

potassium chlorate/
manganese (IV) oxide mixture

three-way tap

gas bottle

water

delivery tube

beaker

FIGURE 9.42

3. Fill the beaker with water to a depth of at least 3 cm. Then fill a 500-mL collecting bottle with water, place the cover over the mouth of the gas bottle, invert the bottle, and place it in the beaker.

4. Place the end of the delivery tube inside the bottle, making sure the tip of the tube reaches high into the bottle.

5. Make sure the solid mixture is spread along the side of the test tube. Begin heating the mixture with a moderate flame, starting with the solid closest to the mouth of the tube and moving the flame slowly toward the bottom of the tube. If, for any reason, water starts being drawn back up the delivery tube toward the tap, twist the tap immediately so that the outside air can enter the test tube. (If water comes in contact with the hot test tube, the test tube may crack.) When the water level reaches the shoulder of the gas bottle, discontinue heating. **MAKE SURE THE END OF THE DELIVERY TUBE INSIDE THE BOTTLE PROJECTS INTO THE GAS. DO NOT REMOVE THE DELIVERY TUBE AT THIS TIME.**

6. When the test tube has cooled to room temperature, remove the delivery tube from the collecting bottle and measure the temperature of the water in the beaker.

(continued)

7. Raise the bottle until the water level inside and outside the bottle are the same. Slide the cover plate over the mouth of the bottle. Lift the bottle from the beaker. Set the bottle right side up on the table, making sure none of the trapped water is lost.

8. Use a graduated cylinder to add additional water to the bottle until it reaches the brim. Record the volume of added water to the nearest 0.5 mL. This will give you the volume of oxygen gas collected.

9. Determine the mass of the test tube and remaining solid to ± 0.01 g.

10. Record the temperature of the water in the beaker and the laboratory atmospheric pressure in the following table:

	Before	After
Mass of Test Tube		
Temperature of Water in Beaker		
Atmospheric Pressure		

Analyzing and Interpreting

1. Write a balanced chemical equation for the reaction of potassium chlorate to give potassium chloride and oxygen gas. The manganese(IV) oxide is used only to speed up the reaction.

2. From the mass of the tube and contents before and after heating, determine the mass of oxygen produced.

3. Calculate the molar volume for the conditions of your experiment.

4. Use the atmospheric pressure and a table of water vapour pressures with respect to temperature to determine the pressure of the oxygen gas collected.

5. Calculate the molar volume at STP and SATP.

Concluding and Communicating

6. Identify the major sources of error in this experiment.

7. Suggest how you could improve the experiment to obtain greater precision.

8. Explain how you would identify the gas produced in this experiment.

Extending

9. Explain why it is important to specify the temperature and pressure when stating the molar volume of a gas.

10. Discuss why molar volume is an important quantity for gases but not for liquids or solids.

Inquiry Skills

▶ Initiating and Planning
Applying Technical Skills
▶ Using Tools, Materials, and Equipment
▶ Conducting and Recording
▶ Analyzing and Interpreting
▶ Concluding and Communicating

Investigation 2 (Section 9.4)

Determining a Value for the Ideal Gas Constant

The ideal gas law is given by $PV = nRT$. If you want to determine the value of R, then the ideal gas equation can be rearranged to give:

$$R = \frac{PV}{nT}$$

Since pressure, volume, moles, and temperature of a gas are all measurable quantities, it is possible to find a value for R.

Problem

To empirically measure the ideal gas constant R.

Materials

- 1 mol·L^{-1} hydrochloric acid
- 1 cm of magnesium ribbon
- 50-mL beaker
- 10-mL syringe with a hole bored by a #4 cork borer through the tip
- hand lens
- ruler
- thermometer
- tweezers

Experimental Design

1. Develop a scientific investigation to show how you would measure the ideal gas constant.

2. Determine the method that you will use to measure the results of your experiment.

3. Have the teacher review your procedure before you carry out the plan.

Analyzing and Interpreting

1. Identify the major sources of error in your experiment.

2. Calculate your value for R. Comment on how close your value is to the theoretical one.

3. Prepare a lab report to summarize your findings.

Concluding and Communicating

4. Explain how the gas produced in this activity affected your results.

5. Suggest another alkaline-earth metal that could be used in the experiment.

6. Hydrogen gas is referred to as a very clean-burning fuel. Explain why.

Extending

7. Predict if the reaction you used in this activity would be a practical method of making hydrogen on a large scale. Calculate the mass of magnesium that you would need per hour to produce 25 kL of hydrogen gas per hour.

CHAPTER SUMMARY

Key Terms

Antarctic ozone hole
Avogadro's hypothesis
chlorofluorocarbon (CFC)
Gay-Lussac's law of
    combining volumes

greenhouse effect
hydrochlorofluorocarbon
    (HCFC)
hydrofluorocarbon (HFC)
Kyoto Protocol

Montreal Protocol
Newton's Third Law of
    Motion
ozone cycle
perfluorocarbon (PFC)

radiation trapping
stratosphere
troposphere

Essential Understandings

- A knowledge of gas properties and chemical reactions is directly applicable to technologies like rockets and air bags.

- Applying the gas laws to chemical reactions allows us to predict the volume of gas either produced or required for the reaction to take place.

- The relationship between the volume of a gas and the number of gas molecules or atoms was used to determine the molecular formula for a number of compounds.

- Gas reactions that take place in the atmosphere have a significant impact on life on Earth.

- Despite the Montreal Protocol and the Kyoto Protocol agreements, the health of the atmosphere largely depends on individual citizens acting in an environmentally responsible manner.

Consolidate Your Understanding

1. Summarize the chemical reactions that are specific to the atmosphere.

2. Construct a concept map that starts with the word "atmosphere."

3. This chapter has shown some important roles that gases play in our lives. Describe how our lives would be affected if all gases were to change into liquids or solids.

4. Look at Figure 9.17 on page 399. Write a paragraph that describes the key ideas this figure is representing for solving stoichiometric problems.

Understanding Concepts

1. For a good rocket propellant, the product gas molecules must have:
   a) high molecular masses
   b) low velocities
   c) low molecular masses
   d) low toxicity

2. Carbon monoxide burns in oxygen to form carbon dioxide:
   $$2\ CO(g) + O_2(g) \rightarrow 2\ CO_2(g)$$
   To completely react with 24 mL of carbon monoxide, at the same temperature and pressure, you will need:
   a) 24 mL of oxygen
   b) 12 mL of oxygen
   c) 48 mL of oxygen
   d) none of the above

3. Hydrogen reacts with oxygen to form water:
   $$2\ H_2(g) + O_2(g) \rightarrow 2\ H_2O(l)$$
   If the hydrogen gas is at twice the pressure of the oxygen gas but at the same temperature, then for a particular volume of oxygen, you will need:
   a) the same volume of hydrogen
   b) twice the volume of hydrogen
   c) four times the volume of hydrogen
   d) half the volume of hydrogen

4. The mass of a particular volume of an unknown gas is twice that of a sample of oxygen gas under the same conditions of temperature and pressure. The unknown gas must be:
   a) PH_3
   b) SO_2
   c) CH_4
   d) none of the above

5. Identify which one of the following reactions is not a significant component of the ozone cycle:
   a) $O(g) + O_2(g) \rightarrow O_3(g)$
   b) $2\ O(g) \rightarrow O_2(g)$
   c) $O_3(g) \xrightarrow{\text{uv light}} O_2(g) + O(g)$
   d) $O_2(g) \xrightarrow{\text{uv light}} 2\ O(g)$

6. Identify and describe the factors that determine the atmospheric level of carbon dioxide.

7. Explain why water vapour is a better propellant than nitrogen gas.

8. List the criteria of an explosive. Using the chemical equation below, explain how nitroglycerin satisfies one of the criteria.
   $$4\ C_3H_5(NO_3)_3(l) \rightarrow 12\ CO_2(g) + 10\ H_2O(g) + 6\ N_2(g) + O_2(g)$$

9. Most cosmo-chemists believe that Mars once had a much denser atmosphere, rich in carbon dioxide, and water-filled rivers and lakes on its surface.

a) Explain how the presence of high concentrations of carbon dioxide would have affected the atmospheric temperature.
b) The Martian landscape now has many large but inactive volcanoes. Describe the effect the volcanoes would have had on the planet when they were active.
c) Keeping in mind the lower gravity of Mars compared to Earth, suggest a probable fate of much of the carbon dioxide.
d) With the disappearance of a thick atmosphere, speculate on what you think would have happened to most (or all) of the water.

10. If early Earth had possessed as little carbon dioxide in its atmosphere as it does now, it would have been a giant snowball in space. Explain this statement.

11. Describe the differences between the Montreal Protocol and the Kyoto Protocol.

12. Explain why CFCs such as CF_2Cl_2 are considered to be greenhouse gases.

13. Explain the difference between a solid rocket propellant and an explosive.

Applying Inquiry/Communication Skills

14. Ammonia reacts with oxygen to produce nitrogen monoxide and water according to the equation:
    $$4\ NH_3(g) + 5\ O_2(g) \rightarrow 4\ NO(g) + 6\ H_2O(g)$$
    Assume that all gases are at the same temperature and pressure.
    a) Calculate the volumes of ammonia and oxygen that would be required in order to prepare 20.0 L of nitrogen monoxide.
    b) Name the law that enables you to solve this problem.

15. The major ingredient in many solid air fresheners is a compound known as paradichlorobenzene. The compound sublimes in air and is believed to function by blocking the scent detectors in your nostrils while the molecules are in the vapour phase. If a 9.87-g block of air freshener is vaporized in a 1.50-L container at 125°C, the resulting pressure is 148 kPa.
    a) Determine the molar mass of paradichlorobenzene.
    b) Determine the molecular formula of paradichlorobenzene if its empirical formula is C_3H_2Cl.

16. A charcoal briquette has an average mass of 32 g. Assuming that the briquette consists of pure carbon, its combustion in a barbecue can be represented as:
    $$C(s) + O_2(g) \xrightarrow{\Delta} CO_2(g)$$
    a) Calculate the volume of carbon dioxide produced at SATP by one charcoal briquette.
    b) Assuming 50 briquettes are burned in a barbecue, calculate the total volume of gas produced.

c) Suppose, on a typical summer day, there are 100 000 barbecues in use across Canada. Calculate the volume of gas this represents.

d) Assuming this is an average value per day from June 1 through August 31, calculate the total volume of carbon dioxide sent into the atmosphere.

17. The compound $C_8(NO_2)_8$ is a powerful explosive. Given that its decomposition produces only carbon dioxide and nitrogen gas, write a chemical equation for the reaction that occurs when it explodes. Calculate the total volume of gas that would be produced at SATP when 100 g of it explodes.

18. Custom agents seized a contraband cylinder of a perfluorocarbon, and you are given the task of identifying which perfluorocarbon it contains. You determine that the compound consists of 82.6% fluorine, the remainder being carbon. A flask filled with this gas has a mass of 2.870 g, compared with 0.582 g for the same volume of nitrogen gas at the same temperature and pressure. Determine the molecular formula of the gas.

19. The space shuttle uses a mixture of ammonium perchlorate and aluminum metal in its solid boosters. If a pair of boosters contains 700 t of ammonium perchlorate (the limiting reagent), calculate the total volume of gas that will be produced at 500°C and 70 kPa.

$$6\ NH_4ClO_4(s) + 8\ Al(s) \rightarrow$$
$$4\ Al_2O_3(s) + 3\ N_2(g) + 3\ Cl_2(g) + 12\ H_2O(g)$$

20. In commercial aircraft, the emergency oxygen is often provided by the decomposition of potassium chlorate:

$$2\ KClO_3(s) \xrightarrow[MnO_2]{\Delta} 2\ KCl(s) + 3\ O_2(g)$$

a) Calculate the volume of oxygen gas that could be supplied by 5.00 kg of potassium chlorate at a pressure of 75.0 kPa and a temperature of 23°C.

b) Suppose the aircraft used a tank of oxygen gas (at a pressure of 20 MPa) instead of potassium chlorate as an oxygen source. Calculate the volume the oxygen tank would have to be in order to store the same amount of oxygen as your answer to a).

c) Suggest why aircraft carry their emergency oxygen supply as potassium chlorate and not as oxygen gas.

21. Carbon dioxide is commonly prepared by reacting calcium carbonate (marble chips) with dilute hydrochloric acid (3.00 mol·L^{-1}) according to the reaction:

$$CaCO_3(s) + 2\ HCl(aq) \rightarrow CaCl_2(aq) + CO_2(g) + H_2O(l)$$

a) Calculate the maximum mass of calcium carbonate that will react with 0.200 L of hydrochloric acid.

b) Calculate the volume of carbon dioxide that will be produced at 18°C and 104 kPa from the quantities used in a).

22. A student wished to determine the molar mass of oxygen experimentally. A sample of potassium chlorate was heated until it decomposed and the released oxygen was collected in a graduated cylinder by the downward displacement of water. The data was recorded in the table below. The reaction is represented as follows:

$$2\ KClO_3(s) \rightarrow 2\ KCl(s) + 3\ O_2(g)$$

Calculate the molar mass of oxygen from the following data.

TABLE 9.5

Mass of test tube and contents before heating	18.93 g
Mass of test tube and contents after heating	18.81 g
Mass of oxygen liberated	0.12 g
Volume of oxygen collected (room conditions)	92 mL
Temperature of oxygen (equals temperature of water)	24°C
Atmospheric pressure	100.37 kPa
Vapour pressure of water at 24°C	2.98 kPa
Pressure of dry oxygen	97.39 kPa

Compare the student's result to the true value for the molar mass of oxygen gas, and calculate the percent error for the experiment.

Making Connections

23. Write a newspaper article that discusses the major contributors to the increase in methane concentration in the atmosphere. Provide supporting evidence on the relevance of this issue to atmospheric pollution, and suggest ways in which these contributions can be reduced.

24. Nitroglycerin is used for destructive purposes and medical uses. Research this substance, and create a chart outlining the positive and negative uses of nitroglycerin. Provide a summarizing paragraph on the importance of manufacturing nitroglycerin. Include the chemical structure of this molecule.

25. Write a report on the current status of Canada's progress on meeting its commitments under the Kyoto Protocol. Assess whether or not you feel Canada is honouring its commitments. Provide evidence to support your viewpoint.

26. Methyl bromide is a potent destroyer of the ozone layer. Research the use of methyl bromide and why there is considerable difficulty in phasing the gas out of use. Write an action plan that you would propose to the government to reduce the use of this gas.

Preparing for a Career in Chemistry

Hi. My name's Kandra. We have this assignment to write about our career goals. I know what you're thinking: same old stuff, new package. But some of my friends really do know what they want to do after they graduate. Makes life easier for them, that's for sure. They know exactly what courses to take next year—even what summer jobs they want. Me? I've no idea. I guess it's time I did.

Time. Funny I thought of that. You see, we did this peer activity where we had to compare our feelings about our classes, and I said that chemistry always seems to be over too soon while other classes take forever. Not everyone agreed with me, that's for sure. But I think the labs are fun and it's my best mark. But what can I do with that? I doubt being a chemistry student counts as a career goal.

Hey. I'm Jase and this is my "career goals" writing assignment. I suppose these things help some kids make up their minds. Doesn't matter to me because I know what I want to do. I want to be a forensic chemist—you know, the kind of scientist who analyzes evidence and solves the crime. Oh, I know it's not like in the TV shows, where the scientist chases suspects down dark alleys. I've been collecting articles and reading about real criminal investigations since I was eleven. I went on a university tour last month and talked to a professor of forensic biochemistry. Sounded too good to be true, let me tell you.

But maybe it is. I was so excited finally to be taking chemistry and the other sciences. Was. Now it's midway through the term and I'm having serious problems. My chemistry mark is pretty good, but math and English? Guess I got behind earlier this year and it's tough catching up. I have two projects to do and exams are coming fast. Figures my basketball team made the playoffs and the coach has scheduled extra practices. On the bright side, I heard the pizza place is hiring students to work weekends. Maybe that's the kind of career goal I need. What else can I do?

You've learned about the variety of careers in chemistry and how to assess the skills you will need for any career. You've also considered how to find out more about a career by interviewing someone working in it. However, your future, and how you will prepare for it, is up to you. Keep in mind that you will probably change your specific career goals several times in your life—and even during your further education. What won't change is your need to plan and think ahead.

Making Plans and Taking Charge

There seems to be one in every class. The popular student who does well in all subjects and knows exactly which career he or she wants. Most students, however, are trying to decide between what feels like either too many choices or not enough. At the same time, they can be struggling to achieve in this class or that. The best approach in both situations is to plan ahead.

1. Pick one of the written assignments to the left and compose a letter to the student containing a plan to help that student with his or her career goals. Follow these steps:
   - Identify the problem.
   - How is the problem related to the student's career goals? (Hint: What needs to be done for this student to succeed?)
   - Make a plan for this student to follow. Include simple, straightforward steps and be as specific as possible. If your plan involves investigating careers in chem-

istry, supply details on how to do that investigation, what to look for in terms of information, and any contacts you would recommend in or out of school. If it involves seeking extra help, find out exactly how to obtain that extra help in your school.

- Check your plan. Is it positive? Reasonable? Does it allow the student to make mistakes and still continue? Is it flexible? Can the student accomplish most or all of this plan without outside help?
- Compare your plan with those of others in your class. Discuss any differences. See if you can improve your plan.

Now, how about setting some goals and making a plan for yourself? Being able to plan, and following your plan, will help you achieve any of your goals.

2. Take a moment and sketch out a plan for yourself, being sure to break the tasks into several reasonable, clear steps.

For example, if your goal is to learn to drive, your plan could include talking to your family about car insurance and other issues, phoning for information on driver training courses, scheduling a ride to the licensing bureau to obtain the materials you need to write your first test, and so on. Each of these steps is a task you need to perform on the way to achieving your goal. Writing them out this way means you will be aware of what needs to be done and who you will need to contact.

Looking Outward

3. Plan a trip to visit a university. In your plan, include contacting the department offering the courses that interest you for a personal tour. Before you go, make a list of the questions you want answered.

Remember, there are no "dumb" questions. University staff and students are accessible, friendly, and knowledgeable. They also started out asking the same questions you are asking.

There is one thing you should keep in mind as you do this and other activities: you are looking for a direction rather than a final goal. Even if you've discovered a career choice that excites you—perhaps a field or career type or business opportunity—you should consider this a starting point. Most people fine-tune or alter their careers as they gain education and experience, or as opportunities to do something new come along. The key is to begin with what suits you. Your destination will be subject to change without notice.

FIGURE 1 The work of a forensic chemist is important in helping to solve many crimes.

A Fundamental Constant

Background Information

Most people will recognize $E = mc^2$ as being the most famous equation in science. They will also know that Albert Einstein developed the equation. But they may not know that c, the speed of light, is known as a fundamental constant. A **fundamental constant** is a quantity whose value remains constant anywhere in the universe. Other examples of fundamental constants are the electrical charge of an electron e, the mass of an electron m_e, and the universal gas constant R.

You have seen that the gas constant R enables chemists to relate the pressure, volume, and temperature of a gas to the amount (moles) of gas in the container. This number appears in many other mathematical formulas used in chemistry. For example, the difference between the quantity of heat needed to raise the temperature of any gas at constant pressure versus that at constant volume has the numerical value of 8.31 $J \cdot mol^{-1} \cdot °C^{-1}$ (that is, R). The constant R appears in equations relating to electrochemistry, thermodynamics, chemical equilibria, rates of reactions, and osmotic pressure. In fact, R is the most important constant in chemistry. Because this constant is so crucial to chemical calculations, it is vital that the numerical value be known precisely. The precision and accuracy of the constant must be greater than that of our experimental measurements; otherwise careful and precise measurements are pointless.

Science is not always about making new discoveries; it is also about establishing more precise values. Experimental results and discoveries are documented and shared with other colleagues in journals and periodicals. This sharing of information allows other researchers to validate the results of an experiment.

SCENARIO

In this simulation, you are a chemist who has been asked by IUPAC (International Union of Pure and Applied Chemistry) to co-ordinate and take part in a worldwide exercise to obtain the best value for *R* by carrying out a series of suitable experiments.

You are required to:

- share your procedures and results with other chemists
- write a report to IUPAC headquarters in Geneva summarizing the results of this worldwide exercise

As co-ordinator of this exercise, you plan to submit an abstract to a scientific journal describing this project.

Note: The required repetitions of the experiments simulating worldwide results can be accomplished by pooling the results of other students in the class.

Part A: Researching Current Values of R

1. Use electronic and print resources to find the best values of R to date. Summarize the various values, including their units, and indicate the source of information for each one.

Part B: Determining the Value of R by Experiment

2. Obtain oxygen gas by the decomposition of potassium chlorate with manganese dioxide. Follow the procedure in Investigation 1, p. 422 to obtain the volume of oxygen gas, the pressure of oxygen (corrected for pressure of water vapour), and the mass of oxygen.

3. Obtain carbon dioxide by the decomposition of sodium bicarbonate. Use the same procedure as in Investigation 1, p. 422.

4. Obtain hydrogen gas by the reaction of calcium metal in water. A small chunk of calcium metal, when dropped into water, will result in the production of hydrogen gas. Design a procedure that will allow you to collect the hydrogen gas. Measure its volume, mass, and temperature. Have your teacher approve your plan before carrying it out. Make sure you identify all safety precautions.

Part C: Analyzing and Interpreting the Data

5. Design a table that shows all measured data obtained in each of your experiments. Show all calculations made in each experiment. (Note: A spreadsheet can be used to summarize the measured data.)

6. Compare the values of R obtained experimentally with the value obtained from Part A. Discuss all discrepancies between the experimental and researched values. In addition, discuss and explain any differences among the experimental values. Write out the chemical equations for the three reactions.

7. Obtain the values for R from each experiment from other student groups. These will be added, along with your results, in a summary table as part of your final report.

Part D: Communicating Results

8. Write a summary report to IUPAC that includes:
   - a rationale for this worldwide exercise
   - a summary of the current values of R
   - a summary of the procedures that were followed and an explanation why
   - a complete data table of all results
   - a description of possible sources of experimental error

9. Write an abstract for an article in a scientific journal about this worldwide exercise. Include in your abstract a reason why this exercise was commissioned by IUPAC and the implications if a fundamental constant, such as R, varies.

UNIT 4 REVIEW

Understanding Concepts

1. The property of gases that accounts for pressure is:
   a) the space between molecules
   b) the density of the gas
   c) the motion of the gas molecules
   d) the identity of the gas

2. Real gases behave like ideal gases when:
   a) the pressure is high and the temperature is low
   b) the pressure is low and the temperature is high
   c) the pressure is low and the temperature is low
   d) the pressure is high and the temperature is high
   e) none of the above

3. According to Boyle's Law, the volume of a given mass of gas is inversely proportional to the pressure, at a constant temperature. Therefore, it would be expected that an increase in the pressure exerted on a gas would cause the density to:
   a) increase
   b) decrease
   c) remain the same
   d) increase for some gases and decease for others

4. The mass of a fixed quantity of a gas:
   a) increases when the volume increases, at constant temperature
   b) decreases when the absolute temperature decreases, at a constant pressure
   c) does not change at any temperature or pressure
   d) decreases as the density increases

5. The solubility of a gas in water increases with:
   a) an increase in pressure and a decrease in temperature
   b) a decrease in pressure and a decrease in temperature
   c) an increase in pressure and an increase in temperature
   d) a decrease in pressure and an increase in temperature

6. The vapour pressure of a liquid depends on the:
   a) temperature of the liquid
   b) area of exposed surface of the liquid
   c) atmospheric pressure
   d) volume of the container above the liquid

7. At a constant volume, the pressure of a gas Y increases with temperature because:
   a) the molecules of Y move faster
   b) the volume of Y increases
   c) collisions of Y molecules are more elastic
   d) the mass of Y increases

8. Hydrogen gas reacts with oxygen gas at 120°C according to the equation:
   $$2 \ H_2(g) + O_2(g) \rightarrow 2 \ H_2O(g)$$
   If 52 mL of hydrogen gas are reacted with 26 mL of oxygen gas at the same temperature and pressure, the volume of water produced will be:
   a) 52 mL   b) 26 mL
   c) 78 mL   d) 39 mL

9. Oxygen gas can be obtained from the decomposition of hydrogen peroxide:
   $$2 \ H_2O_2(l) \xrightarrow{\text{MnO}_2} 2 \ H_2O(l) + O_2(g)$$
   From 1.00 mol of hydrogen peroxide, at SATP, you can collect the following volume of oxygen gas:
   a) 24.8 L
   b) 12.4 L
   c) 49.6 L
   d) none of the above

10. Identify which one of the following gases are *not* covered by the Kyoto Protocol:
    a) perfluorocarbons (PFCs)
    b) hydrofluorocarbons (HFCs)
    c) hydrochlorofluorocarbons (HCFCs)
    d) sulfur hexafluoride

11. State the combined gas law in your own words.

12. State the assumptions of the kinetic-molecular theory in your own words, and apply these to explain the behaviour of gases.

13. Make a chart summarizing the gas laws. Name each law, and provide the mathematical relationship for each.

14. Explain why opening a bottle of a carbonated beverage causes the liquid to bubble (release gas).

15. Live fish are found at the very bottom of the oceans, yet when samples of these fish are brought to the surface, they are almost always dead. Describe why the trip to the surface might kill them.

16. In chloroflurocarbons, name the element that causes destruction of the ozone layer. Use a graphic organizer to illustrate how this destructive process occurs.

17. Write a paragraph stating your opinion as to whether it would be possible to ship natural gas (methane) from the Arctic by filling balloons with the gas and flying them south. Provide supporting evidence for your opinion.

18. Use electronic and print materials to research why a mixture of helium and oxygen, rather than nitrogen and oxygen, is used for deep-sea divers. Summarize your findings in a paragraph.

19. Dinitrogen oxide is only one of a number of chemicals that can be used as an anesthetic. Use reference books to find out what other compounds are used for this purpose. Prepare a report on these chemicals.

20. The molecules of a gaseous halogen have an average velocity $\sqrt{2}$ times that of argon. Identify the halogen, and describe its properties.

21. Name the three classifications of compressed gases, and compare how they are different from one another.

22. Write a description comparing the air pressure in front of you when you are walking into a wind to the air pressure behind you.

23. Of the percentage of ultraviolet radiation that makes it through the ozone layer, a significant proportion is scattered in Earth's atmosphere. Explain why this is so.

24. Write a paragraph that explains why a major volcanic eruption is more catastrophic than any other natural phenomenon on Earth.

25. The innermost planet, Mercury, does not possess a significant atmosphere. Suggest an explanation.

Applying Inquiry/ Communication Skills

26. Design and conduct an experiment to determine the rates at which two different gases escape through the walls of a balloon.

27. A colourless gas, W, with the smell of rotten eggs is reacted with a colourless, acidic gaseous oxide, X, to give a yellow solid element, Y, and a colourless liquid, Z, whose boiling point at sea level is 100°C.
a) Identify W, X, Y, and Z.
b) Write a balanced chemical equation for the reaction.

28. An observation balloon with a volume of 1.53×10^4 L is filled with helium at a temperature of 18°C and a pressure of 101 kPa. The balloon rises into the stratosphere until the volume of the balloon is 8.18×10^4 L and the pressure is 15.1 kPa. Determine the air temperature at this altitude.

29. A balloon contains 5.0 L of air at a pressure of 149 kPa. If the temperature remains constant, calculate the pressure in the balloon if the volume is decreased to 4.0 L.

30. A cylinder of volume 1.50 m^3 contains compressed air at a pressure of 10.0 MPa. Calculate the volume that the air would occupy at the same temperature and a pressure of 101 kPa.

31. A balloon contains 5.0 L of air at 35°C. Calculate the new volume of the balloon if the temperature drops to −35°C while the pressure is kept constant.

32. A balloon contains 5.0 L of air at 25°C. Calculate at what temperature the balloon will shrink to half that volume. Assume that the pressure is held constant.

33. A gas in a rigid container with a volume of 2.50×10^2 mL has a pressure of 99.7 kPa at 25°C. Calculate the pressure inside the container if:
a) the Celsius temperature is doubled
b) the Kelvin temperature is doubled

34. A certain mass of gas has a volume of 4.50 L at 95.6 kPa and 28°C. Calculate the missing value for each set of conditions given in Table 6.

TABLE 6

Pressure	Volume	Temperature
74.4 kPa	2.80 L	? K
? kPa	8.75 L	259°C
715 kPa	? L	58 K

35. The self-contained breathing apparatus (SCBA) worn by firefighters has a volume of 7.85 L and, at 22°C, contains air at a pressure of 1.55×10^4 kPa.
a) Calculate the volume of air that will be supplied to the lungs at a pressure of 101 kPa and a temperature of 36°C.
b) The SCBA is designed to supply air for 30.0 min. If the firefighter takes 15 breaths per minute, use your answer from a) to calculate the volume of air taken into the lungs during each breath.

36. Fill in the spaces in the following table:

TABLE 7

Gas	Mass	Pressure	Volume	Temperature
NH_3	?	158 kPa	0.500 L	27°C
H_2	2.00 g	124 kPa	20.0 L	?
CO	4.00 g	?	0.500 L	21°C

37. You want to transport chlorine gas (Cl_2), a highly poisonous gas, safely from Vancouver to Toronto. You have a 5-L cylinder that will withstand a pressure of 100 atm. The cylinder will be kept at 0°C throughout the trip. Calculate how many moles of chlorine you will be able from transport safely.

38. Acetylene gas, $C_2H_2(g)$, is widely used in welding.
a) Discuss how a cylinder of acetylene is very different from one of another compressed gas.
b) A cylinder of acetylene gas has a pressure of 1.72×10^3 kPa at a temperature of 20°C. If the volume of the cylinder is 87.0 L, calculate the mass of acetylene present.
c) Write a balanced equation for the reaction of acetylene with oxygen gas.
d) Calculate the volume of oxygen gas at a temperature of 18°C and a pressure of 102 kPa needed to react completely with 1.50 kg of acetylene.

39. a) Identify the gaseous chemical elements.
b) Calculate the density of the least dense gaseous element at 120°C and 103 kPa.
c) Calculate the density of the densest gaseous element at 120°C and 103 kPa.
d) Calculate the ratio of the two densities.
e) Calculate the ratio of the molecular masses of the two gases.
f) Explain why there is a relationship between your answers to d) and e).

40. A gas formed by uranium and fluorine, formula UF_X, is used to assist in the separation of the isotopes U-235 and U-238. At a temperature of 75°C and a pressure of 98.5 kPa, 1.00 g of this uranium-fluorine compound occupies a volume of 83.3 mL. Determine the molar mass of the gas, and deduce its formula.

41. A gas has the formula $CH_3CH_2CH_3$. Calculate the volume that 2.00 g of this gas will occupy at 27°C and 750 mm Hg.

42. Heptane, $CH_3(CH_2)_5CH_3$, a component of gasoline, burns in oxygen to give carbon dioxide and water vapour.
    a) Write a balanced equation for the reaction.
    b) Calculate the volume of oxygen that would be required at 20°C and 102 kPa to completely burn 10.0 kg of heptane (equivalent to about a small tankful of gasoline). Determine the volume of air that would be needed if air contains only 20% oxygen.
    c) Calculate the volume of carbon dioxide that would be produced from this mass of heptane.
    d) If you used one tank of heptane per week, calculate how many tonnes of carbon dioxide you would contribute to the atmosphere in one (1.00) year.

43. Because of the high density of its vapour, carbon tetrachloride was at one time used in fire extinguishers. Calculate the density of carbon tetrachloride, $CCl_4(g)$, at 200°C and 101.3 kPa.

44. Carbon dioxide is bubbled into 100.0 mL of a sodium hydroxide solution until it has been completely converted to sodium carbonate. When the solution is evaporated until dry, 2.50 g of sodium carbonate is formed. Calculate the initial concentration of the sodium hydroxide solution. Calculate the volume of carbon dioxide gas that had been absorbed at 29°C and 102 kPa.

45. Aliens land on an island in the Pacific and see a strange sight—a smoke-like gas coming out of a cone-like part of the island. They collect 600 mL of this gas at 227°C near the cone. Calculate the volume of gas they would have if the temperature were 30°C. Assume that the pressure of the atmosphere is constant.

46. Deduce the best gas for passenger-carrying balloons. Confirm your answer by calculating the density of the gas at a temperature of 18°C and a pressure of 102 kPa, and compare it to the density of air.

47. Zinc metal reacts with dilute hydrochloric acid to give zinc chloride solution and hydrogen gas. When 4.21 g of an impure sample of zinc was treated with an excess of hydrochloric acid, 1.24 L of hydrogen gas was collected over water at a temperature of 20°C and a total pressure of 104.7 kPa. (The vapour pressure of water at 20°C is 2.3 kPa.)
    a) Write a balanced equation for the reaction.
    b) Calculate the mass of zinc present in the sample.
    c) Find the percent purity of the zinc.

48. To determine the purity of a sample of calcium chloride, 2.86 g of the sample was dissolved in water and reacted with an excess of aqueous silver nitrate:
    $CaCl_2(aq) + 2\ AgNO_3(aq) \rightarrow 2\ AgCl(s) + Ca(NO_3)_2(aq)$
    Calculate the percent purity of the sample if 4.41 g of silver chloride is obtained.

49. A 25.0-g sample of impure silver was treated with excess nitric acid to produce a solution of silver nitrate. On the addition of an excess of sodium iodide solution to the silver nitrate solution, 25.0 g of silver iodide was precipitated. Determine the purity of the original sample of silver.

50. Gaseous hydrogen fluoride, produced from the reaction of liquid hydrogen and liquid fluorine, was once considered a possible rocket propellant.
    a) Write a balanced chemical equation for the reaction.
    b) Describe one of the criteria for a propellant that this reaction meets.
    c) Calculate the volume of hydrogen fluoride gas that would be produced at 800°C and 100.0 kPa if 50.0 t of liquid fluorine were reacted with an excess of liquid hydrogen.
    d) Suggest reasons why you think this combination was not adopted.

51. Suppose you were to travel to either of our neighbouring planets, Mars or Venus.
    a) Describe the main chemical components of their atmospheres.
    b) In addition to the chemical difference of the atmospheres, the pressures and temperatures are quite different. To illustrate, calculate the volume that 1.00 mol of an ideal gas will occupy:
       i) on the surface of Venus where the temperature is about 470°C and the pressure is 9.3 MPa
       ii) on the surface of Mars where the temperature is about −10°C and the pressure is 0.60 kPa

52. Chlorofluorocarbons, CFCs, are among the densest gases in the atmosphere.
    a) Calculate the density of dichlorodifluoromethane, CF_2Cl_2, one of the CFC family, at 20°C and 102 kPa.
    b) It has been argued that the chlorofluorocarbons (CFCs) cannot be contributing to the decrease in the ozone layer concentration as they are dense gases and will sink to the ground. Explain the fallacy in this argument.

53. Saturn's moon, Titan, has a high atmospheric concentration of a gas that contains 75.0% carbon, the remainder being hydrogen.
    a) Calculate the empirical formula of the compound.
    b) On the surface of Titan, where the temperature is 95 K and the pressure is 150 kPa, 1.00 L of this gas has a mass of 3.0 g. Calculate the molar mass of the gas.
    c) Use the results of your calculations in parts a) and b) to determine the molecular formula of the gas.

54. The inflation of an air bag involves the sudden decomposition of sodium azide:

$$2 \, NaN_3(s) \rightarrow 2 \, Na(l) + 3 \, N_2(g)$$

a) Calculate the mass of sodium azide required to inflate the bag to a volume of 5.00 L at 31°C and 225 kPa.

b) Lead(II) azide, $Pb(N_3)_2$, is used in warning detonators for trains. In an emergency, disks containing lead(II) azide are placed on the track. The slightest pressure of the engine wheels causes the lead(II) azide to explode, and the noise warns the engineer of trouble ahead. Write a balanced equation for the decomposition of lead(II) azide. Describe why you think sodium azide, and not lead(II) azide, is used for air bags. Provide supporting evidence for your opinion.

55. Calculate the density of helium gas at a temperature of 18°C and a pressure of 102 kPa. Comparing your answer to the density of hot air at 100°C, determine which is the better lifting gas, hot air or helium.

56. A certain compound contains 69.6% sulfur, the remainder being nitrogen.

a) Calculate the empirical formula of the compound.

b) When 1.00 g of this compound was vaporized at 300°C in a 0.500-L container, the pressure in the container was 51.6 kPa. Determine the molar mass of the compound.

c) Use the results of your calculations in parts a) and b) to determine the molecular formula of the compound.

Making Connections

57. In the 1970s, in order to address consumers who were becoming energy-conscious, builders began to construct airtight homes and buildings, cutting fuel and heating costs substantially but causing other problems. Because fresh air could not get in, contaminants accumulated indoors, causing people to complain about their health and comfort. This condition became generally known as "sick-building syndrome." Interview some building contractors and architects to gather primary source information on issues regarding indoor air quality, which designers and builders should consider. Prepare a guide sheet for consumers who are interested in purchasing a house comparing the costs of different building materials and showing how the use of these materials would affect house and fuel costs.

58. In unpolluted air, ozone at ground level is a natural gas occurring in small concentrations that do not affect health. However in polluted air, ozone can increase to unhealthy levels. High concentrations of ground-level ozone often occur in or near heavily populated areas, where vehicles and industry emit the abundance of chemicals necessary to produce and trap ground-level ozone. Many researchers feel that ozone is the common air pollutant that is most detrimental to human health. Analyze the validity of this belief by examining primary and secondary environmental and health sources. Write a report summarizing your findings.

59. If the release of greenhouse gases by human activities remains unchecked, the potential for overall global climate changes increases, as does the threat to the survival of many species. Create a poster that informs the public on how human activities can affect other living things, including long-range economic and environmental consequences.

60. In 1987, Canada was a key player at an international conference on substances that deplete the ozone layer, which led to the signing of the Montreal Protocol. The protocol was further amended at meetings in London, England, in June 1990. Only countries that have signed and ratified the protocol are obligated to phase out the production and consumption of CFCs, halons, carbon tetrachloride, and methyl chloroform. Prepare a convincing argument to nations that have not signed the protocol that will encourage them to consider signing it. Remember to consider heath, economic, and environmental factors.

61. The Climate Summit talks held at the end of November 2000 in The Hague broke down when the European Union delegates rejected the United States' proposal to use its managed forests to count for carbon credits in place of cutting greenhouse emissions. Write a briefing paper to the Canadian government on whether or not you would support this proposal. Include in your paper any political, economic, and environmental consequences.

62. Some years ago, a 21-year-old Canadian flying cadet was learning scuba diving. As part of the training, he had to take a lungful of air from an air tank at the bottom of a swimming pool and then swim to the surface. The cadet did so but forgot one important instruction. As a result, the cadet's lungs ruptured on reaching the surface, and he died the following day. Design and make a poster outlining the health risks associated with scuba diving and the appropriate precautions.

5 Hydrocarbons and Energy

OVERALL EXPECTATIONS

By the end of this unit, you will be able to:

- demonstrate an understanding of the structure and properties of hydrocarbons, especially with respect to the energy changes that occur in their combustion reactions

- describe and investigate the properties of hydrocarbons, and apply calorimetric techniques to the calculation of energy changes

- evaluate the impact of hydrocarbons on our quality of life and the environment through an examination of their uses

Every day, new technology makes things possible that many of us may not even have dreamed of. Most of us expect that technology will continue to advance and find new ways to solve problems or enrich our lives. But have you considered that the resources we use to create and fuel our technological society are hundreds of millions of years old? These resources include the oil, natural gas, and coal that supply us with hydrocarbons.

Before humans evolved, the remains of prehistoric vegetation and marine life were deposited in thick layers on Earth's surface. Over time, these layers became buried and pushed into Earth's crust, where they were subjected to extreme heat and compression. These forces converted the decayed matter into deposits of coal, petroleum, and natural gas, which we now rely on for energy and chemical building blocks.

Without these resources, the Industrial Revolution could not have occurred; we might still be riding in horse-drawn carts, wearing only wool and cotton clothing, and using only herbal medicines. Today, we rely on these resources to supply us with energy for our vehicles and machinery. Many new materials are synthesized from the compounds found in these reserves, from plastics to pharmaceuticals.

Coal, petroleum, and natural gas have many benefits and therefore are extremely valuable to the world economy. However, using these resources is not without cost. Pollution of our air, land, and water can in large part be traced to burning the compounds in these reserves. We also have only a limited supply of coal, petroleum, and natural gas, and so we cannot rely on them indefinitely.

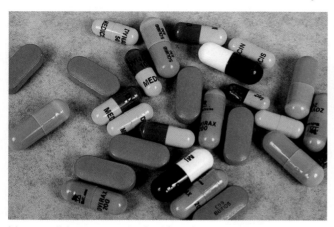

Many medicines are synthesized from hydrocarbons.

Plastics are also synthesized from hydrocarbons.

■ Landfill Liners of Asphalt

Asphalt has many uses, from roofing to paving. Now researchers at the University of Missouri think they have yet another use for this petroleum product: making liners to prevent leakage at potentially hazardous landfills. These scientists say asphalt liners contain waste in landfills far better than the liners currently in use.

■ Cleaning Up

Oil spills are extremely hard to clean up. Professor Subhasis Ghoshal and his team at McGill University have found that when crude oil is immersed in water, it forms rigid skins. The scientists have found that these skins can prevent toxic contaminants from leaching into water. They are trying to understand how these skins form, in the hope they will be able to make other fuels form skins as well. Then, even if the entire spill cannot be recovered, the toxic effects on the environment could be reduced.

■ Plastics and Computers

Many parts of the average computer are constructed of plastic, but a new technology is currently being tested that may allow plastic chips to replace silicon chips in some devices. If they work as hoped, the plastic chips would be much cheaper to produce. Since they would also be flexible and more durable than silicon chips, they would be more suitable for use in toys, touch screens, and credit cards.

••••• ••••• ACHIEVEMENT TASK (PREVIEW)

At the end of this unit, you will demonstrate your learning by completing the task "Survival Kit." You will prepare a brief to the directors of a manufacturing company on the advantages and disadvantages of using different hydrocarbons to produce components of an emergency survival kit. Your brief will summarize the sources, properties, waste product recovery options, economic factors, and social issues involved in using hydrocarbons. See page 518.

We rely on hydrocarbon fuels for our transportation.

Hydrocarbons

Petroleum, coal, natural gas: you read about them in the newspaper and hear about them on the news. Wars have been waged and international agreements brokered by hard negotiation, just to ensure their continuing supply. But what exactly are these resources? Is petroleum made of one type of compound or of many? Are these resources important only for energy, or do they have other uses?

Petroleum, coal, and natural gas are our main supply of a class of compounds called hydrocarbons. **Hydrocarbons** are compounds that contain only hydrogen and carbon atoms. You might be surprised at the many different uses we have for hydrocarbons.

If the world's hydrocarbon supplies were suddenly cut off, your life would become a lot different. Your travelling would be limited to the distance you could cover under your own power. You would have trouble getting groceries

FIGURE 10.1   Many industries in Canada, such as those of the Chemical Valley in Sarnia, Ontario, are based on hydrocarbon compounds.

because supermarkets would not be able to ship many of their goods. Only hydro- and nuclear-powered electric generating stations could operate, so you would have to use far less electricity. You also would not be able to get many synthetic materials: there would be no polyester fleece for your sweat-shirt, no nylon for your backpack, not even any latex elastic to hold up your socks! Computers, telephones, televisions, automobiles, cooking utensils—all the things we now produce using plastics would disappear. There would even be fewer pharmaceuticals, so some diseases might no longer be treatable.

Hydrocarbons are members of a huge group of compounds based on the carbon atom. In this chapter, you will find out where carbon-based compounds come from. You will classify and name hydrocarbons and explore their structure. You will find out about their physical and chemical properties. You will also explore some of the many substances we make from hydro-carbons and evaluate their role in our society.

Discovering Chemistry

Getting along Like Oil and Water

Oil is a hydrocarbon. How do ionic and covalent compounds behave in oil?

Materials
  vegetable oil
  water
  NaCl, an ionic compound
  sugar, a covalent compound

1. Consider what you already know about the behaviour of ionic and cova-lent compounds in water, and then predict how these compounds might behave in the oil.

2. Develop an experimental procedure that will allow you to test your predictions.

3. Carry out your procedure.

■ In two or three sentences, explain what you observed.

■ Can you think of other properties of oil and water that might be differ-ent? How about those that would be the same? How could you find out?

CHECK**POINT**

1. Identify the kinds of elements that form cova-lent bonds.

2. Write a list of guidelines that you would use to determine if the bonds in a compound were covalent, polar covalent, or ionic.

3. Describe the type of bonding that is present in ethane (CH_3CH_3). Draw the Lewis struc-ture for ethane.

10.1 Organic Compounds

Key Understandings

When you have completed this section, you will be able to:

- identify the origins and sources of organic compounds
- understand the special characteristics of the carbon atom that allow it to form so many organic compounds
- use scientific vocabulary to communicate ideas related to hydrocarbons

FIGURE 10.2 Some inorganic compounds

FIGURE 10.3 Some organic compounds

An **organic compound** is commonly defined as any compound that contains covalently-bonded carbon atoms. **Inorganic compounds** are all the remaining compounds. There are, however, some simple carbon-containing substances that are considered to be inorganic. These substances are compounds and polyatomic ions that contain only one carbon atom, such as the oxides carbon monoxide and carbon dioxide, and the polyatomic ions carbonate (CO_3^{2-}) and cyanide (CN^-).

Although inorganic compounds can be made from any combination of over 100 elements, more than 80% of all the chemicals we know (over 10 million) are in fact organic. Organic compounds form the basis of life. Your skin, bones, hair, and even your DNA are made of organic compounds. Plants, bacteria, fish, and insects—in fact, almost every form of life is composed of organic compounds.

The Origins of Organic Chemistry Before 1828, any substance that was isolated from animal or plant material (that is, an organism) was thought to contain a "vital force." The study of compounds made by living things came to be called organic chemistry. Because the vital force was believed to occur only in living things, it was thought that organic compounds could not be prepared in a laboratory. However, in 1828, Friedrich Wöhler successfully synthesized the organic compound urea from inorganic chemicals, thus disproving the existence of a vital force.

Sources of Organic Substances

Most organic compounds are obtained from living sources. For example, the food you eat is composed of organic substances that maintain your health, including carbohydrates, proteins, fats, and vitamins. The cotton in your clothing is an organic product of the cotton plant; the wood that supports your house is also composed of organic molecules. Almost all the living things on Earth are made of compounds based on the carbon atom.

Although organic compounds can be synthesized in a laboratory, it is often much cheaper to have living organisms do the chemical synthesis for us. For example, it is much cheaper to obtain the organic compound we call table sugar (sucrose, $C_{12}H_{22}O_{11}$) from sugar beets or sugar cane than to assemble the atoms from simpler molecules.

FIGURE 10.4 A molecule of vitamin C has the same structure and properties whether it is synthesized by a living plant or in a chemical laboratory.

Fossil Fuels Many other important organic compounds are obtained from deposits of materials formed by decomposition of living organisms. These

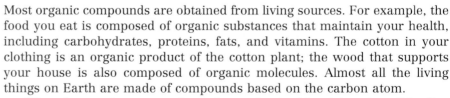

deposits are collectively referred to as fossil fuels. **Fossil fuels** are the products of decomposition of once-living organisms, formed beneath the Earth's surface by the action of great pressure and high temperature over millions of years. The heat and pressure convert the remains of the organisms into a complex mixture of organic compounds—mainly hydrocarbons. Organic compounds produced from oil or natural gas are called **petrochemicals**.

Properties of the Carbon Atom

What makes the carbon atom so special? Is life based on the carbon atom just by chance, or is there something unique about carbon that makes possible all these different kinds of molecules with so many different properties? There are three factors:

- The carbon atom can bond with as many as four other atoms. When you think about the number of other elements in the periodic table, you can see that the ability to bond to four other atoms is one feature that allows the carbon atom to form many different compounds. However, carbon is not the only atom that can form four covalent bonds. In fact, all the other atoms in the same group as carbon have this ability. So why don't they also form millions of compounds?

- Carbon atoms readily bond with other carbon atoms to form chains, rings, spheres, sheets, and tubes of almost any size. This property is known as **catenation**.

- When carbon bonds to another carbon atom, the bond that forms is very hard to break. As you can see from Figure 10.5, the other members of this periodic group form much weaker bonds.

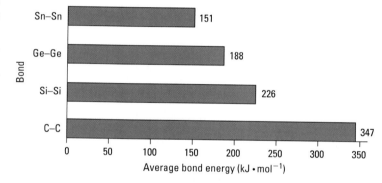

FIGURE 10.5 Average bond energy between the same atoms of group 14 (IVA) elements of the periodic table.

Hydrocarbons

Hydrocarbon molecules are composed of only carbon and hydrogen atoms. The carbon atoms in hydrocarbons may be bonded either to each other or to atoms of hydrogen. To understand and predict the behaviour of the many hydrocarbon compounds, scientists have organized them into families based on their structure (Figure 10.6). The two main types of hydrocarbons are aliphatic and aromatic.

Aliphatic compounds can be either open-chain or cyclic molecules. Open-chain hydrocarbons are subdivided into alkanes, alkenes, and alkynes. **Alkanes**, such as ethane ($H_3C–CH_3$), contain only carbon-carbon *single* bonds. **Alkenes**, such as ethene ($H_2C=CH_2$), contain one or more carbon-carbon *double* bonds, while **alkynes**, such as ethyne ($HC\equiv CH$), contain carbon-carbon *triple* bonds. **Alicyclics**, such as cyclopentane C_5H_{10}, are a special class of aliphatic hydrocarbon in which the arrangement of the carbon atoms is **cyclic**; i.e, it forms a *ring structure*.

Aromatic hydrocarbons are also cyclic. However, some electrons in aromatic compounds are shared between the carbon atoms in the ring. This arrangement gives aromatics different properties from those of aliphatics. You will study this group of hydrocarbons in your grade 12 course.

WORD**ORIGIN**

Aliphatic comes from the Greek *aleiphatos* meaning "fat."

FIGURE 10.6 Flowchart of the families of hydrocarbons

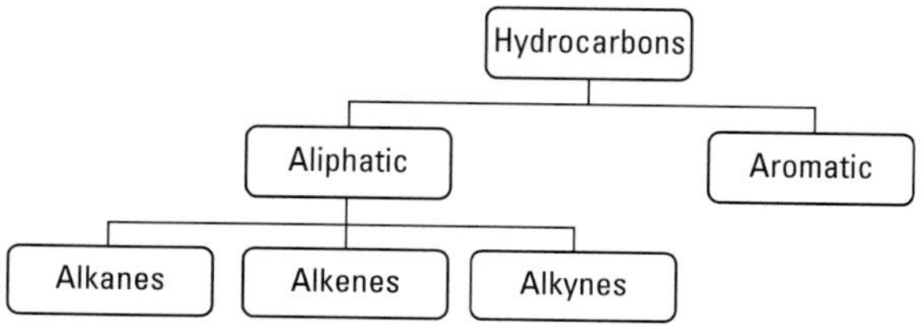

```
                    Hydrocarbons
                    /          \
              Aliphatic      Aromatic
              /   |   \
        Alkanes Alkenes Alkynes
```

FIGURE 10.7 Gas stoves burn methane gas.

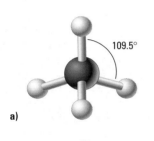

a)

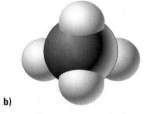

b)

FIGURE 10.8 a) Ball-and-stick and b) space filling representations of the methane molecule

INFO**BIT**

If your home is heated with natural gas, you may be familiar with the distinct smell of this fuel. This odour in fact does not come from the gas, but from the compound ethane thiol (C_2H_5SH). Small amounts of ethane thiol are added to natural gas for safety; without it, you would not be able to detect a leak in your system, which could have deadly consequences.

10.2 Alkanes

Key Understandings

When you have completed this section, you will be able to:
- identify alkanes and describe their characteristics
- define the term "constitutional (structural) isomer"
- identify constitutional (structural) isomers for given compounds
- use molecular models to construct models of alkanes including constitutional (structural) isomers
- name alkanes using IUPAC rules
- use scientific vocabulary to communicate ideas about alkanes

Alkanes are hydrocarbon molecules that have only single bonds. Each carbon atom in an alkane is therefore bonded to four other atoms. This is the maximum number of other atoms to which carbon can bind according to the octet rule. This pattern of bonding determines the shape and the reactivity of alkanes.

Methane

The simplest alkane is methane (CH_4). At room temperature, methane is a colourless, odourless gas; it is a major component of natural gas. Methane is also an important starting material for the synthesis of methanol (CH_3OH), chloroform ($CHCl_3$), and many other organic compounds.

Methane is produced as a by-product of bacterial decomposition in the absence of air (anaerobic decomposition). Methane is produced in large quantities in waterlogged areas such as bogs and swamps. High levels of methane can also be produced in landfills if garbage is buried. Landfills therefore often have gas vents to prevent methane buildup.

The carbon atom of methane is bonded to four hydrogen atoms. The hydrogen atoms are located at sites in three dimensions around the carbon atom, giving methane a tetrahedral shape (Figure 10.8). **Tetrahedrons** are geometric structures in which all the angles are the same; methane molecules are tetrahedral where the angles are 109.5°. Use a molecular model kit to construct a model of methane, and check this yourself.

The Canary in the Coal Mine

An early-warning system is sometimes referred to as "a canary in a coal mine." Like many expressions, this one is based in truth. Coal mining, particularly underground coal mining, is one of the most dangerous jobs in the world. Methane, carbon monoxide, and other gases are often trapped inside coal deposits. When miners drill or blast into the deposits, these gases can escape through the cracks and pores that are created. If the coal is being mined underground, the gases quickly build up inside the mine shafts. Methane is highly flammable and will be ignited by the smallest spark, while carbon monoxide is toxic. Unfortunately, both these gases are colourless and odourless, so miners must have some way of detecting them before they reach dangerous levels.

In the 1800s, the most reliable gas detection system was a caged canary. When methane or carbon monoxide leaked into a closed shaft, the oxygen level decreased. Canaries show symptoms of oxygen deprivation at much lower gas levels than humans. Therefore, if the canary fell unconscious from its perch, the men knew they had but a short time to leave the mine. Unfortunately, this was often not long enough, and many lives were lost.

The worst Canadian coal mine disaster occurred in 1914 in the Hillcrest Collieries, located on the Alberta side of the Crowsnest Pass. One hundred and eighty-nine men were killed, either directly by the methane explosion, by gas poisoning, or in the collapse of the tunnels that followed.

Improving the safety of miners depended on the invention of new technology for gas detection. By 1938, miners were working with handheld combustible gas indicators (the Explosimeter®) that were much more sensitive than the poor canaries. Today's devices are miniature gas chromatographs that can gather data on a range of gases at very low levels, which can be downloaded to a computer. This allows mine workers to analyze gas levels in an entire mine and map when and where problems develop.

FIGURE 10.9 Modern gas monitors have greatly improved mining safety.

Of course, no tool is effective if it is not used properly. In 1993, 26 men were killed in an explosion in the Westray mine in Plymouth, Nova Scotia. Inadequate gas monitoring and a lack of safety training played a large role in this disaster, and led to strict new laws for mine safety that included better guidelines for gas monitoring.

Ethane

Ethane (CH_3CH_3) is the second member of the alkane series. Like methane, ethane is a gas at room temperature and is also a component of natural gas. Ethanol (CH_3CH_2OH) and ethylene glycol antifreeze ($HOCH_2CH_2OH$) are also made from ethane.

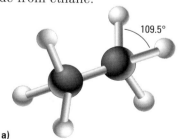
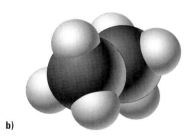

109.5°

a)

b)

FIGURE 10.10 a) Ball-and-stick and b) space-filling representations of the ethane molecule

The carbon atoms in the ethane molecule are bonded to three hydrogen atoms as well as the other carbon atom. From the ball-and-stick representation in Figure 10.10, you can see that, as for methane, all the bond angles of ethane are the same. The space-filling model shows that ethane is shaped somewhat like a short tube.

FIGURE 10.11 Propane is used as a low-polluting fuel in fleet vehicles such as buses and taxis.

Propane

Propane, C_3H_8, is the third member of the alkane series. You and your family may have used propane as fuel in an RV camper or a gas barbecue. Some vehicles have been modified to run on propane, because propane gas produces fewer pollutants (Figure 10.11). When propane is used as fuel, it is usually in a container that keeps it under pressure. This pressure forces the propane into a liquid state, so that more propane molecules can be transported in a smaller space.

Although structural formulas are useful for showing the arrangement of atoms in a molecule, they are cumbersome to draw. Therefore, a more compact form called a **condensed formula** is used. Figure 10.12 shows the structural formula and the condensed formula of propane. To write the condensed formula of a hydrocarbon, you write the hydrogen atoms beside the carbon atom to which they are attached. Although it is not apparent from the condensed formula of a hydrocarbon, remember that each hydrogen atom forms only one bond and therefore always ends a chain of atoms: it is the carbon atoms that are bonded together.

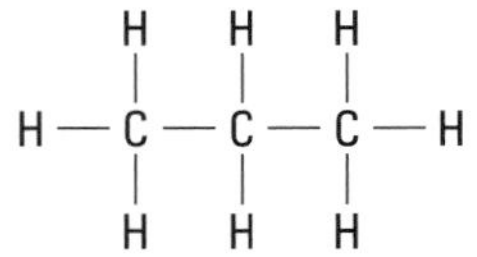

FIGURE 10.12 a) Structural formula and b) condensed formula of propane

Butane

Butane, C_4H_{10}, is a component of both natural gas and of crude oil. Butane is used as a fuel in products like pocket lighters. It can also be converted into 1,3-butadiene, which can, in turn, be polymerized to make synthetic rubber. Figure 10.13 shows the structural formula and the condensed formula of the chain of four carbon atoms. Do you think butane would become a liquid easily under pressure? Why?

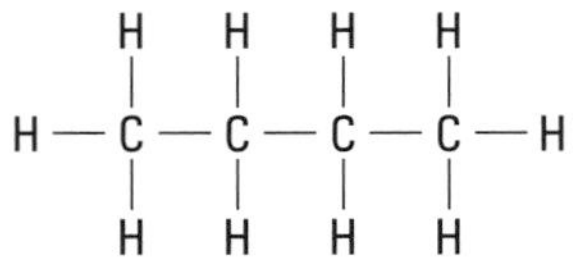

FIGURE 10.13 a) Structural formula and b) condensed formula of butane

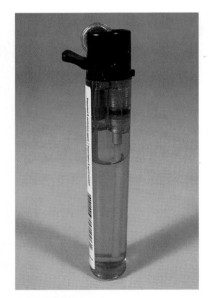

FIGURE 10.14 Butane is the fuel in pocket lighters.

Constitutional Isomers (Structural Isomers)

There is another compound with the molecular formula C_4H_{10}. In this other molecule, three carbon atoms are attached to one central carbon atom. Figure 10.15 shows the structural formula and the condensed formula of this molecule. Describe how this structural isomer of butane differs from the molecule in Figure 10.13.

a) CH_3—$\overset{\displaystyle \overset{H}{|}}{\underset{\displaystyle \underset{CH_3}{|}}{C}}$—$CH_3$

b) CH_3—$CH\,(CH_3)$—CH_3

FIGURE 10.15   a) Structural formula and b) condensed formula of an isomer of butane

These two compounds are **constitutional isomers** (formerly called **structural isomers**). They are compounds that have the same molecular formula but different connectivity. By **connectivity**, chemists mean that the atoms are bonded in different orders. There are several types of constitutional isomer.

The molecule in Figure 10.13 is butane; its isomer in Figure 10.15 is 2-methylpropane. Butane is a **straight-chain** alkane, in which each carbon atom is bonded to a maximum of two other carbon atoms. 2-methylpropane is a **branched-chain** alkane; that is, one in which one or more of the carbon atoms in the molecule is bonded to three or four carbon atoms. Each of these two structures has the molecular formula of C_4H_{10}, but the *arrangement* of the atoms in the carbon chain is different. These two compounds are called **skeletal isomers** (formerly called **chain isomers**), because the carbon atoms in the "backbone" of the molecule are arranged differently.

WEBLINK

To view a simulation of structural isomerism, go to **www.pearsoned.ca/chemistry11**.

Discovering Chemistry   *Skeletal Isomers*

How many constitutional (structural) isomers of the molecular formula C_5H_{12} are possible?

Materials

a molecular model kit or modelling software

1. Make as many different arrangements of the carbon chain as you can.

2. Write down the condensed formula of each of your models.

- Compare the isomers you were able to construct with those of a fellow student. Did you both come up with the same number?

An even simpler way to draw hydrocarbons is to omit the C-C bond entirely and add similar units together. For example, you can write the condensed formula of butane as CH_3—$(CH_2)_2$—CH_3 or $CH_3(CH_2)_2CH_3$. Similarly, 2-methylpropane can be written as $CH_3CH(CH_3)CH_3$ or $CH_3CH(CH_3)_2$. This super-condensed representation is particularly useful when a long chain of CH_2 units is present in a molecule.

As you work through this chapter, you will often find that two structures that first appear to be different actually represent the same compound. You will need practice to develop skill at relating a two-dimensional condensed formula to a three-dimensional molecular shape. Work through Example 1 to try this out.

INFOBIT

All branches of chemistry, including nomenclature, continually advance. The International Union of Pure and Applied Chemistry (IUPAC) is active in making the terminology used in chemistry more systematic. The terminology for organic compounds emphasized in this text (such as constitutional isomer) was recommended by IUPAC in 1993 and 1996. The older terms (such as structural isomer) are also mentioned, since you might see these in older texts and articles.

Identify all the different isomers of C_6H_{14} from the molecules below.

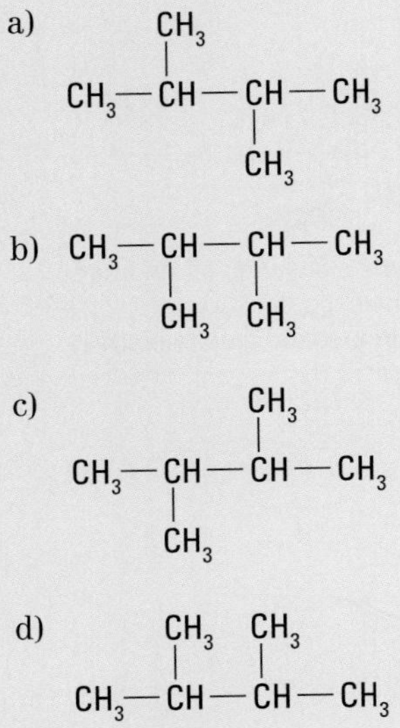

a)

CH$_3$
|
CH$_3$—CH—CH—CH$_3$
|
CH$_3$

b) CH$_3$—CH—CH—CH$_3$
| |
CH$_3$ CH$_3$

c)

CH$_3$
|
CH$_3$—CH—CH—CH$_3$
|
CH$_3$

d)

CH$_3$ CH$_3$
| |
CH$_3$—CH—CH—CH$_3$

FIGURE 10.17

EXAMPLE 1

How many different isomers of C_6H_{14} are shown below?

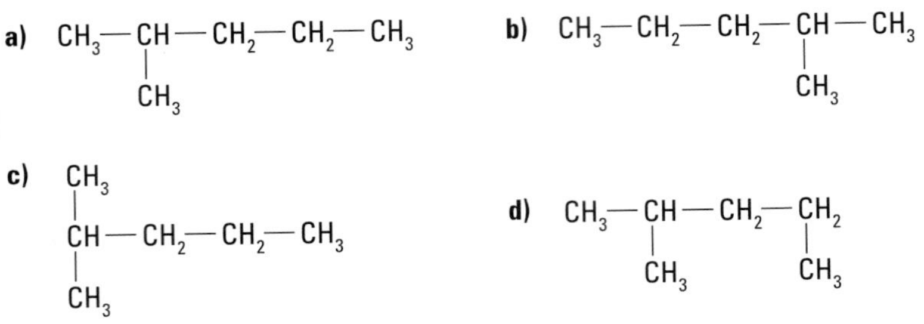

a)   CH$_3$—CH—CH$_2$—CH$_2$—CH$_3$
          |
          CH$_3$

b)   CH$_3$—CH$_2$—CH$_2$—CH—CH$_3$
                          |
                          CH$_3$

c)   CH$_3$
      |
      CH—CH$_2$—CH$_2$—CH$_3$
      |
      CH$_3$

d)   CH$_3$—CH—CH$_2$—CH$_2$
          | |
          CH$_3$ CH$_3$

FIGURE 10.16

Given
four condensed formulas for C_6H_{14}

Required
number of different isomers

Analysis
Count the number of carbons in the longest chain in each molecule, and then in any side chains.

Solution
All the structures represent the same isomer. If you look carefully, you will see that each structure has a main chain of five carbons with a one-carbon side chain attached to the second carbon of the main chain.

Statement
All the formulas represent the same isomer.

The number of possible constitutional (structural) isomers increases very rapidly as the number of carbon atoms increases. A set of complex mathematical expressions is used to calculate this; the results for some saturated hydrocarbons are shown in Table 10.1.

TABLE 10.1 Number of Carbon Atoms versus Number of Constitutional (Structural) Isomers

Number of Carbon Atoms	Number of Isomers
2	1
5	3
7	9
10	75
15	4 347
20	366 319
25	36 797 588

Naming Alkanes

Many organic compounds are still known by their historic common (or trivial) names, which people have used for centuries. For example, rubbing alcohol is the common name of a compound derived from propane with the formula $CH_3CH(OH)CH_3$. Unfortunately, these names tell us little about the structures of the compounds. Therefore, the International Union of Pure and Applied Chemistry (IUPAC) established a systematic way of naming organic compounds that allows you to deduce the structure of a compound from its name. This is very different from the system you used to name inorganic compounds in previous units.

Straight-Chain Alkanes In general, the IUPAC system for naming hydrocarbons uses prefixes to indicate the number of carbon atoms in the chain. Most of these prefixes are derived from the Greek words for each number. The suffix *–ane* then completes the name. Table 10.2 gives the prefixes used for alkanes that are up to 10 carbon atoms.

TABLE 10.2 Prefixes Indicating Number of Carbon Atoms in a Straight-Chain Alkane

No. of C Atoms	Prefix	Condensed Formula	Alkane Name
1	meth-	CH_4	methane
2	eth-	CH_3CH_3	ethane
3	prop-	$CH_3CH_2CH_3$	propane
4	but-	$CH_3(CH_2)_2CH_3$	butane
5	pent-	$CH_3(CH_2)_3CH_3$	pentane
6	hex-	$CH_3(CH_2)_4CH_3$	hexane
7	hept-	$CH_3(CH_2)_5CH_3$	heptane
8	oct-	$CH_3(CH_2)_6CH_3$	octane
9	non-	$CH_3(CH_2)_7CH_3$	nonane
10	dec-	$CH_3(CH_2)_8CH_3$	decane

EXAMPLE 2

Give the IUPAC name for the following molecule:

$CH_3 - CH_2 - CH_2 - CH_2 - CH_2 - CH_3$ FIGURE 10.17

Given
structural formula

Hexane

Required
IUPAC name

Analysis and Solution

$CH_3 - CH_2 - CH_2 - CH_2 - CH_2 - CH_3$ FIGURE 10.18

PRACTICE PROBLEMS

1. Deduce the name of the hydrocarbon given by the formula $CH_3CH_2CH_2CH_2CH_2CH_2CH_2CH_2CH_3$.
2. Write the condensed formula of heptane.

Count the number of carbon atoms in the chain and choose the appropriate prefix. There are six carbon atoms, so the prefix is *hex-*.

Examine the structural formula to see that there are only single carbon–carbon bonds. You therefore know that this is an alkane molecule, so add the suffix *–ane*.

Statement

The IUPAC name for the compound is hexane.

TABLE 10.3 Prefixes for Naming Alkane Substituent

No. of C Atoms	Prefix	Substituent Formula	Substituent Name
1	*meth-*	CH_3—	methyl
2	*eth-*	CH_3CH_2—	ethyl
3	*prop-*	$CH_3CH_2CH_2$—	propyl
4	*but-*	$CH_3(CH_2)_2CH_2$—	butyl
5	*pent-*	$CH_3(CH_2)_3CH_2$—	pentyl
6	*hex-*	$CH_3(CH_2)_4CH_2$—	hexyl
7	*hept-*	$CH_3(CH_2)_5CH_2$—	heptyl
8	*oct-*	$CH_3(CH_2)_6CH_2$—	octyl
9	*non-*	$CH_3(CH_2)_7CH_2$—	nonyl
10	*dec-*	$CH_3(CH_2)_8CH_2$—	decyl

Branched-Chain Alkanes To name branched-chain hydrocarbons, you must first identify the parent (or base) chain. The **parent chain** is the longest continuous chain of carbon atoms in the alkane molecule. You name the parent chain exactly the same way that you name straight-chain alkanes. Count the number of carbon atoms in this chain, and then name the compound using the appropriate prefix and the *-ane* suffix. This process is the same as you used for straight-chain alkanes.

The side chain of atoms linked to the parent chain is called a **substituent**. You name the substituents by counting the number of carbon atoms each substituent contains, and then assigning the appropriate prefix. However, as you can see in Table 10.3, you complete the name by adding the suffix *–yl*. For example, the substituent $-CH_3$ has one carbon atom, so it must be given the prefix *meth-*. The name is completed by adding *–yl*, to give methyl.

To derive the IUPAC name of a branched-chain alkane, you follow the steps below:

1. Identify the parent chain. Choose the correct prefix to describe the number of carbon atoms in the substituent and add the suffix *–ane*.
2. Identify any substituents. Choose the correct prefix according to the number of carbon atoms in the substituent chain and add the suffix *–yl*.
3. Number the carbon atoms in the parent chain in the direction that gives the lowest number to the substituent at the first branch point (Figure 10.19). This means you start from the end nearest to a substituent.
4. Add the location of each substituent before its name. Separate the number and name using a hyphen.
5. Complete the IUPAC name by writing the names of all the substituents with their locations in front of the parent name in *alphabetical order*. For example, if both methyl and ethyl substituents are present, ethyl is written before methyl. The completed name is written as one word.

Follow how these steps are applied in Examples 3 and 4, and then try the Practice Problem. Example 5 shows the steps in reverse, beginning with the IUPAC name of a compound to determine the formula.

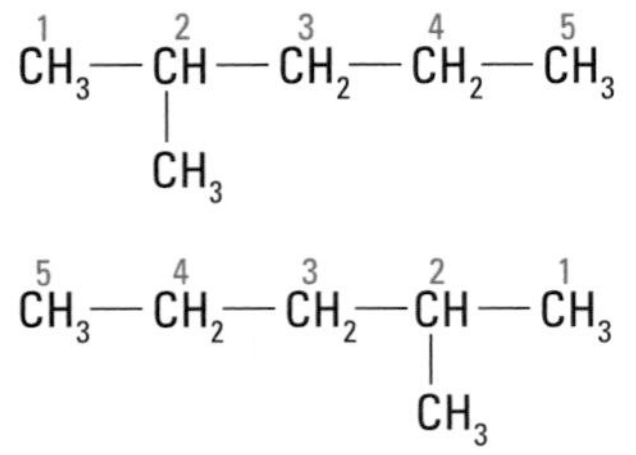

FIGURE 10.19 You must always number the carbon atoms in the parent chain in the direction that will give any substituents the lowest number at the first point of branching, no matter how the molecule appears on the page. Both of these structures represent 2-methylpentane.

EXAMPLE 3

Name the following compound using the IUPAC system:

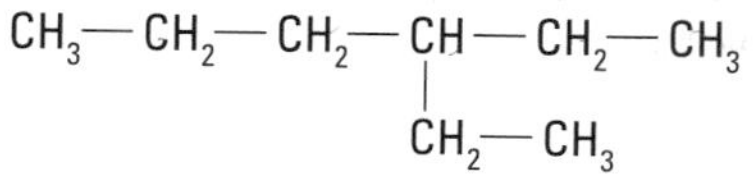

$$CH_3-CH_2-CH_2-CH-CH_2-CH_3$$
$$|$$
$$CH_2-CH_3$$

FIGURE 10.21

Given
structural formula

Required
IUPAC name

Analysis
Follow the steps to determine the names of the parent chain and any substituents. Locate any substituents on the parent chain.

Solution
The longest continuous carbon chain contains six carbon atoms and is an alkane; therefore, the parent name is *hexane*. An ethyl substituent is present. Combine this with the parent name to obtain *ethylhexane*. Now, count from the end of the parent chain closest to the location of the substituent, and you will find that the substituent is on the third carbon atom. Hence the name of the compound, written as a single word, is *3-ethylhexane*.

Statement
The IUPAC name is 3-ethylhexane.

PRACTICE PROBLEM

The original way of naming branched-chain hydrocarbons was to use various Greek prefixes. For example, $CH_3CH(CH_3)CH_2CH_3$ was called *isopentane* while $CH_3C(CH_3)_2CH_3$ was called *neopentane*. Name these isomers using IUPAC rules.

EXAMPLE 4

Write the IUPAC name for the following hydrocarbon:

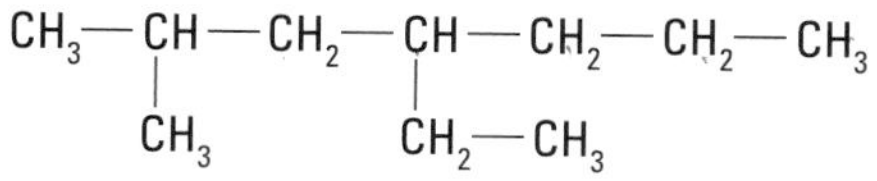

$$CH_3-CH-CH_2-CH-CH_2-CH_2-CH_3$$
$$|\qquad\qquad|$$
$$CH_3\qquad\quad CH_2-CH_3$$

FIGURE 10.22

Given
structural formula of a hydrocarbon molecule

Required
IUPAC name

Analysis
Use IUPAC rules for naming branched-chain alkanes.

Solution
Identify the longest continuous chain of carbon atoms and assign the name of the parent chain.

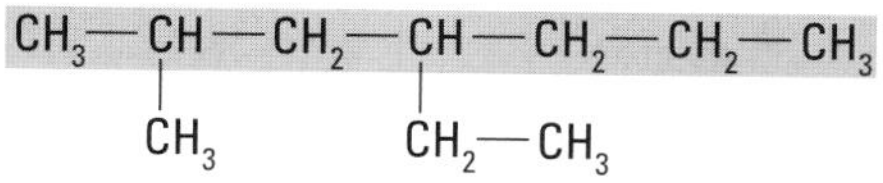

$$CH_3-CH-CH_2-CH-CH_2-CH_2-CH_3$$
$$|\qquad\qquad|$$
$$CH_3\qquad\quad CH_2-CH_3$$

FIGURE 10.23

The longest chain has 7 carbons with only single bonds between carbon atoms, so the parent name is *heptane*.

Identify and name any substituents. You should see an ethyl and a methyl substituent. Now, number the carbon atoms along the parent chain, beginning at the *end of the carbon chain that will result in the lowest possible number at the first branch*. This is the end nearest to the methyl group.

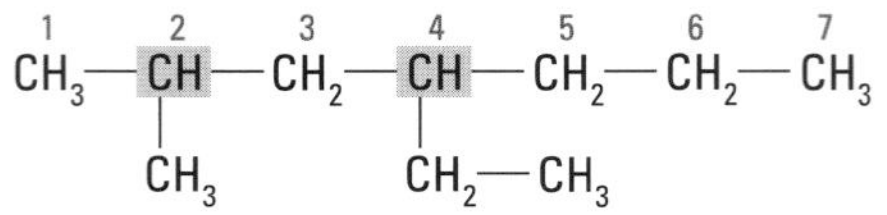

$$\overset{1}{C}H_3 - \overset{2}{C}H - \overset{3}{C}H_2 - \overset{4}{C}H - \overset{5}{C}H_2 - \overset{6}{C}H_2 - \overset{7}{C}H_3$$
$$|\qquad\qquad\quad|$$
$$CH_3 \qquad CH_2 - CH_3$$

FIGURE 10.23

Note that if the molecule were numbered from the other end, you would get number 4 for the ethyl group as the first substituent. Therefore, the correct numbering puts the methyl substituent at carbon 2 and the ethyl at carbon 4.

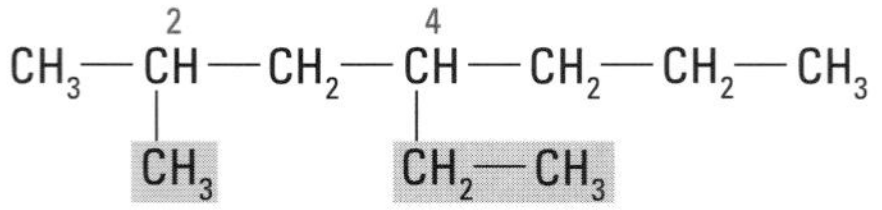

$$CH_3 - \overset{2}{C}H - CH_2 - \overset{4}{C}H - CH_2 - CH_2 - CH_3$$
$$|\qquad\qquad\quad|$$
$$CH_3 \qquad CH_2 - CH_3$$

FIGURE 10.24

Construct the name of the compound by listing all the substituents in alphabetical order. Use commas to separate numbers that are grouped together. Separate numbers from names of substituents by hyphens. Merge the name of the last substituent with the name of the parent hydrocarbon. *Remember:* Write the name as a single word.

Statement
The IUPAC name of the hydrocarbon is 4-ethyl-2-methylheptane.

PRACTICE PROBLEM

Determine the location of each of the substituents on this molecule using IUPAC rules.

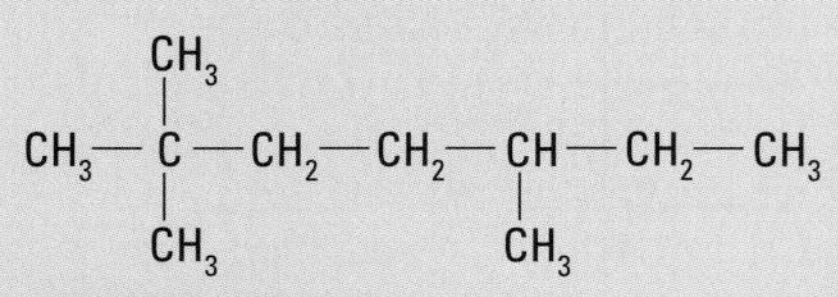

$$\begin{array}{c}CH_3\\|\\CH_3 - C - CH_2 - CH_2 - CH - CH_2 - CH_3\\|\qquad\qquad\qquad|\\CH_3\qquad\qquad\quad CH_3\end{array}$$

FIGURE 10.25

EXAMPLE 5

Draw the condensed formula for 3-ethylheptane.

Given
IUPAC name 3-ethylheptane

Required
condensed formula

Analysis
Determine the number of carbons in the longest chain from the parent name. Look at the prefix for the presence of substituents and their positions on the parent chain.

Solution
Since the name of the compound ends with the suffix *-ane*, you know that this is an alkane. The prefix *hept-* tells you that the longest carbon chain contains seven carbon atoms.

$$C - C - C - C - C - C - C$$

FIGURE 10.26

450 UNIT 5 Hydrocarbons and Energy

From the prefix, you can determine that an ethyl substituent is attached at the third carbon in the chain, as shown in the following formula:

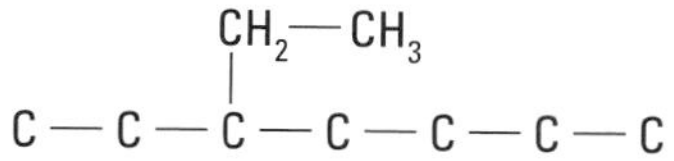

$$CH_2 - CH_3$$
$$C - C - C - C - C - C - C$$

FIGURE 10.27

Statement

The condensed formula of 3-ethylheptane is

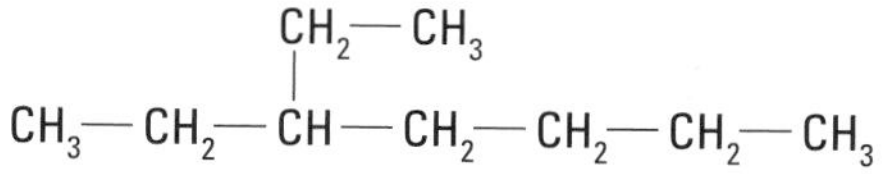

$$CH_2 - CH_3$$
$$CH_3 - CH_2 - CH - CH_2 - CH_2 - CH_2 - CH_3$$

FIGURE 10.28

or $CH_3 CH_2 CH (C_2H_5) CH_2 CH_2 CH_3$

PRACTICE PROBLEM

Draw the condensed formulas of:
a) 2,2-dimethylbutane
b) 2,3-dimethylbutane

Sometimes a particular substituent will occur more than once in a compound. IUPAC rules for naming this type of hydrocarbons are:

1. Indicate the number of times the substituent occurs by adding the correct prefix. These are given in Table 10.4.
2. Write the number of each carbon atom on which the substituent is located, making sure that each has the lowest number possible.
3. List all the substituents in alphabetical order, *ignoring the prefixes di-, tri-,* etc., and separating the substituents with a hyphen.
4. Write the IUPAC name as one word.

Work through Example 6, which illustrates these steps, and then do the Practice Problem.

TABLE 10.4 Prefixes for Multiple Substituents

Number of Occurrences of Substituent	Prefix
2	di-
3	tri-
4	tetra-
5	penta-
6	hexa-
7	hepta-

EXAMPLE 6

Write the IUPAC name of the following compound:

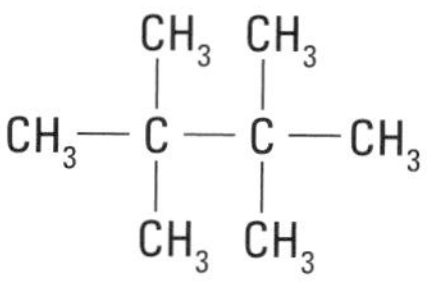

$$CH_3 \quad CH_3$$
$$CH_3 - C - C - CH_3$$
$$CH_3 \quad CH_3$$

FIGURE 10.29

Given
structural formula

Required
IUPAC name

Analysis
Use IUPAC rules for naming branched-chain alkanes.

Solution
The longest continuous carbon chain contains four carbon atoms and is an alkane; therefore, the parent name is *butane*.

There are four methyl substituents. Indicate these four identical substituents by using the prefix *tetra-* to give you the name *tetramethylbutane*.

Name the molecule represented by the structure below according to IUPAC rules.

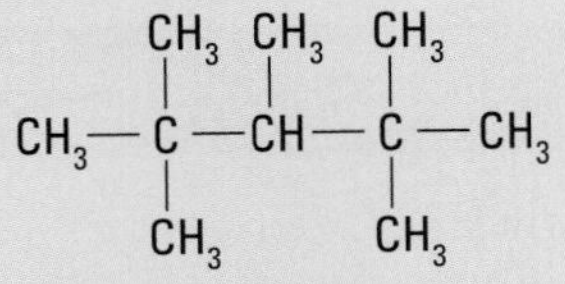

$$CH_3 - \underset{\underset{CH_3}{|}}{\overset{\overset{CH_3}{|}}{C}} - \underset{}{\overset{\overset{CH_3}{|}}{CH}} - \underset{\underset{CH_3}{|}}{\overset{\overset{CH_3}{|}}{C}} - CH_3$$

FIGURE 10.31

Two of the methyl groups are on carbon atom number 2, and the other two are on carbon atom 3. Noting the numerical location of each methyl group appropriately will give you the complete name *2,2,3,3-tetramethylbutane*.

Statement
The IUPAC name is 2,2,3,3-tetramethylbutane.

Discovering Chemistry   *Isomers of C_6H_{14}*

Gasoline is a mixture of different hydrocarbons, including isomers of hexane, C_6H_{14}. What do these isomers look like?

Materials
   molecular model kit or molecular modelling software

1. Construct models of as many isomers of C_6H_{14} as you can.

2. Draw and name each constitutional (structural) isomer.

- Is a branched-chain model of C_6H_{14} containing three carbon atoms in the straight chain possible? Explain your answer.

Cycloalkanes

Cycloalkanes are alkane molecules with a cyclic structure. The simplest cyclic hydrocarbon is cyclopropane, C_3H_6. The cyclopropane molecule has the three carbon atoms joined to form a triangle, and each carbon atom is attached to two hydrogen atoms (Figure 10.32).

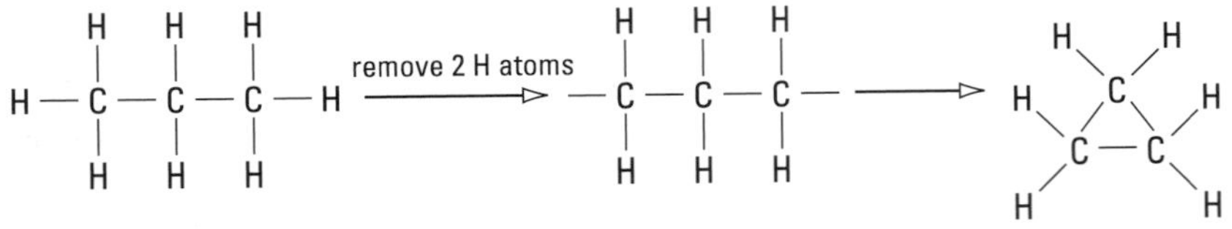

FIGURE 10.32

You can draw the structural formula of cyclopropane starting from the structural formula of propane. First remove a hydrogen atom from each end, and then join the two end carbon atoms together to form the ring.

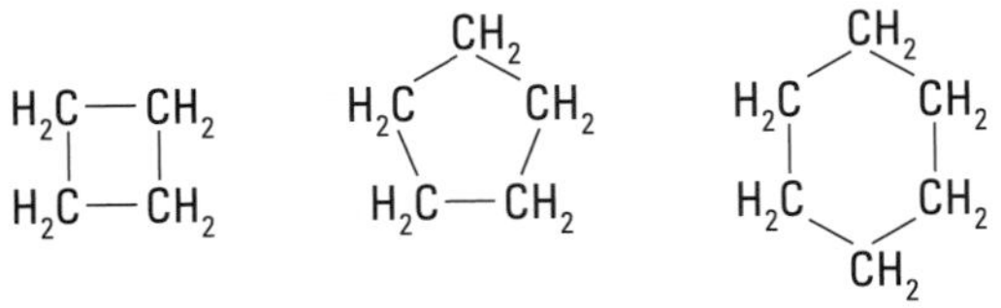

FIGURE 10.33

If you remove two hydrogen atoms from the end carbon atoms of the structural formula of butane (C_4H_{10}), you will have the four-carbon ring structural formula of cyclobutane (C_4H_8). Also shown are cyclopentane and cyclohexane.

You can also see from Figure 10.32 that you can derive the structure of a cyclohexane from the corresponding alkane. Try to derive the structural formula of cyclopentane (C_5H_{10}) from that of pentane (C_5H_{12}) and of cyclohexane (C_6H_{12}) from hexane (C_6H_{14}) for yourself.

You can also represent cycloalkanes in a simpler way that depicts only their ring structure. In this type of representation, you retain the lines of the carbon–carbon bonds but remove the CH_2 symbols. Each corner in the resulting geometric representation marks the location of the $-CH_2$ unit. Figure 10.33 shows the correct way to represent the structure of three-, four-, five-, and six-carbon rings.

FIGURE 10.33

Cycloalkanes are named in much the same way as straight-chain alkanes. You first indicate the presence of a ring by adding the prefix *cyclo-* to the correct alkane name. Then, if any substituents are attached to any of the carbons in the ring, you write the name(s) of the substituent(s) before the name of the ring. Number the carbon atoms in the ring so that any substituents will have the lowest possible number, and then indicate the position of the substituent in the prefix.

Step 1. Identify the ring of carbon atoms and assign the base name. Since the ring has 5 carbon atoms arranged in a ring with only single bonds, the base name is cyclopentane.

FIGURE 10.34

WEBLINK

SIMULATION

To view and manipulate 3-D models of cycloalkanes, go to
www.pearsoned.ca/chemistry11.

Step 2. Number the ring beginning with the location that will result in the lowest possible numbers for the substituents. There are alkyl groups at carbon 1 and carbon 3.

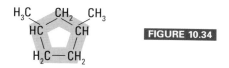

FIGURE 10.35

Step 3. Name each substituent and indicate its position by the number of the carbon atoms on the ring to which it is attached. There is a methyl at carbon 1 and at carbon 3. Separate the numbers from each other by commas and the numbers from the substituents by hyphens, and write the name as a single word. This gives the name *1,3-dimethylcyclopentane* for the molecule in Figure 10.36.

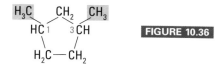

FIGURE 10.36

Section 10.2 Review

Understanding Concepts

1. Define the term constitutional (structural) isomer in your own words.

2. Identify which of the compounds below represents a compound that is different from all of the others.

a) 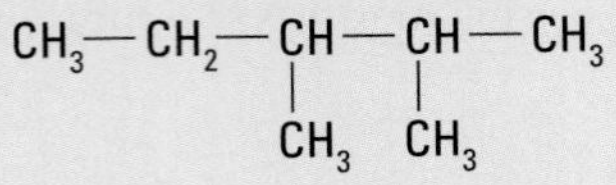 $CH_3-CH_2-CH-CH-CH_3$
    with CH_3 and CH_3 below

b) 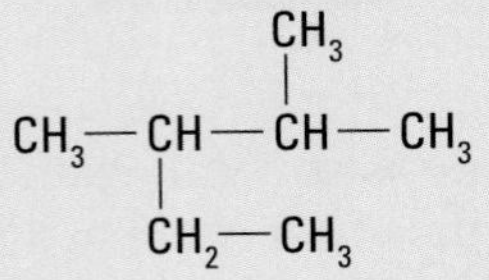
   CH_3 above
   $CH_3-CH-CH-CH_3$
   with CH_2-CH_3 below

c) 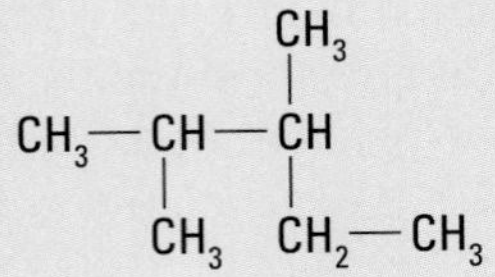
   CH_3 above
   $CH_3-CH-CH$
   with CH_3 and CH_2-CH_3 below

d) 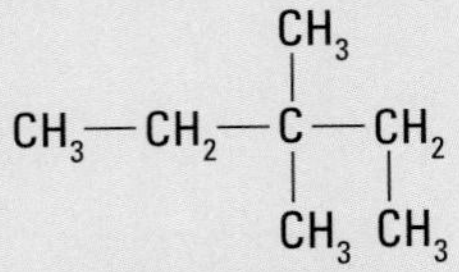
   CH_3 above
   $CH_3-CH_2-C-CH_2$
   with CH_3 and CH_3 below

FIGURE 10.38

3. Differentiate between a straight-chain alkane and a branched-chain alkane.

Applying Inquiry/Communication Skills

4. Draw the electron-dot formula for propane, C_3H_8, and butane, C_4H_{10}. Identify the type of carbon–carbon bonds in these two compounds.

5. Draw the condensed formula for each of the five isomers of C_6H_{14} and name each one.

6. Write the condensed formulas for each of the following hydrocarbons:
   a) ethane, C_2H_6
   b) propane, C_3H_8
   c) butane, C_4H_{10}
   d) hexane, C_6H_{14}
   e) heptane C_7H_{14}

7. Give the IUPAC name of each of the following compounds. The carbon atoms that form the longest chain are not necessarily shown in a straight chain.

a) 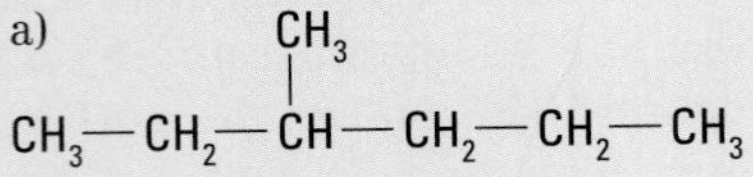
   CH_3 above
   $CH_3-CH_2-CH-CH_2-CH_2-CH_3$

b) 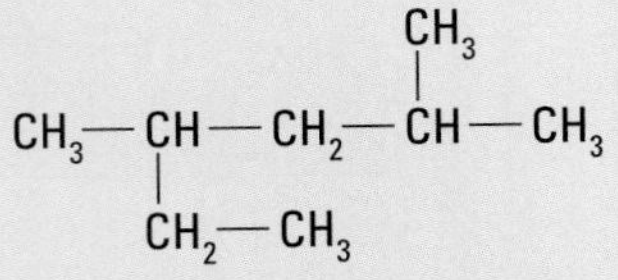
   CH_3 above
   $CH_3-CH-CH_2-CH-CH_3$
   with CH_2-CH_3 below

c) 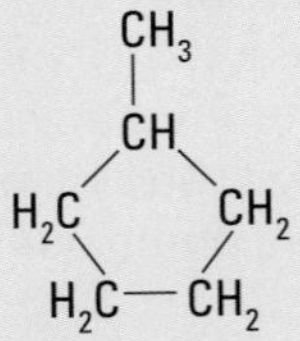
   CH_3 above
   CH
   $H_2C \quad CH_2$
   H_2C-CH_2

d) 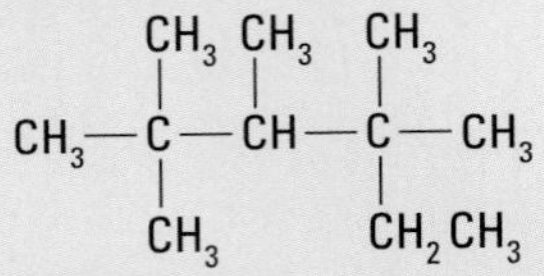
   $CH_3 \quad CH_3 \quad CH_3$ above
   $CH_3-C-CH-C-CH_3$
   with CH_3 and CH_2CH_3 below

FIGURE 10.39

8. Use the IUPAC system to name the following compound:

   $CH_3-CH_2-CH_2-CH-CH_2-CH_3$
   with CH_2-CH_3 below

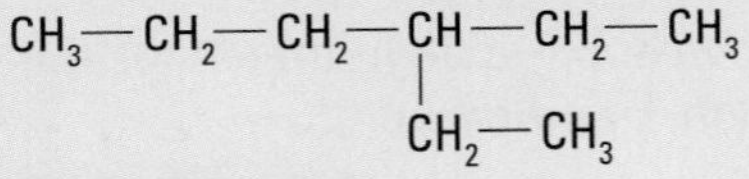

FIGURE 10.40

9. Use the IUPAC system to name the following compound:

   $CH_3 \quad CH_2 \quad CH_3$ above
   $CH_3-C-C-CH_3$
   with $CH_3 \quad CH_2CH_3$ below

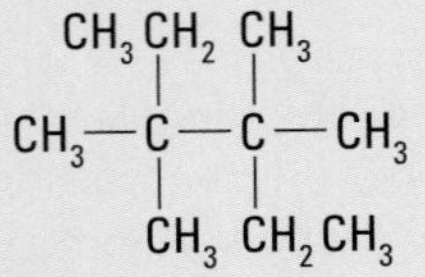

FIGURE 10.41

10. Use the IUPAC system to name the following compound:

   $CH_3CH_2CH(CH_3)CH_3$

FIGURE 10.42

10.3 Alkenes and Alkynes

Key Understandings

When you have completed this section, you will be able to:

- identify alkenes and alkynes and describe their characteristics
- define the term "stereoisomer" and "geometric isomer"
- identify geometric isomers for given compounds
- use molecular models to construct models of alkenes and alkynes
- use scientific vocabulary to communicate ideas about alkenes and alkynes
- name alkenes and alkynes using the IUPAC system, and draw their constitutional (structural) formulas
- explain the relationship between multiple bonds and constitutional (structural) isomers in unsaturated hydrocarbons
- make molecular models demonstrating how atoms are arranged in isomers of unsaturated hydrocarbons
- identify hydrocarbons that are commonly used by industries and consumers

The presence of a double bond in alkenes or a triple bond in alkynes gives them many common properties. Chemists therefore often group these two families together as unsaturated hydrocarbons. An **unsaturated compound** is any organic compound that contains at least one double or triple bond between its carbon atoms. In contrast, **saturated compounds** have only single carbon-carbon bonds. Alkanes are saturated hydrocarbons.

You may have heard the terms "saturated" and "unsaturated" in discussions about food and health, especially the fats in food. A saturated fat is one that contains only single bonds. People who have too much saturated fat in their diet are far more likely to develop heart disease. Saturated fats are found in high levels in animal products such as bacon and cheese. In contrast, fats from plants such as olive and canola are mostly unsaturated (Figure 10.43).

FIGURE 10.43 Hydrogenation is used to convert liquid vegetable oils to solid margarine.

Ethene: The Simplest Alkene

The simplest alkene is ethene, C_2H_4. The common name of ethene is ethylene; it is a sweet-smelling gas at room temperature. Ethene is an important reagent in the petrochemical industry, where it is used to produce plastics such as those in products like plastic bags and lawn furniture.

Ethene is also important to the agricultural industry. This hydrocarbon is a plant hormone that controls, among other things, the rate at which fruits and vegetables ripen. To ensure that fruits and vegetables arrive at the grocery store at just the right stage, they are stored at low temperature under reduced CO_2 levels after they are harvested. Carbon dioxide prevents the tissues from producing ethene, and the colder temperature slows down all biological processes in the produce. Producers may sometimes release ethene to ripen the fruits prior to putting them on the grocer's shelf (Figure 10.44).

Figure 10.45 shows the Lewis structure and the structural formula for ethene. Because each carbon atom in ethene is bonded to only two hydrogen atoms, a double bond between the carbon atoms is required to satisfy the octet rule.

FIGURE 10.44 This device produces ethene, allowing the producer to control when the fruit will ripen.

FIGURE 10.45 a) Lewis structure and b) structural formula of ethene, C_2H_4

Decision-Making Skills

▶ Defining the Issue
Developing Assessment Criteria
▶ Researching the Issue
▶ Analyzing Data and Information
▶ Proposing a Course of Action
▶ Justifying the Course of Action
▶ Communicating Your Proposal

Case Study

The Carbon–Carbon Bond and Your Health

BACKGROUND INFORMATION

When you and your friends meet at a fast-food restaurant to buy a hamburger and chat about the day, chances are the last thing you would think about is the type of carbon-carbon bonds in the burger. But did you know that a hamburger contains about 40 g of fat, most of which has single carbon-carbon bonds. Fats with single carbon-carbon bonds are saturated fats. If you are eating almost 40 g of saturated fat in one item, you might be consuming too much saturated fat per day.

Fat is actually not a bad thing. Fat is an important part of healthy eating, and is essential for maintaining your nervous system. But fat is not a single compound. It is a group of different molecules that have different properties. Most fats from animal products, such as those in a burger, are saturated fats. Saturated fats should only be a very small part of your diet, because consuming large amounts of saturated fat is associated with many health problems, especially heart disease. Unsaturated fats are those that contain one or more carbon-carbon double bond. Unfortunately, most people in Canada eat far too much saturated fat, in part because we eat a lot of fast food.

Do you know how much fat and what kinds of fat you should eat? You might not. Much of the information available on fats and healthy eating is aimed at adults 40 years of age and older. However, the food choices you are making now can seriously affect your health in the future. This means that teenagers need to be better informed about the kinds and quantities of fats in their diet so that they can make informed choices about the food they eat.

FIGURE 10.46 Fast foods contain high levels of saturated fats.

Analyzing the Issue

1. Explain in your own words the issue related to this case study.

2. Research the differences between saturated and unsaturated fats, and how your body uses fats from foods.

3. Survey the class on their favourite fast foods. Research the amount of saturated and unsaturated fats that are contained in the top three favourites.

4. Plan an information brochure that is directed specifically at high school students informing them of short-term and long-term health consequences of choosing foods with high fat content. Your brochure should include:
   • the distinction between saturated and unsaturated fats
   • the recommended fat intake for teenagers
   • a chart showing the amount and type of fats in the three favourite fast foods of your class
   • health effects related to eating saturated and unsaturated fats

If you construct a ball-and-stick model, you will find that the angles between the bonds of ethene are wider than those of ethane, which gives the molecule a flat, or **planar** shape. (Figure 10.47). Compare the shape of alkenes with that of alkanes. Are they similar?

Naming Alkenes

Naming alkenes by the IUPAC system is similar to how you named alkanes in the previous section. However, an important difference is that when you identify the parent hydrocarbon, you must choose the carbon chain that contains both carbon atoms of the double bond, even if it is not the longest chain. The presence of a double bond is indicated by the ending *-ene* instead of *-ane* (Table 10.5).

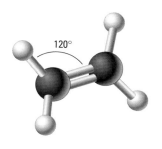
a)

b)

FIGURE 10.47 a) Ball-and-stick and b) space-filling representations of ethene

TABLE 10.5 Names and Formulas of the Simplest Alkenes

Formula	Name	Structure
$CH_2{=}CH_2$	ethene	2 carbon atoms
$CH_2{=}CHCH_3$	propene	3 carbon atoms
$CH_2{=}CHCH_2CH_3$	1-butene or but-1-ene	double bond at carbon 1
$CH_3CH{=}CHCH_3$	2-butene or but-2-ene	double bond at carbon 2
$CH_2{=}CHCH{=}CH_2$	1,3-butadiene	double bonds at carbon 1 and 3

When there are more than three carbon atoms in the parent chain, a number must be used to indicate at which carbon atom the double bonds start. This number should be as low as possible. If two double bonds are present, the ending *-diene* is used and *two numbers* are required to specify the positions of both the double bonds. Examples of these situations are given in Table 10.5.

Note that 1-butene and 2-butene are constitutional (structural) isomers, since they have the same molecular formula (C_4H_8). They represent a second type of constitutional isomer known as positional isomers. In alkenes, **positional isomers** have the same carbon skeleton but differ in the position of the multiple bonds.

Work through the following example to practise naming the alkene in Figure 10.48 using IUPAC rules.

$$CH_3 - \underset{\underset{\displaystyle CH_3}{|}}{C} = CH - CH_2 - \underset{\underset{\displaystyle CH_3}{|}}{CH} - CH_3$$

FIGURE 10.48

Step 1. Identify the longest continuous chain of carbon atoms containing the double bond and assign the parent name to it. The longest chain containing C=C is six carbons, so the parent name is *hexene*.

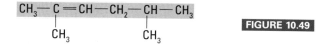

FIGURE 10.49

Step 2. Number the main chain, beginning at the end that will result in the lowest possible number for the double bond. The double bond starts at carbon 2, hence *2-hexene* (or *hex-2-ene*).

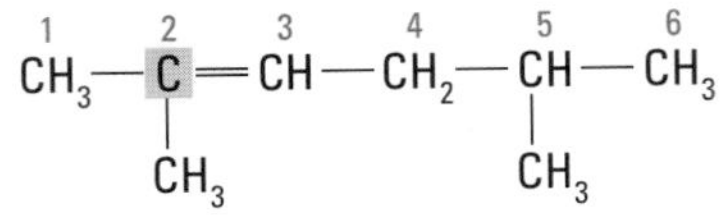

$$CH_3 \overset{2}{\underset{\underset{CH_3}{|}}{C}} = \overset{3}{CH} - \overset{4}{CH_2} - \overset{5}{\underset{\underset{CH_3}{|}}{CH}} - \overset{6}{CH_3}$$

FIGURE 10.50

$$CH_3 - \overset{2}{\underset{\underset{CH_3}{|}}{C}} = CH - CH_2 - \overset{5}{\underset{\underset{CH_3}{|}}{CH}} - CH_3$$

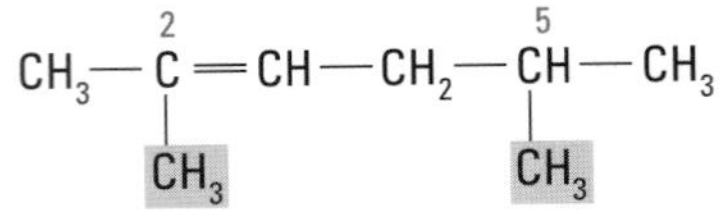

FIGURE 10.51

Step 3. Identify each substituent and indicate its position by the number of the carbon atom on the main chain to which it is attached. A methyl group is at carbon 2 and at carbon 5. Write the name as one word: this gives you the name *2,5-dimethyl-2-hexene* or *2,5-dimethylhex-2-ene*.

Geometric Isomers

If you made ball-and-stick models of ethane and ethene, you may have noticed another difference between the two molecules. If you hold the ethane model by one carbon, you will find you can rotate the other $-CH_3$ unit like a propeller. That is, there is rotation about the carbon-carbon single bond. If you try this with a model of ethene, however, you will find you cannot rotate around the double bond. The carbon-carbon double bond is rigid, so the hydrogen atoms must remain in the same plane as the carbon atoms.

This is one case where the model reflects reality. Alkenes are in fact locked into a planar arrangement because of the presence of the double bond. This rigidity allows for another type of isomer to occur, resulting in **geometric isomers**. Geometric isomerism is a type of stereoisomerism. **Stereoisomers** are two or more compounds having their atoms connected in the same order but with different three-dimensional arrangements. Geometric isomerism can occur when alkenes contain different substituents on each of the double-bonded carbon atoms. Geometric isomers are also called *cis-trans* isomers.

$$CH_3 - HC = CH - CH_3$$

a)
$$\underset{H}{\overset{CH_3}{\diagdown}} C = C \underset{H}{\overset{CH_3}{\diagup}}$$

b)
$$\underset{H}{\overset{CH_3}{\diagdown}} C = C \underset{CH_3}{\overset{H}{\diagup}}$$

FIGURE 10.52 a) *cis*-2-butene and b) *trans*-2-butene

The simplest alkene in which geometric isomerism occurs is 2-butene (Figure 10.52). The two methyl groups in 2-butene can be either on the same side of the double bond or on opposite sides. Since bond rotation cannot occur, the 2-butene isomers cannot interconvert. They are two different compounds that can be obtained in pure form. The isomer with both methyl groups on the same side of the double bond is called *cis*-2-butene, and the isomer with the methyl groups on opposite sides is *trans*-2-butene.

Use a molecular modelling kit or software to construct all the possible alkene isomers of C_4H_8, then name each one using IUPAC rules. Hint: There are 5 structural isomers, and one of these has 2 geometric isomers.

Investigation

Refer to page 475, Investigation 1

WEBLINK

SIMULATION

To view a simulation of geometric isomerism, go to **www.pearsoned.ca/chemistry11**.

WORDORIGIN

The prefix *cis-* means "on the same side," and the prefix *trans-* means "across." The latter prefix is used in common speech; for example, it occurs in words such as "transatlantic," "transplant," and "transmute."

WEBLINK

Sites on the Internet are available that allow you to construct and manipulate three-dimensional models of chemical molecules. Compare the shapes of isomers using computer-generated virtual models made with these programs. Begin your work at **www.pearsoned.ca/chemistry11**.

Other Alkenes

Many compounds in nature contain double bonds. One example is limonene, the major component of citrus peel oil. This compound (Figure 10.52) gives oranges, lemons, and grapefruit part of their characteristic odour. Limonene is a botanical insecticide, being effective against ticks, lice, and mites.

FIGURE 10.52 Limonene, a diene, is found in citrus peel.

Ethyne: The Simplest Alkyne

The simplest alkyne is ethyne, C_2H_2, which is commonly called acetylene. Ethyne is a colourless gas with a pleasant odour.

a)   H:C:::C:H   b)   H—C≡C—H

FIGURE 10.53 a) Lewis structure and b) structural formula of ethyne, C_2H_2

At one time, acetylene was most important for use in household lighting. Before reliable batteries were available, miners and cave explorers used ethyne-burning lamps to see as they worked (Figure 10.54). Today, acetylene is used most commonly to provide heat for welding (Figure 10.55). When the ratio of oxygen to ethyne is properly adjusted in an acetylene torch, the flame can reach a temperature of 3,300°C.

If you construct a ball-and-stick model of ethyne, you will see that the ethyne molecule is linear (Figure 10.56). This linearity around the triple bond is characteristic of all alkynes.

a)   b)

FIGURE 10.56 a) Ball-and-stick and b) space filling models of the ethyne molecule

FIGURE 10.54 The lamp on this coal miner's helmet burned acetylene, which provided enough light to see in dark underground mine shafts.

FIGURE 10.55 Acetylene burns at temperatures high enough to melt metal.

"Carbide" Willson

FIGURE 10.57 | Thomas L. Willson

Ethyne (acetylene) is a gas of major industrial importance, used to provide the hot flame of a welder's torch. However, its usefulness was recognized only when an experiment failed. Thomas L. Willson, who was born in Princeton, Ontario, in 1860, wanted to devise a process to produce alu-

minum. He tried to reduce aluminum ore (aluminum oxide, Al_2O_3) with carbon in a high temperature electric furnace. The reaction he predicted was:

$$Al_2O_3(s) + 3\ C(s) \rightarrow 2\ Al(l) + 3\ CO(g)$$

However, only a few small globules of aluminum formed. Willson then decided to first prepare calcium metal by the same procedure. He reasoned that since calcium is above aluminum in the activity series, the calcium metal formed in this reaction could be used to react with aluminum oxide, producing aluminum metal and calcium oxide.

When he tried this reaction, a product was formed. To check that the reaction he predicted had taken place, Willson threw some of the product into water. (Calcium reacts with water to give calcium hydroxide and hydrogen gas.) Although a gas was produced, it burned with a sooty flame, and not the colourless flame of hydrogen.

Willson hired Francis Venable, a respected American chemist, to identify the product. Venable identi-

fied the solid product as calcium carbide, CaC_2, and the gas product as acetylene, C_2H_2. The initial reaction had been:

$$CaO(s) + 3\ C(g) \rightarrow CaC_2(s) + CO(g)$$

The calcium carbide had reacted with water as follows:

$$CaC_2(s) + 2\ H_2O(l) \rightarrow$$
$$Ca(OH)_2(aq) + C_2H_2(g)$$

Rather than admit defeat, Willson patented the process and set up a laboratory to find applications for acetylene gas. He found the gas could be used for lighting and for welding, and he also synthesized a range of compounds from acetylene.

Unexpected discoveries such as this are called *serendipity*; that is, they occur by chance rather than as part of a plan. Unanticipated discoveries are part of the excitement of a science. Even though chemists these days process much more knowledge of chemical reactions to base their prediction on than did Willson, it is still only by actually mixing chemicals together that they can find out if the predicted product really forms.

Homologous Series

The compounds ethyne, propyne, 1-butyne, and 2-butyne are the first members of a homologous series. Since all alkynes contain the C≡C bond, they form a homologous series.

Homologous series of aliphatic hydrocarbons have the following four characteristics:

1. All members of a homologous series differ by a simple repeating unit. In aliphatic hydrocarbons, this is CH_2, the methylene group. Thus for alkanes, the first five members of the series are methane, CH_4; ethane, C_2H_6; propane, C_3H_8; butane, C_4H_{10}; and pentane, C_5H_{10}. For alkenes, the first four members are ethene, C_2H_4; propene, C_3H_6; butene, C_4H_8; and pentene, C_5H_{10}.
2. All members of a homologous series can be represented by a general formula. The alkanes (except cycloalkanes) have a general formula of C_nH_{2n+2}, the alkenes are all C_nH_{2n}, and the alkynes are all C_nH_{2n-2}.
3. All members of a homologous series exhibit similar chemical properties.
4. All members of a homologous series exhibit a gradual change in physical properties. For example, as the size and molar mass increase in the alkanes, so do the melting and boiling points.

Naming Alkynes

The rules for naming alkynes are the same as those for alkenes, except that the ending *-yne* is used to denote the presence of the triple bond (Table 10.6). What do you think is the difference between the structure of 1-butyne and 2-butyne?

TABLE 10.6 Names of Simple Alkynes

Formula	Name	Structure
$HC\equiv CH$	ethyne	2 carbon atoms
$HC\equiv CCH_3$	propyne	3 carbon atoms
$HC\equiv CCH_2CH_3$	1-butyne or but-1-yne	triple bond begins at carbon 1
$CH_3C\equiv CCH_3$	2-butyne or but-2-yne	triple bond begins at carbon 2

To name a more complex alkyne, you follow the same steps that you used for alkenes. Follow through the worked example below to name the alkyne in Figure 10.59.

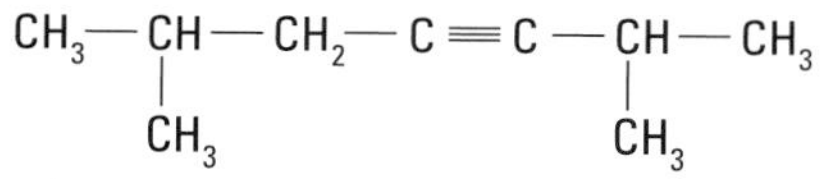

$$CH_3-CH-CH_2-C\equiv C-CH-CH_3$$

(CH₃ below second carbon; CH₃ below sixth carbon)

FIGURE 10.59

Step 1. Identify the longest continuous chain of carbon atoms containing both carbon atoms of the triple bond, and assign the name of the parent hydrocarbon. The longest chain containing the carbon-carbon triple bond has seven carbon atoms, so the parent hydrocarbon is *heptyne*.

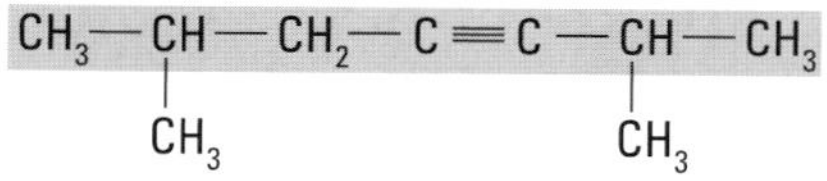

$$CH_3-CH-CH_2-C\equiv C-CH-CH_3$$

FIGURE 10.60

Step 2. Number the main chain beginning at the end that will result in the lowest possible number for the triple bond. The triple bond starts at carbon 3, hence *3-heptyne* (or *hept-3-yne*).

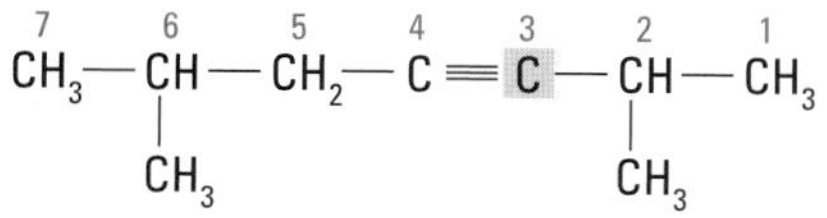

$$\overset{7}{CH_3}-\overset{6}{CH}-\overset{5}{CH_2}-\overset{4}{C}\equiv\overset{3}{C}-\overset{2}{CH}-\overset{1}{CH_3}$$

FIGURE 10.61

Step 3. Name each substituent and indicate its position by the number of the carbon atom on the main chain to which it is attached. Methyl groups are located on carbons, 2 and 6. Write the name as one word. This gives the complete IUPAC name of *2,6-dimethyl-3-heptyne* or *2,6-dimethylhept-3-yne*.

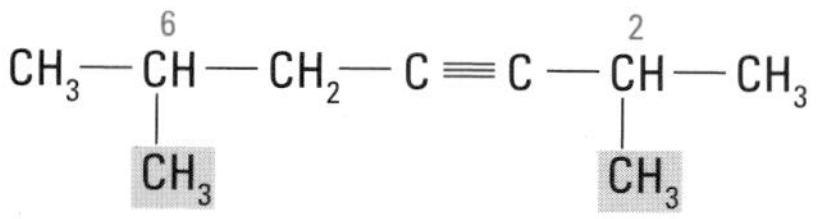

$$CH_3-\overset{6}{CH}-CH_2-C\equiv C-\overset{2}{CH}-CH_3$$

FIGURE 10.62

Section 10.3 Review

Understanding Concepts

1. Describe what is meant by a homologous series. Provide an example.

2. Differentiate between unsaturated and saturated hydrocarbons.

3. Define the terms "steroisomer" and "geometric isomer."

4. Explain whether or not geometrical isomerism occurs in either 1-butene or 2-butene.

5. Can there be a compound called 3-pentyne? Explain your answer.

Applying Inquiry/ Communication Skills

6. Draw and name all of the alkenes with the molecular formula C_4H_8.

7. Draw a structural formula for each alkene with the molecular formula C_5H_{10}. Name each compound.

8. Draw structural formulas for the following alkenes. If a compound has geometric isomers, draw both the *cis* and *trans* forms.

    a) 1-pentene

    b) 2-hexene

    c) 2-methyl-2-hexene

    d) 2,3-dimethyl-2-butene

9. Name the following alkenes according to the IUPAC system:

    a) $CH_3 - C \equiv C - CH_3$

    b)

    $$CH_3 - C \equiv C - \underset{\underset{CH_3}{|}}{\overset{\overset{CH_3}{|}}{C}} - CH_3$$

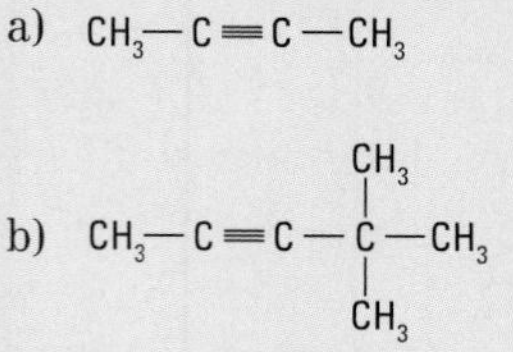

    FIGURE 10.62

10. Name the following alkynes according to the IUPAC system:

    a) $CH_3 - CH_2 - C \equiv C - CH_3$

    b)

    $$CH_3 - \underset{\underset{CH_3}{|}}{\overset{\overset{CH_3}{|}}{C}} - C \equiv C - \underset{\underset{CH_3}{|}}{\overset{\overset{CH_3}{|}}{C}} - CH_3$$

    c)

    $$CH_3 - \underset{\underset{CH_3}{|}}{\overset{\overset{CH_3}{|}}{C}} - CH_2 - \overset{\overset{CH_3}{|}}{CH} - CH_2 - CH = CH - CH_3$$

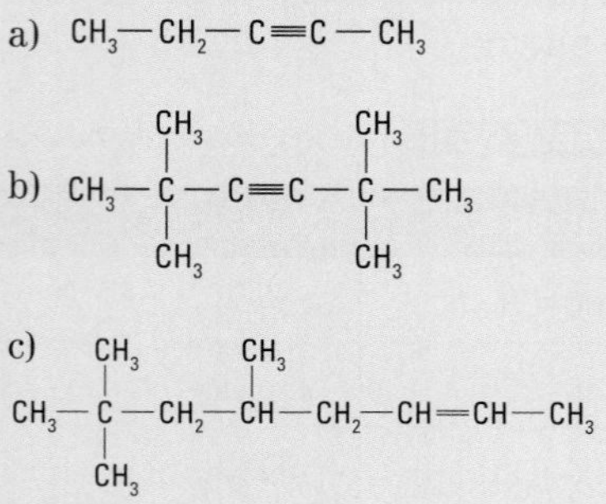

    FIGURE 10.63

11. Draw the condensed formula of

    a) 1-hexene

    b) 1,3,5-hexatriene

    c) 2-pentyne

12. Write the condensed formula of each of the alkenes having molecular formula C_5H_{10}. Identify which of these alkenes exhibit constitutional (structural) isomerism and give their names.

13. Write the condensed formula for each of the following alkynes:

    a) 1-heptyne

    b) 3-hexyne

    c) 3, 4-dimethyl-1-pentyne

    d) 2,3-dimethyl-4-octyne

    e) 2,2,5,5-tetramethyl-3-hexyne

Making Connections

14. Describe how ethylene is used in the food industry. Create a chart outlining the advantages and disadvantages of using this hydrocarbon, and its impact on consumerism.

15. Write a persuasive paragraph that would convince a consumer to switch from using a product with saturated fats to a product that uses unsaturated fats.

10.4 Properties of Hydrocarbons

Key Understandings

When you have completed this section, you will be able to:

- describe some of the physical and chemical properties of hydrocarbons
- communicate ideas about hydrocarbons using scientific vocabulary
- carry out experiments to explore the properties of hydrocarbons
- write balanced chemical equations for the complete and incomplete combustion of hydrocarbons
- identify ways in which we use hydrocarbons in our lives

Organizing scientific information can make it easier to find information. More importantly, you can also make predictions based on the patterns in the organized information. You saw in Unit 1 how information about the elements is arranged to form the periodic table. By organizing hydrocarbons into homologous series, chemists can more easily predict the characteristics of particular hydrocarbons. New ways of using hydrocarbons are constantly being found based on these predictions. In this section, you will explore some of the properties of alkanes, alkenes, and alkynes that make them so useful to our society.

Physical Properties of Hydrocarbons

The physical properties of a substance refer to those such as its boiling point, melting point, solubility, and density. These properties can be very important in determining how a substance can be used.

The physical properties of alkanes can be predicted by a molecule's position in the homologous series. The straight-chain alkane molecules can be ordered so that each molecule differs from the preceding one by a single CH_2 unit. For example, ethane (CH_3CH_3) becomes propane ($CH_3CH_2CH_3$) with the addition of one CH_2 unit. As the length of the carbon chain increases in the alkane series, the attraction between neighbouring molecules (intermolecular force) also increases in a predictable manner, due to the additional electrons from each CH_2 unit.

FIGURE 10.65 The hydrocarbons in this petroleum spill float on the water because they are non-polar molecules of low density.

Boiling Point   The boiling point of straight-chain alkanes increases with the number of carbon atoms. Since molecules with longer carbon chains have greater intermolecular forces, they require more energy to enter the gaseous state. However, as the length of the carbon chain increases, there is a progressively smaller increase in these forces with each CH_2 group. The difference in the boiling points between consecutive alkanes therefore decreases. If you were to plot the boiling points of alkanes against the number of carbon atoms, you would get a smooth curve. Check this for yourself using the values in Table 10.7.

FIGURE 10.66 The branched-chain alkane 2,2-dimethylpropane has a boiling point of 9.5°C, compared to 36°C for its straight-chain isomer, pentane.

TABLE 10.7 Boiling Points of Straight-Chain Alkanes

Name	Molecular Formula	Structural Formula	Boiling Point (°C)
methane	CH_4	CH_4	−161.0
ethane	C_2H_6	CH_3CH_3	−88.5
propane	C_3H_8	$CH_3CH_2CH_3$	−42.0
butane	C_4H_{10}	$CH_3CH_2CH_2CH_3$	0.5
pentane	C_5H_{12}	$CH_3CH_2CH_2CH_2CH_3$	36.0
hexane	C_6H_{14}	$CH_3CH_2CH_2CH_2CH_2CH_3$	68.7
heptane	C_7H_{16}	$CH_3CH_2CH_2CH_2CH_2CH_2CH_3$	98.5
octane	C_8H_{18}	$CH_3CH_2CH_2CH_2CH_2CH_2CH_2CH_3$	125.6
nonane	C_9H_{20}	$CH_3CH_2CH_2CH_2CH_2CH_2CH_2CH_2CH_3$	150.7
decane	$C_{10}H_{22}$	$CH_3CH_2CH_2CH_2CH_2CH_2CH_2CH_2CH_2CH_3$	174.1

Branched-chain alkane molecules are not cylindrical but are more compact in shape. As a result, fewer atoms in a molecule are able to interact with their neighbours, which affects the boiling point. Consider the two isomers of C_5H_{12} shown in Figure 10.66. Pentane has a cylindrical shape, but 2,2-dimethyl-propane is almost spherical, giving it a smaller surface area than pentane. This results in weaker intermolecular forces between neighbouring molecules of 2,2-dimethylpropane, and therefore a lower boiling point. In general, branched-chain alkanes have lower boiling points than straight-chain molecules with the same number of carbon atoms.

Melting Point Melting point generally increases as the mass and chain length of alkanes increase. However, plotting melting point against the number of carbon atoms does not produce a smooth curve (Figure 10.67).

Alkanes with an even number of atoms tend to have slightly higher melting points than those with an odd number. When the molecules form solids, they are arranged in a highly ordered manner in which the carbon chains form a zigzag pattern. Chains with an even number of carbon atoms can pack together more closely than those with an odd number. Check this out for yourself by building a molecular model. Will the intermolecular force be higher in alkanes with an even or an odd number of carbon atoms?

Density The density of an alkane is also related to the forces between the molecules. Recall that density is the mass of a sample divided by its volume. Strong intermolecular forces attract neighbouring molecules closer to one another, so they take up a smaller volume. Therefore, the higher the intermolecular forces, the greater the density.

Alkanes have low densities, generally being lower than that of water. For example, the density of pentane at 20°C is 0.63 g·mL^{-1}, compared with 1.0 g·mL^{-1} for water. As the number of carbon atoms in the alkane chain increases, the density of the molecule also slowly increases.

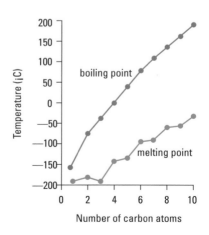

FIGURE 10.67 Alkanes with long carbon chains tend to have higher melting and boiling points than those with short chains.

The alkenes and alkynes show similar patterns in boiling point, melting point, and density to those of the alkanes. Use a data book or the Internet to obtain values of the boiling points of the following alkenes: ethene, propene, 1-butene, 1-pentene, 1-hexene, 1-heptene, and 1-octene. Plot the boiling point of each molecule against its molar mass. Describe the resulting line.

Solubility   Hydrocarbons are non-polar molecules; that is, the charges on the molecule are distributed evenly. Because they are non-polar, hydrocarbons are not soluble in water and other polar solvents. On the other hand, oil is soluble in non-polar solvents, such as benzene and hexane. Chemists use the general rule "like dissolves like." Two polar substances will generally dissolve in each other, as will two non-polar substances, but a non-polar compound generally does not dissolve in a polar solvent.

Discovering Chemistry

Solubility of Some Common Hydrocarbons

How soluble are hydrocarbons in various solvents? Recall that rubbing alcohol (C_3H_7OH) and water are polar compounds, whereas vegetable oil is non-polar.

Materials
  solutes: petroleum jelly, baby oil, suntan oil
  solvents: vegetable oil, rubbing alcohol, water
  Petri dish
  pipette dropper
  glass stirring rod

1. Predict which solute will dissolve in which solvent in the Materials list. Make a chart using the headings below. Record your prediction in your chart.

Combination of Solute and Solvent Tested	Prediction	Observation

2. Test your prediction by mixing equal volumes of each solute with equal volumes of each solvent in a Petri dish. Mix the solvents and solutes together with the glass rod.

3. Record your observations in your chart.

■ Was your prediction accurate? Write two or three sentences to explain your observations.

Chemical Properties of Hydrocarbons

One important use of hydrocarbons not yet discussed is as a raw material for making new molecules. Knowledge about the kinds of chemical reactions in which hydrocarbons can engage and the conditions needed for these reactions guides chemists in making new substances. For example, plastics are synthesized from hydrocarbons (often with additional elements). The production of new pharmaceuticals often starts from hydrocarbons and depends on the chemist's knowledge of their chemical properties.

INFOBIT

The hazard of a liquid fuel is measured as its flash point. **Flash point** is that temperature at which the proportion of the fuel in the vapour phase is high enough that it will be ignited by a spark. The flash point of gasoline is −38°C. When the temperature of gasoline is raised to this temperature, a spark will cause the gasoline vapour to burn. What is the flash point of diesel fuel? Which fuel do you think is safer to store?

WORDORIGIN

Paraffin, from the Latin word for "little affinity," was historically the name used for alkanes.

Combustion Reactions The one chemical property common to all hydrocarbons is that they are **combustible**; that is, they burn. The energy from combustion of hydrocarbons makes them extremely valuable as fuels.

In the presence of an excess of oxygen, combustion of a hydrocarbon yields only water vapour and carbon dioxide. For example, the complete combustion of methane can be expressed by the following equation:

$$CH_4(g) + 2\ O_2(g) \rightarrow CO_2(g) + 2\ H_2O(l) + \text{energy}$$

However, when there is insufficient oxygen for complete combustion, hydrocarbons produce different products. During incomplete combustion, poisonous carbon monoxide is formed, as well as solid carbon (soot). Depending on the amount of oxygen, incomplete combustion of methane can give the products in these equations:

$$CH_4(g) + O_2(g) \rightarrow C(s) + 2\ H_2O(l)$$

$$2\ CH_4(g) + 3\ O_2(g) \rightarrow 2\ CO(g) + 4\ H_2O(l)$$

You have probably seen black soot particles from the emissions of some motor vehicles. This too is usually the result of burning a hydrocarbon in insufficient air. Using octane, C_8H_{18}, one of the hydrocarbons in gasoline, as an example, the following balanced equations illustrate how the products of combustion change as the proportion of oxygen decreases.

$$C_8H_{18}(l) + {}^{25}/_2\ O_2(g) \rightarrow 8\ CO_2(g) + 9\ H_2O(l)$$

$$C_8H_{18}(l) + 12\ O_2(g) \rightarrow CO(g) + 7\ CO_2(g) + 9\ H_2O(l)$$

$$C_8H_{18}(l) + 11\ O_2(g) \rightarrow C(s) + CO(g) + 6\ CO_2(g) + 9\ H_2O(l)$$

$$C_8H_{18}(l) + 9\ O_2(g) \rightarrow 2\ C(s) + 3\ CO(g) + 3\ CO_2(g) + 9\ H_2O(l)$$

A car left running in a closed garage can have deadly consequences, because as combustion continues, oxygen levels fall and carbon monoxide levels rise. Carbon monoxide interferes with oxygen transport in the body, and deprives the cells of oxygen. If oxygen is not supplied, then coma, respiratory failure, and finally death result.

Substitution Reactions Since alkanes are saturated hydrocarbons, the only way they can react chemically is by atoms of hydrogen being replaced by some other atom. Since carbon and hydrogen form a strong bond, alkanes are very unreactive.

These reactions usually require additional energy if they are to occur. For example, the following reaction occurs only under ultraviolet light or at high temperatures.

$$CH_4(g) + Cl_2(g) \xrightarrow{\text{uv light}} CH_3Cl(g) + HCl(g)$$

Addition Reactions However, the presence of the double or triple bond provides a reaction centre in unsaturated hydrocarbons. These bonds cause alkenes and alkynes to be more reactive than the alkanes. They typically participate in *addition* reactions, in which a multiple bond is converted to a single bond. This reaction type can be illustrated by the bubbling of ethene or ethyne gas into an aqueous solution of bromine. Note that the alkyne requires 2 mol of bromine for complete reaction while the alkene requires only 1 mol.

$$H_2C{=}CH_2(g) + Br_2(aq) \rightarrow CH_2BrCH_2Br(l);\ \text{1,2-dibromoethane}$$

$$HC{\equiv}CH(g) + 2\ Br_2(aq) \rightarrow CHBr_2CHBr_2(l);\ \text{1,1,2,2-tetrabromoethane}$$

Decision-Making Skills

Defining the Issue

Developing Assessment Criteria

▶ Researching the Issue

▶ Analyzing Data and Information

▶ Proposing a Course of Action

▶ Justifying the Course of Action

▶ Communicating Your Proposal

Case Study

Detecting a Silent Killer

BACKGROUND INFORMATION

On March 8, 2000, a husband and wife in Portage la Prairie, Manitoba, died in their beds from carbon monoxide poisoning. On November 27, 2000, a man and his son died while they were sleeping, again of carbon monoxide poisoning. These deaths could all have been prevented had the people installed a carbon monoxide detector in their homes.

Carbon monoxide is an odourless, colourless gas that cannot be detected by the human senses. In most cases of carbon monoxide poisoning, the victims were unaware they were even at risk. When a person breathes low levels of carbon monoxide, they are likely to first feel tired or develop a headache. Later on, they might feel weak and nauseous, as if they have the flu. If exposure continues, it can lead to brain damage, suffocation, and death.

Carbon monoxide is the product of incomplete combustion of hydrocarbons. Some home appliances use hydrocarbon fuels; for example, gas and oil furnaces, water heaters, clothes dryers, gas ovens, and even small space heaters. If they are not regularly maintained, such appliances can produce carbon monoxide. The carbon monoxide can quickly reach toxic levels in a home if there is inadequate ventilation.

To reduce the number of deaths due to carbon monoxide poisoning, government and community safety workers recommend that all homes and offices have a working carbon monoxide detector. Most new homes have both smoke and carbon monoxide detectors installed during construction.

Before installing a carbon monoxide detector, you need to think about where to install it and what type to buy. Most fire departments recommend that at least one detector be installed in a home, outside the main bedroom, because most deaths from carbon monoxide occur when people are asleep and therefore are unaware of any symptoms. There are three types of carbon monoxide detectors to choose from, each of which uses a different technology to detect carbon monoxide. These three types are:

- a biomimetic or gel cell detector, which contains a light source that shines through a chemically treated cell
- an electrochemical detector, which operates by detecting changes in electric current
- a semiconductor detector; semiconductors are substances that conduct electricity only above a certain temperature

FIGURE 10.68 An electrochemical CO detector

Analyzing the Issue

1. Research the three different kinds of technology used in manufacturing carbon monoxide detectors. In a Venn diagram compare the similarities and differences between each type of carbon monoxide detector.

2. Based on the results of your research, write a summary paragraph describing which type of detector is best. Provide evidence to justify your choice.

3. Create a public service announcement informing consumers about potential household sources of carbon monoxide and ways consumers can reduce their risk of being exposed to this poisonous gas.

4. Several communities are now requiring households to have a carbon monoxide detector. Write a PMI on this issue. Would you recommend all municipalities to have this by-law? Explain why or why not.

Investigation

Refer to page 476,
Investigation 2

The carbon-carbon double bond and carbon-carbon triple bond in unsaturated compounds are two examples of a functional group. A **functional group** is an atom or a group of atoms responsible for the typical reactions of a compound. Table 10.8 is a summary of the functional groups in aliphatic hydrocarbons and the characteristic reactions they undergo.

TABLE 10.8 Characteristic Reactions of Hydrocarbon Functional Groups

Family of Hydrocarbons	Functional Group Present	Characteristic Reaction
alkanes	C–C; carbon-carbon single bonds	unreactive at ordinary temperatures due to saturation
alkenes	C=C; carbon-carbon double bonds	addition reaction due to presence of C=C
alkynes	C≡C; carbon-carbon triple bonds	addition reaction due to presence of C≡C

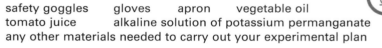

Discovering Chemistry

A Test For Unsaturation: The Baeyer Test

The Baeyer test is used to determine if a hydrocarbon is unsaturated. This test involves using alkaline potassium permanganate ($KMnO_4$), which has a distinct purple colour in solution. When potassium permanganate reacts with an unsaturated hydrocarbon, a colour change occurs. The product has two −OH groups, one on each C atom on which the double bond occurred. What happens when you perform the Baeyer test on vegetable oil and tomato juice?

CAUTION: Potassium permanganate will cause stains. Wear gloves, an apron, and safety goggles.

Materials

safety goggles   gloves   apron   vegetable oil
tomato juice   alkaline solution of potassium permanganate
any other materials needed to carry out your experimental plan

1. Plan an experiment to determine if vegetable oil or tomato juice contains unsaturated compounds. Include a list of any materials you will need, including those items on the Materials list. Your plan should clearly state what you will be looking for and how you will record your observations.

2. Write your experimental plan clearly, then give it to your teacher to check over. Do not proceed without your teacher's instructions.

3. Carry out your experiment and record your observations.

- Did either of the samples contain an unsaturated compound?

- Tomato juice contains an organic compound called lycopene. Research the structure of lycopene. Use the information you find to write a short paragraph that explains your observations.

Another example of an addition reaction is that of an alkene (or alkyne) and hydrogen gas. This process, called **hydrogenation**, proceeds under quite mild conditions to produce the corresponding alkane (Figure 10.69).

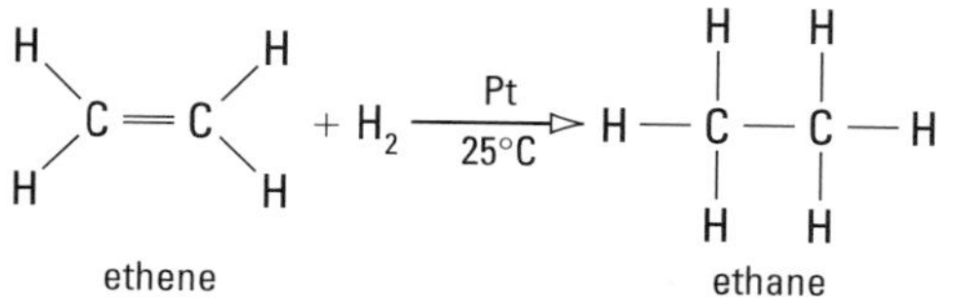

The reaction at top (Figure 10.69):

$$\underset{\text{ethene}}{CH_2{=}CH_2} + H_2 \xrightarrow[25°C]{Pt} \underset{\text{ethane}}{CH_3{-}CH_3}$$

FIGURE 10.69

Alkenes also react with hydrogen halides. For example, hydrogen chloride reacts with ethene to produce chloroethane, CH_3CH_2Cl (Figure 10.70).

$$CH_2{=}CH_2(g) + HCl(g) \longrightarrow CH_3{-}CH_2Cl(g)$$

FIGURE 10.70

In acidic solution, alkenes undergo an addition reaction with water to produce an alcohol (Figure 10.71). Most industrial ethanol is made by this reaction.

$$CH_2{=}CH_2(g) + H_2O(l) \xrightarrow[100°C]{H_2SO_4} CH_3{-}CH_2OH(aq)$$

FIGURE 10.71

If an alkene is bubbled through a dilute alkaline solution of potassium permanganate, the purple colour of the permanganate ion disappears and a brown precipitate of manganese(IV) oxide is formed (Figure 10.72). This is also a common test for the presence of an unsaturated carbon-carbon bond.

$$3\,CH_2{=}CH_2(g) + 2\,KMnO_4(aq) + 4\,H_2O(l) \longrightarrow 3\,\underset{OH\quad OH}{CH_2{-}CH_2}(aq) + 2\,MnO_2(s) + 2\,KOH(aq)$$

FIGURE 10.72

Polymerization Reactions   A **polymer** is a large organic molecule that consists of many identical units. **Polymerization** is the chemical reaction that forms polymers. For example, polyethylene is a polymer that you might use to wrap your sandwiches to keep them fresh (Figure 10.73). Polyethylene is formed from the polymerization of ethene; its correct chemical name is polyethene.

During polymerization, the carbon-carbon double bonds in the ethene molecules are broken. New single bonds are then formed between neighbouring ethene molecules. In a typical polymerization reaction, between 2000 and 50 000 alkene units may become bonded together. To represent this large and variable number of units, you place the symbol n outside the parentheses that contains the repeating unit. This is shown below by the equation in Figure 10.74, representing the formation of polyethene.

$$n\,\underset{\text{ethene}}{CH_2{=}CH_2}(g) \xrightarrow[\text{high pressure}]{\text{high temperature}} \underset{\text{polyethene}}{{+}CH_2{-}CH_2{+}_n}(s)$$

FIGURE 10.74

Although most of the polymers we use today are synthetic, the first polymer widely used by humans is from a natural source. Rubber is 98% composed of a naturally occurring polymer of an alkene. Natural rubber is tapped from rubber trees, just like we tap maple trees for syrup (Figure 10.75). The repeating unit in rubber is C_5H_8, and there about 20 000 of these units in one molecule of rubber.

FIGURE 10.73 Polyethene can be formed into thin films.

WEBLINK

Natural rubber was and still is an important material. Research how liquid latex from the rubber tree is converted into solid rubber. Write a brief report. Begin your research at **www.pearsoned.ca/chemistry11**.

FIGURE 10.75 Natural rubber is a polyalkene.

Section 10.4 Review

Understanding Concepts

1. Identify which compound you would expect to have the higher boiling point, hexane or 2,2 dimethylbutane. Give reasons for your answer.

2. Explain why oil is immiscible with water.

3. Suggest a hypothesis to explain why alkanes have low reactivity.

4. Explain why members of a homologous series exhibit similar chemical properties.

5. Explain how the addition reactions of alkynes differ from the addition reactions of alkenes.

Applying Inquiry/ Communication Skills

6. Write an equation to describe the combustion of pentane in air.

7. Write the equation for the following:
   a) the reaction of propene with hydrogen at 25°C in the presence of a platinum catalyst
   b) the reaction of propene with potassium permanganate

8. C_5H_{10}, C_6H_{14}, and C_7H_{16} are hydrocarbons found in gasoline. Identify each as a saturated or unsaturated hydrocarbon. Describe how you would confirm your identification experimentally.

9. Complete the following equations:
   a) $C_7H_{16} + 11\ O_2 \rightarrow$
   b) $C_7H_{16} + 10\ O_2 \rightarrow$
   c) $C_7H_{16} + 7\ O_2 \rightarrow$

10. You are provided with a bottle of canola oil and a bottle of olive oil. Design an experiment to determine the degree of unsaturation for each type of oil.

11. Write balanced chemical equations for complete combustion of:
    a) ethanol, C_2H_5OH
    b) benzene, C_6H_6
    c) acetic acid, CH_3COOH

12. In the presence of a limited amount of oxygen, benzene (C_6H_6) undergoes partial combustion. One mole of benzene produces 1 mol of carbon, 1 mol of carbon monoxide, 4 mol of carbon dioxide, and water. Write a balanced chemical equation for the reaction.

13. Compound A melts at 801°C and is very soluble in water, whereas compound B melts at 24°C and is insoluble in water. Determine which of these two compounds is more likely to be a hydrocarbon. Explain your choice.

14. You have a bottle of hexane and a bottle of octane. However, the labels have fallen off. Suggest two physical properties that you could use to distinguish between the substances.

15. Write the constitutional (structural) formulas for all possible isomers of hexane. Give the IUPAC name for each of them.

16. Assuming that the average composition of gasoline can be represented by the formula C_8H_{18}:
    a) write a balanced equation for the reaction of gasoline with oxygen
    b) calculate the amount of carbon dioxide gas produced from the combustion of 1.00 mol of gasoline

Making Connections

17. Explain why the higher molar mass alkanes are not appropriate for use as fuel for automobiles.

18. From a consideration of the boiling points of octane (C_8H_{18}) and decane ($C_{10}H_{22}$), suggest which hydrocarbon would be a better fuel for an automobile. Explain your answer.

10.5 Petrochemicals

Key Understandings

When you have completed this section, you will be able to:

- describe the importance of hydrocarbons in making polymers and other petrochemicals
- discuss the risks and benefits of using hydrocarbons to make petrochemicals
- use appropriate scientific vocabulary to communicate ideas related to hydrocarbons

Consider a school ski trip. How would you, as a skier, be equipped? Skis, ski poles, moulded boots with plastic straps, and unbreakable goggles would be some of your equipment. You would be wearing thermal longjohns, polyester pants, synthetic-fibre sweater and socks, a GoreTex® jacket, and Thinsulate® gloves to keep you warm. Very likely you would carry a backpack made of synthetic materials containing an extra pair of waterproof nylon pants, tennis shoes of synthetic fibres, and a plastic bottle to carry water. All these are examples of plastics and synthetic materials made from hydrocarbons.

Petrochemicals are organic compounds found in or derived from **petroleum** (crude oil) and used in the production of products other than fuels. Over the last 50 years, the petrochemical industry has produced a remarkable number of chemicals. You do not have to go far to find something that was originally made from petroleum. Think about the products you use in your home that come from petroleum. Among them would be clothing, plastics, detergents, synthetic rubbers and fibres, paints, solvents, toys, garden chemicals and medicines, to name just a few.

FIGURE 10.75 Hydrocarbons form the base of many synthetic materials.

Polymers

Ethene, C_2H_4, and propene, C_3H_6 are used extensively in the manufacture of plastics such as polyethene, polypropene, and synthetic fibres.

Ethene-based Polymers The simplest polymer formed from ethene is polyethene (polyethylene). There are two types of polyethene, which are made by polymerizing ethene under different conditions. Both of these are **thermoplastics**, or plastics that harden when cooled but soften again when heated. Thermoplastics can be moulded, extruded to form tubes or rods, and formed into sheets; in fact, they can be made into almost any shape we want.

FIGURE 10.76 Plastics can be modified to suit many purposes.

Low-density polyethenes have relative molecular masses ranging from 10 000 to 100 000. They are soft, transparent, not damaged by acids or bases, and not very strong. Low-density polyethene is used for making items such as grocery bags, squeeze bottles, food wrap, and plastic packaging.

High-density polyethenes have relative molecular masses of up to 3 000 000. They are much stronger than low-density polyethene, and are used to make rigid articles such as chairs, tables, buckets, disposable syringes, gas tanks, canisters, and heavy-duty pipes.

By adding other compounds to polyethylene, plastics with entirely different properties can be made. For example, plastic bottles are made from a compound called polyethylene terephthalate (PET). PET plastic is transparent like polyethylene, but is much stronger.

Propene-based Polymers The simplest polymer made from propene is polypropene or, more commonly, polypropylene. Polypropylene can be made into very strong fibres and is used in making items such as ropes and carpets.

Other Petrochemicals

Many useful products contain petrochemicals, including paints, perfumes, detergents, medicines, and dyes. Petrochemical research is an exciting area, and scientists are finding they can create polymers with unexpected characteristics. Many devices used in medicine are made with petrochemicals; because polymers are so durable, these can outlast the natural parts of the human body.

Recycling Petrochemicals

Do you recycle all your plastics? One reason to remember to recycle plastics is that they are made from petroleum, a non-renewable resource. The other reason is that plastics are so durable; once they enter a landfill site, they will be around for a very long time. Although the garbage that the average North American throws away is only about 10% plastic, plastic products take up almost a third of the volume of landfills. To address this problem, scientists have come up with biodegradable plastics. However, these are often not as strong as regular plastics and are more expensive to make, so we still need to use other ways, such as recycling to reduce the amount of plastic we throw away.

However, there are problems with recycling plastics as well. Not all types of plastics are recyclable, and those that can be recycled cannot be processed in the same way. Recyclable plastic items usually have a symbol stamped on them that indicates what type of polymer they contain. Before they can be recycled, all the plastic you throw away has to be separated according to these symbols. Recycling therefore requires a lot of labour, which can be very expensive. Recycled plastics cannot be used for certain products. For example, to ensure that they are safe, the bottles that contain juice or milk cannot be made from recycled plastics.

Case *Study*

Reducing Plastic Waste

Decision-Making Skills

▶ Defining the Issue
  Developing Assessment Criteria
▶ Researching the Issue
▶ Analyzing Data and Information
  Proposing a Course of Action
  Justifying the Course of Action
▶ Communicating Your Proposal

BACKGROUND INFORMATION

When you have finished the yogurt you brought with your lunch or used up the last of your shampoo, what do you do with the empty plastic container? If you are like many people in Canada, you put it into the recycling box to be taken away. But where exactly is "away"? And what happens to the plastic once it goes there?

At present, Canada does not have a standard policy for managing waste, including plastic recycling. Some provinces have waste legislation, but in general, each municipality is responsible for its own recycling program. Not only does the municipality have to arrange to pick up the material in your blue box, it also has to provide and pay for recycling the material, instead of the manufacturers who made the plastic products.

Most communities have done a good job of recycling items such as paper and metal. But when it comes to plastic, each different area often has very different programs. Since each type of plastic has to be handled differently, municipalities often have the resources to recycle only one or two specific types of plastic. Unfortunately, this means that a good deal of these valuable products do not get re-used.

FIGURE 10.78 As the volume of garbage increases, the need to recycle becomes more urgent.

Analyzing the Issue

1. Find out who is responsible for the waste management policy in your municipality.

2. Research the kinds of plastics that can be recycled in your area.

3. Address a letter to the politicians responsible for waste management policy, pointing out the advantages of recycling any of the types of plastic that are not being used in your area. Make your arguments as specific as possible to that type of plastic. You might want to do more research and find out how much of the plastic is used and the kinds of products that can be produced after recycling.

Section 10.5 Review

Understanding Concepts

1. In your own words, define the term "petrochemicals."

2. Provide three examples of petrochemicals found in the home and five that are used in sports.

3. Describe two types of polymers and their characteristics. Name a product made by each of these types.

4. List two key hydrocarbons obtained from petroleum that are used in the manufacture of plastics. Name the two plastics formed.

5. Deduce the type of plastic that is being produced in Figure 10.78. Explain your choice, and give two examples of items that might use plastic with these characteristics.

FIGURE 10.78

Making Connections

6. The chemicals produced from petroleum can be converted into a wide variety of useful products ranging from edible oil products, such as powdered coffee whiteners or whipped cream substitutes, to plastics and synthesized fibres. The petrochemical industry is very important to the Canadian economy. Prepare a report on this industry, giving details of the range of petrochemical products that are made in Canada and their impact on our economy.

7. Prepare a risk/benefit chart of the widespread use of plastics by consumers. Create a public service information brochure on the advantages and disadvantages of using plastic products that would help consumers make informed choices.

8. A community group is attempting to organize a plastic recycling program in your area. Curbside pickup can be done with the regular garbage collection already taking place, but the only recycling facility is 300 km away. The collected plastic would therefore have to be hauled by truck to the facility. Determine if recycling plastic would be good environmental practice in this case. Give reasons for your answer.

Investigation 1 (Section 10.3)

Exploring the Shapes of Hydrocarbons

Inquiry Skills

Initiating and Planning

Applying Technical Skills

Using Tools, Materials, and Equipment

▶ Conducting and Recording

▶ Analyzing and Interpreting

▶ Concluding and Communicating

Scientists have organized hydrocarbons into families and homologous series as a tool for understanding and predicting their properties. In this chapter, you have had an opportunity to learn about some of the physical and chemical properties of hydrocarbons, and how they change within a group. Using molecular models, you will now have an opportunity to explore the shapes of hydrocarbons and to investigate how the type of carbon–carbon bond changes the shape of a molecule.

Problem

To determine how the number and type of carbon-carbon bonds in a hydrocarbon molecule affect its three-dimensional shape.

Materials

- ball-and-stick molecular modelling kit
- protractor

Experimental Design

1. Using paper and pencil or a spreadsheet, create a table similar to the one below to record your observations. Your table should have more rows than this sample.

Data Table for Models of Hydrocarbons

Group	Number of Carbon Atoms	Bond Angle	Type of Bond	Formula	IUPAC Name	Number of Isomers
alkanes						
alkenes						
alkynes						
alicyclics						

2. For each of the four groups of hydrocarbons, construct models of members of the group, starting with the smallest member. For example, for alkanes, you would begin with methane, then proceed to ethane, propane, and so on. Continue up to five carbon atoms in a chain.

3. For each model you construct, use the protractor to measure the angle between the sticks that represent bonds. Record your measurement.

4. Write the formula and the IUPAC name of each molecule.

5. Repeat steps 2 to 4 for each of the four groups of hydrocarbons on your table.

Analyzing and Interpreting

1. Compare the shape of molecules within a group as the number of carbon atoms increases. Describe any patterns you find.

2. Compare the shape of analogous members between groups. For example, compare ethane to ethene to ethyne. Describe any patterns you find.

3. Describe what happens to the number of possible isomers as the number of carbon atoms increases. Draw a diagram to explain how the nature of the carbon-carbon bond affects the number of possible isomers.

4. Compare the size of the bond angles for single, double, and triple carbon-carbon bonds and between the carbon atoms in the alicyclics.

Concluding and Communicating

5. Use the data in your table to explain why carbon can form so many different kinds of molecules.

6. Comment on how strained the rings become as the number of carbon atoms in cycloalkanes decreases from 5 to 4 to 3.

7. Is there any rotation around a single bond or a double bond or the ring structure? Explain the consequence of the presence of double bonds or ring structure to the shape of the molecule.

Extending

8. Describe what occurs in an unsaturated hydrocarbon when it is hydrogenated.

9. When the degree of unsaturation is reduced in a vegetable oil, the oil becomes solid at room temperature. The molecules in solids are packed closer together than molecules in liquids. Consider the differences in shape between a saturated and an unsaturated hydrocarbon. Relate this to the change in melting point that occurs in vegetable oil when it is hydrogenated.

Investigation 2 (Section 10.4)

Tests for Unsaturation

Inquiry Skills

Initiating and Planning
► Applying Technical Skills
► Using Tools, Materials, and Equipment
► Conducting and Recording
► Analyzing and Interpreting
Concluding and Communicating

Problem

Bromine has a very distinct blood red-orange colour (depending on dilution), whereas the product is clear. The decolouration of bromine is used as a test for unsaturation.

> **CAUTION: Bromine vapour is toxic and should only be used in a properly ventilated laboratory. Keep all organic chemicals, bromine, and potassium permanganate in the fume hood.**
>
> **Do not discard organic chemicals down the drain. Dispose all waste chemicals in specially marked containers.**
>
> **Wear gloves, safety goggles, and apron.**

Materials

- apron
- gloves
- safety goggles
- bromine water ($Br_2(aq)$, 0.1 mol·L^{-1})
- cyclohexene, C_6H_{12}
- hexane or petroleum ether
- labelled dropper pipettes
- 2 test tubes

Procedure

1. Place 2 mL of bromine water in each of two test tubes.
2. Gently add 3 mL of hexane in the first test tube and 3 mL of cyclohexene in the second test tube. Do not shake the test tubes.
3. Do the two liquids mix? If they do not, record whether the aqueous or the organic layer is the top layer.
4. Shake the test tube so that the two reactants mix.
5. Record and explain your observations.
6. Dispose of any chemicals according to your teacher's instructions.

Analyzing and Interpreting

1. What is the typical reaction of alkenes and why?
2. Is water polar or non-polar? Is alkene polar or non-polar?
3. Describe the forces of attraction between two alkene molecules.

Concluding and Communicating

4. List two tests for unsaturation.
5. Write balanced chemical equations using structural formulas for the hydrocarbons where the reactions took place.
6. Explain why alkanes do not undergo addition reactions. Account for the absence of reactivity of alkanes.

Extending

7. The reaction of iodine with unsaturated compounds has important applications. Iodine number is a value representing the number of grams of iodine that will react with 100 g of an unsaturated fat. Addition of iodine to an unsaturated molecule causes the double bonds to break to form single-bonded carbon atoms. Saturated and unsaturated fats and oils are colourless. The red-violet colour of iodine turns clear as the iodine is used up in the addition reaction. Therefore, the amount of iodine that reacts with 1 mole of fat indicates the number of double bonds present. Design an investigation to determine the iodine number of olive oil and canola oil using iodine.

CHAPTER SUMMARY

Key Terms

addition
alicyclic
aliphatic
alkane
alkene
alkyl group
alkyne
aromatic

branched-chain
catenation
chain isomer
cis-trans isomer
combustion
condensed formula
constitutional isomer
cyclic

functional group
geometric isomer
homologous series
hydrocarbon
isomer
IUPAC system
organic
petrochemical

polymer
saturated
stereoisomer
straight-chain
structural formula
structural isomer
substituent
unsaturated

Essential Understandings

- Hydrocarbons are compounds containing only carbon and hydrogen atoms.

- Carbon forms stable single, double and triple covalent bonds with other carbon atoms.

- Hydrocarbons can be classified into groups. The members of these groups have different physical properties and some different chemical properties from one another.

- Isomers are different compounds with the same molecular formula containing different arrangements of atoms.

- Two important types of isomers are constitutional isomers and stereoisomers.

- All hydrocarbons undergo combustion.

- Hydrocarbons undergo chemical reactions such as addition, substitution, and polymerization, depending on the functional group present.

- Petrochemicals are important sources of many of today's consumer products.

Consolidate Your Understanding

1. Make a chart comparing the rules for naming compounds (nomenclature) in organic chemistry with those used in inorganic chemistry.

2. Construct a concept map that starts with the word "hydrocarbons."

3. Explain how the connections between molar mass and structure in hydrocarbons affect their physical properties. Use examples to support your explanation.

4. Models are used to help us understand things that are difficult to comprehend, or too small or too large to see. Describe how using models has helped your understanding of hydrocarbons.

CHAPTER 10 REVIEW

Understanding Basic Concepts

1. Identify which one of the following describes the difference between pentane and cyclopentane:
   a) Pentane contains only single bonds; cyclopentane contains a C=C double bond.
   b) Pentane contains 2 more carbon atoms than does cyclopentane.
   c) Pentane contains 2 more hydrogen atoms than does cyclopentane.
   d) Pentane contains 2 less hydrogen atoms than does cyclopentane.

2. The substance with the highest boiling point is:
   a) $CH_3(CH_2)_3CH_3$ b) $CH_3(CH_2)_2CH_3$
   c) $CH_3CH(CH_3)CH_2CH_3$ d) $C(CH_3)_4$

3. The total number of isomers for the formula C_4H_8 is:
   a) 2   b) 3   c) 4   d) 5

4. Identify the reagent that will react with propane.
   a) H_2SO_4 b) Br_2
   c) NaOH   d) O_2

5. The general formula of an alkyne is:
   a) C_nH_{2n-4} b) C_nH_{2n-2}
   c) C_nH_{2n} d) C_nH_{2n+2}

6. Define the term "hydrocarbons" and then list three major sources of hydrocarbons.

7. Use diagrams to illustrate the two conditions necessary for geometric isomers to occur.

8. Describe how geometric isomers differ from constitutional (structural) isomers.

9. Make a chart that describes the characteristics of an alkane, an alkene, and an alkyne.

10. Classify each of the following compounds as an alkane, an alkene, or an alkyne, and name each one.

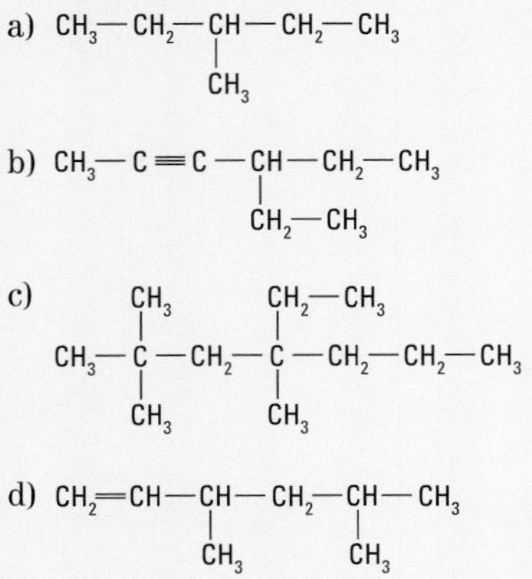

   a)

   b)

   c)

   d)

   FIGURE 10.79

11. Using your own words, define the term "homologous series," and then list the four characteristics of a homologous series.

12. Explain why alkanes have low reactivity.

13. Write a comparison statement differentiating addition reactions and substitution reactions.

Applying Inquiry/ Communication Skills

14. When 1 mol of a particular alkane undergoes combustion, 10 mol of carbon dioxide and 11 mol of water are produced. Determine the molecular formula of the alkane.

15. Give the IUPAC name for each of the following alkanes:

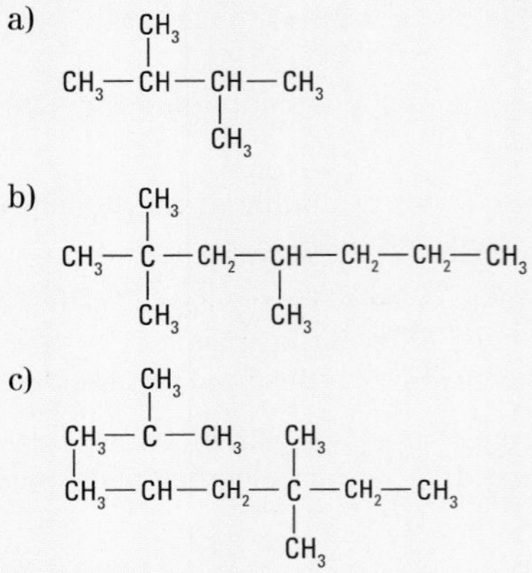

   a)

   b)

   c)

   FIGURE 10.80

16. Give the IUPAC name for each of the following alkenes:

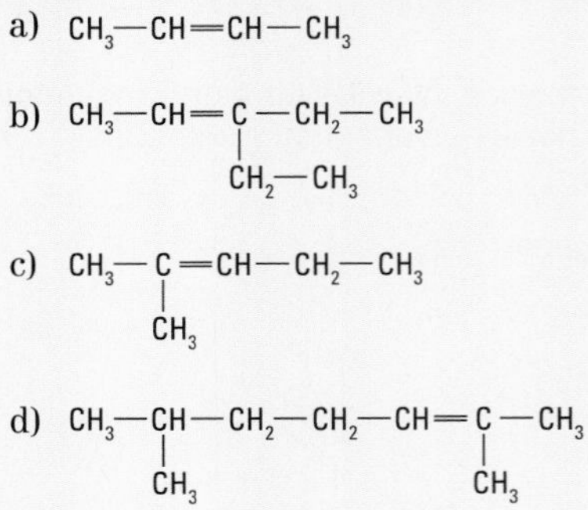

   a) $CH_3-CH=CH-CH_3$

   b)

   c)

   d)   FIGURE 10.81

17. Give the IUPAC name for each of the following alkynes:

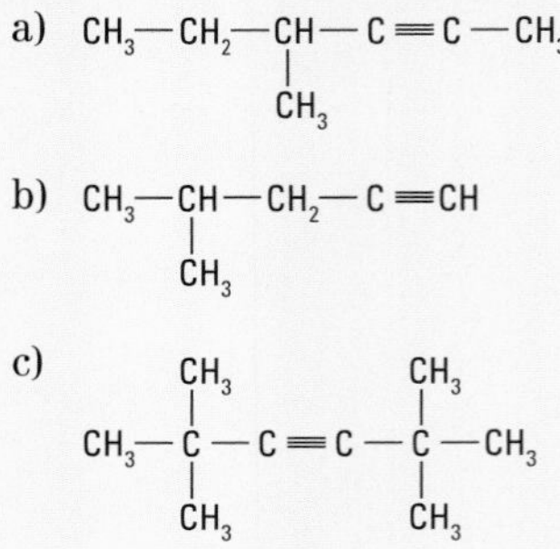

   a)

   b)

   c)   FIGURE 10.82

18. Write the condensed formula for each of the following alkanes:
    a) 5-propylnonane
    b) 3,4-diethylhexane
    c) 2,2,3-trimethylpentane
    d) 1,4-diethylcyclohexane

19. Write the condensed formula for each of the following alkenes:
    a) 2,4-dimethyl-3-heptene
    b) 2,3-dimethyl-2-pentene

20. Draw the structure of each of the following compounds
    a) a cyclic alkene containing 5 carbon atoms in a ring
    b) a branched-chain alkane containing 4 carbon atoms
    c) a straight-chain alkane that is isometric with 2,2,4-trimethylpentane

21. Draw the structure of each of the following compounds:
    a) 2-butyne
    b) 3,3,-dimethyl-1-pentyne

22. Use structural formulas to show how 1-pentene can be changed to pentane by reaction with hydrogen.

23. Molecular models enable us to obtain a much better understanding of the three-dimensional nature of organic compounds. Obtain a set of molecular models and construct examples of each of the four classes of hydrocarbons that you have studied in this chapter. Prepare a display of these models, giving information about the names, properties, and uses of each of the compounds exhibited.

24. Use a molecular model kit to illustrate which of the following compounds can exist in two isometric forms.
    a) 1,2-dichloroethene
    b) 1, 2-dichloroethane

25. Write a series of equations for the reaction of methane with bromine.

26. Write an equation to describe the combustion of octane in air.

27. Write the equation for the reaction of 1 molecule of propyne and
    a) 1 molecule of bromine
    b) 2 molecules of bromine
    Name the products in each case.

Making Connections

28. "The human race is in danger of being smothered in its own plastics." Decide how each of the following people might respond to this statement, and then write a paragraph from each person's perspective.
    a) an environmentalist
    b) a consumer
    c) a chemistry researcher
    d) an economist

29. Rubber and nylon were originally developed to meet military needs. Developing these compounds spurred the invention of new technology for making large quantities of these compounds and for manufacturing products from them. These technologies were eventually adopted by society at large for peaceful purposes. Draw a chart to illustrate the possible consequences that should be considered during the development of new products. Include the following areas in your chart:
    a) immediate consequences
    b) short-term consequences (1 to 5 years)
    c) medium-term consequences (5 to 25 years)
    d) long-term consequences (over 25 years)

30. The increasing rate of heart disease in the Canadian population is a major health-care concern. There is a lot of evidence showing that proper diet can help to decrease a person's risk of developing heart disease. Unsaturated fats may help to lower blood cholesterol levels. Foods we eat contain either saturated or unsaturated fat products. Using Canada's Food Guide to Healthy Eating, design a diet for someone who would like to eat foods that may help to prevent the development of heart disease.

31. Plastic products have contributed to the volume of waste in landfill sites because they do not decompose readily. Design a public awareness campaign that encourages people to recycle plastic products as much as possible.

32. Products made from petrochemicals are at the core of our society. Imagine that our supplies of these products are cut off. Write a descriptive essay describing the change in your lifestyle if products made from petrochemicals were no longer available. Include a description of the immediate change, the change in 5 to 10 years, and the long-term change.

Chemical Energy and Hydrocarbon Fuels

Since the time we first began to use fire to keep warm and cook food, humankind has depended on the energy that is stored in fuels. A fuel is any substance that, when burned, releases energy that we can use. Today, fuels allow us to drive our vehicles and to heat our homes, and provides the energy for most of our manufacturing, either directly or by converting their energy to another form, such as electricity. The most important fuels to our society today are the fossil fuels: natural gas, petroleum, and coal. Fossil fuels are primarily composed of a complex mixture of hydrocarbons, along with a small amount of other compounds.

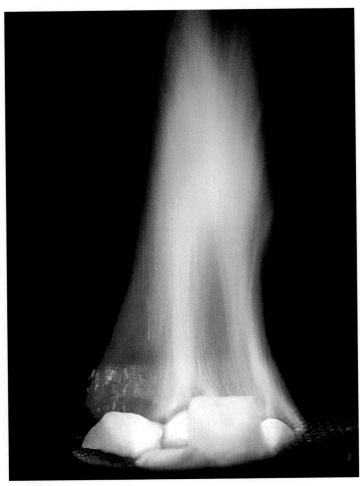

FIGURE 11.1 Combustion of methane hydrate releases the energy contained in its chemical bonds, which can then be used for other purposes.

What makes fossil fuels such a good source of energy? One factor is that they are very abundant and relatively easy to extract. But it is the energy stored in the bonds of the hydrocarbons of fossil fuels that makes them so useful. This energy can be released by combustion reactions; that is, by burning.

Because much of our technological society depends on a steady supply of energy, fossil fuels are extremely important to the world economy. However, using the compounds in these reserves is not without a cost. Pollution of our air, land, and water can in large part be traced to the use of fossil fuels. Furthermore, since fossil fuels are a non-renewable resource, we cannot continue our dependence on them indefinitely.

In this chapter, you will learn about some fundamental properties of energy. You will explore the quantitative energy changes that occur during chemical reactions. You will have an opportunity to measure the amount of energy that is released by combustion of a hydrocarbon. You will learn about the major sources of hydrocarbons and how we extract and isolate the particular substances we need. You will also be asked to consider the impact of using hydrocarbon fuels on technology, society, and the environment.

Discovering Chemistry

Burning the Candle at Both Ends?

Candle wax is a mixture of hydrocarbons called paraffin. What products form when paraffin is burned?

Materials

    glass jar with lid
    candle on a watch gas
    heatproof mat
    limewater

1. Assume that the formula for paraffin is $C_{24}H_{50}$. Predict the products of combustion of paraffin.

2. Put the candle on the watch glass, and set them on the heatproof mat. Light the candle, and then cover it with the glass jar.

3. When the candle burns out, lift the jar and quickly place the cover over its mouth. Hold the lid in place and turn the jar upside down.

4. Add about 10 mL of limewater (calcium hydroxide solution) to the jar, put the lid back on, and shake the jar. Record your observations.

■ Based on your results, write a balanced equation for the combustion of paraffin.

■ Suggest a reason why it is not possible to make a candle from very long chain hydrocarbons like $C_{50}H_{102}$.

CHECK**POINT**

1. Using your own words, define the term "fossil fuels." List three examples of fossil fuels.
2. Name the main products of combustion of fossil fuels.
3. Write a balanced chemical equation for the combustion of methane, CH_4.

11.1 Energy and Bonds

Key Understandings

When you have completed this section, you will be able to:

■ compare the energy change when chemical bonds are broken and when they are formed

■ describe how energy changes during endothermic and exothermic reactions

■ write thermochemical equations for endothermic and exothermic reactions

■ use appropriate scientific vocabulary to communicate ideas related to energy changes involved in hydrocarbon combustion

In previous units, you investigated how elements and compounds interact to form new substances under a variety of conditions. All of these reactions resulted in a change in the arrangement of the atoms in the reactants. Chemical reactions do not involve simply moving atoms around, however. Chemical reactions also involve changes in energy.

Measuring Energy

Energy may be defined as the ability to do work or the capacity to produce change. **Heat** is the flow of thermal energy from a warmer object to a cooler one. **Temperature** is a measure of the average thermal energy of a substance. The terms "heat" and "temperature" are often used interchangeably in common language. In chemistry, however, these terms have different meanings. For example, if a 250-mL and a 500-mL container of water are both at the same temperature, the larger container will have more thermal energy.

Thermochemistry is the study of heat changes associated with chemical reactions, and is a part of **thermodynamics**. The principles of thermodynamics enable chemists to understand why some chemical and biochemical reactions occur and others do not.

The Joule   The SI unit for measuring energy is the **joule** (J), named after the British scientist James Joule. Heat is expressed in joules, whereas temperature is measured in degrees Celsius or in kelvins. A joule is quite a small quantity of energy. For example, it takes 4.18 J of energy to increase the temperature of 1 g of water by 1°C. It is therefore more common to use kilojoules (kJ) and megajoules (MJ) to measure energy.

One example of an energy measurement you may be familiar with is that of the energy content of food. The different nutrients in food contain different amounts of energy. The values given in Table 11.1 can be used to calculate the energy value of a particular food item. For example, a hamburger

INFOBIT

Geologists use thermodynamics to explain why certain rocks formed at a particular site and not others. Physicists and engineers use thermodynamics to solve many practical problems, such as the development of refrigeration systems and heat pumps.

WEBLINK

The unit of energy was named after James Joule to commemorate his outstanding contribution to our knowledge of energy. Create a Web page or paper on the life and work of Joule. Begin your research at **www.pearsoned.ca/chemistry11**.

TABLE 11.1 Energy Values of Various Food Components

Food Component	Energy Value in $kJ \cdot g^{-1}$
fats	39
carbohydrates	16
protein	17

patty might be 49% water, 15% protein, 0% carbohydrate, 36% fat, and 0.7% minerals. Using the values in Table 11.1, you can calculate the energy content of a 100-g piece of hamburger meat as follows:

Nutrient	Energy = (mass × energy content)
water	= 49 g × 0 kJ·g^{-1}
	= 0 kJ
protein	= 15 g × 17 kJ·g^{-1}
	= 255 kJ
carbohydrate	= 0 g × 16 kJ·g^{-1}
	= 0 kJ
fat	= 36 g × 39 kJ·g^{-1}
	= 1404 kJ
Total energy	= 1659 kJ
	= 1.6 MJ

Forms of Energy

There are many different forms of energy, including electrical, chemical, light, heat, sound, nuclear, and mechanical energy. Energy can make something useful happen because it can be converted from one form to another. In fact, many common devices work by changing one energy form to another. For example, when you turn on a cellular phone, the chemical energy in the battery is converted into electrical energy, the form of energy needed to run the phone. When hydrocarbon fuels are burned, the chemical energy in the hydrocarbon molecules is converted into other energy forms that we need, such as heat energy, light energy, or sound energy.

Whenever energy is converted from one form to another, the total amount of energy remains the same. Therefore, energy is never lost or used up. This principle is described in the **law of conservation of energy**, which states:

Energy can be neither created nor destroyed.

In other words, energy can only be converted from one form to another, with no net loss or gain.

So why is it that batteries, for example, run out of energy? The energy does not in fact run out, it just becomes converted to a form you cannot use. Say you put the batteries in your calculator. The chemical energy in the batteries is converted to electrical energy for the electronic circuits and to light energy for the number display. You might even have noticed that some of it gets converted to heat energy. Eventually, none of the energy is in a form that can run your calculator. You then must replace the chemical energy by getting new batteries or by recharging them.

FIGURE 11.2 M.C. Escher's *Waterfall*, ©2001, Cordon Art B.V., Baarn, Holland. All rights reserved. The action shown here could never occur in the real world, because it defies the law of conservation of energy.

Energy in Chemical Reactions

Chemical reactions involve the breaking and forming of bonds. In order to understand the energy involved in a chemical reaction, it is useful to divide the reaction process into two theoretical steps.

Step 1. First the chemical bonds in the reactants are broken, leaving the component atoms free to make new bonds. Energy is required to break the bonds in the reactants.

Step 2. The atoms of the reactants come together in new combinations and form new bonds in the products of the reaction. When chemical bonds are formed, energy is released.

The **energy change** in a chemical reaction is the difference between the energy required to break chemical bonds in the reactants and the energy released by the formation of the bonds in the products.

Endothermic and Exothermic Reactions In some reactions, the energy required to break the bonds in the reactants is greater than the energy released by the formation of the products. Such chemical reactions are **endothermic** (energy-requiring). In other reactions, the energy required to break the bonds in the reactants is less than the energy released by product formation. These reactions are **exothermic** (energy-releasing).

An energy diagram such as Figure 11.4 can help you to picture the energy changes in these two classes of chemical reactions. Remember that the steps in these diagrams are only theoretical steps to help you to understand these changes. Reactants are shown at the lower left. The bond-breaking steps require an input of energy (shown on the left-hand side). The bond-forming step is then shown descending on the right-hand side to the product. The change in energy of the reaction is the *difference in energy between the reactants and the products*.

Predicting Energy Changes in Chemical Reactions In all scientific investigations, it is important to have as much information as possible in order to make reasonable predictions, as well as to ensure that you are working safely. Chemists often combine chemicals together, and must be able to predict whether a particular reaction will be exothermic or endothermic. To help make such predictions, the strength of the common covalent bonds have been measured and tabulated. Table 11.2 presents some of these average values.

Since the energy of an individual covalent bond is very small, the values refer to the energy needed to break 1 mol of a particular type of bond. You can see that the single bonds between 2 hydrogen atoms or 2 carbon atoms are both significantly stronger than single bonds between other atoms on the table. All single bonds between any element and hydrogen atoms are also strong, but the strongest bonds are multiple bonds.

FIGURE 11.3 The bonds in compounds that are explosive are much weaker than the bonds of the products formed in these reactions. Such reactions are very exothermic.

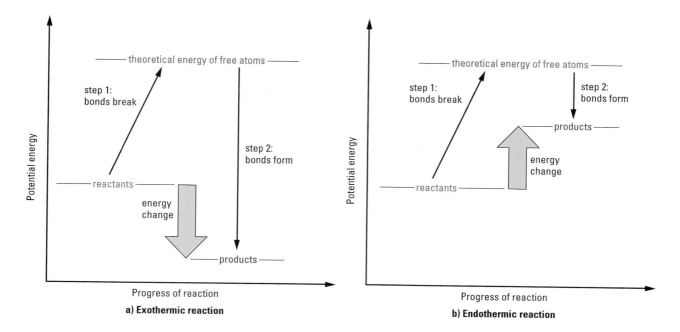

a) Exothermic reaction

b) Endothermic reaction

FIGURE 11.4 Theoretical steps in breaking and making covalent bonds of different strengths in a) an exothermic and b) an endothermic reaction

TABLE 11.2 Average Bond Energies of Some Common Covalent Bonds

Bond Type	Bond	Average Bond Energy (kJ·mol⁻¹)
single bond to same atom	C–C	346
	N–N	158
	O–O	144
	F–F	159
	H–H	436
	Cl–Cl	242
single bond to hydrogen	C–H	414
	N–H	391
	O–H	463
	F–H	567
	Cl–H	431
multiple bond	C=C	614
	C≡C	839
	C=O	804
	N≡N	945
	O=O	498

WEBLINK

For a simulation of an experiment to show energy changes, go to **www.pearsoned.ca/chemistry11**.

To calculate the energy change in a reaction, you must first calculate the energy required to break the bonds in the reactants. You then determine the amount of energy released by the formation of the bonds in the products. The energy change of the reaction is the difference between these two values.

EXAMPLE 1

Hydrogen gas and oxygen gas combine to give water vapour. Use the average bond energy values in Table 11.2 to calculate the net energy change for this reaction. Note that the bond in molecular oxygen is a double bond.

$H_2(g) + \frac{1}{2} O_2(g) \rightarrow H_2O(g)$

Given
average bond energies of H-H and O=O bonds

Analysis
bonds broken: 1 mol H-H bonds + $\frac{1}{2}$ mol O=O bonds
bonds formed: 2 mol O-H bonds (in 1 mol H_2O)

Solution
bonds broken:

energy of 1 mol H-H bonds $= 1 \times (436 \text{ kJ})$
                                              $= 436 \text{ kJ}$

energy of $\frac{1}{2}$ mol O=O bonds $= \frac{1}{2} \times (498 \text{ kJ})$
                                              $= 249 \text{ kJ}$
total energy input $= 685 \text{ kJ}$

bonds formed:
energy of 2 mol O-H bonds $= 2 \times (463 \text{ kJ})$
                                              $= 926 \text{ kJ}$
total energy output $= 926 \text{ kJ}$

energy change:
net energy change $= 685 \text{ kJ} - 926 \text{ kJ}$
                               $= -241 \text{ kJ}$

Statement
The net energy change of the reaction is -241 kJ.

PRACTICE PROBLEM

Methane burns in the presence of oxygen to form carbon dioxide and water. Use the average bond energy values in Table 11.2 to calculate the net energy change for this reaction.

Since the formation of bonds corresponds to the release of energy (i.e., an exothermic reaction), the value of the net energy change is negative. Since bond energies are only average values, the net energy change that is calculated from bond energies is only approximate.

Thermochemical Equations Recall that a balanced chemical equation has the same number of atoms in the reactants and in the products. A **thermochemical equation** is a chemical equation in which the heat of reaction is included. Therefore, to write a thermochemical equation, you must first determine the energy change of the reaction. Example 2 demonstrates how to derive a thermochemical equation.

EXAMPLE 2

One mole of hydrogen chloride gas forms from gaseous reactants according to the following equation:

$$\frac{1}{2}\ H_2(g) + \frac{1}{2}\ Cl_2(g) \rightarrow HCl(g)$$

Using the following average bond energy data, determine the change in energy and write the thermochemical equation for this reaction.

H−H	436 kJ·mol^{-1}
Cl−Cl	242 kJ·mol^{-1}
H−Cl	431 kJ·mol^{-1}

Given
average bond energy of H−H, Cl−Cl, and H−Cl bonds

Required
change in energy when hydrogen chloride gas forms

Analysis
bonds broken: $\frac{1}{2}$ mol (H−H) + $\frac{1}{2}$ mol (Cl−Cl)

bonds formed: 1 mol (H−Cl)

Solution
bonds broken:

energy input of $\frac{1}{2}$ mol H−H bonds	$= \frac{1}{2} \times 436$ kJ
	$= 218$ kJ
energy input of $\frac{1}{2}$ mol Cl−Cl bonds	$= \frac{1}{2} \times 242$ kJ
	$= 121$ kJ
total energy input	$= 218$ kJ $+ 121$ kJ
	$= 339$ kJ
energy output of 1 mol H−Cl bonds	$= 1 \times 431$ kJ
	$= 431$ kJ
total energy output	$= 431$ kJ
net energy change	$= 339$ kJ $- 431$ kJ
	$= -92$ kJ

You now have the value for the heat term of the thermochemical equation. Because there is less energy in the bonds of the reactants than in the products, this is an exothermic reaction. Therefore, to balance the energy content, you must *add* 92 kJ to the right side of the equation.

Statement
There is a net energy change of -92 kJ. The thermochemical equation is:

$$\frac{1}{2}\ H_2\ (g) + \frac{1}{2}\ Cl_2\ (g) \rightarrow HCl\ (g) + 92\ kJ$$

PRACTICE PROBLEMS

1. Use the data from Table 11.2 to calculate an approximate value for the energy change when 1 mol of hydrogen fluoride is formed from its constituent elements, then write the thermochemical equation. The balanced chemical equation is:

$$\frac{1}{2}\ H_2(g) + \frac{1}{2}\ F_2(g) \rightarrow HF(g)$$

8. Use the data from Table 11.2 to write the thermochemical equation for the reaction of ammonia gas with oxygen gas to form nitrogen gas and water vapour.

$$NH_3(g) + \frac{3}{4}\ O_2(g) \rightarrow$$
$$\frac{1}{2}\ N_2(g) + \frac{3}{2}\ H_2O(g)$$

You can see from the net energy change values why some reactions are strongly exothermic, particularly the combustion of hydrocarbons. Consider the reaction of methane with oxygen (Example 3). Because the bond energies of the products are greater than those of the reactants, you can predict that this reaction will be strongly exothermic.

EXAMPLE 3

Using the values in Table 11.2, calculate the energy change in the following reaction. Write the thermochemical equation for this reaction, and state whether this is an exothermic or an endothermic reaction.

$CH_4(g) + 2 O_2(g) \rightarrow CO_2(g) + 2 H_2O(g)$

Given
average bond energy for C-H, O=O, C=O, and O-H bonds

Required
energy change of the reaction

type of reaction

Analysis
bonds broken: 4 mol C-H bonds + 2 mol O=O bonds

bonds formed: 2 mol C=O bonds + 4 mol O-H bonds

Solution
bonds broken:

energy of 4 mol C-H bonds	= 4 × 414 kJ
	= 1656 kJ
energy of 2 mol O=O bonds	= 2 × 498 kJ
	= 996 kJ
total energy input	= 1656 kJ + 996 kJ
	= 2652 kJ

bonds formed:

energy of 2 mol C=O bonds	= 2 × 743 kJ
	= 1486 kJ
energy of 4 mol O-H bonds	= 4 × 463 kJ
	= 1852 kJ
total energy output	= 1486 kJ + 1852 kJ
	= 3338 kJ
net energy change	= 2652 kJ − 3338 kJ
	= −686 kJ

Statement
The thermochemical equation for the reaction is:

$CH_4(g) + 2 O_2(g) \rightarrow CO_2(g) + 2 H_2O(g) + 686$ kJ

The reaction is exothermic.

PRACTICE PROBLEMS

1. The combustion of 1 mol of octane, C_8H_{18}, produces carbon dioxide, water, and 5512 kJ of energy. Write the balanced thermochemical equation for this reaction.

2. Methanol is used as a fuel in racing cars. The combustion of 0.20 mol of methanol produces carbon dioxide, water, and 143 kJ of energy. Write a balanced thermochemical equation for the production of 1 mol of methanol.

Discovering Chemistry — Running Hot and Cold

When two compounds are mixed, is the reaction endothermic or exothermic?

You will mix the following solutions together:

a) aqueous sodium hydroxide and hydrochloric acid

b) citric acid and aqueous sodium hydrogen carbonate

Materials

    2 Styrofoam cups
    2 test tubes and a test-tube rack
    50-mL graduated cylinder
    balance
    thermometer or temperature probe
    stirring rods
    sodium hydroxide solution (1 mol·L^{-1})
    hydrochloric acid (1 mol·L^{-1})
    sodium hydrogen carbonate solution (1 mol·L^{-1})
    citric acid

1. Use the bond energies in Table 11.2 to predict whether the reaction will be exothermic or endothermic.

2. Put on your gloves and safety goggles. Measure and pour 10 mL of the sodium hydroxide solution in one of the Styrofoam cups, and 10 mL of the hydrochloric acid into a test tube. Determine the starting temperature of each solution.

3. Carefully add the hydrochloric acid to the sodium hydroxide solution and stir it with a stirring rod for about 30 s. Measure and record the temperature of this solution.

4. Now place about 5 g of citric acid into the other Styrofoam cup. Determine the temperature of the sodium hydrogen carbonate solution.

5. Pour 10 mL of the sodium hydrogen carbonate solution into the cup and stir it with the stirring rod. Measure and record the temperature as you are stirring.

6. Write balanced chemical and thermochemical equations for the two reactions.

- Was your prediction correct?

Section 11.1 Review

Understanding Concepts

1. Define energy and explain how energy and heat are related.

2. Two beakers of water, one containing 50 mL and the other containing 250 mL, are heated to 75°C. Using these beakers as examples, explain the difference between heat and temperature.

3. Describe what happens to the energy in chemical bonds during a chemical reaction.

4. When potassium nitrate (KNO_3) dissolves in water, the solution cools. Is this process exothermic or endothermic? Explain your answer.

5. Using energy always involves a conversion between one form of energy to another. State the energy conversions that occur in the following situations.
   a) Kerosene burns in an outdoor lantern.
   b) You recharge your cell phone and call a friend.
   c) You are relaxing in a propane-heated sauna and pour water over the heated rocks.

6. Identify whether the following reaction is endothermic or exo-thermic and explain your choice.
   $4 NH_3 + 3 O_2 \rightarrow 2 N_2 + 6 H_2O$
   Use the bond energies in Table 11.2 for the compounds in this reaction.

7. The bond energy of F_2 is 153 kJ and the bond energy of Cl_2 is 242 kJ. Calculate the bond energy of $F-Cl$ if the reaction $F_2 + Cl_2 \rightarrow 2 FCl$ liberates 69.4 kJ of energy.

8. Write a thermochemical equation for each of the following reactions:
   a) The combustion of octane C_8H_{18}, which has an energy change of -5470.6 kJ·mol^{-1}.
   b) The combustion of ethanol, CH_3CH_2OH, which has an energy change of -1368 kJ·mol^{-1}.

Applying Inquiry/ Communication Skills

9. Identify whether the reaction in the following graph is endothermic or exothermic. Write an equation for a reaction represented by the graph.

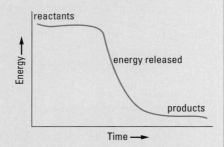

10. Describe why it is possible to get an accurate measurement for the bond energy of the H—H bond but not for the C—O bond.

Making Connections

11. You have just purchased a large soft drink in a bottle. You want a drink from it as soon as possible, but the pop is warm. Identify which method would cool the pop in the bottle the fastest: immersing the bottle in a bucket of ice-cold water, or wrapping the bottle in a cold, wet towel. Explain your choice.

11.2 Heat Change

Key Understandings

When you have completed this section, you will be able to:

- explain the relationship between mass, heat capacity, and temperature change
- gather and use experimental data to solve problems concerned with heat changes using the equation $Q = mc\Delta T$
- use appropriate scientific vocabulary to communicate ideas related to energy changes involved in hydrocarbon combustion

In order to test predictions about the compounds in chemical reactions, chemists often need to measure the energy changes that result. **Calorimetry** is the field of science involved with measurement of heat changes. Calorimetry relates changes in temperature to changes in amount of heat.

Temperature Change

Recall that heat refers to the flow of thermal energy from a warmer object to a cooler one, and temperature to the average thermal energy of a substance. Chemists have given change in temperature the symbol ΔT (pronounced "delta T"). Suppose you have two objects made of iron, one of mass 10 g and the other of mass 100 g. Both objects have a temperature of 20°C. You need to increase the temperature of both to 30°C, or $\Delta T = 10$°C. Do you need to add the same quantity of heat to each object?

The answer is no. The amount of heat you need to add so that the 100-g object has a ΔT of 10°C is 10 times the amount of heat you would need for the 10-g object to have a ΔT of 10°C. The heat required to raise the temperature of an object or substance by a specific amount always depends on the mass of the substance.

Now suppose you wanted to change the temperature of the 10-g iron object by 20°C ($\Delta T = 20$°C). You would need twice the amount of heat you used to change the temperature of the object by 10°C. Similarly, to change the temperature of the 100-g iron object by 20°C, you would need to add twice the heat you used to increase its temperature by 10°C. That is, the amount of heat required depends on both the magnitude of ΔT and on the mass of the substance.

FIGURE 11.6 The amount of heat energy required to raise the temperature of each of these pieces of metal to 30°C depends on their mass.

Heat Capacity

Now suppose you had a 10-g mass of iron and a 10-g mass of aluminum. In order for ΔT to equal 10°C in both of these blocks, would you need the same quantity of heat? Again the answer is no. Scientists have found that it takes different amounts of heat to raise the temperature of different substances by the same amount. Scientists refer to this property as heat capacity. **Heat capacity** is the amount of heat required to raise the temperature of an object by one degree Celsius or one kelvin. Heat capacity depends on both the mass and chemical composition of an object or substance. It takes a lot of energy to increase the temperature of a substance with a high heat capacity. It will also take a long time for a substance with a high heat capacity to cool down.

If you have ever baked cookies, you probably used oven mitts or a cloth to handle the cookie sheet so you would not burn yourself. But did you worry about putting the unprotected parts of your arms into the oven when you removed the cookies? Probably not. You know not to touch the cookie tray without some protection from the heat, but you are not concerned that the hot air in the oven will burn the rest of your arms. Why will the cookie tray burn you but not the hot oven air?

When you reach your arms into the hot oven, you place them in contact with the heat energy stored by the air. Air has a low heat capacity, so it cools down quickly when you open the door. Therefore, the air that reaches your arms will not be at the temperature that you set the oven.

FIGURE 11.7 The heat capacity of water is much higher than that of ethylene glycol, the main component of antifreeze. Explain why the coolant in most engines is at least 50% water.

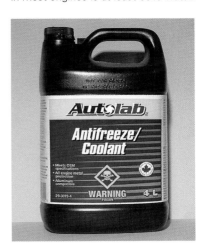

The metal in the cookie sheet, however, has a high heat capacity, so it will take a long time to cool. If you happen to touch the cookie sheet without any protection as you bring it out of the oven, your skin will be exposed to a lot more heat energy than is present in the air inside the oven.

Specific Heat

Since the heat capacity of a substance varies with its mass, scientists use specific heat capacity to compare various substances. **Specific heat capacity**, (symbol c), is the heat capacity of 1 g of a substance; it is the amount of heat required to raise the temperature of 1 g of a substance by 1°C or 1 K. Specific heat capacity is also called **specific heat**, and is expressed in units of $J \cdot g^{-1} \cdot °C^{-1}$ or $J \cdot g^{-1} \cdot K^{-1}$. Table 11.3 gives the specific heat of aluminum, iron, and water. You can see that it takes much more energy to increase the temperature of 1 g of water than for 1 g of either of these metals.

TABLE 11.3 Specific Heat of Three Common Substances

Substance	Specific Heat ($J \cdot g^{-1} \cdot °C^{-1}$)
Al(s)	0.903
Fe(s)	0.449
H_2O(l)	4.184

The **molar heat capacity** of a substance is the amount of heat required to raise the temperature of 1 mol of a substance by 1°C or 1 K. Molar heat capacity is equal to specific heat times molar mass of the substance. The units of molar heat capacity are $J \cdot mol^{-1} \cdot °C^{-1}$ or $J \cdot mol^{-1} \cdot K^{-1}$.

Water has a high specific heat. This means that it can absorb a lot of heat energy with only a small increase in its temperature. Water can also release a lot of heat energy with only a small decrease in temperature. Large bodies of water such as the Great Lakes moderate the temperature of the area around them, because they absorb a great deal of heat from the air during the summer and give off heat to the air in the winter.

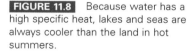 **FIGURE 11.8** Because water has a high specific heat, lakes and seas are always cooler than the land in hot summers.

Decision-Making Skills

▷ Defining the Issue

Developing Assessment Criteria

▷ Researching the Issue

▷ Analyzing Data and Information

▷ Proposing a Course of Action

▷ Justifying the Course of Action

▷ Communicating Your Proposal

Geothermal Energy: Using the Heat Capacity of Water

BACKGROUND INFORMATION

A school in Markham, Ontario, has taken advantage of the heat capacity of water to save money and reduce pollution, while maintaining a comfortable temperature inside the school. Father Michael McGivney Senior High School was designed with a geothermal heat pump. **Geothermal energy** is the energy stored inside Earth itself. Geothermal energy comes from the molten core deep in Earth as it continuously flows outward. The molten magma can also seep through cracks in Earth's crust. This energy is tapped by drawing the stored heat up from the Earth through water-filled pipes. The water in the pipes absorbs and stores the heat energy by virtue of its high heat capacity. This heated water is then pumped back to the surface and through the building. Geothermal energy systems can also cool the air in the summer. The system is essentially run in reverse; the water draws the heat from the building and returns it to the ground.

Father Michael McGivney Senior High School has more than 90 water-to-air heat pumps in ceiling spaces outside individual classrooms and offices. A further 20 water-to-water heat pumps are located in 3 separate rooms to provide hot water. The individual heat pumps are connected to over 250 wells, each 60 m deep. More than 43 km of plastic pipe form long U-tubes that run through the wells, and continuously circulates the water in a closed-loop system. Although winter temperatures above ground may drop below 0°C, the temperature of the ground surrounding the 60 m wells remains constant year-round. Even when the outdoor temperatures are below 0°C, the water in the tubes remains between 7°C and 9°C.

Geothermal heat pumps are more expensive than a conventional heating system but are far less expensive to run. The heat pump system at Father McGivney cost \$2.6 million; a conventional system would have cost about \$2.5 million. However, Father Michael McGivney Senior High uses almost half the energy of schools of comparable size in the same area. The system also requires less maintenance than a conventional system, which will save even more money over time.

Analyzing the Issue

1. Identify the issue from an environmental perspective and from an economic perspective.

2. Research geothermal energy systems and summarize the advantages and disadvantages of their use in a T-chart.

3. Draw a diagram to illustrate the direction of heat transfer in a geothermal system during the winter. Explain how this same system can be used to cool air in the summer.

4. Using geothermal energy requires that a building can be connected to a large field of wells. Explain reasons why geothermal energy may not be appropriate for all buildings.

5. The success of the high school's heating system leads you to believe that it should be made available to any residents or businesses in the region. Write a proposal for the regional council that is persuasive for funding more geothermal energy projects.

EXAMPLE 4

Using the values for specific heat capacity given in Table 11.3, determine the change in heat that occurs when the temperature of 125 g of aluminum increases from 25°C to 100°C.

Given

$m = 125$ g

$c_{Al} = 0.903$ J·g^{-1}·°C^{-1}

$\Delta T = (100°C - 25°C)$

$\quad\;\; = 75°C$

Required

heat change, Q

Analysis

$Q = mc\Delta T$

Solution

$Q = (125$ g$)(0.903$ J·g^{-1}·°C$^{-1})(75°C)$

$\quad = 8.5 \times 10^3$ J

$\quad = 8.5$ kJ

Statement

The heat change is 8.5 kJ.

PRACTICE PROBLEMS

1. Calculate the heat required to raise the temperature of 2.0 kg of copper from 20°C to 80°C. The heat capacity of copper is 0.385 J·g^{-1}·°C^{-1}.

2. Calculate the final temperature when 10 kJ of heat is added to 15 g of iron at 15°C. The heat capacity of iron is 0.449 J·g^{-1}·°C^{-1}.

EXAMPLE 5

A metallurgist is working with pure samples of copper, silver, and gold. The mass of each sample is 10.0 g. The specific heat of copper is 0.385 J·g^{-1}·°C^{-1}, of silver is 0.237 J·g^{-1}·°C^{-1}, and of gold is 0.130 J·g^{-1}·°C^{-1}. Using the equation $Q = mc\Delta T$, determine which metal reaches the highest temperature when a heat change of 10 J occurs in each sample.

Given

m_{Cu}, m_{Ag}, and $m_{Au} = 10.0$ g

$c_{Cu} = 0.385$ J·g^{-1}·°C^{-1}

$c_{Ag} = 0.237$ J·g^{-1}·°C^{-1}

$c_{Au} = 0.130$ J·g^{-1}·°C^{-1}

$Q = 10$ J

Analysis

For the equation $Q = mc\Delta T$, all terms other than ΔT are known. Therefore, you need to solve for ΔT, or $\Delta T = \dfrac{Q}{mc}$

Solution

$$\Delta T_{Cu} = \frac{10 \text{ J}}{10 \text{ g} \times 0.385 \text{ J}\cdot\text{g}^{-1}\cdot^\circ\text{C}^{-1}}$$

$$= 2.6^\circ\text{C}$$

$$\Delta T_{Ag} = \frac{10 \text{ J}}{10 \text{ g} \times 0.237 \text{ J}\cdot\text{g}^{-1}\cdot^\circ\text{C}^{-1}}$$

$$= 4.2^\circ\text{C}$$

$$\Delta T_{Au} = \frac{10 \text{ J}}{10 \text{ g} \times 0.130 \text{ J}\cdot\text{g}^{-1}\cdot^\circ\text{C}^{-1}}$$

$$= 7.7^\circ\text{C}$$

Statement
The gold metal will have the greatest increase in temperature.

PRACTICE PROBLEM

Use the equation $Q = mc\Delta T$ to compare the amount of each product that is formed by combustion of 1 kg of methane to the amount formed by combustion of 2 kg of methane. Identify which quantities stay the same and which change. Describe the relationship between the quantities that change.

Calculating Heat Change

You can calculate the heat change of a substance (symbol Q), if you know its specific heat capacity (c), mass (m), and the temperature change that takes place, ΔT. Heat change is calculated from the formula $Q = mc\Delta T$. The values for any one of c, m, or ΔT can also be calculated from this equation if the other three terms are known.

Investigation
Refer to page 511, Investigation 1

Measuring Heat Change

Heat changes are measured by a **calorimeter**, which is any device used to measure heat change. A calorimeter can be as simple as a Styrofoam cup or a coffee can. We can measure heat change because of the law of conservation of energy. Since energy is never created or destroyed, the heat released by a chemical reaction or physical change must equal the heat absorbed by the calorimeter and its contents.

A Simple Calorimeter Figure 11.9 shows a simple constant-pressure calorimeter made from a Styrofoam cup. This type of calorimeter is used for reactions involving aqueous solutions, so it is sometimes known as a *solution calorimeter*.

Whenever you use a simple calorimeter, you make the following assumptions:

- The water in the solution absorbs all the released heat.
- The calorimeter (the Styrofoam cup) does not absorb any heat.
- If the simple calorimeter is covered, no heat is lost to the surroundings, such as the air or the tabletop.

Because you must make these assumptions, you can use a simple calorimeter to measure relatively small heat changes only. When large heat changes take place in a

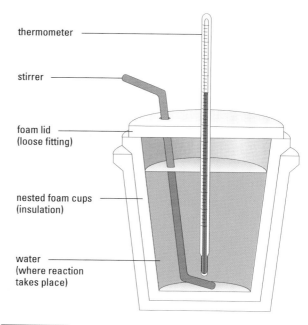

thermometer

stirrer

foam lid (loose fitting)

nested foam cups (insulation)

water (where reaction takes place)

FIGURE 11.9 A simple calorimeter

simple calorimeter, a significant amount of heat is lost, so your results would not be accurate.

You can use a simple calorimeter for calorimetric measurements of many aqueous solutions. Provided that the solutions that you use are dilute (i.e., mostly water), you can also assume that the solutions have the same specific heat as water.

EXAMPLE 6

A mass of 100. g of water is placed in a coffee-cup calorimeter. The temperature of the water before the reaction is 14.4°C. A mass of 0.412 g of calcium metal is placed in the calorimeter. When the reaction is complete, the temperature is 24.6°C. Given that the specific heat of water is $4.18 \text{ J} \cdot \text{g}^{-1} \cdot ^\circ\text{C}^{-1}$, calculate the heat change (Q) for this reaction:

$$Ca(s) + 2 \text{ H}_2O(l) \rightarrow Ca(OH)_2(aq) + \text{H}_2(g)$$

Given

mass of solution	= 100. g
mass of calcium solid	= 0.412 g
specific heat	= $4.18 \text{ J} \cdot \text{g}^{-1} \cdot ^\circ\text{C}^{-1}$
temperature of the solution before reaction	= 14.4°C
temperature of the solution after reaction	= 24.6°C

Required
heat change, Q

Analysis
$Q = mc\Delta T$

$\Delta T = (24.6 - 14.4)°C$
$\quad = 10.2°C$

Solution
$Q = 100. \text{ g} \times 4.18 \text{ J} \cdot \text{g}^{-1} \cdot ^\circ\text{C}^{-1} \times 10.2°C$
$\quad = 4.26 \times 10^3 \text{ J}$
$\quad = 4.26 \text{ kJ}$

Statement
The heat change for the reaction of calcium metal with water is 4.26 kJ.

PRACTICE PROBLEMS

1. A mass of 100. g of dilute hydrochloric acid is placed in a coffee cup calorimeter. The starting temperature of the solution is 11.2°C. A 0.18-g mass of magnesium ribbon is placed in the acid and then the lid is replaced. The final temperature is 20.0°C. Calculate the molar heat change for this reaction:

$$Mg(s) + 2 \text{ HCl}(aq) \rightarrow$$
$$MgCl_2(aq) + \text{H}_2(g)$$

2. A 24.6-g sample of nickel is heated to 110.00°C. It is then placed in a coffee-cup calorimeter containing 125 g of water at a temperature of 23.00°C. The highest temperature reached by the metal and water is 24.83°C. Calculate the specific heat of nickel.

Discovering Chemistry   *How Much Energy Does It Take to Melt Ice?*

If you want to melt ice, you have to add heat energy. For example, you might hold an ice cube in your hand. As it melts, it turns into water at 0°C. According to the kinetic molecular theory, the heat energy that is applied is converted to the kinetic energy of the water molecules in the liquid state. You can measure this amount of energy using a simple calorimeter.

Materials
    water
    100-mL graduated cylinder
    ice cubes
    2 Styrofoam cups
    lid
    thermometer or graphing calculator with temperature probe

1. Place one Styrofoam cup inside another one. Using the graduated cylinder, add 50.0 mL of warm water (about 40°C) to the cup. Measure the temperature of the water to the nearest 0.2°C.

2. Add two ice cubes to the cup and stir the water. As soon as both ice cubes have completely melted, accurately measure and record the temperature. Record your data.

3. Transfer the water to the graduated cylinder and determine its volume. Subtract the initial volume of 50.0 mL to determine the volume of ice that you melted. Given that the density of water is 1.0 g·mL^{-1}, determine the mass of the two ice cubes.

■ The heat capacity of water is 4.18 J·g^{-1}·°C^{-1}. Use the equation $Q = mc\Delta T$, calculate the change in heat that occurred when the ice melted.

■ Write a short paragraph explaining why the amount of heat in water can change but its temperature can stay the same.

The Flame Calorimeter Fossil fuels release a lot of heat during combustion, so you cannot use a simple calorimeter to measure the energy changes of these reactions. Large heat changes are measured with a flame calorimeter instead. Figure 11.10 shows a commercial flame calorimeter. However, you can construct a flame calorimeter using a coffee can and some metal tubing (even just a coffee can may be used) to measure large heat changes reasonably accurately.

To measure heat change with a flame calorimeter, a sample is placed inside the burner. After the initial temperature is measured, the wick inside the burner is lit and the sample is burned. As the air inside the calorimeter gains heat energy, it rises through the metal tube and heats the water and the metal calorimeter itself. The final temperature inside the calorimeter is then measured. This value can then be used to calculate ΔT, the change in temperature.

To calculate Q, the heat change of the combustion reaction, you must know the mass, m, of the sample, the mass of the water, and the mass of the calorimeter. You also need to know the heat capacity, c, of the kind of metal in the calorimeter and the heat capacity of water. Heat change can then be calculated by the same equation that is used for a simple calorimeter: $Q = mc\Delta T$.

Chemists have determined the value of Q for the combustion of most of the fossil fuels using very accurate flame calorimeters. Some of these values are given in Table 11.4; you can see that natural gas produces the most heat energy per gram mass of these common fuels.

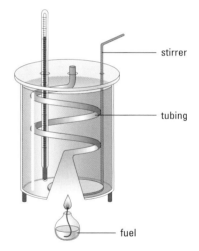

stirrer

tubing

fuel

FIGURE 11.10   A flame calorimeter

Investigation
Refer to page 512, Investigation 2

TABLE 11.4 Heat Change, Q, of Combustion of Fossil Fuels

Fuel	Q
coal	33 kJ·g^{-1}
natural gas	55 kJ·g^{-1}
gasoline	48 kJ·g^{-1}

WEBLINK

For a simulation of an experiment
showing how a flame calorimeter
works, go to
www.pearsoned.ca/chemistry11.

EXAMPLE 7

A steel flame calorimeter of mass 322 g is filled with 225 g of water. The
starting temperature of the water and calorimeter is 10.6°C. When 1.02 g
of ethanol, CH_3CH_2OH, is burned, the temperature of the calorimeter
rises to 38.4°C. The heat capacity of steel is 0.44 J·g^{-1}·°C^{-1}, and the heat
capacity of water is 4.18 J·g^{-1}·°C^{-1}. Calculate the heat change of combustion of ethanol.

Given

mass of steel calorimeter	= 322 g
mass of water	= 225 g
starting temperature of calorimeter	= 10.6°C
final temperature of calorimeter	= 38.4°C
specific heat of steel	= 0.44 J·g^{-1}·°C^{-1}
specific heat of water	= 4.18 J·g^{-1}·°C^{-1}

Required
heat change, Q

Analysis
$\Delta T = (38.4 - 10.6)°C$
$\quad\quad = 27.8°C$

Assume that all the heat energy will be absorbed by the water and
calorimeter.

Therefore, the total energy change will be the energy changes of the water
and the steel:

$Q_{total} = Q_{water} + Q_{steel}$

Solution
$Q_{water} = 225 \;g \times 4.18 \;J·g^{-1}·°C^{-1} \times 27.8°C$
$\quad\quad\;\; = 2.61 \times 10^4 \;J$

$Q_{steel} = 322 \;g \times 0.44 \;J·g^{-1}·°C^{-1} \times 27.8°C$
$\quad\quad\; = 3.9 \times 10^3 \;J$

$Q_{total} = Q_{water} + Q_{steel}$
$\quad\quad\; = (2.61 \times 10^4 \;J) + (3.9 \times 10^3 \;J)$
$\quad\quad\; = 3.0 \times 10^4 \;J$

Statement
The heat change that occurs from the combustion of 1.02 g of ethanol is
3.0×10^4 J, or 30 kJ.

PRACTICE PROBLEM

A flame calorimeter made of
copper has a mass of 587 g and
is filled with 314 g of water.
The starting temperature of the
water and calorimeter is 12.2°C.
When 0.920 g of 1-propanol,
$CH_3CH_2CH_2OH$, is burned, the
temperature rises to 32.3°C.
Calculate the change in heat of
this reaction for the combustion
of 1 mol of 1-propanol, given the
following additional information:
the specific heat of water is
4.18 J·g^{-1}·°C^{-1}; the specific heat
of copper is 0.385 J·g^{-1}·°C^{-1}.

The Human Calorimeter With current concern about diets and excess body weight, you may have wondered how energy measurements are calculated for people. One way involves the use of a human calorimeter, which mainly consists of a well-insulated room. Volunteers live in this room, performing different tasks, while the heat energy released is monitored continuously. From these measurements, scientists can calculate the energy consumed in performing specific tasks by people with different metabolic rates.

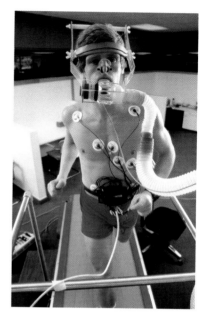

Section 11.2 Review

Understanding Concepts

1. Define heat capacity in your own words, and compare the difference between it and specific heat.

2. Compare the heat capacity of a 10-g water sample and a 100-g water sample.

3. Explain why the concrete deck around an outdoor swimming pool becomes hot on sunny days, while the water in the pool stays cool.

4. Explain the purpose of a calorimeter.

5. Identify the two similarities and one difference between a thermochemical equation and a chemical equation.

6. Determine the specific heat capacity of the metal gold if a 227-g gold piece has a heat capacity of 29.5 J·°C·g^{-1}.

7. Calculate the molar heat capacity of water, given that the specific heat of water is 4.18 J·g^{-1}·°C^{-1}.

Applying Inquiry/ Communication Skills

8. Design an experiment to measure the specific heat capacities of brass, lead, and zinc. Have your teacher approve your design and then, if possible, obtain the necessary materials and perform the investigation. Compare your experimental results with the values from a chemical reference book.

9. You and a classmate are asked to determine the heat change of the reaction of magnesium metal with aqueous hydrochloric acid. You both have 100 g of dilute hydrochloric acid and 0.18 g of magnesium ribbon. You are also provided with a Styrofoam cup to use as a simple calorimeter. Explain why the value for heat change that you calculate might be different from that of your classmate.

10. A candle of mass 24.7 g was burned in a steel calorimeter of mass 143 g that contained 340 g of water. The combustion of the candle increased the temperature of the water and calorimeter from 15.0°C to 31.2°C. The final mass of the candle was 23.6 g. If the specific heat of steel is 0.44 J·g^{-1}·°C and the specific heat of water is 4.18 J·g^{-1}·°C, calculate the heat of combustion of the candle wax in J·g^{-1}.

Making Connections

11. When people exercise regularly, they are able to use the energy in their food far more efficiently. Imagine that an unfit person volunteers to be tested in a human calorimeter. If this same person exercises three times a week for three months and is then tested in the same human calorimeter, would you expect them to produce more or less heat energy? Explain your answer.

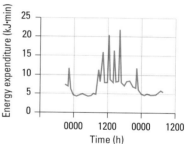

FIGURE 11.11 A human calorimeter. In a perfectly insulated room, the heat released from the body of a volunteer can be measured and related to activity over several days.

11.3 Fossil Fuels

Key Understandings

When you have completed this section, you will be able to:

- describe how petroleum is refined
- describe some of the products we make from petroleum
- understand the importance of hydrocarbons as fuels
- identify the risks and benefits to society and the environment of using hydrocarbons as fuels
- use appropriate scientific vocabulary to communicate ideas related to hydrocarbons

Hydrocarbons have been an integral part of Canada's development as a country. In Canada, petroleum was first discovered in Petrolia, Ontario, in 1861. This discovery eventually led to the development of the neighbouring city of Sarnia as a leading centre of the petrochemical industry. Similarly, when oil was discovered in Leduc, Alberta, in 1947, Alberta's economy was transformed from an agricultural base to the oil-based economy of today. Now the rich oil and gas fields off the Atlantic coast of Newfoundland and Nova Scotia are poised to transform the economy of these traditionally poorer regions of our country.

FIGURE 11.12 We live in an oil-based economy. Canada relies on oil reserves, such as those of the Hibernia oilfield off the eastern coast of Newfoundland.

Fossil Fuel Deposits

There are five main types of fossil fuel deposits that supply hydrocarbon fuels: coal, petroleum, natural gas, tar sands, and oil shale.

WEBLINK

Bio-diesel is a fuel of the future that is already here today. Investigate the benefits of this fuel over conventional diesel fuel. Research possible reasons why this fuel is not more widely used. Report on the potential of this fuel in the future. Begin your research at **www.pearsoned.ca/chemistry11**.

TABLE 11.5 Composition of the Main Types of Fossil Fuels

Deposit	Principal Constituents	Other Constituents
natural gas	up to 99% methane, CH_4	up to 10% ethane, C_2H_6 up to 20% propane, C_3H_8 other hydrocarbons up to 95% CO_2 up to 30% H_2S
petroleum	0%–75% straight-chain alkanes 20%–70% cycloalkanes 5%–40% other cyclic hydrocarbons	0%–5% organic compounds of nitrogen and/or sulfur
tar sands	complex hydrocarbon mixture (bitumen)	clays, sands, and/or sandstone, water
oil shale	hydrocarbon polymer	various minerals
coal	complex cyclic structure with high C:H ratio	some sulfur and nitrogen combined in structure

Then &NOW

Petroleum and Fossils

Fossil fuels are the remains of ancient organisms that have been transformed over time beneath Earth's crust. Sometimes, these buried remains also leave traces of their bodies in the form of fossils. This is not surprising, since the forces that produce fossil fuels are often the same as produce the fossilized remains. The work of two of Canada's most successful scientists benefited greatly from this link, and provided Canadians with two rich heritages.

Abraham Gesner is often referred to as the father of the petroleum industry. Gesner was born in Nova Scotia in 1797, and first trained as a physician. However, he had such a great interest in rocks and fossils that he set up his first medical practice near Parrsboro, Nova Scotia, because he knew he could find fossils in that area.

Gesner gathered a large collection of fossils during his travels to make house calls. Eventually, he became so knowledgeable about the geology of New Brunswick that he was appointed first Provincial Geologist. While in this post, Gesner came across large deposits of bituminous coal. Although coal was used extensively for heating at that time, Gesner thought he could make the low-grade coal in New Brunswick into a better fuel. Working towards this goal, Gesner invented and patented a distillation process that refined coal oil into kerosene. Kerosene became an important fuel, since kerosene lanterns were the only alternative to candles until the invention of the electric light bulb. Gesner's process laid the groundwork for petroleum refining and Canada's petroleum industry.

It was an interest in fossils that led Gesner to a career in geology. And it was during an expedition to map Canada's western areas that the geologist and adventurer Joseph Tyrrell uncovered the first fossilized dinosaurs in Canada.

Joseph Burr Tyrrell was born in Weston, Ontario, in 1858, and spent much of his career mapping what was then unexplored western wilderness. In 1884, Tyrrell was Canada's senior geologist, and worked for the Canadian Geological Survey mapping and exploring the geological features of Canada. In the summer of that year, Tyrrell led an expedition to the area of Alberta now known as the Badlands. On June 9, he discovered dinosaur bones. Three days later, he discovered coal deposits in the same area.

Tyrrell had found one of the richest deposits of fossils in the world. He is often remembered for only that accomplishment, but Tyrrell provided us with a wealth of information on Canada's geology. He also contributed greatly to the material wealth of Canada, in the coal industry in what is now Drumheller, Alberta, and in the gold mining industry in the Timmins and Kirkland Lake regions of Ontario.

FIGURE 11.13 Albert Gesner

FIGURE 11.14 Joseph B. Tyrrell

Coal Coal was the earliest fossil fuel that humans learned to exploit. Coal was formed predominantly from the remains of plants that grew during the Carboniferous era. This plant material became buried deep under Earth's crust, where it was subjected to high pressures and temperatures and was transformed into coal (Figure 11.15).

Coal has a complex chemical composition, consisting of molecules with enormous chains of carbon linked to hydrogen and sometimes nitrogen and sulfur atoms as well. Coal is graded according to its moisture content. Lower grades of coal have moisture contents greater than 25%, which makes them less efficient fuels than coal grades with less moisture.

There are several types of coal, each of which was formed under different conditions. **Anthracite** is a hard coal, formed when buried plant material was subjected to

FIGURE 11.15 A deep coal face in an underground mine

FIGURE 11.16 Although natural gas causes fewer airborne pollutants, it must be transported through pipelines which may cross fragile environments.

very great pressure. Anthracite coal has the lowest amount of moisture of any coal and is a very efficient fuel. Soft or **bituminous** coal formed at lower pressures. This coal has a higher percentage of moisture and is the most plentiful.

The major coal deposits in Canada are in Alberta, British Columbia, and Nova Scotia. The world reserves of coal are enormous, far more than those of petroleum. However, coal is the least convenient fuel, since it is a solid and difficult to transport. Coal can have a high level of sulfur-containing compounds, so coal combustion is a large contributor to acid rain. Coal combustion is used, however, to generate a lot of the world's electricity. Coal mining can be dangerous as well, especially in underground mines. However, open-pit mining has improved working conditions in this industry (Figure 11.15).

Scientists have been able to convert coal into more usuable fuels known as synthetic natural gas (SNG) and synthetic natural liquid (SNL). Although these fuels have the advantages of gaseous and liquid fuels, the cost of their production is currently too high for large-scale use.

Natural Gas Although most natural gas seems to have been formed along with petroleum deposits, there is some evidence that very deep methane deposits may have an inorganic origin. However, all the reserves that are currently tapped are of biological origin.

Natural gas is found in porous sedimentary rocks in Earth's crust, often floating on top of a petroleum deposit. In Canada, large quantities of natural gas are found in Alberta, British Columbia, and off the coast of Nova Scotia.

Petroleum Petroleum, or crude oil, is a homogenous mixture of hydrocarbons formed from the decay of marine plant and animal life under high pressure and temperature (Figure 11.17). The main constituents of petroleum are aliphatic hydrocarbons, but the exact composition of petroleum varies between different sites. Some petroleum has mainly long-chain molecules, which makes the oil highly viscous. When oil has a very high percent of long-chain hydrocarbons, it is as viscous as thick syrup.

There is usually a proportion of sulfur compounds in the oil. Petroleum with lower quantities of sulfur (so-called "sweet crude") has a higher market value. Canadian oil reserves are predominantly in Alberta and offshore Newfoundland.

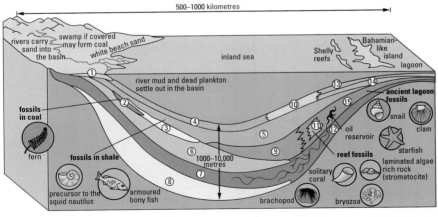

① Delta sand
② Coal
③ White sandstone (compacted beach sand)
④ Black mud settled from ocean water
⑤ Shale formed by compaction of mud
⑥ Brown sandstone (formed by compaction of river and delta sand)
⑦ Ancient shale (the heat down here turns organic matter into oil)
⑧ Ancient sandstone
⑨ Limestone (compacted lime mud)
⑩ Lime mud washed offshore
⑪ Ancient reef
⑫ Oil moves from shale to the dolomites and forms an oil reservoir
⑬ Lime, sand and shell debris
⑭ Limestone rock formed by compaction of lime sediment
⑮ Dolomite formed by groundwater altering limestone

FIGURE 11.17 Formation of petroleum occurs over millions of years.

Controlling Oil Spills

Decision-Making Skills

▶ Defining the Issue

Developing Assessment Criteria

Researching the Issue

▶ Analyzing Data and Information

▶ Proposing a Course of Action

▶ Justifying the Course of Action

▶ Communicating Your Proposal

BACKGROUND INFORMATION

Twelve years after the oil tanker *Exxon-Valdez* leaked crude oil, destroying wildlife and fish stocks in Prince William Sound, Alaska, another unique and fragile ecosystem was again threatened by an oil spill. The tanker *Jessica* leaked heavy oil after it ran aground on January 16, 2001, outside the port of Baquerizo Moreno on San Cristobal Island, an island in the Galapagos archipelago. The tanker was carrying 606 000 L of diesel for the fuel dispatch station on Baltra Island and 303 000 L of bunker fuel for the tourism vessel *Galapagos Explorer*.

Environmentalists pointed out that both the *Jessica* and its more infamous predecessor, the *Exxon-Valdez*, were single-hulled, not double-hulled, tankers. Double-hulled vessels became required by law in the United States as a result of the *Exxon Valdez* spill. Similarly in Europe, after a wreck that killed fish and birds throughout Brittany in 2000, double-hulled ships became far more common.

However, experts are far from agreed on the value of double- versus single-hulled vessels. Double-hulled tankers were developed to offer a second barrier against leakage if a ship were to run aground. However, the strength of each individual wall is less than that of the heavier single-walled tankers. Environmentalists, who once demanded double-hulled tankers, now seem to support a return to single-hulled vessels, since these vessels can better withstand high seas. Other changes, such as the use of smaller tankers that would have less fuel and tankers that are compartmentalized, so that the entire cargo would not be lost in the event of a rupture, have been proposed.

Each of these proposals would add to the cost of transporting oil, which is passed on to consumers. Compartmentalization and the use of double hulls also increases the amount of corrosion that occurs, which increases the amount of maintenance required. Smaller tankers are less stable in high seas, and require more personnel per unit of oil than large tankers.

In the end, oil companies are unwilling to cut into their profits and consumers are never happy to pay more for fuel. As a result, protecting the environment against oil spills will depend as much on a change in attitude as on further regulations in tanker design.

Analyzing the Issue

1. Define the issue described and create a mind map of sub-issues related to it.

2. Identify the principal stakeholders affected by the major issue. Summarize their perspectives in a chart.

3. Construct a table of the risks and benefits associated with each proposed solution outlined in the article.

4. Oil companies will continue to transport crude petroleum and fuels by sea for the foreseeable future. Propose a method of decreasing the risk of contaminating sensitive environments by oil spills. Develop a prototype for your new method of crude oil transport. Draw diagrams or build a model to present your ideas.

5. Prepare a presentation to persuade others that your method will work.

FIGURE 11.18 The cost of the heavy machinery required to mine tar sands makes this resource far more expensive than conventional petroleum sources.

Tar Sands In most petroleum deposits, the crude oil is trapped beneath the ground under a cap of impervious rock which keeps it contained in a large pool. However, some petroleum deposits lack this rock cap, and can seep up through the ground to the surface. As the petroleum rises, the components with lower boiling points evaporate, leaving the longer-chain molecules. Tar sands likely formed by this process.

Tar sands, or oil sands, are a mixture of about 85% sand and mineral-rich clays, 4% water, and 10% bitumen. **Bitumen** is a dense, sticky, semi-solid mixture of hydrocarbons that is about 83% carbon. Canada has the largest deposits of tar sands in the world, equivalent to approximately 900 billion barrels of oil. Large tar-sand deposits are found in the Lloydminster, Peace River, and Athabasca regions of Alberta. The Lloydminster deposits flow sufficiently freely to be pumped directly from the ground. At Peace River, the mixture is about 1000 times more viscous, and the Athabasca deposits are 10 times more viscous again.

Mining tar sands is difficult. The high sand content makes tar sand extremely abrasive, and wears out mining equipment rapidly. The sticky particles cling to everything, including machinery, clogging moving parts.

Processing tar sand is relatively simple. The mixture is first treated with hot water. The sand and clays sink to the bottom, while the bitumen floats to the top. The bitumen is separated and then subjected to **pyrolysis**, which is the process of strongly heating a substance in the absence of air. Pyrolysis is known industrially as "coking." During pyrolysis, the large carbon-rich molecules are broken down into **coke**, an impure form of carbon, and smaller hydrocarbons that can be used commercially.

Oil Shale Oil shale also forms from petroleum deposits that lack an impervious rock cap, but differs markedly from tar sands. Oil shale looks like rock, but can burn when the fuel content is sufficiently high. The United States has enormous reserves of oil shale, approaching the equivalent of 172 trillion barrels of oil. However, the difficulties involved in extracting the oil from the shale mean that much of this oil is unobtainable. To extract the hydrocarbons and other organic compounds, the shale first must be crushed. The crushed material is then subjected to a coking process similar to that used to process tar sands. The high cost of processing oil shale has prevented widespread use of this type of fossil fuel reserve, but increasing prices and declining reserves of more conventional fossil fuels may change this situation.

FIGURE 11.19 Methane hydrates are another potential source of hydrocarbon fuels.

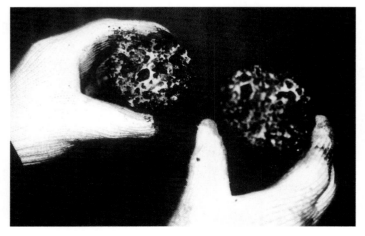

Methane Hydrates In recent years, scientists have found ice deposits on the sea floor that contain methane molecules trapped in the ice structure. These trapped molecules are called **methane hydrates**. Some scientists believe that undersea deposits of methane hydrates could supply us with energy for centuries into the future, if a method of extracting them can be found. Other scientists fear that global warming will cause these methane hydrates to melt, releasing the methane gas into the atmosphere and causing catastrophic and rapid climate change.

Petroleum Refining

Although petroleum is a major source of hydrocarbon compounds, petroleum is not useful in its crude state. **Petroleum refining** is the process of turning crude oil into useful products. During refining, the various types of hydrocarbons that we use are separated from one another.

Fractionation **Fractionation** is the process that is used to partially separate the components of crude petroleum *according to their boiling points* (Table 11.6). Crude petroleum is pumped through pipes into a furnace, where it is heated to about 350°C. The resulting mixture of gases and liquids is then passed to a distillation tower, where the gases are cooled as they rise. The different compounds cool and condense at different temperatures, which are determined by their boiling points. The condensed fractions are then collected on trays placed at different levels in the tower and drawn off.

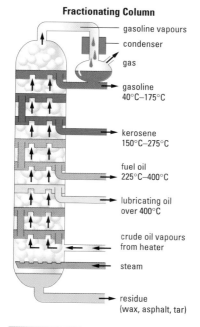

Fractionating Column

gasoline vapours
condenser
gas
gasoline 40°C–175°C
kerosene 150°C–275°C
fuel oil 225°C–400°C
lubricating oil over 400°C
crude oil vapours from heater
steam
residue (wax, asphalt, tar)

FIGURE 11.20 The compounds that condense at a particular temperature in the distillation tower all have very similar boiling points. These are drawn off as a fraction and may be further refined.

TABLE 11.6 Boiling Points of Petroleum Fractions

Fraction	Length of Carbon Chain	Boiling Point Range (°C)
natural gas	1 to 4 atoms	below 20
petroleum ether (solvent)	5 to 6 atoms	30 to 60
naphtha (solvent)	7 to 8 atoms	60 to 90
gasoline	6 to 12 atoms	40 to 175
kerosene	12 to 15 atoms	150 to 275
fuel oils, mineral oil	15 to 18 atoms	225 to 400
lubricating oil, petroleum jelly, greases, paraffin wax, asphalt	16 to 24 atoms	over 400

Any material that is not vaporized in the first tower is passed to a second tower, which operates at reduced pressure. This tower is therefore called a vacuum distillation tower. Because the air pressure is lower, the remaining materials boil at a lower temperature. Many compounds with high boiling points that cannot be vaporized in the first column will vaporize and fractionate in the vacuum distillation tower. The material that cannot be vaporized in the second tower, pitch, is used in asphalt.

Unfortunately, the chain lengths and types of molecules that occur naturally in petroleum do not match our needs. In particular, demand for short carbon-chain molecules (6 to 12 carbon atoms) is far greater than is their prevalence in crude oil. Petroleum also contains many straight-chain molecules, but we use more branched-chain molecules, since these are better fuels. Chemists and chemical engineers have therefore developed chemical processes to change the product to fit our needs.

WEBLINK

SIMULATION

For a simulation of how petroleum refining works, go to **www.pearsoned.ca/chemistry11**.

Catalytic Cracking **Catalytic cracking** decomposes long-chain (less desirable) hydrocarbons into shorter fragments. Cracking involves heating the hydrocarbons under pressure in the presence of a catalyst, such as specially processed clays. For example, hexadecane, $C_{16}H_{34}$, can be broken into octane and octene by cracking.

$$C_{16}H_{34}(l) \xrightarrow{\Delta,\ \text{pressure, catalyst}} C_8H_{18}(l) + C_8H_{16}(l)$$

Alkylation The process of **alkylation** can combine very short-chain hydrocarbon molecules together, giving molecules with longer carbon chains. For example, propene can be reacted with methylpropane according to the following formula:

$$CH_2{=}CH{-}CH_3(g) + CH_3{-}CH(CH_3){-}CH_3(g) \xrightarrow{\text{catalyst}} CH_3{-}C(CH_3)_2{-}CH_2{-}CH_2{-}CH_3(l)$$

For the actual process, dozens of different short-chain alkenes would be reacting with different alkanes, so the product of the reaction would be a mixture of a large number of different hydrocarbons with carbon chains from 6 to 12 atoms long.

Catalytic Reforming Using heat and a very specialized catalyst, **catalytic reforming** rearranges the bonds in hydrocarbons, converting them from straight-chain to branched-chain molecules. One example of this process is the conversion of pentane to 2-methylbutane:

$$CH_3{-}CH_2{-}CH_2{-}CH_2{-}CH_3(g) \xrightarrow{\Delta,\ \text{catalyst}} CH_3{-}CH(CH_3){-}CH_2{-}CH_3(g)$$

Products of Petroleum Refining

The typical output of an oil refinery is given in Table 11.7. Between 70% and 90% of the hydrocarbons are burned as fuel. The remainder is used to produce petrochemicals such as plastics and pharmaceuticals.

TABLE 11.7 Products of Petroleum Refining

Component	Use	Typical Percent in Crude Petroleum
natural gas	fuel, organic chemicals	
petroleum ether	solvents	10
napthalene	solvents, synthetic organic resins	
gasoline	motor fuel, organic chemicals	40
kerosene	jet fuel, oil furnace fuel, other fuels	10
fuel oils, mineral oil	diesel fuel, pharmaceuticals, other chemicals	30
lubricating oil, petroleum jelly, greases, paraffin wax, asphalt	lubrication, water repellents, moisturizers, paving, roofing, other chemicals	10

Gasoline The great advantage of gasoline is that it is a liquid fuel. Liquid fuel is a more concentrated source of energy than gases like methane and easier to transport than solids like coal. Although gasoline engines have become more efficient, many people still prefer to drive large vehicles that use a lot of fuel. This increases not only gasoline consumption, but also air pollution.

Gasoline is available in more than one grade; the higher grades have a higher octane rating. What exactly does this number refer to? To understand octane ratings, you first need to understand some of the processes inside the internal combustion engine (Figure 11.22). When an engine is started, liquid gasoline is sprayed into the combustion chambers (the cylinders) by the fuel injectors. Here the gasoline vaporizes, creating an air/gasoline mixture. Gasoline must contain short-chain molecules with lower boiling points in order for this vaporization to be possible. The piston moves up the cylinder and compresses the air/gasoline mixture, which is ignited by a spark from the spark plugs. The resulting explosion produces a large amount of hot gases. The pressure from the gases pushes the piston down. This motion is then conveyed through the transmission to the wheels of the vehicle.

Straight-chain hydrocarbons will readily react with air simply by compression, but branched-chain molecules need the energy of the spark for a reaction to occur. You may have heard a knocking sound coming from an engine. Engine knock is often caused by gasoline that contains too many straight-chain molecules.

The octane rating is a scale that measures the proportion of branched-chain molecules in gasoline. The octane scale is a relative scale. When the scale was developed, heptane was assigned a rating value of 0, while 2,2,4-trimethylpentane (commonly called iso-octane) was given a value of 100. The octane rating of a gasoline is determined by using the fuel in a standard engine and recording how much knocking occurs. The compression at which knocking starts is compared to that of a specific mixture of n-heptane and iso-octane. For example, a gasoline that causes an engine to knock at the same compression as a mixture of 9% heptane and 91% iso-octane will be assigned an octane rating of 91.

Gasoline engines are now designed to run with up to 10% of methanol or ethanol in the fuel mix. These compounds raise the octane rating, and the products of their combustion are less polluting. Methanol is easily obtained from surplus natural gas, and ethanol is produced during fermentation of grains or sugars. Unfortunately, the demand for transportation fuels is so great

FIGURE 11.21 Gasoline is composed of a mixture of different hydrocarbons designed to burn efficiently in an internal combustion engine. Many gasoline producers offer more than one formulation of gasoline to consumers.

FIGURE 11.22 Operation of the internal combustion engine. a) Fuel is injected into the cylinder; b) the piston compresses the fuel-air mixture, which is then ignited by the spark plug; c) the exploding gases force the piston down; and d) the products of combustion are pushed out of the cylinder by the next upward stroke of the piston.

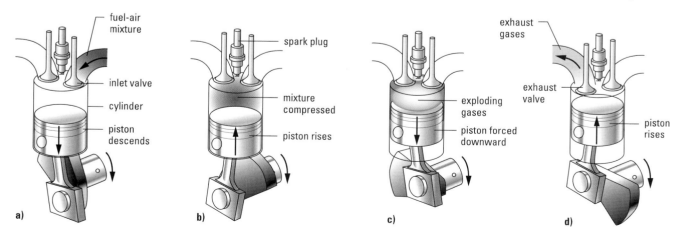

a)
fuel-air mixture
inlet valve
cylinder
piston descends

b)
spark plug
mixture compressed
piston rises

c)
exploding gases
piston forced downward

d)
exhaust gases
exhaust valve
piston rises

INFO BIT

Many oil wells also contain natural gas. It is often cheaper for companies to burn this natural gas (flaring off) at the wellhead than to collect it. This is a horrendous waste of our energy resources.

that even if all the corn, wheat, and sugar cane currently grown were converted to ethanol, it would supply only about 6% of the world's present needs.

Diesel Fuel Because diesel engines rely on compression to ignite the fuel mixture, the best fuel for a diesel engine has a high proportion of straight-chain hydrocarbons. In fact, diesel fuels are rated on a scale that is the converse of the octane rating scale. Diesel engines tend to give higher fuel economy, but they also produce soot particles that are sufficiently small to enter our lungs, where they may cause cancer. As a result of these concerns, fuel chemists and engine designers are trying to find ways to reduce the particulate matter from diesel engines.

Natural Gas Methane is the main component of natural gas. Methane can be liquified only under low temperature and high pressure, so natural gas is best used as a piped energy source for electrical power plants and home use. Since combustion of natural gas produces carbon dioxide and water, natural gas is one of the cleanest burning hydrocarbon fuels. Carbon dioxide is nevertheless a greenhouse gas.

Two of the minor components of natural gas, propane and butane, are also used as fuels. Propane, commonly known as bottled gas, is used in recreational vehicles and gas barbecues. Since propane and butane are easy to compress and store, they are also used for domestic purposes, such as pocket lighters.

Fuel Oil The higher-boiling fraction of crude oil used for home and commercial heating is called fuel oil. The cheaper grades of fuel oil contain significant amounts of sulfur-containing molecules, which are a major contributor to acid rain.

FIGURE 11.24 The fuel oil is the most convenient and economical fuel for home heating in many areas not served by natural gas.

A Way of Life Under Attack

Decision-Making Skills

▶ Defining the Issue

▶ Developing Assessment Criteria

▶ Researching the Issue

▶ Analyzing Data and Information

▶ Proposing a Course of Action

▶ Justifying the Course of Action

▶ Communicating Your Proposal

BACKGROUND INFORMATION

The Gwich'in people are the most northern of all Native Peoples in North America, with some 15 communities spread across Alaska, the Yukon, and the Northwest Territories. For thousands of years, Gwich'in ancestors have relied on caribou for food, tools, and clothing. Beyond this, the caribou are considered spirits that offer guidance and in return, require respect. The caribou herd the Gwich'in people rely on, known as the Porcupine Herd, are now in potential danger, and the issues surrounding this cross international borders, involving the American and Canadian governments, and the future of the Gwich'in people.

The Arctic National Wildlife Refuge was set up in Alaska to protect the environment of the untouched Arctic. The Refuge is part of the migration route of the Porcupine Herd, which does not respect international borders. In 1988, for the first time in a hundred years, the Gwich'in People met and then organized the "Gwich'in Steering Committee" and elected leaders to lobby the American and Canadian governments to stop oil exploration in the Refuge. They had been successful in keeping out the oil companies until now. A new American government under President George W. Bush wants to open up the Refuge to oil and gas exploration. A Gwich'in leader, who lives on the Canadian side in Fort McPherson, knows the power of the oil companies. If they want to open up the Refuge, however they will not open it without a fight.

Oil experts in the United States say that the development of the Refuge will be so slight that the environment and the Porcupine Herd will be hardly touched. New technologies will allow the oil companies to explore, drill, and remove the oil and gas with very minimal impact. In one scenario, the oil companies extract the oil and gas only during the winter on the frozen Tundra. By the spring, when the caribou migrate, all the equipment would be removed. Due to a looming energy shortage for hundreds of millions of people in the United States, the President and other members of the government say the American economic future is far too important to let the Refuge go unexplored. Environmental groups along with Gwich'in leaders on both sides of the border will continue to fight to save the Gwich'in way of life.

Analyzing the Issue

1. Identify the issue described in the text.

2. Use electronic and print resources to research the history and culture of the Gwich'in people. Summarize how their history and culture rely on the environment.

3. Identify criteria that in your opinion could direct the decision-making of oil company executives in this instance. Justify your choice for each criterion.

4. Examine the two points of view described in the text. Write a position paper to address whether preservation of a traditional way of life should outweigh any decision to proceed with research for new sources of energy.

5. Propose a compromise position that might satisfy both the oil companies and the Gwich'in people. Explain why you feel each side will accept your compromise.

Section 11.3 Review

Understanding Concepts

1. Describe in your own words how fossil fuels are formed.

2. Describe the process of cracking, and explain why it is carried out in the absence of air.

3. Identify what physical characteristic of hydrocarbons is used to fractionate petroleum during refining. Explain how fractionation is carried out.

Applying Inquiry/ Communication Skills

4. Figure 11.25 shows the carbon dioxide emissions of some of the world's countries in 1995.
   a) Write two or three sentences describing any patterns you see in this illustration.
   b) In 1995, North America had a population of approximately 302 million people. China had a population of approximately 1244 million people. Does this new information change the interpretation you made in part a)? Why or why not?

5. Explain why branched-chain molecules make better fuels.

6. Some experts believe that the tar sands are not as economically important as petroleum deposits. Explain why it is more expensive to extract fuel from the tar sands than from petroleum deposits.

Making Connections

7. Both natural gas and coal can be used as a fuel in a manufacturing plant. To use natural gas, the manufacturing plant must transport it from the well to the plant, which requires many kilometres of pipelines that pass through environmentally sensitive areas. To use coal, miners must work underground in sometimes-lethal conditions, and the coal must be transported the same distance as the natural gas, but by truck or rail. If you were a consultant, which fuel source would you recommend? Explain your reasons why.

8. Some scientists believe that we have already found most of the world's fossil fuel reserves. Do you agree or disagree with this statement? Write a persuasive report that supports your position.

9. Research and describe an alternate source of energy to relieve the demand on the current non-renewable sources of energy.

10. Identify the source of hydrocarbons that you think is most important to our society: petroleum, natural gas, or coal. Explain your choice.

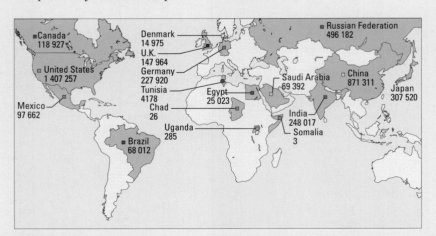

FIGURE 11.25 Carbon dioxide emissions, in thousands of metric tonnes (1995)

Investigation 1 (Section 11.2)

Inquiry Skills

	Initiating and Planning
▶	Applying Technical Skills
▶	Using Tools, Materials, and Equipment
▶	Conducting and Recording
▶	Analyzing and Interpreting
▶	Concluding and Communicating

Comparing the Energy Content of Foods

Problem

Each of us requires between about 8400 kJ and 12 500 kJ each day, depending on the activity level and the size of the person. Since the chemical processes in our bodies obey the law of conservation of energy, any energy that you do not convert to heat and kinetic energy by physical activity or other body processes must still be accounted for. If you conserve more energy than you use, the excess energy is converted to chemical energy in the bonds of fat molecules.

In this investigation, you will use a coffee can calorimeter to measure the energy content of different foods. You will then compare your results to the content given by the manufacturer of each item.

Materials

- food items (e.g., marshmallows, potato chips, pasta, dried bread, dried white beans)
- 100-mL beaker
- 50-mL or 100-mL graduated cylinder
- centigram balance
- mounting needle
- retort stand
- ring clamp
- small piece of cork
- thermometer or graphing calculator with temperature probe
- tweezers
- gas burner

> **CAUTION: Wear safety glasses. Handle the calorimeter with care. Take extreme caution in burning the samples.**
>
> **At the end of the investigation, wet the burnt samples under the water tap before discarding them.**
>
> **Always wash your hands after every investigation.**

Procedure

1. Weigh an empty 100-mL beaker. Fill the beaker with 50.0 mL of water using the graduated cylinder, and record its temperature to the nearest 0.2°C.

2. Set up the retort stand. Clamp the beaker to it approximately half way up the stand.

3. Accurately weigh a small piece of one sample (between 2 g and 3 g) and fix it to one end of the needle. Attach the other end of the needle onto the cork.

4. Burn the sample on a Bunsen burner until it catches fire. Immediately hold the burning sample under the beaker of water, with the top of the flame as close to the bottom of the beaker as possible. Stir the water.

5. When the temperature of the water has risen by about 20°C, extinguish the sample and accurately record the highest temperature that was reached.

6. Cool the unburned food sample and weigh it.

7. Repeat the procedure with the other samples. Record all qualitative observations and present your quantitative data in a tabular form.

Analyzing and Interpreting

1. Explain why the mass of the beaker is required.

2. Describe how you would determine the heat absorbed by the water?

3. Describe how you would determine the heat absorbed by the glass calorimeter. The heat capacity of glass is $0.84 \text{ J·g}^{-1} \cdot {}^{\circ}\text{C}^{-1}$.

4. How would you calculate the energy content of the sample in J·g^{-1} and kcal·g^{-1}?

Concluding and Communicating

5. Compare the energy content of each sample. Did you observe a trend?

6. Comment on your results and explain any differences.

Extending

7. The systematic errors in such an investigation can be rather large. Evaluate the procedure, identify sources of errors and weaknesses in the procedure, and suggest ways in which the method can be improved.

Investigation 2 (Section 11.2)

Inquiry Skills

Initiating and Planning

▶   Applying Technical Skills

▶   Using Tools, Materials, and Equipment

▶   Conducting and Recording

▶   Analyzing and Interpreting

▶   Concluding and Communicating

Heat of Combustion of Alcohols

Problem

Our energy demands require that any source of energy must be available in large quantities and be an efficient source of energy. The purpose of this investigation is to determine the heat change that occurs during combustion of several alcohols, and to identify which is the most efficient fuel.

Materials

- safety goggles
- ethanol
- methanol
- 1-butanol
- 1-propanol
- pipette
- 50-mL or 100-mL graduated cylinder
- bench mat
- centigram balance
- metal alcohol lamp in safety stand
- thermometer or graphing calculator with temperature probe
- tweezers

> **CAUTION: All alcohols are flammable and poisonous. Transfer the liquids only in the fume hood.**
>
> **Stopper all alcohol containers when not in use and keep them away from any flame.**
>
> **Always wash your hands after every investigation.**

Procedure

1. Calculate the percent mass of carbon and hydrogen in each of the alcohols in the Materials list: methanol (CH_3OH), ethanol (CH_3CH_2OH), 1-propanol ($CH_3CH_2CH_2OH$), and 1-butanol, ($CH_3CH_2CH_2CH_2OH$).

2. Predict which alcohol will produce the most energy per gram.

3. Weigh a dry 100-mL beaker. On a bench mat, place an alcohol lamp on a retort stand. Clamp the beaker so that the bottom of the beaker is approximately 2 cm from the top of the wick.

4. Measure 50.0 mL of water using the measuring cylinder, transfer water to the beaker and measure its temperature to the nearest 0.2°C.

5. Use a pipette to half-fill the alcohol lamp with an alcohol. Determine its mass to at least two decimal places.

6. Light the spirit lamp and immediately place it under the beaker. Use the pair of tweezers to adjust the height of the wick so that the flame is about 1 cm high.

7. Gently stir the water. When the temperature of the water rises about 20°C, extinguish the flame and record accurately the highest temperature reached.

8. Let the spirit lamp cool. Weigh the lamp and its contents to determine the mass of alcohol burned.

9. Record all qualitative observations and present your quantitative data in a tabular form.

10. Repeat the procedure with another alcohol.

Analyzing and Interpreting

1. The heat released on combustion of each alcohol is used to raise the temperature of the water and the calorimeter. Write balanced chemical equations for the complete combustion of the four alcohols.

2. Determine the heat absorbed by the glass calorimeter. The heat capacity of glass is 0.84 $J \cdot g^{-1} \cdot °C$.

3. Determine the heat absorbed by the water.

4. Calculate the heat change for each alcohol in $J \cdot mol^{-1}$ and $J \cdot g^{-1}$. Write thermochemical equations for the combustion of each alcohol using these values.

Concluding and Communicating

5. Draw a graph of heat produced ($kJ \cdot mol^{-1}$) versus molar mass of the alcohol. Comment on your results.

6. Compare the number of atoms in each pair of alcohols: methanol/ethanol, ethanol/1-propanol, and 1-propanol/1-butanol. Relate this information to your graph.

Extending

7. Design an experiment to prove that water is one of the products of combustion of alcohol.

8. Research the advantages and disadvantages of methanol as a fuel for automobilies. Present your research using presentation software or a poster.

CHAPTER SUMMARY

Key Terms

alkylation
bond energy
calorimeter
calorimetry
catalytic cracking
coal
combustion
diesel fuel

endothermic reaction
energy
exothermic reaction
fractionation
fuel oil
gasoline
heat
heat capacity

heat change
joule
law of conservation of
  energy
molar heat capacity
methane hydrate
natural gas
octane number

oil shale
petroleum
petroleum refining
specific heat
tar sand
temperature
thermochemistry
thermochemical equation

Key Equation

$Q = mc\Delta T$

Essential Understandings

■ A thermochemical equation describes both a chemical reaction and its heat change.

■ The heat change in a chemical reaction is measured experimentally using a calorimeter.

■ Heat change can be measured quantitatively using the equation $Q = mc\Delta T$.

■ A chemical reaction is exothermic when the bonds of the reactants contain less energy than the bonds of the products. An exothermic reaction releases energy.

■ A chemical reaction is endothermic when the bonds of the reactants contain more energy than the bonds of the products. An endothermic reaction requires the addition of energy.

■ Fossil fuels were formed millions of years ago from the decomposed remains of living organisms, which were buried and subjected to extreme heat and pressure.

■ Fossil fuels occur as deposits of coal, natural gas, and petroleum. Petroleum deposits can be found as liquid reserves under a rock cap, or in tar sand and oil shale.

■ Fractional distillation of petroleum separates components of crude oil, according to their boiling points, to produce many important substances such as gasoline, jet fuel, kerosene, candle wax, and asphalt.

Consolidate Your Understanding

1. Use the concept of bond energy to explain what happens in an endothermic chemical reaction and in an exothermic chemical reaction.

2. Construct a concept map that starts with the words "bond energy."

3. You used the equation $Q = mc\Delta T$ in this chapter. Write an explanation for this equation using words. Explain the significance of this formula, and describe how formulas communicate information in general. Reflect on why formulas are used for scientific communication instead of written descriptions.

4. Make a chart summarizing the advantages and disadvantages to society if fossil fuel resources were to be depleted. Consider social, environmental, economic and technological impacts.

CHAPTER 11 REVIEW

Understanding Concepts

1. Identify all the reactions that are endothermic:
   I) $H_2O(s) \rightarrow H_2O(l)$
   II) $CO_2(g) \rightarrow CO_2(s)$
   III) $N_2(g) \rightarrow 2\ N(g)$

   a) I only
   b) II only
   c) I and II only
   d) I and III only

2. Identify the energy released by the condensation of 4.50 g of water. The molar heat of vaporization of water is 40.7 kJ·mol^{-1}.
   a) 0.25 kJ
   b) 10.2 kJ
   c) 42.0 kJ
   d) 100. kJ

3. The specific heat of metallic lead is 0.129 J·g^{-1}·°C^{-1}. If 74.0 J of heat is added to a 125-g sample of lead at 23.0°C, identify the final temperature of the lead.
   a) 18.4°C
   b) 26.4°C
   c) 27.6°C
   d) 28.4°C

4. One hundred millilitres of 0.050 mol·L^{-1} HCl(aq) is mixed with 100 mL of 0.050 mol·L^{-1} NaOH(aq) in a Styrofoam cup. The temperature increases by 3.3°C. Assume that the specific heat of the mixture is 4.2 J·g^{-1}·°C^{-1}. Identify the change in heat, Q, of this reaction:
   a) 2.77 kJ
   b) 0.069 kJ
   c) 0.138 kJ
   d) 0.38 kJ

5. The molar heat of combustion of methane, CH_4, is -890 kJ. Identify the correct thermochemical equation for this reaction:
   a) $C(g) + 4\ H(g) + 890\ kJ \rightarrow CH_4(g)$
   b) $C(s) + 2\ H_2(g) + 890\ kJ \rightarrow CH_4(g)$
   c) $CH_4(g) + \frac{3}{2}\ O_2(g) + 890\ kJ \rightarrow CO(g) + 2\ H_2O(l)$
   d) $CH_4(g) + 2\ O_2(g) \rightarrow CO_2(g) + 2\ H_2O(l) + 890\ kJ$

6. Define the law of conservation of energy in your own words.

7. Using the example of combustion of methane gas in oxygen, explain how chemical reactions follow the law of conservation of energy.

8. Define exothermic and endothermic. Write a chemical equation for an example of each of these types of reactions.

9. Identify whether the following reactions are exothermic or endothermic.
   a) combustion of methane:

   $CH_4(g) + 2\ O_2(g) \rightarrow CO_2(g) + 2\ H_2O(l) \qquad Q = -890\ kJ$

   b) decomposition of hydrogen chloride:

   $2\ HCl(g) \rightarrow H_2(g) + Cl_2(g) \qquad Q = +185\ kJ$

   c) combustion of ammonia:

   $4\ NH_3(g) + 5\ O_2(g) \rightarrow 4\ NO(g) + 6\ H_2O(l) \qquad Q = -1169\ kJ$

10. State whether the following equations are endothermic or exothermic:
    a) $C_2H_5OH(l) + 3\ O_2(g) \rightarrow 2\ CO_2(g) + 3\ H_2O(l) + 1367\ kJ$
    b) $H_2O(l) \rightarrow H^+(aq) + OH^-(aq) - 56.2\ kJ$
    c) $H_2O(s) + 6.01\ kJ \rightarrow H_2O(l)$
    d) $CS_2(l) + 3\ O_2 \rightarrow CO_2(g) + 2\ SO_2(g) + 105\ kJ$

11. Identify whether the melting of ice is an endothermic reaction or an exothermic reaction. Explain why.

12. Explain why tabulated bond energies are usually average values.

13. Define the term "calorimetry" in your own words.

14. Describe how a simple calorimeter operates.

15. Explain why an experimenter must determine the heat capacity of his or her own calorimeter to use in calculations, rather than using the value obtained on another calorimeter.

16. Explain the difference between specific heat and heat capacity.

17. Explain why burns from steam are more severe than burns from boiling water.

18. Which food will warm you up fastest when you are cold, a bowl of hot soup or hot buttered toast? Explain why.

19. Define the following terms in your own words:
    a) fractionation
    b) cracking
    c) pyrolysis
    d) reforming
    e) petroleum refining

20. Describe the process of fractionation and its significance.

21. Draw a diagram illustrating the refinement of petroleum to obtain gasoline.

22. When 1.5×10^3 J of heat energy is absorbed by a beaker of water, its temperature rises by 3.1°C. Calculate the heat capacity of the beaker of water.

23. A 75-g sample of a viscous liquid requires 850 J to increase its temperature from 25.0°C to 30.0°C. Calculate the specific heat of the liquid.

24. The molar heat capacity of liquid sodium is 28.4 J·K^{-1}·mol^{-1}. Calculate the heat required to raise the temperature of 5.67 g liquid sodium by 3.75 K.

25. A 1.89-g sample of solid benzoic acid, C_6H_5COOH, was placed in a bomb calorimeter in the presence of excess oxygen. The calorimeter contained 18.94 kg of water. Complete combustion of the acid raised the temperature of the water 0.076°C. Calculate the heat of combustion for 1 mol of benzoic acid.

26. A copper flame calorimeter of mass 305 g contains 255 g of water. When 1.01 g of 1-propanol, $CH_3CH_2CH_2OH$, is burned in the calorimeter, the calorimeter and contents increase in temperature by 28.8°C. Calculate the molar heat change of this reaction given the specific heat of copper is 0.385 $J \cdot g^{-1} \cdot °C^{-1}$.

Applying Inquiry/ Communication Skills

27. Design an investigation to determine the value for the heat change that occurs during combustion of ethanol. Prepare a list of chemicals and equipment you will require and outline the experiment in detail. Describe how you would collect data to meet the objectives of the investigation.

28. Design a calorimeter. Choose your materials carefully so that you maximize its efficiency. Make a list of the components and explain why you chose each one.

29. When hydrocarbons are heated to high temperatures in the absence of air, they often decompose into related compounds of similar properties. Design a procedure that can be used to separate the mixtures into pure substances.

30. You are asked to determine the heat change of the endothermic reaction that occurs when a small amount of ammonium nitrate is added to 100 mL of water. Outline the steps you would take to carry out this experiment, and then describe the calculations you would need to make.

31. From the following data, calculate the molar heat of combustion of 3-pentanone, $CH_3CH_2COCH_2CH_3$:

mass of 3-pentanone burned	1.00 g
mass of water in calorimeter	500. g
initial temperature of water	25.0°C
final temperature of water	42.1°C

32. You are asked to determine the heat change that occurs when a piece of calcium metal reacts with water to form calcium hydroxide and hydrogen gas. Outline the steps you would take in the lab to carry out this experiment.

33. Make a model of a two-cylinder gasoline engine. Use this model to demonstrate and explain how a two-cylinder engine operates.

34. Write a balanced chemical equation for the combustion of $C_9H_{20}(l)$.

35. One mole of ethyne gas $HC{\equiv}CH$ (commonly called acetylene) undergoes complete combustion in the presence of oxygen gas to produce carbon dioxide gas, water, and 1300 kJ of energy. Write a thermochemical equation for the reaction.

36. When 5.16 kJ of heat is added to 167 g of gaseous ammonia at 45.0°C, the temperature of the gas rises to 60.0°C. Draw a visual organizer such as a flowchart to summarize the process that occurs.

37. From the data in the question above, determine:
a) the specific heat of $NH_3(g)$
b) the molar heat capacity of $NH_3(g)$

Making Connections

38. A magazine advertisement claims that a new method of weight loss requires no dieting or exercise. Discuss the validity of this claim in relation to the law of conservation of energy.

39. Discuss the following question: As a society, should we allow our non-renewable hydrocarbon reserves to be used as fuel or should we save them for use as petrochemicals?

40. Many areas of the world use wood as a primary fuel source. This has led to depletion of forests, which is now causing erosion and desert formation. Use electronic and print sources to find out where this problem is occurring. Write a report suggesting what possible alternative fuels or technologies might be used to provide energy to these populations.

41. Write a paper from the perspective of a scientist who is responding to the popular idea that technology can solve the energy crisis.

42. From your home electricity bill, estimate how much electric energy your household uses in 1 year. Assume that your electricity is generated from coal. Determine how much coal is required to serve your electrical consumption. Assuming your requirements are average, estimate the amount of fuel required by your entire city or town. Suggest how this amount might be reduced.

43. Write an essay describing how our lifestyle in Canada would change if we were unable to use large amounts of energy such as gasoline and electricity. Speculate on whether or not we could reduce our energy consumption without changing our standard of living.

44. A nutritional chart states that the average apple supplies 418 kJ. Discuss whether this information is sufficiently specific to use in designing a diet. List all the factors that must be considered by someone designing a nutritional diet to maintain, lose weight, or gain weight.

After Class

You've seen how you can do a great deal of career exploration and preparation on your own—but that's only the beginning. Eventually, you will go out into the world and that involves communicating with others about who you are and what you want to do. It's not something that comes easily to most of us, but, like anything else, it's something you can practise and improve.

Laboratory Assistant

Summer

Ramblewood Environmental Consultants Ltd. requires three general duty laboratory assistants for summer field work.

Duties include assisting with obtaining soil and water samples, recording on-site observations, transporting and storing samples, and performing chemical assays in a laboratory setting. Experience with titration, measuring, operating a balance, and using a spectrophotometer is essential. Other training will be provided.

Must be available to work some weekends.

Successful applicants will be familiar with government workplace hazardous materials symbols (WHMIS) and safe practices in a laboratory. A valid St. John's Ambulance First Aid Certificate would be an asset.

Interested applicants are invited to apply in writing to:

Human Resources,
Ramblewood Environmental Consultants Ltd.,
10 Dodge Street North,
Anytown, Ontario N2Z 3K2
email: humanresources@ramblewood.ca
1-888-555-5678 ext 1234

The Cover Letter

When you see "apply in writing," it means you will be judged by what you put into the envelope or include with your email. It's as if your letter and résumé are going to the job interview in your place. If you think of your résumé as what you'd like to say in that interview, your letter is the smile and handshake making that important first impression.

1. Write a cover letter as if you were applying for the job listed here. Your letter should be no more than one page long. When you have finished your first draft of this letter, check it against these criteria:
   - Have you included your complete address, including a phone number where you can be reached during business hours? (Hint: Include this in your letter because it may be filed separately from your résumé.)
   - Have you included the company's address? (Hint: Check the spelling. If you have someone's name to use, be sure it's correct.)
   - Is it easy to see the date and the position you are applying for? (Hint: Under the date or before the body of your letter begins, put "Re: Laboratory Assistant Position" in boldface or underlined. This makes it easy for the person opening your letter to pass it to the right person.)
   - Have you stated, in your first paragraph, the position you are applying for and how you found out about it? Did you mention that you have attached your résumé?

- Did you include a brief second paragraph about yourself and why you would be a good candidate for this position? (Hint: Look at the requirements in the ad. Your letter can repeat these. For example, state "I am familiar with ...")
- Did you finish with a polite offer to supply more information upon request?
- Did you sign the letter? (Hint: Make sure you have the correct spelling of your full name somewhere in the letter even if you do have a clear, legible signature.)

2. If you wish, rewrite this letter as an email. It will be essentially the same, except that you would attach the file containing your résumé. If you have never done this before, practise by emailing your résumé to a friend. (Hint: Keep your résumé plain and simple if you are going to email it. Do not use fancy fonts or unusual formatting. These may not come out as intended on someone else's computer.)

The Cold Call

A cold call is when you are phoning someone for the first time. This person has no idea who you are or what you want. You don't know who you will be talking with or whether that person will be interested in what you have to say. It's stressful and difficult, but it's something you'll need to do at some point. A little practice now will go a long way.

Ramblewood Environmental Consultants Ltd. has asked for applications in writing. You have some questions about the job that affect whether or not you apply, so you decide

FIGURE 1 Soil scientist at work

to call the number provided and ask for more information. Most classified ads do not include phone numbers, but you can usually find business numbers in the phone book or on-line. Be aware: some ads state "no phone calls please." Make sure you follow the instructions in the ad.

3. Working with a partner, role-play a cold call to find out about the starting date for the advertised job.

Looking Outward

Practise your interview skills as well. You need to be comfortable talking about your skills and qualifications with a prospective employer. Communicating well is a vital part of any career, but it's especially important in science, where people tend to work in groups that share complex information.

Survival Kit

Background Information

Petroleum-based products have been widely available only since the 1950s, when the first plastic was invented. Many different kinds of plastics can be produced, each with properties that make them suitable for specific uses. Synthetic polymers can also be formed into just about any shape and in any colour we want. Petrochemical polymers are also more durable than natural polymers.

Unfortunately, using plastics and other petrochemicals also has negative consequences. Petroleum is a nonrenewable resource, so it is unwise to assume it will always be there. The durability of plastics means that many plastic products outlast their intended use. Toys, clothing, plastic packaging—these petrochemical products are often discarded after no more than a year of use, but they will not degrade for many years to come.

One solution is to recycle plastics. However, the different types of plastic must be sorted and recycled separately, which is expensive. Unsorted plastic can be melted to produce a mixed plastic product, but this has limited use. Finally, recycling requires that people change long-term habits, which can be a major stumbling block.

There is another solution to the problem of petrochemical waste. If manufacturers of these products took responsibility for their products after they reach the consumer, then each type of plastic would be returned directly to a facility that uses it. The cost of recovering and recycling the plastics would also be carried by the manufacturer.

SCENARIO

You are a member of the research department in a company that is planning to produce low-cost emergency survival kits for use in the home during power outages. One of the founding principles of this company is "cradle to grave" stewardship. This means that the company considers all social, environmental, and cost factors related to their products. This includes being responsible for disposing of the product after the consumer no longer needs it.

Your department has been asked to assess the suitability of some materials that might be used to produce the utility cords and candles that are to be in the survival kit. The utility cord is to be made from a synthetic polymer and must be flexible, lightweight, and durable. The candle is to be made from hydrocarbon wax and is to be used in a metal can to provide emergency heat and light.

You must prepare a brief summarizing the different products available. Your brief must include:

- the origin of the raw materials for the utility cords and candles
- the procedure and results of testing two different synthetic polymers used in making utility cords
- the procedures and results of testing two different waxes made from hydrocarbons
- a comparison chart summarizing the advantages and disadvantages of the materials tested
- disposal options for the materials in the utility cords and candles

Part A: Information on the Petrochemical Industry

1. Use electronic resources, print resources, and the information you have learned from this unit to summarize how fractionation of petroleum provides the hydrocarbon molecules needed to produce both synthetic polymers and hydrocarbon waxes.

2. Identify the technologies needed for fractional distillation and for manufacturing synthetic polymers and hydrocarbon waxes. Describe the environmental and social advantages and disadvantages associated with these technologies.

3. Create a flowchart showing all the products that can be obtained from crude oil. Indicate the percent of crude oil that is used for plastic production on your chart.

4. Write a summary of all the factors related to waste disposal of petrochemical products.

Part B: Testing Properties of Products

5. From your research, select two types of synthetic polymers that would be suitable for making a utility cord. Obtain small strips of each polymer. Outline a procedure to test the material for:
   a) flammability
   b) density

   Only conduct the tests after your teacher approves of your procedure. Make a note of any safety precautions you will take in your procedure.

6. Obtain two candles that appear to be made from different types of wax. Design a procedure to test each for:

a) hardness
b) heat of combustion in $J \cdot g^{-1}$
c) rate of burning in $g \cdot s^{-1}$

Only conduct the tests after your teacher approves of your procedure. Note of any safety precautions you will take in your procedure.

Part C: Analyzing the Results

7. Create a comparison chart that clearly outlines the advantages and disadvantages of each type of polymer and each type of candle wax.

8. Write a summary chart outlining factors to consider regarding the disposal of the materials in the utility cords and the candles. Suggest a variety of disposal options.

Part D: Communicating Your Results

9. Prepare a brief to the managers of the company summarizing the results of your research. Your brief should include:

   a) a graphical summary of the origin and production process of the products tested
   b) the procedures used in testing the products, including possible sources of experimental error
   c) a comparison chart for both utility cords and candles summarizing your testing procedures
   d) a chart that visually displays the advantages and disadvantages of various methods of disposing of the products when they are no longer needed
   e) your recommendations for the type of petrochemical to be used in the utility cords and the candles that will be in the survival kit, including references to any supporting evidence for your choices.

Understanding Concepts

1. Identify the correct formula for 3-methylheptane.
   a) $CH_3CH_2CH_2CH_2CH_2CH_2CH_3$
   b) $CH_3CH_2CH(CH_3)CH_2CH_2CH_2CH_3$
   c) $CH_3CH_2CH_2CH(CH_3)CH_2CH_2CH_3$
   d) $CH_3CH_2C(CH_3)_2CH_2CH_2CH_3$

2. Identify in which type of compound geometric isomers are usually found:
   a) alkanes
   b) alkenes
   c) alkynes
   d) benzene

3. Identify which is a structural isomer of ethanol:
   a) CH_3CHO
   b) CH_3OH
   c) CH_3OCH_3
   d) CH_3CH_3

4. Identify which organic products are formed when an alkene is hydrated:
   a) acid
   b) alkyne
   c) alkane
   d) alcohol

5. Identify which statement is true for the reaction:
   $NaCl(s) \rightarrow NaCl(l)$
   a) The reaction is endothermic, and the energy change is positive.
   b) The reaction is endothermic, and the energy change is negative.
   c) The reaction is exothermic, and the energy change is positive.
   d) The reaction is exothermic, and the energy change is negative.

6. Given the heats of combustion for diamond (-395.4 kJ) and graphite (-393.5 kJ), which are both composed of pure carbon, identify which statement is true.
   a) The combustion reactions are endothermic.
   b) The combustion reactions are exothermic.
   c) The combustion reactions depend on the temperature.
   d) There is insufficient information to determine the type of combustion reactions.

7. The bond energies for the halogens F_2, Cl_2, Br_2, and I_2 are 153 kJ, 243 kJ, 193 kJ, and 151 kJ respectively. Identify which compound has the strongest bond:
   a) F_2
   b) Cl_2
   c) Br_2
   d) I_2

8. Identify which is an accurate definition of specific heat:
   a) the heat required to raise the temperature of 1 g of a substance by 1°C
   b) the heat required to raise the temperature of 1 mol of a substance by 1°C
   c) the heat required to raise the temperature of a substance by 1°C
   d) the heat required to raise the temperature of 1 L of a substance by 1°C

9. Hexane (C_6H_{14}) is burned in excess oxygen gas. Identify the correct equation for the complete combustion of hexane:
   a) $C_6H_{14} + {}^{19}\!/_2\,O_2 \rightarrow 6\ CO_2 + 7\ H_2O$
   b) $C_6H_{14} + 19\ O_2 \rightarrow 6\ CO_2 + 7\ H_2O$
   c) $C_6H_{14} + {}^{13}\!/_2\,O_2 \rightarrow 6\ CO + 7\ H_2O$
   d) $C_6H_{14} + 13\ O_2 \rightarrow 6\ CO + 7\ H_2O$

10. Identify which compound is likely to be produced from cracking $C_{16}H_{34}$:
    a) ethyne
    b) octane
    c) carbon dioxide
    d) ethanol

11. Explain the importance of Friedrich Wöhler's discovery of urea in 1828 and how it influenced the development of organic chemistry.

12. Identify the major sources of organic compounds.

13. State at least two general characteristics associated with organic compounds.

14. Describe the features of an organic molecule that influence its chemical behaviour.

15. Describe how aromatic compounds differ from aliphatic hydrocarbons.

16. Explain briefly the difference between alkanes, alkenes, and alkynes.

17. State whether C_3H_8 is an alkane, an alkene, or an alkyne. Explain your answer.

18. Define the term "isomer" in your own words. Give an example.

19. Explain the difference between each of the following:
    a) constitutional (structural) isomers and geometric isomers
    b) addition reactions and substitution reactions
    c) saturated and unsaturated compounds

20. Using a diagram, illustrate the difference in structural formula between a straight-chain alkane and the cycloalkane having the same number of carbon atoms.

21. Identify the structure below that represents a compound that is different from the others.

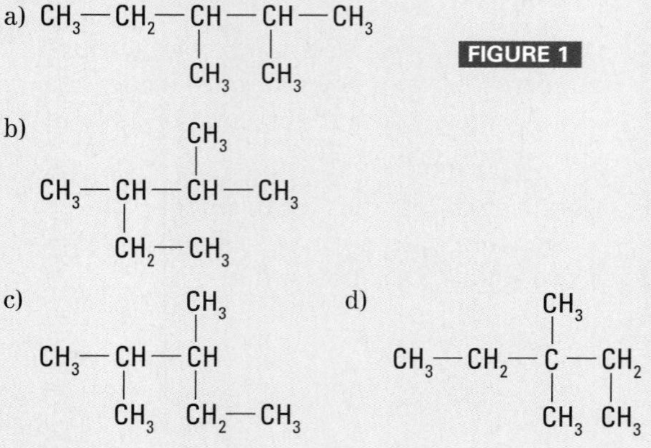

FIGURE 1

22. Identify the class or family to which each of the following compounds belongs:
    a) 3,4-dimethylcycloheptene
    b) 1,3,5-trimethylbenzene
    c) 4-decyne
    d) propylbenzene
    e) 1,2,3,4,5,6-hexamethylcyclohexane

23. Explain why the alkane series of hydrocarbons is called a homologous series.

24. Describe the term "polymerization" in your own words.

25. Explain how high density polymers differ from low density polymers.

26. Describe in your own words the difference between an exothermic reaction and an endothermic reaction.

27. Use the concept of bond energies to explain why combustion reactions are exothermic.

28. When concentrated sulfuric acid, H_2SO_4, is added in a stream to a beaker of water, the water and the beaker get hot. State whether this is an exothermic or an endothermic process. Explain your answer.

29. Identify each change of state by name, and classify each change as exothermic or endothermic:
    a) 1 mol $C_3H_8(l) \rightarrow$ 1 mol $C_3H_8(g)$
    b) 1 mol NaCl(s) + 3.88 kJ/mol $\rightarrow$ 1 mol NaCl(aq)
    c) 1 mol NaCl$(s) \rightarrow$ 1 mol NaCl(l)
    d) 1 mol Hg$(l) \rightarrow$ 1 mol Hg(s)

30. Identify which of the following exothermic reactions can be classified as combustion reactions.
    a) $CH_4(g)$ + 2 $O_2(g) \rightarrow CO_2(g)$ + 2 $H_2O(l)$
    b) $C_2H_4(g)$ + $Br_2(l) \rightarrow C_2H_4Br_2(l)$
    c) $CH_3CH_2OH(l)$ + 3 $O_2(g) \rightarrow$ 2 $CO_2(g)$ + 3 $H_2O(l)$

31. Calculate the heat of combustion per gram of cooking oil if burning 20 g of the oil changes the temperature of 250 mL of water from 20°C to 100°C.

32. A 60-g mass of gasoline undergoes combustion. Estimate the mass of carbon and carbon monoxide that is produced when 1% of the mass is converted to carbon particles and 5% is converted to carbon monoxide. If C_8H_{18} is the average molecular formula of the components of gasoline, estimate the amount (in moles) that undergoes combustion.

33. Distinguish between specific heat, heat capacity, and molar heat capacity.

34. The mining town of Flin Flon, Manitoba, is at approximately the same latitude (54°) as the coastal community of Prince Rupert, British Columbia, and yet Prince Rupert has a far milder climate than Flin Flon. Explain this phenomenon using your knowledge of heat capacities.

35. Explain why it is important to give the physical state of a substance in a thermochemical reaction.

36. Explain why methanol produces less energy per mole (726 kJ) than methane (890 kJ), although it contains the same number of carbon and hydrogen atoms per molecule.

37. Calculate the molar heat capacity of ethanol, $C_2H_5OH(l)$. The specific heat of ethanol is 2.46 $J \cdot g^{-1} \cdot {}^\circ C^{-1}$.

38. The molar heat capacity of liquid sodium is 28.4 $J \cdot mol^{-1} \cdot K^{-1}$. Calculate how much heat is required to raise the temperature of 5.67 g of liquid sodium by 3.75 K.

39. Determine the heat required to raise the temperature of 100 g of water from 298.0 K to 373.0 K.

40. 10.5 g iron at 25.0°C absorbs 128 J of heat. Determine the final temperature of the metal given that the specific heat of iron is 0.449 $J \cdot g^{-1} \cdot {}^\circ C^{-1}$.

41. Identify the experimental errors that can be expected in a calorimetric experiment.

42. Name four processes used in the petroleum industry to improve the amount and quality of gasoline produced. Give an example of a reaction that might occur in each process.

43. Describe two ways in which the octane rating of gasoline can be increased.

44. Describe what changes cracking and hydrogenation make in the products obtained from petroleum.

45. Describe why it is possible to use fractional distillation to separate hydrocarbons in petroleum.

46. Discuss what might happen to a hydrocarbon with the formula $C_{16}H_{34}$ when it is cracked.

47. Describe how the cracking process affects the efficiencies of gasoline fuels.

Applying Inquiry/ Communication Skills

48. Design an experiment to investigate the difference between saturated and unsaturated fats in human diets.

49. Design an experiment that will distinguish between the differences in the chemical properties of alkenes and alkanes by reacting cyclohexane and cyclohexene with bromine water or alkaline potassium permanganate.

50. You are asked to determine the endothermic heat of reaction when some ammonium chloride is dissolved in water. Outline the steps you would take to carry out this experiment, and then describe the calculations you would need to make.

51. The following data was obtained from an experiment in which a heated mass of aluminum was added to water in a calorimeter. Calculate the specific heat of aluminum.

mass of water in the calorimeter	1000. g
initial temperature of water in the calorimeter	22.4°C
mass of aluminum sample	125.25 g
temperature of boiling water bath and aluminum	99.3°C
final temperature of water	24.4°C

52. The following data was obtained from an experiment in which a heated mass of copper was added to water in a calorimeter. Calculate the specific heat of copper.

mass of water in the calorimeter	500. g
initial temperature of water in the calorimeter	20.0°C
mass of copper sample	482.0 g
temperature of boiling water bath and copper	98.8°C
final temperature of water	26.2°C

53. Methane and ethyne (acetylene) are both hydrocarbons that are used as fuels, but for different situations. Design a procedure to compare the characteristics of these two compounds when they are burned. Write the chemical equations involved. Discuss why the results would differ.

54. Everyone knows that the flame of a candle releases energy. Design an experiment to determine how much energy a candle releases. Include a data sheet on which you could enter the data collected when performing your procedure.

55. Write the procedure you would use to demonstrate that rubber is a polymer that can be stretched without tearing.

56. Write a procedure that uses cobalt chloride paper and limewater to identify the complete combustion of natural gas (mainly methane).

57. Give the IUPAC name for each of the following alkenes:

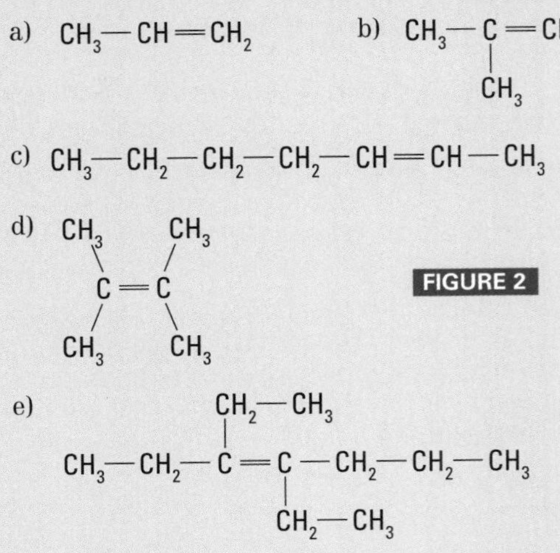

a) $CH_3-CH=CH_2$ b) $CH_3-C=CH-CH_3$ with CH_3 below

c) $CH_3-CH_2-CH_2-CH_2-CH=CH-CH_3$

d)

FIGURE 2

e)

$CH_3-CH_2-C=C-CH_2-CH_2-CH_3$ with CH_2-CH_3 above the first C and CH_2-CH_3 below it

58. Give the IUPAC name for each of the following alkynes:

a) $CH_3-C\equiv C-CH_3$

b)

$CH_3-C\equiv C-C-CH_3$ with CH_3 above and CH_3 below the fourth C

c) $CH_3-CH_2-CH-C\equiv C-CH_3$ with CH_3 below

d) $CH_3-CH-CH_2-C\equiv CH$ with CH_3 below

e) $CH_3-C-C\equiv C-C-CH_3$ with CH_3 above each and CH_2CH_3 below first, CH_3 below second

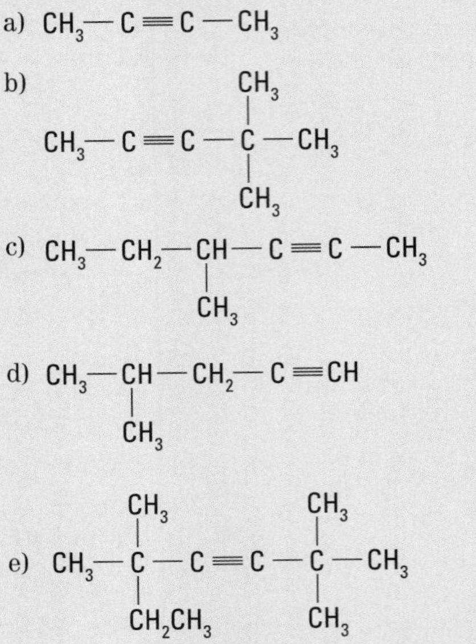

FIGURE 3

59. Write the condensed formula for each of the following alkynes:
a) 2-pentyne
b) 5-methyl-1-hexyne
c) 4,4-dimethyl-2-pentyne
d) 3,3-diethyl-1-octyne
e) 3,3-dimethyl-1-butyne

60. Draw the five structural isomers of the cycloalkane C_6H_{12}, that involve 6-, 5-, or 4-membered rings and name each isomer.

61. Draw formulas and write names for five isomers of hexane, C_6H_{14}.

62. Draw the condensed formula for each of the following:
a) 4-propylheptane
b) 3,3-diethylpentane
c) 2,2,3,3-tetramethylbutane
d) 1,3-diethylcyclopentane

63. Write an equation to show what might happen during the hydrogenation of the alkene C_8H_{16} and the alkyne C_8H_{14}.

64. Write an equation for the reaction of 1-butyne under the following conditions and name the product in each case:
a) excess hydrogen in the presence of a nickel catalyst at 25 °C
b) excess bromine in carbon tetrachloride

65. Solid calcium carbonate, of $CaCO_3$, undergoes decomposition when heated to produce solid calcium oxide and carbon dioxide gas. If 100 g of $CaCO_3$ is decomposed and requires 178 kJ of energy, write a thermochemical equation for the reaction.

66. When 2 mol of solid magnesium combine with 1 mol of oxygen gas, 2 mol of solid magnesium oxide is formed and 1204 kJ of heat is released. Write the thermochemical equation for this combustion reaction.

67. Write balanced chemical equations for complete combustion of one mole of:
   a) propanol, $CH_3CH_2CH_2OH$
   b) methylbenzene, C_7H_8
   c) propanoic acid, CH_3CH_2COOH

68. Write the chemical equations for the complete combustion of the fuels methane gas, CH_4, and methanol, CH_3OH.

69. A light has to be applied to the propane gas, C_3H_8, for it to work in a barbecue. Therefore, a student considers the burning of propane to be an endothermic process. Write a balanced chemical equation for the combustion reaction. Give a reason why energy has to be applied in the first place, and explain whether the student is correct in assuming that this is an endothermic reaction.

70. Assume that the average composition of gasoline can be represented by the formula C_8H_{18}.
   a) Write a balanced equation for the reaction of gasoline with oxygen.
   b) Calculate the mass of carbon dioxide gas produced from the combustion of 120.0 g of gasoline.

71. At 25.0°C, 15.7 g of carbon dioxide absorbs 1.2 kJ of heat. Calculate the final temperature of the gas. The molar heat capacity of CO_2 is 37.11 J·°C^{-1}·mol^{-1}.

72. Calculate the amount of heat 32.0 g of water absorbs when its temperature is changed from 25.0°C to 80.0°C.

73. A piece of silver has a heat capacity of 42.8 J·°C^{-1}. If the silver has a mass of 181 g, calculate the specific heat of silver.

74. Using the following specific heat values, calculate the molar heat capacities of copper, silver, and gold.

Cu(s)	0.3385 J·g^{-1}·°C^{-1}
Ag(s)	0.235 J·g^{-1}·°C^{-1}
Au(s)	0.129 J·g^{-1}·°C^{-1}

   Describe what you observe about these molar heat capacities and compare them to the molar heat capacity of the polyatomic gases.

75. Calculate how many kilojoules of heat are absorbed when 1.00 L of water is heated from 18°C to 85°C.

76. A copper flame calorimeter has a mass of 305 g and contains 255 g of water. When 1.01 g of propanol, $CH_3CH_2CH_2OH$, is burned in the calorimeter, the calorimeter and contents increase in temperature by 28.8°C. Calculate the heat of combustion for 1 mol of propanol. The specific heat of copper is 0.3385 J·g^{-1}·°C^{-1}.

Making Connections

77. Choosing the type of material to use when designing a product requires knowledge of the characteristics and properties of the material. Design and develop a display that describes the properties of a specific type of plastic. Include in your display the properties of the plastic, how those properties can be used in a product, and the advantages and disadvantages of using the plastic.

78. Discuss the implications on the quality of air if 10 million new automobiles are produced every year by manufacturers. Provide scientific evidence to support your statements.

79. As our hydrocarbon resources are used up, we must start using less conventional deposits, such as those in tar sands, the Arctic, and offshore. Prepare a chart that illustrates the advantages and disadvantages associated with each of these sources.

80. List two advantages and three specific risks of using petroleum as an energy source.

81. Use electronic and print sources to research strategies that will extend the available petroleum resources. Prepare a chart that describes the advantages and disadvantages of each strategy.

82. Although Earth receives more energy from the sun each month than the energy stored in the known fossil fuel reserves, solar energy remains relatively unused. Design and construct models of different devices and systems that would put energy from the sun to practical use.

83. Using your family's electricity and gas bills, determine how much energy is being used in your home each day and each month. Compare the difference in the energy use between the seasons. Design an action plan to help your family reduce energy consumption. Describe the consequences of your action plan on the quality of life for each member of your family.

84. Describe your favourite breakfast. Determine where each of the products for that breakfast was grown, processed, and packaged. Indicate which fossil fuel energy is needed to grow, prepare, and deliver the food to your table. Design and develop a display that shares this information with others. Describe what changes you would propose to improve the efficiency of this system and reduce consumption of fossil fuels.

85. Identify four alternative sources of energy to relieve the demand on the current non-renewable sources of energy. Use print and electronic sources to research information about each of these four alternative sources of energy. Create a chart that outlines the advantages and disadvantages of using each source.

Appendix

A. Science and Safety

Doing science and learning science occur in the classroom, in the laboratory, and in the field. Safe practices are essential when students are actively learning science in all environments. Familiarity with the potential hazards makes it possible to take proper precautions and develop a safe learning environment.

Before every investigation, you should review all safety precautions and understand their importance. If you are unsure of any procedure or safety instructions, ask your instructor before you proceed.

The Canadian Hazardous Products Act requires chemical manufacturers to include all hazard symbols and the degree of hazard. You may recognize the household product symbols shown in the photograph. These symbols indicate hazard(s), precaution, and first-aid treatment.

Hazardous Product and WHMIS Symbols

The household hazardous symbols indicate the type of danger and the degree of danger. They appear in either a triangle (which means "caution"), a diamond (which means "warning"), or an octagon (which means "danger").

Below are some of the more common symbols.

Flammable Hazard: Materials could ignite (catch on fire) if exposed to flames, sparks, or friction.

Explosive Hazard: The materials or equipment could explode.

Toxic Hazard: The material is very poisonous and could have immediate and serious effects.

Corrosive Hazard: The material may corrode ("eat away at") clothing, skin, or other materials.

Biological Hazard: Be alert to the possibility of poisoning or infection from microscopic and other organisms.

Electrical Hazard: Be alert to the possibility of an electric spark or shock.

Many of the chemical products used in Canadian schools are manufactured in the United States. To standardize the labelling systems, WHMIS (the Workplace Hazardous Materials Information System) was developed. The symbols belonging to this system appear on materials and products used both in workplaces and our schools.

 compressed gas

 dangerously reactive material

 oxidizing material

 poisonous and infectious causing immediate and serious toxic effects

 flammable and combustible material

 biohazardous infectious material

 corrosive material

 poisonous and infectious causing other toxic effects

Laboratory Safety

Approach all investigations, especially in the laboratory, with maturity. Before the lab activity, read all instructions for the lab experience, noting all safety precautions. In addition, your teacher may provide other safety reminders and rules pertaining to the laboratory activity. It is your responsibility to inform your teacher of medical conditions such as possible allergies to materials used (e.g., latex) or by-products of the activity. If you wear contact lenses, inform your teacher.

1. **Precautions and Safety Equipment**
   a) Identify all safety equipment in the laboratory.
   b) Know the location of and how to operate safety equipment, including the fire extinguisher, fire blankets, eyewash fountains, sand, and the first-aid kit.
   c) Wear appropriate laboratory apparel, which includes safety goggles, rubber gloves, and lab aprons.
   d) Tie back long hair and any loose clothing.

2. **Precautions with Burners or Hot Plates**
   a) Never leave any burner or hot plate unattended.
   b) Before connecting a burner, make sure the gas supply valve is completely closed. Open it only slightly just before lighting the burner.
   c) If the flame keeps going out, turn off the gas before you seek your teacher's help.
   d) Ensure the use of Borosilicate (e.g., Pyrex™) for heating substances.
   e) Use tongs or holders to handle hot glassware or objects.

3. Precautions with Glassware
a) Check for any chipped, cracked or broken glassware.

b) Ensure the glassware is clean before and after use.

c) Use only equipment specified in the laboratory instructions unless advised otherwise by your teacher.

4. Precautions with Chemicals
a) Never smell, touch, or taste substances in the laboratory without your teacher's instruction.

b) Do not inhale fumes directly. Instead, wave the air above the substance toward your nose.

c) Take materials only from labelled containers.

d) Dilute acids by adding only ACID to WATER.

e) Never return unused chemicals to stock bottles or containers.

5. Precautions with Electrical Sources
a) Do not use 110-V ac equipment if it has a damaged plug (e.g., missing the ground pin) or a frayed cord.

b) Keep water and wet hands away from electrical cords.

c) Do not touch a person in contact with live electrical currents. Disconnect the power source first. Then give artificial respiration, if necessary, and treat burns.

d) When unplugging an electrical device, always disconnect the cord from the socket by pulling the plug, not the cord, and make sure electrical cords are not placed where someone could trip over them.

e) Never attempt to recharge a non-rechargeable battery. Always exercise caution in handling any batteries: allowing them to discharge quickly, through a short circuit for instance, can generate dangerous amounts of heat in the wires and in the batteries themselves, and some kinds of batteries could even explode.

f) Never cut open batteries. Their contents can be corrosive and poisonous.

6. Other Precautions and Accident Procedures
a) All accidents (including breakage and spillage) or injuries must be reported to your teacher.

b) With your teacher's help and supervision, clean up all spills and broken glassware.

c) If a chemical splashes into your eyes or on your body, wash at the eyewash for several minutes or add copious amounts of cool water immediately. Ensure your teacher is notified.

d) At the end of all lab activities, ensure the lab bench is clean.

e) Put all cleaned apparatus away.

f) Ensure your hands are washed before you leave the lab.

For any independent investigation:

Before you begin, obtain approval from your teacher for all procedures. Carefully discuss the apparatus and the procedure with your instructor. Learn the appropriate safety measures for your work. Never work without your teacher's supervision and never work alone.

B. The Inquiry Process

What causes bananas to change colour from green to yellow? Why is the sky blue? Why do different types of wood burn to produce different amounts of heat? How does the addition of ethylene glycol to water prevent the water in the radiator of a car from freezing? Why do balloons filled with helium rise in the air? Why did the bacteria die in this petri plate?

All of these are questions asked by scientists as they observe parts of the world around them. While an answer to the last question might be "Let's just throw out this plate's results," a scientist named Alexander Fleming might have asked, "What factors existed in this culture plate to kill these bacteria?" It turns out, Fleming had discovered a mould, called *Penicillium notatum*, that has a lethal effect on many harmful organisms. As a result of his discovery, Oxford researchers Howard Florey and Ernst Chain were able to isolate the active component *penicillin*. Today, penicillin is produced by drug companies to help fight infections and diseases.

Fleming approached the problem from a scientific perspective, using a structured approach to examine the world and answer his questions. This approach is called the **Inquiry Process**. It is a logical reasoning process used to solve problems through observation and measurement, experimentation and research, and analysis and dissemination. It attempts to explain phenomena by examining cause and effect in a controlled situation. Scientists use experiments as a key part of their scientific work. Working scientifically involves being precise and accurate when making and interpreting observations and formulating conclusions from them. It is also important to communicate the results of experimental work clearly to other scientists. The flowchart on this page outlines some of the steps involved in the inquiry process.

Initiating and Planning

Notice a scientific problem or issue, ask a question, and formulate a plan to solve it.
I wonder if? I wonder why?
How can I find out?

Applying Technical Skills

Use your skills to put your play into practice.
Did I read the thermometer accurately?

Using Tools, Materials, and Equipment

Use suitable tools and materials appropriately.
Would sodium hydroxide be a better base to use than ammonium?

Conducting and Recording

Conduct your study in a controlled manner and observe/record appropriate results.
Did I control all of the variables?
Are my results recorded clearly and accurately?

Analyzing and Interpreting

Use various tools to analyze results and figure out what they mean.
Should I use a graph or a calculation to examine these results?
What do my results mean?

Concluding and Communicating

Make a decision about the experimental results and communicate them.
Do my results support my conclusion?
Will others be able to understand my work?
Would they be able to repeat my work?

Initiating and Planning

A scientist notices an event or occurrence and attempts to explain it. If a reasonable explanation does not exist, the scientist may take further steps. He or she will develop a question that can be answered through various means. The question should point to a structured approach to finding the answer or explanation through an experiment, a model, or research. The scientist will make a prediction (hypothesis) of the answer based on his or her scientific knowledge and experience. A plan must then be devised for gathering information and drawing appropriate conclusions.

Question: Will the temperature of my iced cappuccino increase as it sits in the sun?

Hypothesis: The temperature of my iced cappuccino will increase steadily as it sits in the sun.

One scientific plan would be to conduct an experiment. A sequence of steps (method) must be determined to describe how the experiment is to be conducted. The design of the method is essential to ensure that consistent and valid results are obtained. The method should be geared toward collecting data specific to the hypothesis and should identify what tools, equipment, and materials would be necessary. Care should be taken to control as many variables as possible, otherwise results will be difficult to interpret correctly. Any safety considerations should also be included in the method. In addition, the method should be written to allow others to reproduce the experiment.

Method:
1. Place an equal volume (30 mL) of iced cappuccino into 3 beakers.
2. Measure the initial temperature of the beverage.
3. Place the beakers in the sun or under a heat lamp.
4. Stirring constantly, measure the temperature of the iced cappuccino at 2-min intervals.

The method should also clarify the number of beverages, the position of the thermometer, the frequency and length of data collection, and the number of trials to ensure accurate and reliable results that are reproducible.

Applying Technical Skills

To conduct an experiment on temperature change in a liquid, for example, you would need to control a number of variables that may affect the results. The volume of liquid, for example, would affect results, as a larger volume would take longer to heat up. Even the position of the thermometer could skew results if the liquid is not stirred constantly and heats up unevenly. So it is important to use proper technical skills—for example, in measuring the liquid or positioning the thermometer—in applying your method to control all variables and ensure that the data obtained are valid.

Using Tools, Materials, and Equipment

In a laboratory, using tools, materials, and equipment safely and correctly is essential to ensure a secure environment for all. Safety is everyone's responsibility. If you see a fellow student struggling to use equipment properly, it is your responsibility to offer assistance or notify the lab supervisor (your teacher). A review of specific safety considerations and proper use of apparatus may be necessary at the outset of an experiment. Working responsibly includes knowing what to do and when to ask for help.

Materials

3 beakers	safety goggles
3 thermometers (0–100°C, ±0.5°C)	graduated cylinder
timers	stirring rods

Conducting and Recording

While performing an experiment, use your scientific and technical skills to follow the identified method, gathering and recording both qualitative and quantitative observations in your lab notes. The critical functions of lab notes are to state what was done and what was observed. The greatest flaw found in lab notes, even with experienced scientists, is that they are often unreadable. Hard as it is to believe, even the author of a notebook often cannot understand his or her own notes after a few years. The problem is not usually one of legibility, but rather of poorly labelled entries and incomplete descriptions. Writing in complete sentences, indicating units of measurement, and noting possible sources of error are excellent ways to ensure a high-quality record of the experiment.

A table is one method to present results. It offers an organized structure to present experimental results/data. It is apparent from the quantitative observations provided here that the temperature of the iced cappuccino increased over time as the beverage remained in the sunlit location. The data can be manipulated through graphing or calculations to find further relationships. A line graph of the three data sets offers a good visual representation of the melting process.

Observations

Quantitative observations were recorded in Table B.1.

Table B.1: Temperature of Iced Cappuccino Sitting in the Sun

Time (min)	Temperature (°C)		
	Beaker 1	Beaker 2	Beaker 3
0	1.0	0.5	0.5
2	0.0	0.0	0.0
4	0.0	0.5	0.0
6	0.5	1.0	0.5
8	2.0	4.0	3.0
10	6.0	7.0	7.0

Analyzing and Interpreting

A collection of numbers or a list of observations is not sufficient to address your hypothesis. It is necessary to use appropriate analysis tools to find meaning in your experimental results. The tools may include a graphical representation of results, a calculation, a comparison to known data, and an identification of patterns or trends. Often visual representations of data simplify the identification of relationships that exist in data.

<u>Analysis</u>

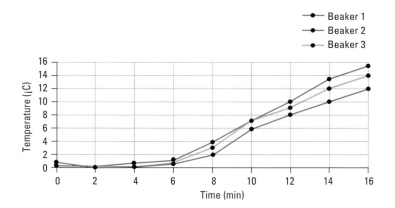

Upon examining Graph B.1, the temperature of the iced cappuccino appears to have remained relatively constant for the first 6 min; after which time, it started to steadily increase. It was also noticed that the ice in the beverage disappeared completely at approximately 6 min. A further experiment heating the beverages to boiling may provide more insight into this temperature study.

Concluding and Communicating

Use your completed analysis to draw conclusions that support or refute your hypothesis. Your conclusion should be written in such a manner that it is clearly linked to your analysis and results. Any errors noted should be addressed, indicating their effect on the observed results.

Your overall inquiry process should be organized in order to communicate your results. Regardless of the form they take, the information and ideas should be communicated with a high degree of clarity and precision, using the correct terminology, symbols, conventions, SI units, and a number of significant figures. It may be necessary to use technology to support the communication of your inquiry process; you may choose to use computers or media tools to enhance your work.

<u>Conclusions</u>

While a solid is melting, the temperature will remain constant. The temperature of the sample will only increase after melting is complete. This statement can be explained using energy concepts. The energy being absorbed from the sun is being used to change the state of the ice, rather than increase the temperature of the sample. Once the ice is gone, the kinetic energy in the particles starts to increase, thus the temperature of the beverage increases.

You can use the following Inquiry Process Checklist to guide your work.

Inquiry Process Checklist

Purpose
- ☐ poses a question
- ☐ question can be answered by following an inquiry process

Hypothesis
- ☐ hypothesis specifically predicts the answer to the question stated in the purpose

Method
- ☐ written in logical steps
- ☐ reproducible by other scientists
- ☐ data collected are connected to the hypothesis
- ☐ variables controlled where necessary
- ☐ diagram included where appropriate

Inquiry Skills
- ☐ demonstrate knowledge of proper use of tools, materials, and equipment
- ☐ use apparatus properly
- ☐ use apparatus safely
- ☐ help others to work safely and properly

Conducting and Recording
- ☐ follow method
- ☐ qualitative observations written with adequate detail
- ☐ quantitative observations include appropriate units and significant figures
- ☐ use table, chart to organize results
- ☐ note errors or discrepancies

Analyzing and Interpreting
- ☐ include a visual representation of results
- ☐ calculations where necessary; clearly organized, units shown

Conclusion
- ☐ stated to link hypothesis with results
- ☐ hypothesis supported or refuted
- ☐ error analysis

Overall
- ☐ spelling and grammar correct
- ☐ written in clear, precise language
- ☐ scientific terms used correctly
- ☐ neat presentation
- ☐ technology used where necessary

C.   The Decision-Making Process

During spring 2000 in Walkerton, Ontario, tainted water killed 7 people and sent 700 to hospital. A potentially deadly strain of bacteria called *E. coli 0157:H7* had leaked into the town's water supply. It was hypothesized that a local farm and its herd of cattle were the source of contamination. There are 150 strains of *E. coli* bacteria, not all of them lethal; however, the form found in Walkerton is stronger than most. *E. coli 0157:H7* is known to cause bloody diarrhea, abdominal cramps, kidney trouble, fever, and possible kidney failure or death. Adequate chlorination of water supplies would destroy such bacteria. Subsequent to the incident, there have been a series of inquiries delving into the mishap and its causes.

The circumstances that surround the tragedy in Walkerton typify the many different issues facing science and scientists today. Some of these issues are ethical in nature, requiring analysis of one's beliefs and values. Others require a consideration of safety. This type of issue and the questions it raises require that an informed decision be made. Some decisions are easier than others. How does one make an informed decision and analyze its validity? Scientists often use an approach called the **Decision-Making Process** as they strive to make prudent choices. The flowchart on this page outlines this process.

Defining the Issue

The issue should be articulated using a brief statement or question. For example, safe water practices is the issue from the above example and the broad question might be: "How can a population be protected from food and water contamination?"

Developing Assessment Criteria

As a means to an end, assessment criteria should be established prior to the in-depth research and analysis of the issue; this will facilitate an objective decision-making process. Some possible criteria include cost, social implications, precedents, norms, environmental impact, and/or feasibility. In this example, one might base a decision on the costs versus benefits to select the appropriate course of action to protect a population.

Defining the Issue

Identify an issue and its context.
Is this ethical? Is this acceptable?
What are the options and which one is better?

Developing Assessment Criteria

Establish criteria to use as the basis for making a final decision.
On what criteria will I base my decision?
What factors are important in making this decision?

Researching the Issue

Find as much information as possible to make an informed decision.
What sources of information can I use?
Are my sources reliable?
Have I considered all aspects of the issue?

Analyzing Data and Information

Select the relevant information, organize it, manipulate it, and examine it.
How can I best present the information?
What method should I use to analyze the data?

Proposing a Course of Action

Make a decision.
Have I considered all of the relevant factors?
Have I put all the possible courses of action in the right order?

Justifying the Course of Action

Determine whether the information supports your decision.
Is there enough data supporting my decision to allow others to reach the same conclusion?
What will I do if my proposed course of action is turned down?
Check for the consequences or impact of the decision.
What are the consequences of this decision?
Have I weighted the consequences in an appropriate way?

Communicating Your Proposal

Decide how you will communicate your findings.
Who is my intended audience?
How will I communicate my findings?
What visuals will I include in my work?

Researching the Issue

To make an informed decision, all related factors must be identified and described. A researcher might consult journals, articles, the Internet, experts, available data, past practice, or precedents to find information, impacts, factors, norms, and connections to other fields. Relevant ethical, moral, and social perspectives should be noted. If relevant information is overlooked, the wrong decision may be reached. For example, the following questions may arise in the case of the Walkerton tragedy:

- *food irradiation:* Will irradiation effectively eliminate all *E. coli* bacteria?
- *water treatment:* Is chlorination the best method of water treatment?
- *guidelines:* Are the policies and procedures for water control safe enough for our population?
- *staffing:* Is there sufficient staff to meet the needs of a water-supply system?
- *protective valves:* Would the general population operate a protective valve properly?
- *cost versus benefit to individuals/society:* Is the solution financially viable under our budget?
- *effectiveness:* What is the certainty of protection for this solution?
- *impact:* Will the solution have an adverse effect on other aspects of the water or its consumers?
- *accessibility to the general public:* Is this solution feasible on a larger scale?

Analyzing Data and Information

The information must be organized in a structured manner to facilitate analysis. Methods for organizing information might be a chart comparing pros and cons, a cost-benefit analysis, a consequences or responsibilities chart, statistical analysis, graphical representation, or a flowchart to illustrate the issue.

Once organized, information can be easily analyzed using the assessment criteria. During analysis, one should consider the relative importance of the factors and how each affects the outcome of the decision in order to weight them accordingly within the decision-making process. For example, the effectiveness of a given solution may be judged on its costs and effectiveness.

Proposing a Course of Action

Taking into account all available research and its analysis, an objective course of action must be chosen. For example, a municipal office might decide to introduce a by-law and policy for using protective valves under the town's backflow prevention program.

Justifying a Course of Action

Your course of action should be directly supported by your analysis of the research. To justify your course of action, it is necessary to evaluate its effect or impact on society. The evaluation can be conducted from two perspectives:

1) the validity of the decision in comparison to the data and criteria *(Is this the best decision possible given the available information and financial resources?)*

2) the impact and effect of a decision over an extended period of time *(How has the course of action affected a population? Were there unforeseen consequences?)*

This evaluation could be accomplished through public polls, expert analysis, and a study of success rates. The method of analysis will depend on the scope of the issue. The argument presented should appeal to the reader's intellect through logic and reason.

Communicating Your Proposal

Any good research project requires clear communication of the work and results. The communication should summarize the goal, the process, and the recommendations of the work in a succinct and concise manner. Regardless of the form used for communication, there are key components to include: an introductory statement of the issue, an accurate and precise description of relevant background information and the research undertaken, an analysis of the information, and a conclusion clearly supported by the analysis.

There are various ways to communicate your work, both orally and in writing. A number of forms of communication are outlined in the table below. The form used should be supported by visual aids to enhance the communication. In addition, the tone and perspective of the work should be matched to its intended audience. For example, an editorial may contain more personal views than a news report.

Forms of Communication

Oral	Written
debate	editorial
presentation (e.g., town meeting, school council)	position paper
radio spot	poster
TV spot	pamphlet or brochure

You can use the following Decision-Making Process Checklist to guide your work.

Decision-Making Process Checklist

Issue
- ☐ clearly articulated as a statement or question

Assessment Criteria
- ☐ clearly identified
- ☐ enables objective, fact-based decision making

Research
- ☐ relevant factors identified
- ☐ factors described in detail and seriated
- ☐ a variety of sources used

Analysis
- ☐ appropriate method(s) used
- ☐ easily interpreted
- ☐ weighted according to relative importance

Decision
- ☐ objective course of action chosen
- ☐ supported by data
- ☐ predicted possible impact or consequence of decision
- ☐ checked validity of decision with respect to data

Evaluation
- ☐ predicted possible impact or consequence of decision
- ☐ checked validity of decision with respect to data

Communication (Overall)
- ☐ information presented clearly and precisely
- ☐ spelling and grammar correct
- ☐ scientific terms used correctly
- ☐ approach appropriate to intended audience
- ☐ content appropriate to intended audience
- ☐ structure of content appropriate to communication form
- ☐ use of technology enhances presentation

D.   Using Graphic Organizers

Graphic organizers are effective tools that can help you learn. They enable you to problem solve and think critically through analyzing similarities and differences, inferring sequences, and establishing cause-and-effect relationships. They generate discussion and negotiation of ideas, extend comprehension of a concept, theme, or topic, and lead to organized representation and presentation of understandings. You can use them to brainstorm, demonstrate what you know, and organize your thoughts before writing a report or essay or planning a presentation. The following chart outlines a number of graphic organizers, their intended purposes, and how to use them as you study science.

Type of Graphic Organizer	Purpose	Method
Concept Map 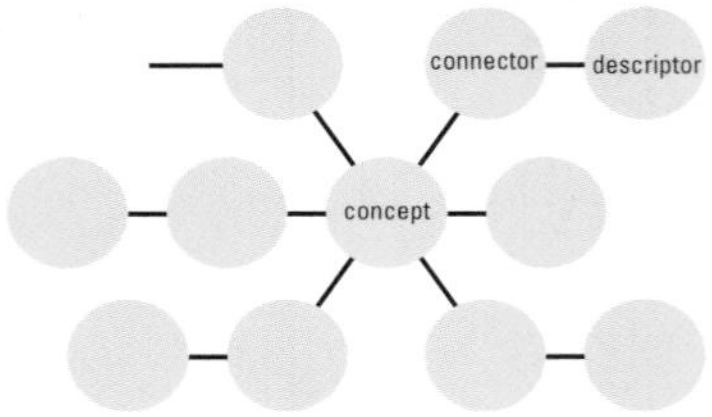	• Used to clarify relationships and linkages between concepts, events, or ideas	Brainstorm ideas and link together from "big to small" with arrows and linking words.
Venn Diagram 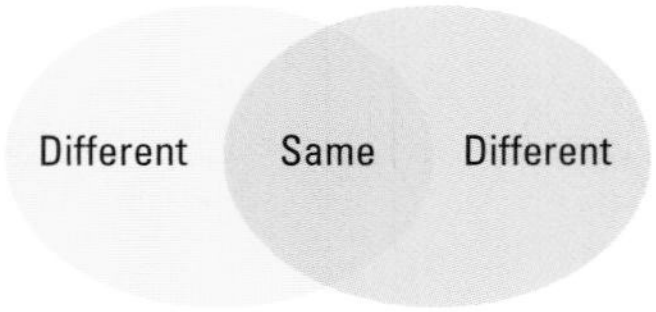	• Used to visualize similarities and differences between two or more ideas, topics, or concepts	Brainstorm similar traits to both topics and list in the overlapping section of the two circles. Repeat for unique traits and list in the non-overlapping sections.
Web Diagram 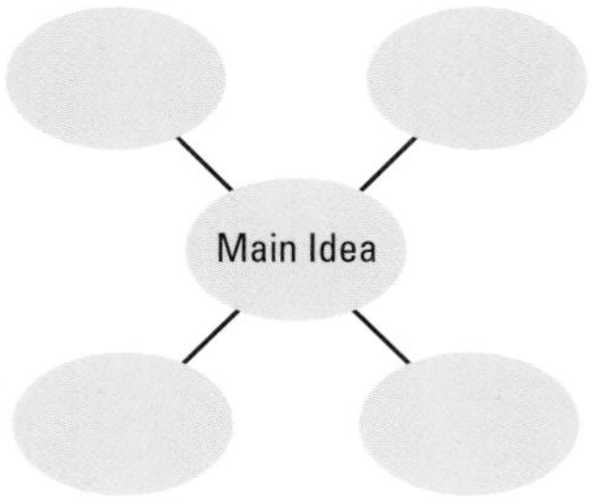	• Used to clarify concepts and ideas by clustering them	Cluster words and/or information around a central object, concept, or idea.
Pie Chart	• Used to estimate the relationship of parts to the whole	Estimate/research the importance or amount of proportionate time of each aspect of an event in relation to the whole.

Type of Graphic Organizer	Purpose	Method
Flowchart/Sequence Chart	• Used to map out your thinking about an issue or to organize ideas for an essay or report	Brainstorm aspects of the whole event. Select important aspects and put them into sequential order.
Ranking Ladder	• Used to rank ideas in order of importance	Brainstorm ideas and rank them in order from most important (bottom rung) to least important (top rung).
Fishbone Diagram	• Used to identify cause-and-effect relationships	Identify a problem to be solved. List the "effect" at the head of the fish. Brainstorm "possible causes" in each bone. Rank the causes and circle the most probable ones with justification.
Right-Angle Diagram	• Used to explore the implications of ideas and reflect on applications of those ideas	Identify an event and show it on the horizontal arrow. Brainstorm traits and list them to the right of the horizontal arrow. Expand on one trait and list details about it along the vertical arrow. Describe social impacts of that trait below the vertical arrow.
Target Diagram	• Used to weigh the importance of facts and ideas	Brainstorm facts and ideas. Rank their importance and place the most important facts/ideas centrally and the least important ones toward the outer ring.
Agree/Disagree Chart	• Used to organize data to support a position for or against an idea or decision	List a series of statements relating to a topic or issue. Survey agree/disagreement before discussion. Survey again after discussion/research.

Type of Graphic Organizer	Purpose	Method
PMI (Plus, Minus, Interesting) Chart Plus / Minus / Interesting	• Used to summarize the positive and negative aspects of a topic or issue, as well as identify interesting aspects of the topic for possible further research	Sort ideas or information about a topic or issue in a three-column chart that has the following headings: Plus (+), Minus (-), and Interesting.
Gathering Grid	• Used to make distinctions between ideas or events	Gather information on a number of ideas or events and arrange it on a grid. Each idea or event is assigned to a separate row. Analyze the information according to selected criteria in each specific column.
Concept Hierarchy Diagram	• Used to identify and sequence the subordinate concepts needed to understand a higher-order concept	Place the higher-order concept at the top of a page. Then consider the question, "What concepts need to be understood before the higher-order concept above can be grasped?" The same question is then asked for each of the subordinate concepts identified and a hierarchy of connected concepts is created.

E. An Introduction to Quantitative Chemistry

In your daily life, you see many examples of chemical measurement: What is the percentage of caffeine in your cola drink? What mass of salt is in your pizza? How many calories are in your dessert? This section will review the key features of measurement to help you gain the basic knowledge for the sections and chapters in this text.

The International System of Units

In 1960, scientists agreed on a standard system of units, the *Système international d'unités*, abbreviated to SI. Under this system, seven *base units* were defined (Table E.1). Everything a scientist needs to measure can be expressed in terms of these fundamental base units.

The four most important base units for this course will be: volume, mass, temperature, and length. There are many *derived units*. These are units that are combinations of the base units. There are four derived units that you will often use in chemistry and these are listed in Table E.2. All of the derived units can be defined in terms of the base units. For example, the energy unit, the joule, is the following combination of base units: $kg \cdot m^2 \cdot s^{-2}$. Dots at half-height are used to separate units, as recommended by the *Canadian Metric Guide*. The dots help prevent confusion, for example, ms is milliseconds while $m \cdot s$ is metres times seconds.

Sometimes the "pure" unit is too large or too small for practical use. For example, in the laboratory, it is unlikely that we will be measuring out a cubic metre of water! Conversely, a pressure of 1 Pa is the pressure that a $20 bill exerts on a tabletop—many times smaller than the pressures that are used in laboratory gas cylinders. To make life easier, there is a set of unit prefixes that enable you to avoid using enormous exponents of numbers. These prefixes are listed in Table E.3. Metric prefixes usually differ by factors of 10^3, but we commonly use tenths and hundredths of units so there are special prefixes for them (*d* and *c*). Also, all prefixes less than the base unit have small (lower-case) letters, while those greater than the base unit have capital (upper-case) letters—except kilo, which traditionally has been written with a small *k*, partially to prevent confusion with the symbol for kelvin.

TABLE E.1 The Seven Base Units of SI

Quantity	Name of Unit	Symbol
length	metre	m
mass	kilogram	kg
time	second	s
temperature	kelvin	K
electric current	ampere	A
luminous intensity	candela	cd
amount of substance	mole	mol

TABLE E.2 Four of the Derived Units of SI

Quantity	Name of Unit	Symbol
volume	cubic metre	m^3
density	kilogram per cubic metre	$kg \cdot m^{-3}$
pressure	pascal	$Pa = kg \cdot m^{-1} \cdot s^{-2}$
energy	joule	$J = kg \cdot m^2 \cdot s^{-2}$

TABLE E.3 Common Metric Prefixes

Prefix	Symbol	Value	Scientific Notation
giga-	G	1 000 000 000	10^9
mega-	M	1 000 000	10^6
kilo-	k	1 000	10^3
–	–	1	10^0
deci-	d	0.1	10^{-1}
centi-	c	0.01	10^{-2}
milli-	m	0.001	10^{-3}
micro-	μ	0.000 001	10^{-6}
nano-	n	0.000 000 001	10^{-9}
pico-	p	0.000 000 000 001	10^{-12}

Volume is one particular case where chemists use quantities far smaller than the base unit, the cubic metre. There are two smaller-sized units that are much more useful: the cubic decimetre (dm^3) and the cubic centimetre (cm^3). Though 1 cm is one-tenth of 1 dm, 1 cm^3 is one-thousandth of 1 dm^3.

Scientists use these SI units for solids, but more commonly, the litre, symbol L, is used for liquids and gases. There is a very simple relationship between the two sets of units:

$$1 \ dm^3 = 1 \ L \quad \text{and} \quad 1 \ cm^3 = 1 \ mL$$

Making Measurements

When you are measuring your weight on bathroom scales, you should be concerned with two things: whether the scales are measuring correctly and how exactly you can read your weight. For example, the reading is not likely to be valid if the scales have not been adjusted to zero when no one is standing on them. Also, it is impossible to read your weight to any more exactness than 1 kg. The closeness to the true value is a measure of the *accuracy* of the measurement, while the number of digits that you can obtain in your reading is a measure of *precision*.

In many cases in chemistry you will need to do a series of measurements of the same property, for example, the density of a liquid. If your values are close together, then they are said to have a *high precision*. On the other hand, if they differ widely, they are said to be of *low precision*. To determine the accuracy, you need to know the correct or *accepted value*. Then you can compare it with your *experimental value*. The absolute value of the difference between the two is known as the *error*.

$$\text{error} = \text{accepted value} - \text{experimental value}$$

There are two types of errors. *Random error* is usually an indication of poor precision. A random error is caused by limitations of the equipment or of the method used. On the other hand, poor accuracy and good precision is an example of a *systematic error*. In the laboratory, a systematic error is an indication of a problem with the equipment that you are using. To minimize systematic errors, equipment is calibrated using a standard. For example, suppose you place a standard 200-g weight on your lab balance and the reading on the balance is 201 g. Then you know the error in the balance is −1 g.

But is a 1 g difference in 200 g really important? To find out, you can calculate the percentage difference:

$$\text{Percent error} = \frac{|\text{accepted value} - \text{experimental value}|}{\text{accepted value}} \times 100\%$$

The lines on either side of the word "error" mean that you use the absolute value of the error, thus percentage error is always positive.

Using your numbers, you would get:

$$\text{Percent error} = \frac{|-1 \text{ g}|}{200 \text{ g}} \times 100\% = 0.5\%$$

This percent error is probably so small compared with the percent error of other measurements that you regard it as negligible. However, in the laboratory you will be measuring very small amounts of substances, so it is important to minimize the percent error when performing experiments.

Significant Figures in Measurement

In the laboratory, you will have to measure masses and volumes of substances. In some cases, you need only approximate values while in others you need the highest possible precision. This is the realm of *significant figures*. A very simple example is the measurement of the length of a piece of wood. If you measure it with the metre-stick shown in Figure E.1 a), you can tell the wood is slightly more than 60 cm long but less than 70 cm. As the wood is only just more than 60 cm, you can estimate that the wood is about 61 cm long. However, using the metre-stick in Figure E.1 b), you can tell immediately that the wood is slightly less than 61 cm, and as the length is closer to 61 cm than 60 cm, you can estimate its length as 60.7 cm or 60.8 cm. The second metre-stick is more precise and it enables you to state your answer with more precision.

PRACTICE PROBLEM

A thermometer read 79.1°C when it was placed in boiling alcohol. The boiling point of alcohol is normally 78.2°C. What is the percent error of the thermometer?

a)

b)

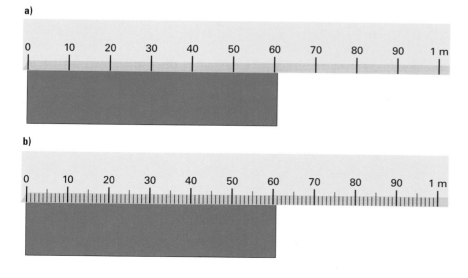

FIGURE E.1 The metre-stick in b) enables you to measure the length of the piece of wood with a greater precision than with the metre-stick in a).

The number of digits in your measurement is known as the number of significant figures. There are rules to determine how many there are in your value.

1. Every non-zero digit in a measurement is significant. For example, 5.37 has three significant figures.
2. Zeros between non-zero digits are significant. For example, 30.15 has four significant digits.
3. Trailing zeros, those to the right of all non-zero digits are significant. For example, 2.10 g shows that you have measured a mass to the nearest 1/100 of a gram and it just happens that value was a zero, not 1 through 9. The mass has three significant figures.
4. Leading zeros, those to the left of all non-zero digits are not significant. They are not real measurements but placeholders, showing where the decimal point is located. For example, 0.002 g means that the mass is two thousandths, not two hundredths nor two tenths. The mass has only one significant figure. It is much easier to deduce the number of significant figures if the number is written in scientific notation. Thus writing 0.002 g as 2×10^{-3} g makes it unambiguously one significant figure.
5. There is a class of numbers to which rules of significant figures do not apply. These are *exact numbers*. For example, suppose you have 31 students in your class. You cannot have 30.5 or 31.2 students. The number of students is an exact number. Similarly, there are exactly 60 s in 1 min.

Zeros are ambiguous in large numbers that do not contain a decimal point. Suppose you are told that the mass of an object is 20 g. Is that mass measured to the nearest gram or to the nearest ten grams? You don't know. It is safer to assume that the mass is only measured to the nearest ten grams; that is, the measurement is only good to one significant figure. Again, scientific notation would have provided an unambiguous answer. A value of 2×10^1 would have indicated a measurement to one significant figure while 2.0×10^1 would have meant the measurement was made to the nearest gram and to two significant figures.

One method of indicating that all digits are significant in whole-number values is to place a decimal point at the end of the number. Thus 20. g would be another way of indicating that the zero was significant.

Significant Figures in Calculations

Suppose you plan to buy a house and want to know the area of the land. The agent tells you that the lot is 16.7 m by 33.3 m. You multiply the two numbers with your calculator and obtain the value 556.11 m². But do you really know the area to the nearest 1/100 of a square metre? No, you do not. **A calculated or derived value cannot be more precise than the measurements that were actually made.**

To determine the number of significant figures in your answer, you need to know the rules applying to significant figures in calculations. There are two sets of rules, one applying to multiplication and division, and the other to addition and subtraction. If you are multiplying numbers, **the answer must have the same number of significant figures as the measurement with the fewest significant figures**. For example, in the area calculation above, both lengths are to three significant figures. Thus the answer can only have three significant figures. To correct the answer, you must round off by deleting the non-significant digits. Then the correct area is 556 m².

Rounding off has its own rules. **If a non-significant digit is less than 5, it is dropped and the preceding digit is unchanged. If a non-significant digit is greater than 5, it is dropped and the preceding digit is increased by one. If a non-significant digit is equal to 5, it is dropped. If the preceding digit is odd, it is increased by one. If the preceding digit is even, it is left as is.**

Suppose you need to find the area of a square object that has sides of length 2.0 cm. Multiplying 2.0 by 2.0 with your calculator gives you an answer of 4. But both numbers had two significant figures, so your answer has to be to two significant figures. The answer should be 4.0—calculators do not display trailing zero significant figures. In such cases, you must add the appropriate number of trailing zeros to your answer.

In the chemistry lab, you are likely to have to add and subtract numbers. These procedures require different significant figure rules. **The answer must be given to the same number of places after the decimal point as the measurement that has the least number of digits after the decimal.** The reason for this is best illustrated by the technique of **weighing by difference.**

It is never permitted to pour chemicals directly on the pan of a balance. Apart from getting the pan messy, you will not know exactly how much of the chemical is actually scraped into the beaker in which you are performing the experiment. Thus you measure the mass of the sample in a container and then determine the mass of the empty container. Suppose you measured the mass of the sample plus container on one balance as 9.82 g, then poured the contents into a beaker and determined the mass of the empty container on a different balance to be 7.4 g. The first balance measured to the nearest 1/100 of a gram while the second only measured to the nearest 1/10 of a gram. You do not know what the second decimal place is for that second measurement. As a result, your answer is only good to the nearest 1/10 of a gram, 2.4 g.

The safest way to determine significant figure rules for addition and subtraction is to write the numbers in line as below:

$$\begin{array}{r} 9.82 \text{ g} \\ -7.4 \text{ g} \\ \hline 2.4 \text{ g} \end{array}$$

Conversion Factors, Dimensional Analysis, and Problem-Solving

Suppose you are given a volume in millilitres—255 mL—and are told to convert it to litres. How can you do the calculation? The first step is to recall the relationship between litres and millilitres:

1000 mL = 1 L

If both sides of the equation are divided by 1 L, then:

$$\frac{1000 \text{ mL}}{1 \text{ L}} = \frac{1 \text{ L}}{1 \text{ L}} = 1$$

Any ratio that relates two quantities expressed in different units of the same type (for example, volume) is called a *conversion factor*. Since the ratio equals one, any measurement can be multiplied by a conversion factor without changing the value of the measurement. How will you convert the volume to litres? First, write the value that you are given:

PRACTICE PROBLEM

1. The dimensions of an internationally approved table-tennis table are 2.74 m by 1.525 m. Calculate the surface area of the table.

2. If 2.125 g of sugar is dissolved in 100.0 g of water in a beaker of mass 64.78 g, what is the total mass of the beaker plus contents?

Volume, $V = 255$ mL

Then multiply it by the conversion factor such that the former units will cancel and your answer has the correct units.

$$\text{Volume, } V = 255 \text{ mL} \times \frac{1 \text{ L}}{1000 \text{ mL}} = 0.255 \text{ L}$$

Notice that the "mL" units cancel. This use of ratios, such that given units cancel to result in required units, is known as *dimensional analysis*. This is the method that will be used throughout this text. Also, as the given value had three significant figures and the relationship between litres and millilitres was an exact number, the answer had to have three significant figures.

Dimensional analysis is a very useful tool for calculating answers to conversion problems. But there is much more to problem solving than simply writing ratios. In fact, problem solving is what you do when you don't know what to do. When you are faced with a numerical problem, where do you start? Throughout this text, a systematic method is used. The method can be summarized as follows:

Given
Among all the words of the question, you will find numerical information that can be used in solving the problem. List it here.

Required
Identify exactly what it is you have to find.

Analysis
Decide your strategy of getting to the answer starting from the provided information.

Solution
Perform the calculation steps that you need using dimensional analysis.

Statement
Answers should be given a context, don't just write the numerical value.

It is easiest to follow these steps if you see the problem-solving method used in practice—first a very simple example, then a more complex problem.

EXAMPLE 2

A baseball pitcher throws a ball with a velocity of 44 m·s^{-1}. How long does the ball take to reach home plate, a distance of 18 m?

Given
$d = 18$ m, velocity $= 44$ m·s^{-1}

Required
time, $t = ?$ s

Analysis
$d \rightarrow t$ (using the proportionality, velocity $= 44$ m·s^{-1})

Solution

time, $t = 18 \text{ m} \times \dfrac{1 \text{ s}}{44 \text{ m}} = 0.41$ s

Statement

The time elapsed to reach home plate is 0.41 s.

EXAMPLE 3

Your school has sold 545 tickets for a fund-raising event. You have volunteered to make enough chili to feed the guests. The recipe requires 1 teaspoon (tsp.) of chili powder for every five portions. You determine the mass of 24 tsp. of chili to be almost exactly 10 g. What mass of chili powder do you need to buy?

Given

quantity, q = 545 portions; 1 tsp. = 5 portions; 24 tsp. = 10 g

Required

mass, m = ? g

Analysis

$q \rightarrow$ tsp. (using the proportionality, 1 tsp. = 5 portions)

tsp. $\rightarrow m$ (using the proportionality, 24 tsp. = 10 g)

Solution

number of tsp. = 545 portions $\times \dfrac{1 \text{ tsp.}}{5 \text{ portions}} = 109$ tsp.

mass, $m = 109 \text{ tsp.} \times \dfrac{10 \text{ g}}{24 \text{ tsp.}} = 45$ g

Statement

You will need at least 45 g of chili powder to make 545 portions.

PRACTICE PROBLEM

1. You have to travel to the United States. If you have Can. $248, how much would that be in U.S. $ if the exchange rate is Can. $1 = U.S. $0.681?

2. How long will it take you to swim the length of a 25-m swimming pool if you can swim at a rate of 1.5 m·s^{-1}?

3. If cabbage costs $1.19 kg^{-1}, what weight of cabbage could you buy for $8.00?

4. You have a favourite recipe that you wish to send to a friend in Australia. The recipe requires 5 U.S. tbsp. (tablespoons) of oil. To the nearest tablespoon, how many tbsp. should your friend use if 1 U.S. tbsp. = 14.2 mL and 1 Aust tbsp. = 20.0 mL?

Density

Density is the compactness of matter. For example, ice floats on liquid water because its structure is less compact than that of liquid water. Density is defined mathematically as:

$$\text{density, } d = \frac{\text{mass, } m}{\text{volume, } V}$$

Though the "pure" SI unit of density is $kg \cdot m^{-3}$, it is much more convenient to measure densities in $g \cdot cm^{-3}$ for solids and $g \cdot mL^{-1}$ for liquids. As $1 \text{ cm}^3 = 1 \text{ mL}$, the values in both unit systems are the same. Water has a density of $1.00 \text{ g} \cdot mL^{-1}$ at 25°C, a very convenient value, and most liquids have densities in the range of 0.5 to $1.5 \text{ g} \cdot mL^{-1}$. Gases are about one thousand times less dense than liquids. For example, air at 20°C and normal atmospheric pressure has a density of $1.2 \times 10^{-3} \text{ g} \cdot mL^{-1}$ (or $1.2 \text{ g} \cdot L^{-1}$). The density of metals is particularly interesting as there is such a wide range of values (Table E.4).

TABLE E.4 The Densities of Some Metals ($g \cdot cm^{-3}$)

Metal	Density
lithium	0.5
aluminum	2.7
titanium	4.5
iron	7.9
lead	11.4
uranium	19.0
gold	19.3
osmium	22.6

Lithium, the least dense metal, has a density half that of water. Unfortunately, it is a very reactive metal so it cannot be used for practical purposes. Aluminum has the lowest density of the less-reactive metals. The low density is the reason why aluminum is used wherever minimizing weight is important, for example, in aircraft bodies. If cost is not a problem, particularly for military applications, titanium, an extremely strong, low-density metal is used.

Though you might think of lead as a dense metal—particularly if you have tried lifting a lead-acid car battery—it is only half as dense as some metals. Osmium is the densest metal of all. Uranium is the densest low-cost metal. For this reason, uranium is sometimes used as counter-weights in aircraft doors, so that pushing open the huge doors requires little effort. Depleted uranium—uranium from which the more useful uranium isotopes have been removed—is used in military shells. The density of the shells gives them greater penetrating-power in their targets.

F. Graphing Techniques

Chemists make extensive use of graphs to convey information and to help determine how one physical quantity is affected by another. To review simple graphical analysis techniques, we will use the data for an experiment similar to that performed by Robert Boyle in 1662. Boyle's experiment was designed to answer the question, "How does the volume of a fixed mass of gas vary with applied pressure?" Boyle applied increasing pressures to a container of gas and measured the volume and the corresponding value of the pressure. (At the time, he was unaware that the pressure and volume also depended upon temperature, but during the course of his measurements, the temperature was fairly constant.)

The Data Table

A data table is the most practical way to record quantitative data. Table F.1 shows the data from an experiment similar to that performed by Boyle. Note that the name of each variable, the symbol, and the unit of measurement are recorded at the top of each column. The unit is enclosed in round brackets and directions are included in square brackets.

TABLE F.1 Table of Volume and Pressure for a fixed mass of gas at constant Temperature

Volume (mL)	Pressure (kPa)
50	40
40	58
30	65
20	100
15	132
10	200

The Title of the Graph

Figure F.1 shows a sample graph for Boyle's experiment. Every graph needs a title to describe what it is about. We place the title at the top of the graph or in a box on a clear area above the graph.

FIGURE F.1 Volume Versus Pressure for a Fixed Amount of Gas at Constant Temperature

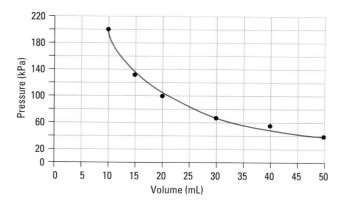

The Axes of the Graph

In chemistry, we usually plot the independent variable on the horizontal x-axis and the dependent variable on the vertical y-axis. The variable that we change intentionally is called the *independent variable*. Volume was the independent variable in Boyle's experiment. The variable that the experimenter observes and measures is called the *dependent variable*. Since Boyle measured the pressure corresponding to each value of volume, the dependent variable in Boyle's experiment was the pressure.

We label each axis with the name, symbol, and unit of the variable being plotted, as shown in Figure F.1. The graphs in this text have origins of (0, 0). Scales are chosen for each axis to spread the measured values across the graph paper without making the plotting difficult and without wasting too much graph paper. The scale on each axis usually has equal divisions and each division represents a whole number.

The maximum value of the volume is 50 mL, while the maximum pressure is 200 kPa. The graph paper has twelve horizontal divisions so each division can represent 5 mL (5 mL $\times$ 12 = 60 mL). Likewise, the twelve vertical divisions can be divided so that each division represents 20 kPa (20 kPa $\times$ 12 = 240 kPa).

Plotting the Data

Use a pencil to plot the data points. Mark the data points with a small visible dot. In this text, we assume that all measured quantities have an error no larger than plus or minus one-half of the smallest division on the measuring instrument. For example, if the volume can be read to the nearest 2 mL, then the error is no larger than plus or minus 1 mL.

Drawing the Line of Best Fit

Once all of the data points and error circles have been plotted, a line of best fit is drawn. A line of best fit is a line that shows the trend of the points. Do not try to have the curve or straight line go through all the dots since most data points have some error. The scatter of the data points from the smooth line indicates the extent of the errors in the data.

Where a point is far off the line, a serious error may have been made. If this occurs, measure the data for that point again. If the same result is obtained, a factor other than those under investigation may be the cause. Notice that the point at (40 mL, 58 kPa) is noticeably off the curve.

Interpolating from the Graph

Interpolation is the process of finding intermediate values between the known or measured points. To interpolate, locate the given value of the variable on its axis. Draw a straight line perpendicular to this axis to intersect the graph. Draw a line at the intersection point perpendicular to the second axis. Read the value of the second variable from this axis.

Figure F.1 shows the process of interpolating the value of the pressure corresponding to a volume of 25 mL. From the graph, what is the interpolated value for the pressure?

Re-Plotting the Data

It is hard to draw curves with any degree of precision. What is more useful is a linear relationship, one that gives a straight line. We can plot different functions of the data and plot combinations until we find one that gives a straight-line plot. For example, we can plot V against $\sqrt{p}$, V against p^2, V against $1/p$, and so on. Let us see the V against $1/p$ plot. First, we need the data:

Volume (mL)	Pressure (kPa)	1/Pressure (kPa^{-1})
50	40	2.5×10^{-2}
40	58	1.7×10^{-2}
30	65	1.5×10^{-2}
20	100	1.0×10^{-2}
15	132	7.6×10^{-3}
10	200	5.0×10^{-3}

If you plot these values, you can see that there is indeed a straight-line relationship.

FIGURE F.2 Volume Versus 1/Pressure for a Fixed Amount of Gas at Constant Temperature

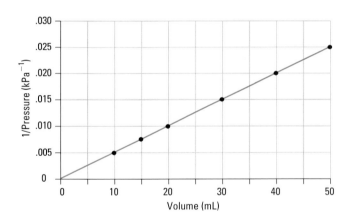

Extrapolating from the Graph

Extrapolation is the process of finding values beyond the limits of the known or measured values. However, there is a considerable risk of inaccuracy because we are assuming that the trend of the curve continues outside the range of the data. When the line is extended, a dotted line is used to show that the extension is little more than guesswork. Figure F.2 shows the process of extrapolating the curve to find the value of the reciprocal pressure corresponding to a zero volume. What is the theoretical value of reciprocal pressure? What would be the theoretical value of the pressure? Is it possible to compress a real gas to zero volume?

Calculating the Slope

If the line of best fit is straight, we can find the slope of the line. The *slope* of the line is defined as the ratio of the rise to the run. Thus

$$\text{slope} = \frac{\text{rise}}{\text{run}}$$

To find the slope, draw any convenient run on the graph. A *run* is a horizontal line drawn below the curve of the graph, touching the curve at one end. The calculations are simplified if the run is a whole number and as large as possible. Then draw in the corresponding rise. A rise is a vertical line joining the free end of the run to the curve.

A run of 30 mL (from 20 mL to 50 mL) is shown in Figure F.2. The rise is 2.0×10^{-2} kPa^{-1} (from 5.0×10^{-3} to 2.5×10^{-2}). The slope is calculated as follows:

$$\text{slope} = \frac{\text{rise}}{\text{run}}$$
$$= \frac{30 \text{ mL}}{2.0 \times 10^{-2} \text{ kPa}^{-1}}$$
$$= 1.5 \times 10^3 \text{ mL·kPa}^{-1}$$

Notice that the slope in this example has units. This is true for many slopes in chemistry.

Writing the General Equation of the Line

If the trend of the curve is a straight line through the origin, the plotted variables are *directly* proportional to each other. As one variable *doubles*, the other doubles, and vice versa. The general equation for a straight line passing through the origin is $y = mx$, where y is the variable on the vertical axis, x is the variable on the horizontal axis, and m is the slope of the line.

As the plot in Figure F.2 was a straight line through the origin, we can assign y as V and x as $1/p$. The equation of the line can be written as $V = k(1/p)$.

Writing the Specific Corresponding Equation

The specific corresponding equation replaces the symbol for the proportionality constant k with its numerical value. The value of the proportionality constant is equal to the slope of the line. Since the slope of the line is 1.5×10^3 mL·kPa^{-1}, the specific corresponding equation in our example is

$$V = (1.5 \times 10^3 \text{ mL·kPa}^{-1})(1/p)$$

Using the Specific Corresponding Equation

It is often more convenient to interpolate or extrapolate using the specific corresponding equation than from a graph. For example, we could use the equation to determine the value of the pressure corresponding to a volume of 90 mL. Perform the calculation and see what pressure you would obtain. The equation can only be used to extrapolate if the trend of the graph is a straight line beyond the plotted points.

The Purpose of the Plot

Though it is a useful skill to be able to plot data, scientists ask the question why? Why is there this relationship between the volume and pressure of a gas? How can the relationship be explained in molecular terms? Thus a graph is only a beginning, not an end in itself.

G.   Tables

G.1   POLYATOMIC IONS

acetate	CH_3COO^-
ammonium	NH_4^+
carbonate	CO_3^{2-}
hydrogen carbonate (bicarbonate)	HCO_3^-
perchlorate	ClO_4^-
chlorate	ClO_3^-
chlorite	ClO_2^-
hypochlorite	ClO^-
chromate	CrO_4^{2-}
dichromate	$Cr_2O_7^{2-}$
cyanide	CN^-
hydroxide	OH^-
nitrate	NO_3^-
nitrite	NO_2^-
oxalate	$(COO)_2^{2-}$
permanganate	MnO_4^-
phosphate	PO_4^{3-}
hydrogen phosphate	HPO_4^{2-}
dihydrogen phosphate	$H_2PO_4^-$
silicate	SiO_4^{4-}
sulfate	SO_4^{2-}
sulfite	SO_3^{2-}
hydrogen sulfide (bisulfide)	HS^-
hydrogen sulfate (bisulfate)	HSO_4^-
hydrogen sulfite (bisulfite)	HSO_3^-
thiocyanate	SCN^-
thiosulfate	$S_2O_3^{2-}$

G.2   CARBON CHAIN NAMES

1	meth-	6	hex-
2	eth-	7	hept-
3	prop-	8	oct-
4	but-	9	non-
5	pent-	10	dec-

G.3   NAMING POLYATOMIC IONS

—ate	most common	thio—	1 less oxygen & 1 more sulfur
per—ate	1 more oxygen		
—ite	1 less oxygen	bi— or hydrogen	1 hydrogen added
hypo—ite	2 less oxygen		

G.4   SOME CONVERSION FACTORS

Length	$1 \text{ m} = 10^9 \text{ nm} = 10^{12} \text{ pm}$
Volume	$1 \text{ L} = 1000 \text{ mL} = 1000 \text{ cm}^3 = 1 \text{ dm}^3 = 10^{-3} \text{ m}^3$
Mass	$1 \text{ kg} = 1000 \text{ g}$ $1 \text{ t} = 1000 \text{ kg} = 1 \text{ Mg}$
Pressure	Standard Pressure = 100 kPa $1 \text{ atm} = 101.3 \text{ kPa} = 760 \text{ torr} = 760 \text{ mm Hg}$
Temperature	Standard Temperature = 25.0°C = 298.15 K $T(K) = T(°C) + 273.15$
Density	$1 \text{ g·cm}^{-3} = 1 \text{ g·mL}^{-1} = 10^3 \text{ g·L}^{-1} = 10^3 \text{ kg·m}^{-3}$

G.5   COMMON ORGANIC FUNCTIONAL GROUPS

STRUCTURE	FUNCTIONAL CLASS	REPRESENTATIVE COMPOUND
$-\overset{\overset{O}{\|\|}}{C}-O-\overset{\|}{\underset{\|}{C}}-$	Ester	$CH_3-\overset{\overset{O}{\|\|}}{C}-O-CH_2-CH_3$ Ethyl ethanoate (ethyl acetate)
$-\overset{\|}{\underset{\|}{C}}-OH$	Alcohol	CH_3-CH_2-OH Ethanol (ethyl alcohol)
$-\overset{\overset{O}{\|\|}}{C}-OH$	Carboxylic acid	$CH_3-\overset{\overset{O}{\|\|}}{C}-OH$ Ethanoic acid (acetic acid)
$-\overset{\|}{\underset{\|}{C}}-O-\overset{\|}{\underset{\|}{C}}-$	Ether	$CH_3-CH_2-O-CH_2-CH_3$ Ethoxyethane (diethyl ether)
$-\overset{\overset{O}{\|\|}}{C}-H$	Aldehyde	$CH_3-\overset{\overset{O}{\|\|}}{C}-H$ Ethanal (acetaldehyde)
$-\overset{\|}{\underset{\|}{C}}-\overset{\overset{O}{\|\|}}{C}-\overset{\|}{\underset{\|}{C}}-$	Ketone	$CH_3-\overset{\overset{O}{\|\|}}{C}-CH_3$ Propanone (acetone)

G.6 COMMON PREFIXES

1	mono-	6	hexa-
2	di-	7	hepta-
3	tri-	8	octa-
4	tetra-	9	nona-
5	penta-	10	deca-

G.7 COMMON MULTIVALENT CATIONS

copper(I)	Cu^+	copper(II)	Cu^{2+}
iron(II)	Fe^{2+}	iron(III)	Fe^{3+}
lead(II)	Pb^{2+}	lead(IV)	Pb^{4+}
mercury(I)	Hg_2^{2+}	mercury(II)	Hg^{2+}
tin(II)	Sn^{2+}	tin(IV)	Sn^{4+}

G.8 ELECTRONEGATIVITIES OF MAIN GROUP ELEMENTS

H 2.1						
Li 1.0	Be 1.5	B 2.0	C 2.5	N 3.0	O 3.5	F 4.0
Na 0.9	Mg 1.2	Al 1.5	Si 1.8	P 2.1	S 2.5	Cl 3.0
K 0.8	Ca 1.0	Ga 1.6	Ge 1.8	As 2.0	Se 2.4	Br 2.8
Rb 0.8	Sr 1.0	In 1.7	Sn 1.8	Sb 1.9	Te 2.1	I 2.5
Cs 0.7	Ba 0.9	Tl 1.8	Pb 1.9	Bi 1.9		

G.9 SOME IMPORTANT CONSTANTS

Absolute zero	$0 \text{ K} = -273.15°C$
Avogadro's number	$N_A = 6.022 \times 10^{23} \text{ mol}^{-1}$
Gas constant	$R = 8.314 \text{ J·K}^{-1}·\text{mol}^{-1}$
Molar volume of a gas at STP (0°C and 101.3 kPa)	$V_m = 22.4 \text{ L·mol}^{-1}$
Molar volume of a gas at SATP (25°C and 100.0 kPa)	$V_m = 24.8 \text{ L·mol}^{-1}$
Specific heat capacity for water	$c = 4.18 \text{ J·g}^{-1}·°C^{-1}$

G.10 SOLUBILITY RULES

All alkali metal and ammonium salts are soluble.

All nitrates are soluble.

All chlorides are soluble except Ag^+, H_2^{2+}, and Pb^{2+}.

All sulfates are soluble except Ca^{2+}, Ba^{2+}, Pb^{2+}, H_2^{2+}, and Ag^+.

All carbonates are insoluble except Group 1 ions and ammonium.

All phosphates are insoluble except Group 1 ions and ammonium.

All hydroxides are insoluble except Group 1 ions, ammonium, and Ba^{2+}.

All sulfides are insoluble except Groups 1 and 2 ions and ammonium.

G.11 ACTIVITY SERIES OF COMMON METALS

Li K Ba Ca Na Mg Al Zn Fe Sn Pb H Cu Hg Ag Au

← react with acids →

← react with water →

G.12 STRONG ACIDS

$HCl(aq)$

$HClO_4(aq)$

$HI(aq)$

$HNO_3(aq)$

$HBr(aq)$

$H_2SO_4(aq)$

G.13 STRONG BASES

$LiOH(aq)$

$NaOH(aq)$

$KOH(aq)$

$HNO_3(aq)$

$Ba(OH)_2(aq)$

GLOSSARY

A

absolute pressure actual pressure exerted by a gas

acid substance that produces hydrogen ions when dissolved in water

acid salt salt whose anion contains one or more covalently bonded hydrogen atoms

acid-base titration method of quantitative analysis that uses the known concentration of an acid or base to determine the unknown concentration of a base or acid through a neutralization reaction

acidic oxide non-metal oxide which reacts with water to form an acid

actinoid any of 14 elements (numbers 89 to 102) placed below the main part of the periodic table

activity series list of metallic elements plus hydrogen placed in order of relative reactivity

actual yield amount of product actually formed when a reaction is carried out

adsorb molecular attraction of a substance at the surface of another substance

alicyclic special class of aliphatic hydrocarbons in which the arrangement of the carbon atoms is cyclic

aliphatic hydrocarbon open chain or cyclic organic molecules subdivided into alkanes, alkenes, alkynes and alicyclics or ring structures

alkali metal any group 1 element except hydrogen

alkaline-earth metal any group 2 element

alkane aliphatic open chain organic compounds containing only single bonds between carbon atoms

alkene aliphatic open chain organic compounds containing one or more carbon-carbon double bonds

alkylation process of combining very short-chain hydrocarbon molecules to form longer carbon chains

alkyne aliphatic open chain organic compounds containing one or more carbon-carbon triple bonds

alpha particle particle consisting of two protons and two neutrons, total charge +2

alpha radiation beam of helium nuclei that are emitted from a radioactive source

amphoteric substances that can behave as an acid in one situation and a base in another

anion negative ion

Antarctic ozone hole massive depletion of ozone in the lower stratosphere above the Antarctic

aqueous solution solution made with water as the solvent

anthracite hard coal formed when buried plant material was subjected to high pressures

aromatic organic compounds that are cyclic and contain carbon-carbon double bonds

Arrhenius theory theory that states an acid is a substance producing H^+ ions when it is dissolved in water and a base is a substance producing OH^- ions when it is dissolved in water

atmosphere non-SI unit of pressure, 1 atm is equal to 760 mm Hg and 101.3 kPa

atmospheric pressure pressure exerted by the gases in the atmosphere

atomic number number of protons in the nucleus of an atom

atomic radius estimate of the size of an atom from its nucleus to its outer perimeter

average atomic mass average mass of the mixture of isotopes of an element that is usually found in nature

Avogadro's hypothesis equal volumes of gases at the same temperature and pressure contain equal numbers of molecules (and moles of molecules)

Avogadro's number (symbol N) number of particles in 1 mole, 6.02×10^{23}

B

ball-and-stick model model showing the type of covalent bond between each pair of bonded atoms

bar unit of pressure, 1 bar equals 100 kPa

barometer device for measuring the absolute pressure of a gas

base substance that contains OH^- ions and produces hydroxide ions when dissolved in water

basic oxide metal oxide which reacts with water to form a base

beta particle electron emitted from a radioactive source

beta radiation radiation consisting of fast-moving electrons

binary compound compound formed from two elements

biochemical reaction chemical change occurring within living cells

bitumen dense, sticky, semi-solid mixture of hydrocarbons that is about 83% carbon

boiling point temperature where the vapour pressure of a liquid equals the external pressure

bonding electrostatic attraction between pairs of atoms or ions

bonding pair two electrons shared between the nuclei of two atoms

Boyle's law at a constant temperature, the volume of a fixed mass of gas is inversely proportional to its pressure

branched-chain organic molecule in which one or more of the carbon atoms in the molecule is bonded to three or four carbon atoms

Brønsted-Lowry acid   any molecule or ion that can give up a hydrogen ion

Brønsted-Lowry base   any molecule or ion that can combine with a hydrogen ion

Brønsted-Lowry theory   theory that states an acid is a molecule or ion that can give up a hydrogen ion and a base is a molecule or ion that can combine with a hydrogen ion

burette   device used for dispensing very precise volumes of solution

C

calorimeter   device used to measure heat changes

calorimetry   field of science involved with measurement of heat changes

carbon bed   activated carbon beds used to absorb organic chemicals from waste water

catalytic cracking   process of decomposing long-chain hydrocarbons into shorter fragments

catalytic reforming   process of rearranging the bonds in hydrocarbons, converting them from straight-chain to branched-chain molecules using heat and a specialized catalyst

catenation   ability of atoms of an element to link together to form chains; catenation is most common for carbon

cation   positive ion

chain isomer   former name for a skeletal isomer

Charles's law   at constant pressure, the volume of a fixed mass of any gas is directly proportional to its Kelvin temperature

chemical bond   electrostatic attraction between pairs of atoms or ions

chemical equation   shorthand description of a reaction using the chemical formulas of the substances

chemical precipitation   formation of a solid compound upon the mixing two solutions

chemical reaction   specific changes in substances

chlorofluorocarbon (CFC)   family of molecules containing carbon, chlorine, and fluorine

cis-trans isomer   geometric isomers of alkenes where substituent groups are located on the same side (cis) or opposite sides (trans) of the carbon-carbon double bond

classical system   nomenclature system which places the name of the least electronegative element first and uses suffixes and prefixes with specific meanings

coefficient   number that describes proportions of reactants and products in a reaction in moles

coke   impure form of carbon, formed by heating carbon in absence chain; used in smelting that can be used commercially

combined gas law   for a fixed amount of gas, the product of the pressure and volume divided by the Kelvin

combustible   ability to burn

compound   pure substance made of two or more elements combined in a fixed ratio

concentrated solution   solution containing a large amount of solute

concentration   measure of the amount of solute dissolved in a solvent

condensed formula   compact form of showing the arrangement of atoms in a molecule

conjugate acid   Brønsted-Lowry acid for a corresponding base

conjugate base   Brønsted-Lowry base for a corresponding acid

connectivity   term used to describe atom bonding order

constitutional isomer   structural isomer; a compound that has the same molecular formula but different arrangement of the atoms

conversion factor   ratio that describes how one unit is related to another unit

co-ordinate covalent bond   covalent bond formed by an electron pair donated by only one of the atoms

covalent bond   shared electrons between the nuclei of individual atoms

covalent compound   pure substance composed of molecules

crystal lattice   three dimensional array of cations and anions

cycloalkane   alkane molecules with a cyclic structure

D

decomposition reaction   complex substance breaks down into two or more simpler substances

diatomic molecule   molecule containing two atoms

diffusion   movement of particles from an area of high concentration to an area of low concentration

dilute solution   solution containing a small amount of solute

dilution   lowering the concentration of a solution by adding solvent

dipole   slight difference in charge within a molecule

dissociation   process of ionic compounds breaking up into ions when dissolved in water. Ions become attracted and surrounded by water molecules

dissociation equation   chemical equation representing the separation of ions in an ionic compound when it is dissolved in water

double bond   two shared pairs of electrons

double displacement reaction   cation of one ionic compound changes place with the cation of another ionic compound

E

effusion   passage of molecules through tiny holes

electrodialysis   technique that uses charged electrodes to remove dissolved ions from water

electrolyte   compound that conducts electricity in the molten state and in solution

electron affinity   energy released when an electron is added to a gaseous atom

electron configuration   arrangement of electrons according to the number in each shell

electron-dot diagram   see Lewis structure

electronegativity   property that determines how strongly the electrons in a chemical compound are held by any one atom

empirical formula   simplest whole-number ratio of atoms (or ions) in a compound

endothermic reaction   reaction that absorbs heat from the surroundings

energy   the ability to do work or the capacity to produce change

energy change   difference between the energy required to break chemical bonds in the reactants and the energy released or absorbed when the products form

Erlenmeyer flask   reaction vessel used in a titration, also known as a conical flask

excess reagent   any reactant that is not completely consumed in a reaction

exothermic reaction   reaction that releases heat to the surroundings

experimental error   variation that occurs between repeated trials of an experiment

F

fissionable   atomic nucleus that is readily split into two major fragments

formula mass   mass of one mole of formula units of an ionic compound

formula unit   smallest unit of an ionic compound that still has the properties of that compound

fossil fuel   one of the deposits of materials formed by decomposition of once-living organisms, formed beneath the earth's surface by the action of great pressure and high temperature over millions of years

fractionation   process that is used to partially separate the components of crude petroleum according to their boiling points

functional group   group of atoms responsible for the typical reactions of a compound

G

gamma radiation   high-energy electromagnetic radiation given off by a radioisotope

gamma ray   most penetrating kind of radiation; gamma rays have no mass and no electrical charge

Gay-Lussac's law   at constant volume, the pressure of a fixed mass of any gas is directly proportional to its Kelvin temperature

Gay-Lussac's law of combining volumes   in any chemical reaction involving gases (at the same temperature and pressure), the volumes of the gases are always in small whole number ratios

geochemical reaction   chemical change occurring over long periods of time involving geologic factors such as high pressure, and temperature

geometric isomer   type of stereoisomer, where two or more compounds have their atoms connected in the same order but with different three-dimensional arrangements

gravimetric analysis   analytical method that relies on mass measurements

green chemistry   use of environmentally responsible strategies in chemical processes

greenhouse effect   term used to describe retention of thermal radiation by infra-red absorbing molecules in the atmosphere

group   family of elements in a column in the periodic table with a similar electron arrangement

H

half-life   time required for half the nuclei in a sample of an element to disintegrate into different nuclei

halogen series   list of halogens in order of relative reactivity

halogens   group 17 elements

hard water   water with a high concentration of calcium ions

heat   flow of thermal energy from a warmer object to a cooler one

heat capacity   heat required to raise the temperature of an object by one degree Celsius or one kelvin

heavy water   water molecules in which the hydrogen-1 atoms have been replaced by deuterium atoms

Henry's law   relationship between gas solubility and gas pressure; the mole fraction of a gas in water is proportional to the applied pressure

hydrated salt   salt containing molecules of water within its crystal structure

hydration when water molecules attach to the surface of other molecules

hydrocarbon compound that contains only hydrogen and carbon atoms

hydrochlorofluorocarbon (HCFC) molecule that contains hydrogen in addition to chlorine, fluorine, and carbon; synthesized to replace CFCs

hydrofluorocarbon (HFC) greenhouse gas listed in Kyoto Protocol containing carbon, fluorine, and hydrogen

hydrogen bond bond formed by the attraction of the partially positive hydrogen atom of one molecule for the partially negative oxygen of a neighbouring molecule

hydrogen-ion acceptor definition of a base according to Brønsted-Lowry theory

hydrogen-ion donor definition of an acid according to Brønsted-Lowry theory

hydrogen-ion exchange reaction (proton transfer reaction) acid-base reaction

hydrogenation chemical process where an unsaturated organic compound becomes saturated

hydronium ion H_3O^+ ion formed by water and a hydrogen atom combining

I

ideal gas gas for which the assumptions of the kinetic-molecular theory are valid

ideal gas constant constant equal to 8.31 $kPa \cdot L \cdot mol^{-1} \cdot K^{-1}$ in SI units

ideal gas law relationship linking moles, pressure, volume, and temperature for a gas

immiscible when two liquids will not dissolve in each other when they are mixed

industrial chemistry use of large-scale chemical processes to convert raw materials into desired end-products

inorganic compound compounds other than organic compounds

insoluble when a solid solute does not dissolve in a given liquid

ion atom that has gained or lost one or more electrons

ion exchange method for removing calcium ions from hard water; calcium ions are replaced with sodium ions

ionic bond electrostatic attractive force between cations and anions

ionic character electronegativity difference between bonding atoms

ionic compound substance that consists of positive ions and negative ions held together by electrostatic attractive forces

ionization process creating ions from molecules

ionization energy energy needed to remove an electron from a gaseous atom

ionization equation chemical equation in which a molecule separates into ions

isomer different compounds with the same molecular formula containing different arrangements of atoms

isotope atom of an element with different atomic masses

J

joule SI unit for measuring energy

K

Kelvin temperature scale absolute temperature scale, $-273.15°C$ is the zero point. One Celsius degree is equivalent to 1 kelvin

Kyoto Protocol international agreement to reduce the production of carbon dioxide, methane, dinitrogen oxide, hydrofluorocarbons, perfluorocarbons, and sulfur hexafluoride

L

lanthanoid any of 14 elements (numbers 57 to 70) placed below the main part of the periodic table

law of conservation of energy energy can be neither created nor destroyed

law of conservation of matter matter is not created or destroyed in a chemical reaction

law of definite proportions composition of a specific compound is constant

law of octaves early belief that, if elements were arranged in order of increasing atomic mass, there would be a repetition of properties with every eighth element

law of partial pressures total pressure of a mixture of gases is equal to the sum of the partial pressures of the component gases

Lewis structure representation of the atom showing the outermost electrons as dots

limiting reagent reagent limiting the amount of product formed in a reaction

logarithm inverse of an exponential relationship

lone pair pair of electrons not involved in bonding

M

main group any of the representative groups (numbers 1, 2, 13 to 18)

manometer device used to measure relative pressure

mass number total number of neutrons and protons in a nucleus

mass percent percent of solute (by mass) in a given mass of solution

mass spectrum   array of ion streams of discrete masses

mass-volume percent   concentration unit equal to mass of solute divided by volume of solution times 100%

methane hydrate   methane molecules trapped in an ice structure

millimetres of mercury   unit used to measure the height of a column of mercury in a barometer

miscible   when two liquids dissolve in each other

molar heat capacity   specific heat of a substance times its molar mass

molar mass   mass of one mole of a substance, expressed in units of $g \cdot mol^{-1}$

molar volume   volume occupied by 1 mole of a gas at STP or SATP

mole   (symbol mol) unit for the amount of a substance (symbol n)

mole fraction   number of moles of a gas in a mixture of gases divided by the total number of moles of gas

molecular formula   actual number of atoms of each element in one mole of the compound

molecular mass   mass of one molecule of a covalent compound

molecule   smallest part of a covalent compound

moles per litre   most common way of representing how much solute is present in a solution, the concentration

Montreal Protocol   international agreement that defined the rate at which replacement of CFCs should occur

N

net ionic equation   simplified equation with only those ions that chemically react

neutralization reaction   acid and base react to form a salt and water

Newton's third law of motion   for every action, there is an equal and opposite reaction

noble gas configuration   eight outer electrons, except for helium

noble gas   any of group 18 elements

nuclear fission   when the nucleus of an atom is struck by a slow-moving neutron, splitting it into two smaller fragments of nearly equal mass

nuclear fusion   reaction where nuclei combine to produce a nucleus of greater mass

nuclear reaction   reaction that involves changes in the atomic nuclei of reactants

O

octet rule   tendency of atoms to form ions having the same electron configuration as the nearest noble gas

organic (compound)   any compound that contains carbon atoms that are covalently linked to each other or to atoms of hydrogen, nitrogen, oxygen, sulfur, phosphorus, or any halogen

oxyanion   polyatomic ion containing oxygen with a net negative charge

ozone cycle   cyclic production of ozone by ultraviolet light fragmentation of oxygen

P

parent chain   longest continuous chain of carbon atoms in an alkane molecule

partial pressure   pressure of the gas of a substance

parts per billion (ppb)   1 part in 10^9

parts per million (ppm)   1 part in 10^6

pascal   SI unit of pressure, symbol Pa

percent composition   proportions of elements in a compound expressed as percents

percent mass-volume   concentration used when the solute is a solid and the solvent is a liquid

percent yield   ratio of actual yield to theoretical yield, expressed as a percent

perfluorocarbon (PFC)   greenhouse gas listed in Kyoto Protocol containing carbon and fluorine

period   any row in the periodic table

periodic law   elements arranged in order of increasing atomic number show a periodic repetition of properties

periodic trend   any pattern in quantitative characteristics of elements e.g. atomic radius, ionization energy, electron affinity, and electronegativity

periodicity   patterns of physical and chemical properties that repeat at regular intervals

petrochemical   any organic compound produced from oil or natural gas

petroleum   crude oil

petroleum refining   process of turning crude oil into useful products

pH scale   scale used to measure hydrogen ion concentration; every increase by one pH unit corresponds to a concentration decrease by a factor of 10. Normal range 0 to 14

pipette   measuring device used to transfer precise and very accurate volumes of a solution

planar   flat

polar   bond between atoms with different electronegativities

polar covalent bond   shared pair of electrons is pulled closer to the atom with the greater electronegativity

polyatomic ion   cluster of atoms held together by covalent bonds having an overall charge

polymer   large organic molecule that consists of many identical units

polymerization   chemical reaction that forms a polymer

positional isomer   isomers of organic molecules that have the same carbon skeleton but differ in the position of the multiple bonds

pounds per square inch   unit of pressure used in some English-speaking countries

precipitate   solid that forms when two solutions are mixed

product   substance resulting from a chemical reaction

proton transfer reaction (hydrogen-ion exchange reaction)   acid-base reaction

pyrolysis   decomposing a compound by heating it strongly in the absence of air

Q

qualitative analysis   technique of identifying which ions are present in solution

R

radiation trapping   atmospheric retention of thermal radiation

radical   atom or ion that possesses unpaired electrons

radioactive decay   process in which certain isotopes of elements are transformed atom-by-atom into other isotopes over time

radioactivity   release of radiation when the atoms of an isotope are transformed into atoms of an isotope of another element or a different isotope of the same element

radioisotope   radioactive isotope

reactant   substance that enters into a chemical reaction

real gas   any gas whose behaviour deviates from that of the Ideal Gas Law (usually at very high and very low temperatures)

recrystallization   method used to purify a solid substance by dissolving it in hot solvent and then cooling the solution, which causes the dissolved solid to crystallize in a very pure form

relative atomic mass   mass of each element relative to carbon-12 which is assigned an atomic mass of 12

relative humidity   ratio of the actual vapour pressure to the saturated vapour pressure expressed as a percent

relative mass   the mass of an object compared to the mass of another object

relative pressure   pressure exerted by a gas relative to atmospheric pressure

reverse osmosis   the application of pressure to reverse the flow of water molecules through a membrane so that the water flows from the side with high concentration of solute to that with low solute concentration

S

saturated compound   organic compounds with single carbon-carbon bonds

saturated solution   solution with the maximum amount of solid or gaseous solute dissolved in a given volume of solvent at a given temperature

saturated vapour pressure   maximum value for the vapour pressure of a liquid at any given temperature

screening effect   reduction in attractive force between nucleus and outer electrons resulting from the presence of the inner electrons

self-ionization   ability of water molecules to ionize to a very small extent

semi-metals   elements which are poor electrical conductors and are shiny and brittle (also called metalloids)

single bond   one shared pair of electrons

single displacement reaction   one element replaces another in a compound

skeletal isomer   isomers formed by different carbon atom arrangement in the backbone of the molecule

soft water   water with a low concentration of calcium ions

solar distillation   process utilizing the sun's energy to evaporate water for subsequent condensation

solar fusion   reaction where hydrogen nuclei(protons) fuse to make helium nuclei

solubility   physical property of a substance describing how soluble or insoluble it is

soluble   ability to dissolve in a solvent

solute   substance dissolved by a solvent

solution   homogeneous mixture of two or more substances; composed of a solvent and solutes

solvation   process by which ions are attracted to and surrounded by water molecules

solvent   liquid in which substances are dissolved

space-filling model   show the space occupied by each atom in the molecule

specific heat   also known as specific heat capacity, expressed in units of $J \cdot g^{-1} \cdot {}^{\circ}C^{-1}$ or $J \cdot g^{-1} \cdot K^{-1}$

specific heat capacity   heat needed to raise the temperature of one gram of a substance by one degree Celcius (or one Kelvin)

spectator ion an ion, in a solution reaction, that does not take part in the reaction

standard ambient temperature and pressure (SATP) 100 kPa and 25°C

standard solution a solution containing a stable solute of precisely and accurately known concentration

standard temperature and pressure (STP) 760 mm Hg and 0°C

stereoisomer any two or more compounds that have their atoms connected in the same order but have different three-dimensional arrangements

Stock system nomenclature system which uses roman numerals to indicate charges

stoichiometry relative proportions in which elements form compounds, or in which substances react

straight chain organic molecule in which each carbon atom is bonded to a maximum of two other carbon atoms

stratosphere 10–15 km of the atmosphere some 50 km above us

strong acid acid that ionizes completely

strong base base that dissociates completely

structural formula representation of a molecule showing each bonding pair of electrons as a solid line

structural isomer constitutional isomer; any compounds that have the same molecular formula but different arrangement of the atoms

sublimation change of state directly from a solid to a gas

substituent side chain of atoms linked to the parent chain of a molecule

synthesis reaction two or more simple substances combine to produce a more complex substance

T

temperature measure of the average thermal energy of a substance; thermal energy is the kinetic energy associated with random molecular motion

tetrahedron three-dimensional geometric structure having four triangular sides and has the same internal angle measurement (109.5°)

theoretical yield maximum amount of product that could be formed from the given amounts of reactants

thermal decomposition complex substance breaks down into two or more simpler substances as a result of heating

thermochemical equation chemical equation in which the heat of reaction is included

thermochemical reaction chemical change involving significant heat change

thermochemistry study of heat changes associated with chemical reactions

thermodynamics study of how and why reactions occur using mathematics and various scientific models

thermoplastic any plastic that hardens when cooled, but softens again when heated

titration procedure used to accurately determine the concentration of an unknown solution

torr unit equivalent to 1 mm of mercury

total ionic equation an equation where every substance that exists as free ions when dissolved in water is written in ionic form

transition metal any element in the middle section of the periodic table

transmutation reaction reaction in which an atom of an element is changed to an atom of a different element

triad historical belief that sets of three elements had related properties

triatomic molecule molecule containing three atoms

triple bond three shared pairs of electrons

troposphere Lower 10–15 km of the atmosphere in which we live

U

unsaturated compound any organic molecule that contains at least one double or triple bond between its carbon atoms

V

vapour pressure pressure exerted by evaporated liquid in a container

volatile substance with high vapour pressure at room temperature

volume percent percent solute by volume when two liquids are mixed to form a solution

volumetric analysis procedure that accurately measures the concentration of an unknown solution

volumetric flask special glassware for precise measurements

volumetric pipette accurately calibrated pipette

W

weak acid acid that ionizes partially

weak base base that partially dissociates

word equation shorthand description of reaction using the names of the substances

UNIT 1

Chapter 1

Section 1.1

Example 1, Practice Problem
density = 4.82 g·cm^{-3},
melting point = 821.0°C,
boiling point = 2431°C

Section 1.1 Review

6. specific gravity = 8.3 g·cm^{-3};
   melting point = 2150°C;
   boiling point = 2800°C

Chapter 1 Review

1. c)
2. e)
3. b)
4. b)
5. a)
17. **a)** 2 (IIA)

Chapter 2

Chapter 2 Review

1. d)
2. c)
3. b)
4. c)
5. b)
27. **c)** 11.4 g

Chapter 3

Chapter 3 Review

1. c)
2. b)
3. c)
4. d)
5. d)

Unit 1 Review

1. b)
2. d)
3. d)
4. b)
5. a)
6. d)
7. c)
8. c)
9. b)
10. c)
16. **a)** 1+, **b)** 2+, **c)** 0, **d)** 2−,
    e) 1−, **f)** 1+
23. 0

UNIT 2

Chapter 4

Section 4.1

Example 1, Practice Problem
35.45

Example 2, Practice Problem
6 gross

Example 3, Practice Problems
1. 2.26×10^{24} atoms
2. 3.3×10^{24} atoms

Section 4.1 Review

5. 55.85
6. 65.39
7. 2.5×10^{24} atoms
8. 1.7×10^{-2} mol

Section 4.2

Example 4, Practice Problems
1. 1.61×10^2 g
2. 67.5 g
3. 3.2×10^{23} g

Example 5, Practice Problem
0.132 mol

Example 6, Practice Problems
1. 1.3×10^2 g
2. **a)** 97.4 g, **b)** 34.9 g

Example 7, Practice Problems
1. 2.56×10^{23} atoms
2. 5.09×10^{23} atoms

Example 8, Practice Problems
1. 44.10 g·mol^{-1}
2. 233.31, 233.31 g·mol^{-1}

Example 9, Practice Problems
1. 197.34
2. 207.32, 207.32 g·mol^{-1}

Example 10, Practice Problems
1. 62.86, 262.86 g·mol^{-1}
2. 68.17, 68.17 g·mol^{-1}

Example 11, Practice Problems
1. 237.93 g·mol^{-1}
2. 204.88 g·mol^{-1}

Section 4.2 Review

3. **a)** 16.8 g, **b)** 16.8 g, **c)** 0.200 g
4. 5.25 mol
5. 5.00×10^{-3} mol
6. 1.25×10^{-5} mol
7. 1.21×10^{23} atoms
8. **a)** 120.91,
   b) 84.31,
   c) 132.14 g·mol^{-1},
   d) 342.30 g·mol^{-1},
   e) 315.47 g·mol^{-1}

Section 4.3

Example 12, Practice Problems
1. 4.1 g
2. **a)** 50.1 g, **b)** 2.98 g

Example 13, Practice Problems
1. 1.64×10^{23} molecules
2. **a)** 1.71×10^{21} molecules,
   b) 3.96×10^{21} molecules

Example 14, Practice Problem
3.76×10^{22} atoms

Example 15, Practice Problem
1.94×10^{22} ions

Example 16, Practice Problems
1. 63.50% Ag, 8.245% N, 28.26% O
2. **a)** 49.5% Co, 10.1% C, 40.4% O;
   b) 54.2% Ba, 20.5% Cr, 25.3% O;
   c) 20.6% Fe, 39.4% Cl, 4.5% H,
   35.5% O

Section 4.3 Review

3. **a)** 8.57×10^{21} molecules,
   b) 1.03×10^{23} atoms
4. **a)** 8.1 g B, **b)** 0.200 mol SO_2,
   c) 1.00 kg $(NH_2)_2CO$
5. **a)** 126.04 g, **b)** 7.1 g, **c)** 585 g
6. 5.77×10^{22} sodium ions
7. **a)** 25.94%, **b)** 17.07%, **c)** 43.74%
8. 9.03×10^{21} molecules
9. **a)** 4.54 mol, **b)** 2.49 mol,
   c) 0.704 mol

10. 8.48×10^{22} molecules

11. 2.51 mol, 7.56×10^{24} atoms

Chapter 4 Review

1. b)

2. b)

3. c)

4. d)

5. c)

20. (helium) 4.00 g·mol^{-1}, 2.0 g, 0.5 mol

(copper) 63.55 g·mol^{-1}, 0.47 mol, 2.84×10^{23} atoms

(water) 18.02 g·mol^{-1}, 2.7 g, 9.03×10^{22} molecules

(carbon dioxide) 44.01 g·mol^{-1}, 1.3×10^2 g, 3.0 mol

23. b) 2.5; **c)** (36.0, 90.1), (48.0, 120)

25. 36.0 g

26. 6.22 g

27. 1.74×10^{22} oxygen atoms

28. 39.8 g

29. 35%

31. a) 2, **b)** 2, **c)** 9, **d)** 10

32. 2.9 mol

33. 17 mol

34. $169 per mole

35. $3170 per mole

36. 15.3 g (acetone), 4.74 g (water)

39. a) 1.777×10^{-4} mol, **b)** 7.30 mol, **c)** 4.99 mol

40. a) 0.498 mol, **b)** 1.45×10^{-8} mol, **c)** 8.3 mol

41. a) 1.77×10^{-22} g, **b)** 1.93×10^{-22} g

Chapter 5

Section 5.1

Example 1, Practice Problem
1. 290 wheels, 145 boards, and 290 handgrips

Section 5.1 Review
6. b) 35 T, 70 W, 35 B, 105 P

Section 5.2

Example 4, Practice Problems
4 molecules of Fe, 3 molecules of O_2, 2 molecules of Fe_2O_3, 4 moles of Fe, 3 moles of O_2, 2 moles of Fe_2O_3

Example 5, Practice Problem
30 mol

Example 6, Practice Problem
17.08 g

Example 7, Practice Problem
a) 1.03×10^{24} molecules, **b)** 226.3 g

Section 5.2 Review
1. (Na) 2 molecules, 2 mol, 45.98 g; (H_2O) 2 molecules, 2 mol, 36.03g; (NaOH) 2 molecules, 2 mol, 79.99 g; (H_2) 1 molecule, 1 mol, 2.02 g

2. (C_8H_{18}) 2 molecules, 2 mol; (O_2) 25 molecules, 25 mol; (CO_2) 16 molecules, 16 mol; (H_2O) 18 molecules, 18 mol

4. a) (Zn) 2 atoms, 2 mol, 130.78 g; (HCl) 4 molecules, 4 mol, 145.84 g; ($ZnCl_2$) 2 molecules, 2 mol, 272.58 g; (H_2) 2 molecules, 2 mol, 4.04 g; **b)** (Mg) 3 atoms, 3 mol, 72.93 g; (H_3PO_4) 2 molecules, 2 mol, 196.00 g; ($Mg_3(PO_4)_2$) 1 molecule, 1 mol, 262.87 g; (H_2) 3 molecules, 3 mol, 6.06 g; **c)** (KIO_3) 2 molecules, 2 mol, 428.00 g; (KI) 2 molecules, 2 mol, 332.00 g; (O_2) 3 molecules, 3 mol, 96.00 g

6. a) 4 mol P, 5 mol O_2, 2 mol P_2O_5; **b)** 9 mol

7. a) 2.9 mol, **b)** 16.6 mol

8. a) 1.17×10^2 g, **b)** 1.28×10^2 g, **c)** 26.3 g

9. 6.77×10^{24} molecules

Section 5.3

Example 8, Practice Problem
b) 106 g

Example 9, Practice Problem
78.4%

Section 5.3 Review
4. a) 7.2 mol P_2O_5, **b)** 3.5 mol $AlCl_3$, **c)** 6.4 mol H_2O, **d)** 0.96 mol H_3PO_4

5. a) 0.1 mol P, **b)** 0.1 mol Al, **c)** 0.2 mol O_2, **d)** 0.08 mol H_2O

6. b) 10.7 g

8. b) 299.3 g

9. b) 0.249 g

10. 70.5%

11. 70.6%

Section 5.4

Example 10, Practice Problems
1. 18

2. 210

Chapter 5 Review

1. a)

2. d)

3. d)

4. d)

5. e)

14. 2 mol $KClO_3$: 2 mol KCl; 2 mol $KClO_3$: 3 mol O_2; 2 mol KCl : 3 mol O_2

15. a) 18.6 mol, **b)** 2.01 g

16. a) 7.88 g, **b)** 65.3 g

17. 0.439 g

18. 71%

19. a) 85.8%, **b)** 2.68

21. b) 61.8 g, **c)** 93.9%

22. b) 3.9 g

Unit 2 Review

1. b)

2. b)

3. a)

4. c)

5. b)

6. d)

7. c)

8. d)

9. b)

10. a)

13. (K) 2 atoms, 2 mol, 78.20 g; (H_2O) 2 molecules, 2 mol, 36.04 g; (KOH) 2 molecules, 2 mol, 112.22 g; (H_2) 1 molecule, 1 mol, 2.02 g

27. a) 91.04%, **b)** 1.693%

28. b) 3.08×10^{24} atoms,
  c) 4.9×10^{23} ions,
  d) 5.74×10^{23} atoms

29. a) 1.88×10^{22} molecules,
  b) 1.85×10^{24} atoms,
  c) 4.37×10^{22} ions

32. a) 141.94 g·mol^{-1},
  b) 103.93 g·mol^{-1},
  c) 181.65 g·mol^{-1},
  d) 221.90 g·mol^{-1},
  e) 279.71 g·mol^{-1}

33. 894 g·mol-1

34. a) 1.32×10^{-2} g, **b)** 2.01×10^{9} g,
  c) 5.05×10^{-11} g

35. a) 1.4 mol, **b)** 1.999 mol,
  c) 2.38×10^{-6} mol,
  d) 2.3×10^{-1} mol,
  e) 9.16×10^{-1} mol

36. a) 11.8 mol, **b)** 2.64×10^{-2} mol,
  c) 1.46×10^{-13} mol,
  d) 4.98×10^{-1} mol,
  e) 1.45×10^{-8} mol, **f)** 8.3 mol

37. a) (KBr) 119 g·mol^{-1}, (AgNO$_3$)
  169.9 g·mol^{-1}; **b)** 7.14 g KBr,
  10.2 g AgNO$_3$; **c)** 1 mol

42. a) 72.3% Fe, 27.7% O;
  b) 7.80×10^{18} atoms

43. a) 17.6% Na, 39.7% Cr, 42.7% O;
  b) 24.7% K, 34.7% Mn, 40.5% O;
  c) 20.2% Mg, 26.7% S, 53.2% O

44. a) 49.5% Co, 10.1% C, 40.4% O;
  b) 54.2% Ba, 20.5% Cr, 25.3% O;
  c) 20.6% Fe, 39.4% Cl, 4.5% H,
  35.5% O

46. a) 7.87 g, **b)** 65.3 g

47. 77.06 g

48. 0.92 g

49. 5.28 mol

51. 3.92 g, 95.2%

52. a) 113%

53. b) 44.3%

54. 87.4%

62. a) 105.5 kg

UNIT 3

Chapter 6

Section 6.3

Example 1, Practice Problem
1.20 mol·L^{-1}

Example 2, Practice Problem
1.54×10^{-2} mol·L^{-1}

Example 3, Practice Problem
4.13×10^{-1} L

Example 4, Practice Problems
  1. 30.0%
  2. 68.8%

Example 5, Practice Problems
  1. 2.0%
  2. 12.0 mol·L^{-1}

Example 6, Practice Problem
$100.$ mg

Example 7, Practice Problem
a) 4.0×10^{-1} g, **b)** 3.1 g

Example 8, Practice Problem
0.267 mol·L^{-1}, 0.133 mol·L^{-1}

Example 9, Practice Problems
  1. 1.60 mol·L^{-1}, 2.40 mol·L^{-1}
  2. 0.445 mol·L^{-1}

Section 6.3 Review

  2. a) 1.00×10^{-1} mol·L^{-1},
    b) 5.00×10^{-2} mol·L^{-1},
    c) 2.00×10^{-1} mol·L^{-1}

  3. 187 g

  4. 41.7 L

  5. 2.25 g

  6. 1.81 g

  7. 4.2×10^{18} g

  8. a) [Na$^+$] $= 1.50$ mol·L^{-1},
    [Cl$^-$] $= 1.50$ mol·L^{-1}

    b) [NH$_4^+$] $= 4.50 \times 10^{-1}$ mol·L^{-1},
    [CO$_3^{2-}$] $= 2.25 \times 10^{-1}$ mol·L^{-1}

    c) [Al^{3+}] $= 2.2$ mol·L^{-1},
    [SO$_4^{2-}$] $= 3.3$ mol·L^{-1}

    d) [K$^+$] $= 3.96 \times 10^{-2}$ mol·L^{-1},
    [NO$_3^-$] $= 3.96 \times 10^{-2}$ mol·L^{-1}

    e) [Pb^{2+}] $= 4.28 \times 10^{-2}$ mol·L^{-1},
    [NO$_3^-$] $= 8.55 \times 10^{-2}$ mol·L^{-1}

  9. 1.57×10^{-1} mol·L^{-1}
  10. 5.2×10^{15} g
  11. 6.42×10^{16} lead ions

Section 6.4

Example 10, Practice Problems
  1. 808 mL
  2. 3.01 L

Section 6.4 Review

  3. 0.15 mol·L^{-1}
  5. 11.1 times
  6. 0.15 mol·L^{-1}

Section 6.6

Example 12, Practice Problem
a) 1.00×10^{-5} mol·L^{-1},
b) 3.72×10^{-9} mol·L^{-1},
c) 9.77×10^{-13} mol·L^{-1}

Example 13, Practice Problem
12.08

Example 14, Practice Problem
2.86, 1.38×10^{-3} mol·L^{-1}

Section 6.6 Review

  4. a) 2.52, **b)** 10.78, **c)** 11.60,
    d) 1.10, **e)** 2.70, **f)** 9.30
  6. 12.83
  7. 12.61

Chapter 6 Review

  1. a)
  2. c)
  3. b)
  4. a)
  5. a)
  19. a) 4.00 g, **b)** 66 g
  21. 2.1×10^{-1} mol·L^{-1}
  22. 2.10×10^{-1} mol·L^{-1}
  24. a) 2.24×10^{-2} mol·L^{-1},
    b) 6.72×10^{-2} mol·L^{-1}
  25. 5.00×10^{-1} mol·L^{-1}
  27. a) 10^2, 10, 1, 10^{-1}, 10^{-2}, 10^{-3};
    b) 2, 3, 4, 5, 6, 7
  28. 58.3%
  29. 5.00×10^{-4} g
  30. c) i) 4.60, ii) 11.00
    d) i) 5.38, ii) 10.04

Chapter 7

Section 7.3

Example 4, Practice Problem
1.82×10^{-1} mol·L^{-1}

Example 5, Practice Problem
2.01×10^{-5} mol·L^{-1}

Section 7.3 Review

1. 4.00×10^{-1} L
2. 7.36 g
3. 7.91×10^{-2} L
4. 6.56×10^{-2} L
6. 3.80×10^{10} g, 2.8×10^7 L

Section 7.4

Example 6, Practice Problems
1. 1.01 mol·L^{-1}
2. 1.42×10^{-1} mol·L^{-1}

Section 7.4 Review

3. 7.469×10^{-2} mol·L^{-1}
4. 4.760×10^{-2} mol·L^{-1}
5. 1.50 mol·L^{-1}
6. 85.3 g·mol^{-1}
8. 2.20 mol·L^{-1}
9. 7.09×10^{-1} g
10. $x = 10$

Chapter 7 Review

1. **b)**
2. **b)**
3. **b)**
4. **a)**
5. **c)**
15. **b)** 1.4 mol·L-1
16. **b)** 5.00×10^{-2} mol·L^{-1}
18. 5.40×10^{-1} g
19. 5.40×10^{-1} L
20. 5.792×10^{-2} mol·L^{-1}
21. 46.0%
22. **b)** 10.7 g
23. 62.38%

Unit 3 Review

1. **e)**
2. **b)**

3. **a)**
4. **e)**
5. **d)**
6. **a)**
7. **e)**
8. **c)**
9. **a)**
10. **a)**
33. 5.03%
34. 21.0 g
35. **a)** 4.60, **b)** 11.00, **c)** 5.38, **d)** 10.04
36. 0.15 mol·L^{-1}
39. 7.36 g
40. **a)** 0.15 mol·L^{-1}, **b)** 5.01×10^{-7} mol·L^{-1}, **c)** 6.31×10^{-4} mol·L^{-1}
42. 8.70×10^{-2} L
43. 7.468×10^{-2} mol·L^{-1}
44. 1.50 mol·L^{-1}
48. 5.05%
52. 1.54×10^{-2} L
53. **a)** 7.67×10^{-3} mol·L^{-1}, **b)** 5.83×10^{-2} mol·L^{-1}, **c)** 4.00×10^{-1} mol·L^{-1}
54. 225 g
55. 1.20 L
56. 4.760×10^{-2} mol·L^{-1}
57. 23 g·mol^{-1}
60. 2.14%
61. **a)** 30 ppm, **b)** 300 mg·L^{-1}, **c)** 85 ppm
62. 41 g·L^{-1}
64. $[H_2SO_4] = 1.38 \times 10^{-1}$ mol·L^{-1}, $[NaOH] = 2.01 \times 10^{-1}$ mol·L^{-1}

UNIT 4

Chapter 8

Section 8.1

Example 1, Practice Problem
109 mm Hg

Example 2, Practice Problem
a) 0.333 atm, **b)** 4.89 lb·in^{-2}

Section 8.1 Review

6. 780 mm Hg
7. 825 kPa
8. 90.9 kPa

Section 8.2

Example 3, Practice Problems
1. 328 kPa
2. 1.27 L

Example 4, Practice Problems
1. 1.08 L
2. 149 K

Example 5, Practice Problems
1. 1.19×10^3 kPa
2. 662 K

Section 8.2 Review

5. $P_2 = 3P_1$
6. 1077 K
7. $V_2 = 2V_1$
8. 617 kPa
9. 379 kPa

Section 8.3 Review

7. $v_{Ra} = 0.36v_{N_2}$

Section 8.4

Example 6, Practice Problems
1. 1.48 L
2. 1.50×10^3 kPa

Example 7, Practice Problem
8.14×10^{-2} g·L^{-1}

Example 8, Practice Problem
1.13×10^3 g

Example 9, Practice Problem
549 kPa

Example 10, Practice Problem
2.43×10^{22} air molecules

Example 11, Practice Problem
3.03 g·L^{-1}

Example 12, Practice Problem
83.8 g·mol^{-1}

Example 13, Practice Problem
b) 112 g·mol^{-1}

Section 8.4 Review

3. $P_2 = 4P_1$
4. 1.9×10^{-2} L
5. 131 g·mol⁻¹
6. 2.12×10^8 L
7. 9.62×10^5 g

Section 8.5

Example 14, Practice Problems
1. $P_{N_2} = 25$ kPa, $P_{CO_2} = 125$ kPa
2. $P_{H_2} = 50$ kPa, $P_{Ne} = 50$ kPa

Section 8.5 Review

5. 20 kPa
6. 0.23
7. $P_{Ne} = 2.89$ kPa, $P_{He} = 102$ kPa
8. 67°C
9. 80°C

Chapter 8 Review

1. a)
2. a)
3. a)
4. a)
5. c)
18. a) -273.15°C
19. 26.66 kPa
20. 0.14 and 50.6 kPa (CO_2), 0.86 and 304 kPa (O_2)
22. 2.08×10^{-4} g
23. 1.5×10^3 K
25. 3.59×10^3 kPa

Chapter 9

Section 9.1 Review

6. 420 kPa

Section 9.2

Example 1, Practice Problem
250 mL

Example 4, Practice Problem
8.0 L

Example 5, Practice Problem
0.669 g

Section 9.2 Review

4. 71.6 g·mol⁻¹
5. a) 1.25 L, b) 0.625 L
6. a) 1.12×10^3 L,
   b) $V_{CO_2} = 675$ L, $V_{H_2O} = 900$ L
7. a) 1.67 g, b) 2.91 g
8. 3.33×10^5 L
9. 0.435 L

Section 9.3

Example 6, Practice Problem
0.667 g

Example 7, Practice Problem
0.28 g

Section 9.3 Review

1. $P_{H_2O} = 200$ kPa, $P_{CO_2} = 400$ kPa, $P_{O_2} = 32$ kPa, $P_{N_2} = 168$ kPa
2. 33 L
3. 1.09 L
4. 7.91×10^{-2} L
5. 2.4×10^{-3} g
6. 6.02×10^{-2} g
7. 1.64×10^{-3} mol, 9.86×10^{21} molecules
8. 96.13 kPa
9. $P_{CO_2} = 32.6$ kPa, $P_{N_2} = 71.6$ kPa, $P_{SO_2} = 35.8$ kPa
10. a) 99.8 kPa,
    b) 2.21×10^{-1} L,
    c) 9.86×10^{-3} mol

Section 9.4

Example 8, Practice Problem
17.4 L

Example 9, Practice Problem
1.2×10^{-2} L

Example 10, Practice Problem
4.9 L

Section 9.4 Review

1. b) 0.669 g
2. 33.9 g
3. a) 2.15×10^3 L;
   b) 2.91×10^3 g (SiO_2), 4.85×10^2 g (C)
4. 80% or ⁴/₅
5. 8.48 L

6. a) 3.26×10^{-2} L,
   b) 1.36×10^{-2} L
7. a) 2.00×10^{-2} L, b) 2.54 L,
   c) 16.9 g
8. a) 4.72×10^{-1} mol·L⁻¹,
   b) 5.74×10^{-1} L
9. 2.4×10^4 L

Chapter 9 Review

1. c)
2. b)
3. a)
4. b)
5. b)
14. a) $V_{NH_3} = 20.0$ L, $V_{O_2} = 25.0$ L
15. a) 147 g·mol⁻¹
16. a) 66 L, b) 3.3×10^3 L,
    c) 3.3×10^8 L, d) 3.0×10^{10} L
17. 64.0 L
19. 1.6×10^9 L
20. a) 2.01×10^3 L, b) 7.53 L
21. a) 30.0 g, b) 6.98 L
22. 33.0 g·mol⁻¹, 3.3%

Unit 4 Review

1. c)
2. e)
3. a)
4. c)
5. a)
6. a)
7. a)
8. a)
9. b)
10. c)
28. 233 K
29. 1.9×10^2 kPa
30. 1.49×10^5 L
31. 3.9 L
32. 149 K
33. a) 108 kPa, b) 199 kPa
34. 146 K, 86.9 kPa, 1.16×10^{-1} L,
35. a) 1.26×10^3 L, b) 2.80 L
36. 5.40×10^{-1} g (NH_3), 28°C (H_2), 698 kPa (CO)

37. 20 mol

38. b) 1.60×10^3 g, **d)** 3.41×10^3 L

39. b) 6.37×10^{-2} g·L^{-1},
c) 9.24 g·L^{-1}, **d)** $d_{\text{Uuo}} : d_{\text{H}_2} = 145$,
e) $M_{\text{Uuo}} : M_{\text{H}_2} = 145$

40. 352 g·mol^{-1}

41. 1.13 L

42. b) 2.62×10^4 L (O$_2$),
1.31×10^5 L (air);
c) 1.67×10^4 L;
d) 1.60 t

43. 3.96×10^{-3} g·L^{-1}

44. 4.72×10^{-1} mol·L^{-1}, 5.80×10^{-1} L

45. 0.364 L

47. b) 3.41 g, **c)** 81.0%

48. 59.7%

49. 46.0%

50. c) 2.35×10^5 L

51. b) i) 6.64×10^{-1} L,
ii) 3.64×10^3 L

52. a) 5.06 g·L^{-1}

53. b) 16 g·mol^{-1}

54. a) 19.3 g

55. 1.69×10^{-1} g·L^{-1}

56. b) 184 g·mol^{-1}

UNIT 5

Chapter 10

Section 10.2 Review

2. d)

Section 10.4 Review

16. 352 g

Chapter 10 Review

1. c)

2. a)

3. c)

4. d)

5. b)

Chapter 11

Section 11.1

Example 1, Practice Problem
-686 kJ

Example 2, Practice Problem
1. -269.5 kJ

Section 11.1 Review

6. -1260 kJ

7. 235.2 kJ

Example 4, Practice Problems
1. 46 kJ

2. 1600°C

Example 6, Practice Problems
1. -5.0×10^2 kJ·mol^{-1}

2. 0.456 J·g^{-1}·°C^{-1}

Example 7, Practice Problem
-2.02×10^3 kJ·mol^{-1}

Section 11.2 Review

6. 0.130 J·g^{-1}·°C^{-1}

7. 75.3 J·mol^{-1}·°C^{-1}

10. -22 kJ·g^{-1}

Chapter 11 Review

1. d)

2. b)

3. c)

4. a)

5. d)

22. 0.48 kJ·°C^{-1}

23. 2.3 J·g^{-1}·°C^{-1}

24. 26.3 J

25. -389 kJ·mol^{-1}

26. -2.03×10^3 kJ·mol^{-1}

31. -3.08×10^3 kJ·mol^{-1}

37. a) 2.06 J·g^{-1}·°C^{-1},
b) 35.1 J·mol^{-1}·°C^{-1}

Unit 5 Review

1. b)

2. b)

3. c)

4. d)

5. a)

6. b)

7. b)

8. a)

9. a)

10. b)

21. d)

30. a), c)

31. 4.18 kJ·g^{-1}

32. 0.60 g (C), 3.0 g (CO), 0.53 mol (C$_8$H$_{18}$)

37. 113 J·mol^{-1}·°C^{-1}

38. 26.3 J

39. 31.4 kJ

40. 52.2°C

51. 0.89 J·g^{-1}·°C^{-1}

52. 0.37 J·g^{-1}·°C^{-1}

70. b) 369.8 g

71. 115.6°C

72. 7.36 kJ

73. 0.236 J·g^{-1}·°C^{-1}

74. 21.51 J·mol^{-1}·°C^{-1} (Cu),
25.3 J·mol^{-1}·°C^{-1} (Ag),
25.4 J·mol^{-1}·°C^{-1} (Au)

75. 280 kJ

76. -2.00×10^3 kJ·mol^{-1}

INDEX

atomic radius 21–2, 39
atomic sizes 47
atomic structure 11
  modern model of 11
atomic theory 53, 300, 368
  of matter 368
attraction 23, 25, 34, 50
  force of 25, 345
attraction, interparticle 345
attractive forces 25, 345, 347, 365, 463
average atomic mass 129–30, 132–3
average bond energy 486–7, 490
Avogadro, Amadeo 133–4
Avogadro's number 127, 132–3,
  135–6, 138, 145–6, 147, 180–1,
  185, 356

B

Babcock, Stephen 285
bacteria 235, 237, 239, 363, 440
  decomposition 440
Baeyer test for unsaturation 468, 476
balanced chemical equation 81, 85–6,
  87–8, 93, 96, 98–9, 102–103,
  175–8, 180–3, 188, 190, 289, 296,
  302, 309, 466, 476, 481, 486, 512
  guidelines for writing 176
balanced molecular equation 76
balanced net ionic equation 288
ball-and-stick models 47
bar 331
barium 9, 10, 92, 99, 294, 297
barium bromide 54
barium carbonate 99, 141, 287
barium chloride 99, 109, 286, 287,
  294, 304
barium hydroxide 230, 297, 303
barium ion 294
barium nitrate 287, 295
barium oxide 230
barium salt 287
barium sulfate 304
barium-142 199
barometer 330, 331, 335
  aneroid, 331
  mercury 331
Bartlett, Neil 46
base 52, 82, 85, 99, 100–102, 174,
  290, 302–303, 472
basic oxide 80, 84–5, 99, 100
beams 131
bee sting 258
benzene 156, 235, 360, 361, 465
Berthollet, Claude 148
beryllium 10, 17, 24
beta decay 195
beta particle 195, 198
beta radiation 195, 198
Bhopal accident 356

big bang 2
binary acids 65
binary compound 54
binary covalent compound 63
binary ionic compound 54, 58, 80
biochemical processes 40
biochemical reactions 74, 322
biochemistry 4
bio-diesel fuel 500
biodegradable plastics 3
biological magnification 249
bioinorganic chemist 366
bismuth 10, 19, 194
bitumen 503–4
bituminous coal 502
black carbon, activated 240
blood 173, 221, 241, 325, 328,
  331–2, 371–3, 479
  pH level of 271
  serum 40
Bohr model of atom 16, 23
Bohr, Niels 16
boiling 345
boiling point 9, 11, 27, 48, 230, 355,
  357–8, 364, 371, 460, 463–5, 470,
  503–4, 505
bond 50, 57, 69, 194, 328, 441, 445
  breaking 484
  energies 488
  formation 57, 484
  rotation 458
bonding 37, 45, 51, 57, 194, 230
  chemical 34
  See also electrostatic attraction
bonding pairs 42
boron 10, 17, 24, 138
Boyle, Robert 337, 339
Boyle's law 333, 336–8, 346–7, 351,
  373
brain 371, 373
branch point 448
branched-chain alkane 445, 448–9,
  451, 464
branched-chain hydrocarbons 449
branched-chain model 452
branched-chain molecules 505–7
bromide 225, 294
  ion 294
bromine 7, 10, 12, 16–17, 50, 91,
  288, 466, 476
bromthymol 309
Brönsted-Lowry theory 257
Brooks, Harriet 13
burette 301, 302, 308–310
  clamp 307
butane 444–5, 451–2, 460, 508
butene 460

C

cadmium 10, 248, 292
calandria 202
calcium 5, 9, 10, 17–18, 28, 40–1,
  50, 54, 92, 95, 115, 225, 229,
  231, 290–1, 292, 496
calcium carbide 183
calcium carbonate 58, 83, 84, 95,
  144–5, 192, 228, 290
  limestone chalk 84
calcium chloride 95, 115, 161, 229, 297
  anhydrous 162
calcium chloride dihydrate 142–3,
  146–7
calcium hydroxide 84, 460, 481
calcium nitrate 59, 141–2, 288, 297
calcium oxide (a base oxide) 82, 84,
  106, 460
  commonly called quicklime 82
calcium sulfate 225, 228, 243
calcium sulfate hemihydrate (plaster
  of paris) 63
calculations 185
  average atomic mass 129
  empirical formula 155
  heat change 494
  mass 135
  molecular formula 156
californium 19
calorie 483
calorimeter 490, 495–9, 511–12
Canada Deuterium Uranium (CANDU)
  reactor 200–2
Canada's Food Guide 479
Canadian Centre for Occupational
  Health and Safety (CCOHS) 185
canary 443
cancer therapy 196
CANDU reactor. See Canada
  Deuterium Uranium reactor.
carbide 460
carbohydrate 440, 482, 483
carbon 3, 10, 15, 17, 45, 49, 50–1,
  79, 81, 126, 128–9, 132, 136,
  150–1, 162–3, 224, 230–1, 246,
  361, 442, 444, 458, 484, 504, 512
carbon atom 438, 439–40, 442–3,
  445–53, 455, 457–8, 461, 463–4,
  475, 505
  properties 441
carbon bed 240
carbon chain 445, 449, 451, 457,
  463, 464
carbon dioxide 3, 45, 47, 48, 77–9,
  82–3, 85, 97, 126, 131, 149,
  162–4, 222–3, 290–1, 322, 328,
  347, 349, 373, 375, 379, 440,
  455, 466, 488, 508, 520
  carbonated drinks 329
  emissions 520

tin 9, 10, 54, 55–6, 90, 247
tin(II) fluoride 55
tin(II) nitrate 88
tin(IV) fluoride 55
tin(IV) perchlorate 61
Titan 404
titanate 298
titanium 10, 17, 39
titanium(IV) 55
titanium carbide 125
titanium dioxide 298
titanium oxide 298
titanium(IV) oxide 298
titanyl 298
titanyl sulfate 298
titrant solution 302
titration 300, 301, 309, 320
toothpaste 55
Torricelli, Evangelista 330–1
torr 333
total ionic equation 286, 289, 290
toxicologists 144
toxicity 108
trace analysis 131
trace gases 131
trans- (prefix) 458
trans-2-butene 458
transistors 3
transition elements 53
transition metal 15
	series 15
transmutation 200
transmutation reactions 200, 203
treatment of drinking water 236
tri- (prefix) 61, 63, 451
triads 7
triatomic molecule 42
trihalomethanes (THMs) 219, 236
trimethylpentane (commonly called
	iso-octate) 507
trioxygen (commonly called ozone)
	327
triple bond 44, 455, 459, 461, 466
triple carbon-carbon bonds 475
tritium (hydrogen-3) 198
troposphere 409
tube 441, 443
tungsten 365
Tyrrell, Joseph Burr 501

U

ultraviolet irradiation 316
ultraviolet light 77, 466
universal indicator 285
universal solvent 228
unreactive gas 360
unsaturated carbon-carbon bond 469
unsaturated compound 455, 468, 476
unsaturated fat 455–6, 462, 476, 479
unsaturated hydrocarbon 455, 466,
	475

unsaturation 476
unstable elements 18
uranium 11–12, 19, 125, 200–2, 349
	hexafluoride, 349
	isotopes 198
	processing 123
U-235 199–202, 349
U-238 196, 349

V

vacuum 330–1, 363
vacuum chamber 131
vacuum distillation tower 505
vanadium 10
van Beethoven, Ludwig 125
vaporization 365, 505
vapour 49, 466
vapour pressure 357, 362–3, 365,
	369, 370–1
	curve 364
velocity 348
	molecular 348
Venable, Francis 460
vibration 345
vinegar 259
viruses 235–6
visible light 196
vitamins 440
vitriol 52
volatile 364
volcanoes 352
volume 181, 185, 296–7, 299–301,
	308–9, 325–6, 336–8, 341–6, 347,
	350–2, 354, 356, 367, 373, 464
	of solution 242
volume and pressure. See pressure
	and volume.
volume and temperature. See
	temperature and volume.
volume, molar. See molar volume.
volume percent 245
volumetric analysis 298–301, 313
	procedure 302
volumetric flasks 254
volumetric pipette 255
von Zeppelin, Count Ferdinand 340

W

Walkerton 36, 240, 316
wasp sting 258
waste disposal 105
water 2, 5, 18–20, 28, 37, 40, 42,
	48–9, 51, 62–3, 65, 75, 77–8, 80,
	82, 84, 86, 98–102, 103, 108,
	139–40, 161–2, 164, 167, 183,
	218, 220, 222–5, 228–32, 235–7,
	247, 284, 290, 298, 301, 307–309,
	316, 321, 324, 326, 328, 331,
	352, 355, 356–7, 362–3, 369–70,
	372–3, 436, 439, 460, 469, 482–3,
	488, 492–3, 495–8, 504, 511–12

content of air 362
	model 78
	molecule 145, 228
	purification 236
	quality 233
	shortages 234
	source 147, 218, 219, 230,
		233, 235, 249
	supply 290, 316
	system 237
	vapour 82, 161, 326, 362, 486–7
water cycle (hydrologic cycle) 233
water-borne diseases 219
water-soluble 94
wavelengths 11, 24
weak acids 262–5
weak bases 265–6
weather 335
	balloon 351
weighing to constant mass 303
Wetterhahn, Dr. Karen 366
white lead 298
whitewash 84
WHMIS 93
Willson, Thomas 460
Wöhler Friedrich 440, 442
Woolner, Ken 244
wood 440
word equation 76
World Health Organization 237, 249

X

X-rays 11, 13, 38, 195
xenon 10, 46, 327
	compounds 46

Y

yield 191
-yl (suffix) 448
-yne (suffix) 461

Z

zeppelin 340
zigzag pattern 464
zinc 10, 40, 80, 88, 90–1, 289
zinc carbonate 86
zinc nitrate 88
zinc sulfate 109

PHOTO CREDITS AND ACKNOWLEDGEMENTS

The publisher wishes to thank the following sources for photographs, illustrations, and other materials used in this book. Care has been taken to determine and locate ownership of copyright material used in this text. We will gladly receive information enabling us to rectify any errors or omissions in credits.

Photography

COVER ©NASA/Science Photo Library. **UNIT ONE** Page 3 Science Photo Library/Photo Researchers, Inc.; p. 6 (far left) National Museums of Kenya/Visuals Unlimited, (centre left) Val & Alan Wilkinson/VALAN Photos, (centre) VALAN Photos, (centre right) Jane K. Hyessen/VALAN Photos, (far right) Martin Bough/Fundamental Photographs; p. 11 Bettmann/Corbis/Magma; p. 13 Miss Harriet Brooks, nuclear physicist, Montreal QC, 1898 #II0123880, Notman Photographic Archives, McCord Museum of Canadian History; p. 16 (left) Richard Megna/Fundamental Photographs, (right) Tom Pantages; p. 32 Kip Peticolas/Fundamental Photographs; p. 37 Charles C. Winters/Photo Researchers, Inc.; p. 38 (left) Science Photo Library/Photo Researchers, Inc., (right) Science Pictures Ltd./Corbis/Magma; p. 42 (top) Paul Silverman/Fundamental Photographs, (bottom left) Science Pictures Ltd./Corbis/Magma, (bottom right) Robert Pickett/Corbis/Magma; p. 45 Richard Megna/Fundamental Photographs; p. 46 Courtesy of Dr. Neil Bartlett; p. 51 Microwave Digestion Oven manufactured by Questron Technologies Corp., Mississauga, ON; p. 53 Richard Kellaway/PC Services and courtesy of Blackwell Science Ltd.; p. 54 Richard Megna/Fundamental Photographs; p. 55 (left) John Fowler/VALAN Photos, (top right) Tony Freeman/PhotoEdit, (bottom right) SuperStock; p. 58 Steve Vivler/SuperStock; p. 59 John Fowler/VALAN Photos; p. 60 (top) Diane Hirsch/Fundamental Photographs, (bottom) David Joyce & Ian Smith/VALAN Photos; p. 61 John Fowler/VALAN Photos; p. 62 (top left) John Fowler/VALAN Photos, (top centre and right) Tom Pantages, (bottom left) FPG International/Dick Makin; p. 63 (top) Richard Kellaway/PC Services, (centre) Tom Walker/Visuals Unlimited, (bottom) SuperStock; p. 72 Bill Beatty/Visuals Unlimited; p. 74 Tom Bean/SuperStock; p. 75 (top) Lester V. Bergman/Corbis/Magma, (bottom left) Tom Pantages, (bottom right) L. S. Stepanowicz/Visuals Unlimited; p. 80 Galen Rowell/Corbis/Magma; p. 83 Tom Pantages; p. 84 (top left and centre left) Tom Pantages, (right) Corbis/Magma; p. 87 L. S. Stepanowicz/Visuals Unlimited; p. 90 Richard Megna/Fundamental Photographs; p. 91 John Fowler/VALAN Photos; p. 94 Tom Pantages; p. 95 Paul Silverman/Fundamental Photographs; p. 98, 99 Richard Megna/Fundamental Photographs; p. 102 Tom Pantages; p. 106 David Guyon/SPL/Photo Researchers, Inc.; p. 108 (top left) CP Picture Archive (John Lehmann), (top right) Adam Hart Davis/SPL/Photo Researchers, Inc., (bottom left) David Parker/SPL/Photo Researchers, Inc., (bottom right) Maximillian Stock Ltd./SPL/Photo Researchers, Inc.; p. 116 (far left) Bob Rowan/Corbis/Magma, (centre left) Jeff Greenberg/Visuals Unlimited, (centre) Geoff Tompkinson/SPL/Photo Researchers, Inc., (centre right) PhotoDisc, Inc., (far right) David Woodfall/Stone; p. 121 David Parker/SPL/Photo Researchers, Inc. **UNIT TWO** Page 124 (left) Richard Megna/Fundamental Photographs, (right) Erwin C. "Bud" Nielson/Visuals Unlimited; p. 125 (left) R. F. Ashley/Visuals Unlimited, (right) Jeff Greenberg/Visuals Unlimited; p. 126 PhotoDisc, Inc.; p. 127 Ivy Images; p. 131 NASA; p. 133 M. & D. Long/Visuals Unlimited; p. 148 (top right) Hulton/Archive, (centre right) The Granger Collection, New York, (bottom left) Richard Kellaway/PC Services; p. 149 Richard Kellaway/PC Services; p. 150 Ivy Images; p. 156 (left) Larry Stepanowicz/Visuals Unlimited, (right) Paul A. Souders/Corbis/Magma; p. 161 Richard Megna/Fundamental Photographs; p. 172 Ed Young/SPL/Photo Researchers, Inc.; p. 174 PhotoDisc, Inc.; p. 179 James Burton/Mach 2 Stock; p. 182 David Cavagnaro/Visuals Unlimited; p. 184 Alex Van Name/Visuals Unlimited; p. 187 Richard Kellaway/PC Services; p. 189 E. R. Degginger/Color-Pic, Inc.; p. 190 Potash Corporation of Saskatchewan Inc.; p. 191 (left) CP Picture Archive (Tannis Toohey); p. 198 SOHO EIT consortium. Soho is a project of international co-operation between ESA and NASA; p. 199 Princeton University; p. 201 Canadian Nuclear Association; p. 210 David Young-Wolff/PhotoEdit. **UNIT THREE** Page 219 Ivy Images; p. 220 Gregg Neelin/Communitas Associates, courtesy of Baxter Canada; p. 222 Richard Kellaway/PC Services; p. 223 Richard Megna/Fundamental Photographs; p. 224 (left) SuperStock, (right) John D. Cunningham/Visuals Unlimited; p. 225 Potash Corporation of Saskatchewan Inc.; p. 227 Norman Piluke/Ivy Images; p. 231 Richard Megna/Fundamental Photographs; p. 234 NASA; p. 235 Chris Bruun/Mach 2 Stock; p. 236 R. Morsch/First Light; p. 238 Ole Tenold/Mach 2 Stock; p. 244 CHEM 13 News; p. 246 (top) The Granger Collection, New York, (bottom) Richard Kellaway/PC Services; p. 249 Liba Taylor/Corbis/Magma; p. 251 PhotoDisc, Inc.; p. 254, 255 Richard Megna/Fundamental Photographs; p. 257 (top left) Wally Eberhart/Visuals Unlimited, (bottom left) Science Photo Library/London UK, (top and bottom right) Richard Megna/Fundamental Photographs; p. 258 Hulton/Archive; p. 262 Richard Kellaway/PC Services; p. 263 (top left and right) Richard Megna/Fundamental Photographs, (inset left) Tom Pantages, (inset right) RDF/Visuals Unlimited; p. 265, 266 Ivy Images; p. 268 Diane Schiumo/Fundamental Photographs; p. 269 (left) CP Picture Archive, (right) Michael Melford Inc./The Image Bank; p. 272 Richard Megna/Fundamental Photographs; p. 273 (top left and right) Richard Megna/Fundamental Photographs, (bottom left and right) Uwe Schneider/Vernier Software &

Technology; p. 274 Fisher/Visuals Unlimited; p. 276 Tom Pantages; p. 284 (top) E. F. Smith Collection, (bottom) Doug Martin/Photo Researchers, Inc.; p. 287 Richard Megna/Fundamental Photographs; p. 290 Judy-Ann Cazemier/Ivy Images; p. 291 (top) Barry L. Runk/Grant Heilman Photography, Inc., (bottom) Richard Megna/ Fundamental Photographs; p. 298 (top) Kronos Canada, Inc., (bottom) NASA; p. 300 (left) E. F. Smith Collection, (right) Richard Kellaway/PC Services and courtesy of Dave Kamatovik, Fort Erie Secondary School; p. 301 (top) Larry Stepanowicz/Visuals Unlimited, (bottom) Richard Megna/Fundamental Photographs; p. 303 Alex Van Name/Visuals Unlimited; p. 314 Tim Lovell. **UNIT FOUR** Page 323 (left) Science VU/Visuals Unlimited, (right) Richard Shiell; p. 324 Kip Peticolas/Fundamental Photographs; p. 327 K. Jordan/Mach 2 Stock; p. 328 Richard Kellaway/PC Services; p. 330 (top) SuperStock, (bottom) Charles D. Winters/Photo Researchers, Inc.; p. 331 (top) Tom Pantages, (centre) Karen Su/Stock, Boston, (bottom) Bob Wickley/SuperStock; p. 335 Blackwell Science Ltd.; p. 336 Tom Pantages; p. 337 (top) The Granger Collection, New York, (bottom) N. R. Rowan/Photo Researchers, Inc.; p. 339 (left) The Granger Collection, New York, (right) Richard Megna/Fundamental Photographs; p. 343 Vedros & Associates Inc./Getty Images; p. 347 Ron Kelly/Mach 2 Stock; p. 349 Tom Murphy/SuperStock; p. 351 Environment Canada; p. 352 CP Picture Archive; p. 356 Tom Pantages; p. 357 Gerald & Buff Corsi/Visuals Unlimited; p. 358 SuperStock; p. 359 Raphael Gaillarde/Getty Images; p. 362 (top) Carolyn A. McKeone/Photo Researchers, Inc., (bottom) Minden/First Light; p. 363 Tom Pantages; p. 365 (left) Richard Megna/ Fundamental Photographs, (right) Tom Pantages; p. 366 Jon Gilbert Fox; p. 367 Paul Silverman/Fundamental Photographs; p. 368 (top) The Granger Collection, New York, (bottom) John Greim/SPL/Photo Researchers, Inc.; p. 371 Thomas H. Kelly/Visuals Unlimited; p. 372 Kristen Brochmann/Fundamental Photographs; p. 373 SuperStock; p. 375, 376 Richard Kellaway/PC Services/and Lab setup courtesy of S17 Science Supplies and Services, www.s17science.com 800-288-7151; p. 380 (top) Richard Megna/Fundamental Photographs, (bottom) Bombardier Inc.; p. 382 Fundamental Photographs; p. 383 NASA; p. 384 Benelux Press/Photo Researchers, Inc.; p. 385 Reprinted with permission from cover of *Science*, 18 December 1992. Copyright 1992 American Association for the Advancement of Science. Photograph: Visuals Unlimited; p. 387 (top) The Granger Collection, New York, (bottom) Richard Megna/Fundamental Photographs; p. 389 (left) The Granger Collection, New York, (top right) Reprinted with permission from cover of *Science*, 28 May 1999. Copyright 1999 American Association for the Advancement of Science. Graphics: GA Neumann, MIT and NASA/GSFC, (bottom right) Reprinted by permission from *Nature*, Volume 409 Front Cover, 4th January 2001. Copyright 2001 Macmillan Magazines Ltd. Photograph:

European Southern Observatory ESO; p. 392 Ping Amranand/SuperStock; p. 395 Jeff Greenberg/Visuals Unlimited; p. 404 NASA; p. 405 Science VU/Visuals Unlimited; p. 407 Bristol Aerospace Limited; p. 409 Joe Waters, Nasa Jet Propulsion Laboratory/NASA; p. 410, 411 NASA; p. 413 R. Barber/Visuals Unlimited; p. 415 (top left) Gordon Hartley/Mach 2 Stock, (top right) Steve Vidler/ SuperStock, (bottom) Environment Canada; p. 416 (top) O. Bierwagen/Ivy Images, (bottom) Steve Vidler/SuperStock; p. 417 Ivy Images; p. 419 Vic Tucker/Mach 2 Stock; p. 421 Honda Canada Inc.; p. 429 Dr. Jurgen Scriba/SPL/Photo Researchers, Inc. **UNIT FIVE** Page 436 (left) Walter Paul Bebirian/Fundamental Photographs, (right) Richard Kellaway/PC Services; p. 437 CP Picture Archive (Damian Dovarganes); p. 438 Wayne Windjack, Sarnia; p. 440 Richard Kellaway/PC Services; p. 442 Jack Piekan/ Fundamental Photographs; p. 443 MSA Instrument Division; p. 444 (top) Peter Saunders/Mach 2 Stock, (bottom) Richard Kellaway/PC Services; p. 455 (top left and right) Richard Kellaway/PC Services, (bottom) Catalytic Generators, Inc., Norfolk, VA., 757-855-0191; p. 456 PhotoDisc, Inc.; p. 459 (top) Amber Britton/D&K Detector Sales, (bottom) Chigmaroff-Davison/SuperStock; p. 460 National Archives of Canada (PAC-53499); p. 463 John Lough/Visuals Unlimited; p. 467 Richard Kellaway/PC Services; p. 469 (top) Ivy Images, (bottom) Michael S. Yamashita/Corbis/Magma; p. 471 (top) Bill Marsh/Mach 2 Stock, (bottom) David Cavagnaro/Visuals Unlimited; p. 473 (left inset) Richard Kellaway/PC Services, (right) SuperStock; p. 474 James Holmes/Zedcor/SPL/Photo Researchers, Inc.; p. 480 J. Pinkston and L. Stern/USGS; p. 483 Waterfall, by M. C. Escher. ©2001 Cordon Art – Baarn – Holland. All rights reserved. p. 484 Ed Lallo/Mach 2 Stock; p. 491 (top) J. Vila/First Light, (bottom left) SuperStock, (bottom right) Richard Kellaway/PC Services; p. 492 Jeff Greenberg/ Visuals Unlimited; p. 499 Roger Allyn Lee/SuperStock; p. 500 CP Picture Archive (Jonathon Hayward); p. 501 (top) Nova Scotia Archives and Records Management (N-0998), (centre) Canadian Mining Hall of Fame, (bottom) Science VU/Visuals Unlimited; p. 502 Joel W. Rogers/ Corbis/Magma; p. 504 (top) Ted Shehinski/Syncrude Canada Ltd., (bottom) Tom Pantages; p. 507 Richard Kellaway/PC Services; p. 508 (top) Peter Saunders/Mach 2 Stock, (bottom) Ivy Images; p. 517 Richard T. Nowitz/ Photo Researchers, Inc.; p. 526 Alex Li; p. 527, 528 Ray Boudreau.

The publisher wishes to thank the following sources for diagram reference. Page 4 Dr. Theodor Benfey; p. 202 Canadian Nuclear Association; p. 235 (top) Electrolux Leisure Appliances Water Purification; p. 239 Regional Municipality of Durham; p. 292 (top) Air And Water Quality, Inc., Windham, Maine www.awqinc.com

Periodic Table of the Elements

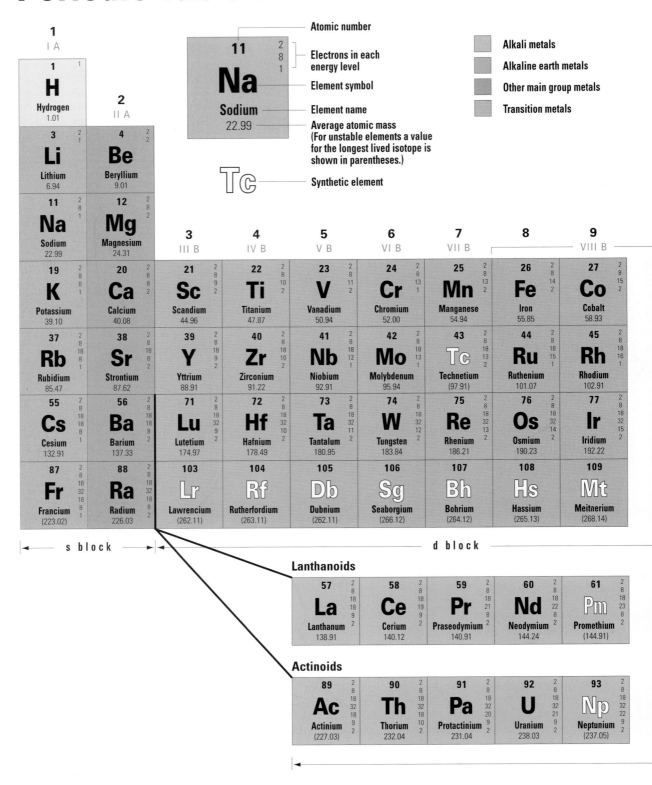

Noble gases

Halogens

Other nonmetals

Lanthanoids and actinoids

Semimetals or metalloids

18
0

← s block →

										13	14	15	16	17	
										III A	IV A	V A	VI A	VII A	

	2
He	
Helium	
4.00	

5	2 3	6	2 4	7	2 5	8	2 6	9	2 7	10	2 8
B		**C**		**N**		**O**		**F**		**Ne**	
Boron 10.81		Carbon 12.01		Nitrogen 14.01		Oxygen 16.00		Fluorine 19.00		Neon 20.18	

13	2 8 3	14	2 8 4	15	2 8 5	16	2 8 6	17	2 8 7	18	2 8 8
Al		**Si**		**P**		**S**		**Cl**		**Ar**	
Aluminum 26.98		Silicon 28.09		Phosphorus 30.97		Sulfur 32.07		Chlorine 35.45		Argon 39.95	

10	11	12
	I B	II B

28	2 8 16 2	29	2 8 18 1	30	2 8 18 2	31	2 8 18 3	32	2 8 18 4	33	2 8 18 5	34	2 8 18 6	35	2 8 18 7	36	2 8 18 8
Ni		**Cu**		**Zn**		**Ga**		**Ge**		**As**		**Se**		**Br**		**Kr**	
Nickel 58.69		Copper 63.55		Zinc 65.39		Gallium 69.72		Germanium 72.61		Arsenic 74.92		Selenium 78.96		Bromine 79.90		Krypton 83.80	

46	2 8 18 18	47	2 8 18 1	48	2 8 18 2	49	2 8 18 3	50	2 8 18 4	51	2 8 18 5	52	2 8 18 6	53	2 8 18 7	54	2 8 18 8
Pd		**Ag**		**Cd**		**In**		**Sn**		**Sb**		**Te**		**I**		**Xe**	
Palladium 106.42		Silver 107.87		Cadmium 112.41		Indium 114.82		Tin 118.71		Antimony 121.76		Tellurium 127.60		Iodine 126.90		Xenon 131.29	

78	2 8 18 32 17 1	79	2 8 18 32 18 1	80	2 8 18 32 18 2	81	2 8 18 32 18 3	82	2 8 18 32 18 4	83	2 8 18 32 18 5	84	2 8 18 32 18 6	85	2 8 18 32 18 7	86	2 8 18 32 18 8
Pt		**Au**		**Hg**		**Tl**		**Pb**		**Bi**		**Po**		**At**		**Rn**	
Platinum 195.08		Gold 196.97		Mercury 200.59		Thallium 204.18		Lead 207.2		Bismuth 208.98		Polonium (208.98)		Astatine (209.99)		Radon (222.02)	

110	111	112	113	114	115	116	117	118
***Uun**	***Uuu**	***Uub**		***Uuq**		***Uuh**		***Uuo**
Ununnilium (272.15)	Unununium (272.15)	Ununbium (277)		Ununquadium (289)		Ununhexium (289)		Ununoctium (293)

*Name not officially assigned.

← p block →

62	2 8 18 24 8 2	63	2 8 18 25 8 2	64	2 8 18 25 9 2	65	2 8 18 27 8 2	66	2 8 18 28 8 2	67	2 8 18 29 8 2	68	2 8 18 30 8 2	69	2 8 18 31 8 2	70	2 8 18 32 8 2
Sm		**Eu**		**Gd**		**Tb**		**Dy**		**Ho**		**Er**		**Tm**		**Yb**	
Samarium 150.36		Europium 151.96		Gadolinium 157.25		Terbium 158.93		Dysprosium 162.50		Holmium 164.93		Erbium 167.26		Thulium 168.93		Ytterbium 173.04	

94	2 8 18 32 24 8 2	95	2 8 18 32 25 8 2	96	2 8 18 32 25 9 2	97	2 8 18 32 27 8 2	98	2 8 18 32 28 8 2	99	2 8 18 32 29 8 2	100	2 8 18 32 30 8 2	101	2 8 18 32 31 8 2	102	2 8 18 32 32 8 2
Pu		**Am**		**Cm**		**Bk**		**Cf**		**Es**		**Fm**		**Md**		**No**	
Plutonium (244.06)		Americium (243.06)		Curium (247.07)		Berkelium (247.07)		Californium (251.08)		Einsteinium (252.08)		Fermium (257.10)		Mendelevium (258.10)		Nobelium (259.10)	

f block →